Museum Publications

Part I
Anthropology, Archeology
and Art

by

Jane Clapp

The Scarecrow Press, Inc.
New York   1962

Foreword

MUSEUM PUBLICATIONS is a classified bibliography of the publications available from 276 museums in the United States and Canada. The publications are arranged, numbered, and indexed separately in two parts:

Part I. Publications in Anthropology, Archaeology, and Art (4416 publications)
Part II. Publications in Biological and Earth Sciences (9231 publications).

Information about the publications listed was obtained from two requests asking Museums (institution members of the American Association of Museums--excluding historic houses, national park sites-- and other sources, including planetariums and observatories; zoos and aquariums; botanical gardens and herbariums) for current lists of their available publications. The first request was made in January 1960; the second request was made in April 1961, when notice of publications issued since the date of the previously received list, and of publications to be issued 1961-2, was requested.

The publications listed are books, pamphlets, and other monographs, and serial reprints. Generally, MUSEUM PUBLICATIONS does not list:

Serials in which articles are not available as separates or reprints (exceptions include University Museum);

Administrative reports;

News bulletins and news sheets issued periodically, and other reports of accessions, current exhibitions, and museum activities;

Geologic Survey Bulletins;

Writings in American history that would be listed in the annual bibliography issued by the American Historical Association;

Publications of the United States National Museum (compiled in the Editorial Division of the Smithsonian Institution); and Publications of the National Museum of Canada, issued by that Museum;

Publications issued by publishers listed in Books in Print (exceptions include Museum of Fine Arts, Boston; Metropolitan Museum).

MUSEUM PUBLICATIONS may list some publications distributed, but not published or issued by, a museum (as some publications available from the Art Gallery of Toronto are distributed through their book shop but not issued by the Gallery).

Prices are given for information, and are subject to change. Series publications may be available to institutions of higher learning on an exchange basis, or may be bought as complete sets (either paper or cloth bound). Also, special discounts may be offered, or publications sent without charge, except perhaps cost of mailing: (1) to educational institutions; (2) to individuals with professional interest in the field of study, or subject--as the publications of Michigan State University Museum; or (3) for quantity purchase.

Each publication listed in MUSEUM PUBLICATIONS is coded to show the symbol of the distributing museum. Museums distributing publications are arranged in two lists:

Museums Distributing Publications (alphabetical by name of museum, giving symbol);

Museums Distributing Publications--Arranged by Symbol.

The symbols used for museums are based on the Library of Congress list: "Symbols used in the National Union Catalog of the Library of Congress."

It is hoped that MUSEUM PUBLICATIONS, by making available in one bibliography popular and scientific publications of Museums, will facilitate the use of these authoritative information sources by teachers; librarians; professional workers in the subject fields of anthropology, archaeology, art, the biological and earth sciences; and by students and general readers.

Appreciation is expressed to the museums for the information regarding their available publications.

Contents

		Page
Foreword		iii
Museums Distributing Publications		vii
Museums Distributing Publications -- Arranged by Symbol		xv
Abbreviations		xlv
Part I		47
Publications in Anthropology, Archaeology, and Art		
Museums and Museum Work		47
Museum Directories		50
Museum Catalogs, Guides, History		50
Anthropology and Archaeology		56
Methodology		57
Regional Anthropology		58
Americas		58

Indians of North America: Eastern Woodlands; Plains and Plateau; Southwest; California Area; Northwest Coast; Eskimo Area; Canada — 61

Indians of Mexico, Central and South America — 99

Europe — 102

Orient — 104

Pacific Area — 117

Art — 126

Language Arts: Folk Literature and Folk Lore; Linguistics and Grammar; Literature

Theatre Arts — 140

Music — 141

Visual Arts — 142

v

Aesthetics   142

Museums and Galleries--Catalogs, Guides,
    History   143

Exhibitions and Private Collections   151

General Art and Painting   153

Drawing and Graphic Arts   158

Photography   159

Sculpture   159

Decorative Arts   160

Regional Art   167

    American: Canadian; United States; Indians of
    North America; Mexico, Central and South
    America   167

    European: Dutch and Flemish; English; French;
    German and Austrian; Mediterranean Area;
    Russian and Eastern European; Spanish; Swiss 209

    Oriental   235

    Primitive: African; Pacific Area; Pre-
    Columbian   250

History, Social Sciences and Technology   257

Health   270

Religion   270

Addenda--Publications in Anthropology, Archaeology and
    Art issued 1960-1961, with other additional publica-
    tions   272

Index   294

Museums Distributing Publications

	Symbol
Academy of Natural Sciences of Philadelphia	PPAN
Addison Gallery of American Art	MAnP-A
Adler Planeterium	ICAP
Alabama State Museum	AU-Mu
Alaska Historical Library and Museum	AkHi
Alaska, University of, Museum	AkU-Mu
Albany Institute of History and Art	NAlAI
Albright Art Gallery	NBuA
Allen's, (Ross), Reptile Institute	FSi
Allied Artists of America	NNAAA
Allyn, (Lyman), Museum	CtNlL
American Antiquarian Society	MWA
American Association of Botanical Gardens and Arboretums	PDel
American Association of Museums	DAMu
American Association of Zoological Parks and Aquariums	WvWA
American Federation of Arts	NNAFA
American Institute of Graphic Arts	NNAIG
American Museum of Natural History	NNM
Arizona, University of, Art Gallery	AzU-A
Arizona State Museum	AzTuMu
Arizona-Sonora Desert Museum	AzTu
Arnold Arboretum	MH-A
Art Institute of Chicago	ICA
Atkins Museum of Fine Arts See Nelson, (William Rockhill), Gallery	
Atlantic County Historical Society	NjSom
Augustana Historical Society	IRi
Baltimore Municipal Museum See Peale Museum	
Baltimore Museum of Art	MdBMA
Baltimore Zoo	MdBZ
The Barnes Foundation	PMeB
Beloit College See Logan Museum of Anthropology	
Berks County Historical Society	PRB
Big Bend Museum See West Texas Historical and Scientific Society	

Birmingham Museum of Art	ABM
Bishop, (Bernice P.), Museum	HB
Bob Jones University Art Gallery	ScGrvB
Boston Athenaeum	MBAt
Boston Public Library	MB
Bronx Zoo See New York Zoological Society	
Brookgreen Gardens Museum	ScGB
Brooklyn Botanic Garden	NBG
Brooklyn Museum	NBB
The Bucks County Historical Society. Mercer Museum	PDoBHi
Buffalo and Erie County Historical Society	NBuHi
Buffalo Museum of Science	NBuM
Butler Institute of American Art	OYoB
Calgary Zoological Gardens	CaACZ
California, University of, Art Galleries	CLU-A
California Academy of Sciences	CSfA
California Palace of the Legion of Honor	CSfPL
Carnegie Institute. Department of Fine Arts	PPiCIA
Carnegie Museum	PPiCM
Central Florida Museum	FOC
Chemung County Historical Center	NElmH
Chicago Academy of Sciences	ICAS
Chicago Historical Society	ICHi
Chicago Natural History Museum	ICF
Chicago Zoological Park	ICZ
Cincinnati Art Museum	OCA
Cincinnati Museum of Natural History	OCMN
Cleveland Health Museum	OClH
Cleveland Museum of Art	OClMA
Cleveland Museum of Natural History	OClMN
Colonial Williamsburg	ViWC
Colorado, University of, Museum	CoU-Mu
Colorado Springs. Fine Arts Center See Taylor Museum	
Colorado State Historical Society	CoHi
Columbia Museum of Art	ScCoM
Connecticut Historical Society	CtHi
Cooper Museum for the Arts of Decoration	NNCoo
Corcoran Gallery of Art	DCGA
Corning Museum of Glass	NCorniC-M
Cranbrook Institute of Science	MiBloC
Crocker, (E. B.), Art Gallery	CSC
Currier Gallery of Art	NhMC
Delaware Art Center See Wilmington Society of the Fine Arts	
Delaware State Museum	De-Ar

Denver Art Museum	CoDA
Denver Museum of Natural History	CoDMNH
Desert Museum See Palm Springs Desert Museum	
Detroit Historical Museum	MiDHi
Detroit Institute of Arts	MiDA
de Young, (M.H.), Memorial Museum	CSfDeY
Dominion Astrophysical Observatory	CaOOO
Dumbarton Oaks Research Library and Collection	DDO
du Pont, (Henry Francis), Winterthur Museum	DeWint
Essex Institute	MSaE
Everson Museum of Art (Formerly, The Syracuse Museum of Fine Arts)	NSyE
Farmers Museum See New York State Historical Association	
Farnsworth, (William A.), Library and Art Museum	MeRF
Fels Planetarium	PPF
Fenimore House See New York State Historical Association	
Field Museum of Natural History See Chicago Natural History Museum	
Fogg Art Museum, Harvard University	MH-FA
Folger Shakespeare Library	DFo
Ford, (Henry), Museum and Greenfield Village	MiDbFM
Franklin Institute See Fels Planetarium	
Freer Gallery of Art	DSI-F
Frick Collection	NNFC
Gardner, (Isabella Stewart), Museum	MBIMu
Georgia Department of Archives and History	G-Ar
Gibbes Art Gallery	ScCG
Gilcrease, (Thomas), Institute of American History and Art	OkTG
Greenfield Village See Ford, (Henry), Museum	
Griffith Park Observatory and Planetarium	CLG
Guggenheim, (Solomon R.), Museum	NNGu
Hall of Fame of the Trotter	NGo
Harvard Observatory	MH-O
Hayden Planetarium	NNM-H
Hebrew Union College. The Museum See Jewish Museum, Hebrew Union College	
Herron, (John), Art Institute	InIJ
Heye Foundation See Museum of the American Indian	
High Museum of Art	GAHM
Hispanic Society of America. Museum and Library	NNH
Honolulu Academy of Arts	HHo
Houston Museum of Fine Arts	TxHM

Idaho Historical Society	IdHi
Idaho State College Museum	IdPI-Mu
Illinois State Museum	ISM
Institute of Contemporary Art	MBI
Jewetts Art Center See Wellesley College	
Jewish Museum	NNJ-Mu
Jewish Museum, Hebrew Union College	OCH-Mu
Kansas, University of, Museum of Natural History	KU-Mu
Kentucky Historical Society	KyHi
Kern County Historical Society	CBakHi
Klamath County Museum	OrK
Laboratory of Anthropology See New Mexico, Museum of	
La Jolla Art Center	CLajA
Lassen National Park See Loomis Museum Association	
Layton Art Gallery now part of Milwaukee Art Center	
Lick Observatory	CMhL
Litchfield Historical Society	CtL
Logan Museum of Anthropology	WBB-Lo
Loomis Museum Association	CMi
Los Angeles County Museum of History, Science and Art	CLCM
Los Angeles Municipal Art Gallery	CLMA
Los Angeles State and County Arboretum	CAr
McGuffey Museum	OOxM-Mc
McNay, (Marion Koogler) Art Institute	TxSaMc
Marineland of the Pacific	CPaM
Mariners Museum	VWa
Maryland Historical Society	MdHi
Mercer Museum See Bucks County Historical Society	
Metropolitan Museum of Art	NNMM
Miami Seaquarium	FMS
Michigan, University of, Museum of Anthropology	MiU-A
Michigan, University of, Museum of Paleontology	MiU-P
Michigan, University of, Museum of Zoology	MiU-Z
Michigan Historical Commission	MiLHi
Michigan State University. The Museum	MiEm-Mu
Middle American Research Institute	LNT-MA
The Miller Art Center	VtSpM
Milwaukee Art Center	WMA
Milwaukee Public Museum	WMMMu
Minnesota, University of, Minnesota Museum of Natural History	MnU-M
Minnesota Historical Society	MnHi
Missouri Historical Society	MoHi

x

Montclair Art Museum	NjMonA
Moravian Historical Society	PNa
Morgan Library See Pierpont Morgan Library	
Morrison Planetarium	CSfA-M
The Mount Vernon Ladies' Association of the Union	ViMt
Mount Wilson and Palomar Observatories	CPal
Munson-Williams-Proctor Institute	NUtM
Museum of Comparative Zoology	MH-Z
Museum of Fine Arts, Boston	MBMu
Museum of History and Industry	WaSMu
Museum of International Folk Art	NmSMI
Museum of Modern Art	NNMMA
Museum of Science and Industry	ICS
Museum of Navajo Ceremonial Art	NmSMN
Museum of Northern Arizona	AzFM
Museum of Primitive Art	NNMPA
Museum of Science and Industry	ICS
Museum of the American Indian, Heye Foundation	NNMAI
Museum of the City of New York	NNMus
Mystic Seaport	CtMy
National Baseball Hall of Fame and Museum	NCooN
National Collection of Fine Arts	DSI-FA
National Gallery of Art	DSI-GA
National Gallery of Canada	CaOONG
National Sculpture Society	NNNSS
Naval Historical Foundation See Truxton-Decatur Naval Museum	
Nebraska, University of, Nebraska State Museum	NbU-Mu
Nebraska State Historical Society	NbHi
Nelson, (William Rockhill), Gallery of Art and Atkins Museum of Fine Arts	MoKNG
Nevada State Museum	NvCM
New Brunswick Museum	CaNBSM
New Jersey State Museum	NjTM
New Mexico Historical Society See New Mexico, Museum of	
New Mexico, Museum of. Historical Society of New Mexico	NmSM-H
Laboratory of Anthropology	NmSM-L
School of American Research	NmSm-S
New York Botanical Garden	NNNBG
New York Historical Society	NHi
New York State Historical Association. Farmers' Museum; Fenimore House	NCooHi
New York State Museum	NAlMu
New York Zoological Society	

Newark Museum	NjNM
North Carolina Department of Archives and History	NcRNC
North Carolina Museum of Art	NcRMA
North Carolina State Museum	NcRSM
North Dakota State Historical Society	NdHi
Oakland Art Museum	COA
Ohio State Historical Society	OHi
Oklahoma, University of See Stovall Museum of Science and History	
Old York Road Historical Society	PJO
Oregon Historical Society	OrHi
Oregon Trail Museum Association	NbG
Palm Springs Desert Museum	CPs
Palomar Observatory See Mount Wilson and Palomar Observatories	
Pasadena Art Museum	CPA
Paterson Museum	NjPatM
Peabody Museum of Archaeology and Ethnology	MH-P
Peabody Museum of Natural History, Yale University	CtY-PM
Peabody Museum of Salem	MSaP
Peale Museum	MdBPM
Pennsylvania Historical and Museum Commission	PHarH
Pennsylvania Historical Society	PHi
Petrified Forest Museum Association	AzH
Philadelphia Commercial Museum	PPComm
Philadelphia Museum of Art	PPPM
Philbrook Art Center	OkTP
Phillips Gallery	DPG
Phoenix Art Museum	AzPhA
Pierpont Morgan Library	NNPM
Pilgrim Society	MP
Portland Art Museum	OrPA
Portland Zoo	OrPZ
Princeton University Art Museum	NjP-A
Rancho Santa Anita Botanic Garden	OCR
Reading Public Museum and Art Gallery	PRM
Remington Art Memorial	NOgR
Rhode Island Historical Society	RHi
Rhode Island School of Design Museum of Art	RPD-A
Ringling, (John and Mabel), Museum of Art	FSR
Rochester Museum of Arts and Sciences	NRM
Rockefeller, (Abby Aldrich), Folk Art Collection	ViWR
Rodin Museum See Philadelphia Museum of Art	
Rogers, (Lauren), Library and Museum of Art	MsLa
Rockwell Museum and Art Center	NmRMA

xii

Royal Ontario Museum	CaOTRM
St. Augustine Historical Society	FStA
St. Louis City Art Museum	MoSCA
Saisset Art Gallery and Museum	CSc
San Antonio Zoo and Aquarium	TxSaZ
San Diego Fine Arts Gallery	CsdF
San Diego Natural History Museum	CSdSNH
San Diego Zoological Society	CSdZ
San Francisco Museum of Art	CSfMA
Santa Barbara Museum of Natural History	CStbMu
Sclamandre Museum of Textiles	NNSM
School of American Research See New Mexico, Museum of	
Science Museum of St. Paul Institute	MnSSci
Seattle Art Museum	WaSA
Seattle Historical Society See Museum of History and Industry	
Shelburne Museum	VtSM
Sleepy Hollow Restorations	NTaS
Smith, (H.V.,) Museum	NNSMu
Smith College Museum of Art	MNS-MA
Smithsonian Institution	DSI
Southern Plains Indians Exhibit	OkA
Southwest Museum	CLSM
Springfield Massachusetts Museum of Fine Arts	MSMFA
Stanford University Museum	CStM
Staten Island Historical Society	NNSI
Stovall Museum of Science and History	OkU-S
Suffolk Museum at Stony Brook	NBLiSt
Syracuse Museum of Fine Arts See Everson Museum of Art	
Taft Museum	OCT
Taylor Museum	CoCF
Texas Memorial Museum	TxAuM
Texas Technological College. The Museum	TxLT-Mu
Textile Museum	DTM
Toledo Museum of Art	OTM
Toronto Art Gallery	CaOTAG
Truxton-Decatur Naval Museum	DN-HF
United States Department of the Interior Museum	DI-M
University Museum	PU-Mu
Utah Field House of Natural History	UV
Valentine Museum	ViRVM
Vassar College Art Gallery	NPV-A
Vermont Historical Society	VtHi
Virginia Museum of Fine Arts	ViRMu
Wadsworth Atheneum	CtHWA
Walker Art Center	MnMW

Walters Art Gallery   MdBWA
Washington County Museum of Fine Arts   MdHagM
Wayne County Historical Society   PHoW
Wellesley College Department of Art. Jewett
   Arts Center   MWelC-A
West Texas Historical and Scientific Society   TxAl
The Whaling Museum   MNBedfW
Whitney Museum of American Art   NNW
Williamsburg See Colonial Williamsburg
Wilmington Society of the Fine Arts   DeWS
Winterthur Museum See du Pont, (Henry Francis),
   Winterthur Museum
Wisconsin State Historical Society   WHi
Wisconsin Union Gallery, University of Wisconsin   WU-G
Witte Memorial Museum   TxSaW
Woolaroc Museum   OkB
Worcester Art Museum   MWM
Yale University Art Gallery   CtY-A
Yale University Peabody Museum See Peabody
   Museum of Natural History
Yellowstone National Parks Museums   WyY
Yosemite Natural History Association   CYo
Zoological Society of Philadelphia   PPZ

Museums Distributing Publications--Arranged by Symbol

Symbol	Museum	Special Information: Serials and Series Listed; Mailing Charges
ABM	Birmingham Museum of Art 8th Ave. & 20th St. N. Birmingham, Ala.	
AU-Mu	Alabama State Museum Alabama Geological Survey, Smith Hall, University, Ala.	Order from: Walter B. Jones, State Geologist, University, Ala. Series listed: MP--Museum Paper
AkHi	Alaska Historical Library & Museum P.O. Box 2051, Juneau, Alaska	
AkU-Mu	Alaska, University of, Museum College, Alaska	
AzFM	Museum of Northern Arizona P.O. Box 402, Flagstaff, Ariz.	Series listed: B--Bulletin C--Ceramic Series (looseleaf) P--Plateau Series R--Reprint Series T--Technical Series
AzH	Petrified Forest Museum Association Box 518, Holbrook, Ariz.	
AzPhA	Phoenix Art Museum Civic Center, 1625 N. Central Ave. Phoenix, Ariz.	
AzTu	Arizona-Sonora Desert Museum P.O. Box 5602 Tuscon, Ariz.	Series listed: AP--Anthropological Papers ES--Educational Series

AzTuMu   Arizona State Museum   Mailing charge $.10
         University of Arizona   each publication
         Tuscon, Ariz.

AzU-A   Arizona, University of, Art Gallery
         Tuscon, Ariz.

CAr   Los Angeles State and County Arboretum
         301 N. Baldwin Ave.,
         Arcadia, Calif.

CBakHi   Kern County Historical Soc.   Mailing charge: $.15
         Kern County Museum,   ea. paperbound publica-
         3801 Chester Ave.   tion; $.25 ea. cloth-
         Bakersfield, Calif.   bound publication

CCR   Rancho Santa Anita Botanic Garden
         1500 N. College Ave.,
         Claremont, Calif.

CLCM   Los Angeles County Museum   Mailing charge, all or-
            of History, Science & Art ders: $.15 min.; addi-
         Exposition Park   tional on larger orders
         Los Angeles 7, Calif.   Series listed: AP--
                                       Anthropology Publica-
                                       tion; CS--Contributions
                                       in Science; PP--Paleon-
                                       tology Publication; ZP
                                       --Zoology Publication

CLG   Griffith Park Observatory
            & Planetarium
         P.O. Box 27787, Los Feliz Station
         Los Angeles 27, Calif.

CLMA   Los Angeles Municipal Art Gallery
         Municipal Art Department, 351 City Hall
         Los Angeles 12, Calif.

CLSM   Southwest Museum
         234 Museum Drive
         Los Angeles 42, Calif.

CLU-A   California, University of, Art Galleries
         405 Hilgard Ave.,
         Los Angeles 24, Calif.

CLajA   La Jolla Art Center
         700 Prospect St.
         La Jolla, Calif.

CMhL   Lick Observatory, University   Order from: Librarian
              of California   Series listed: P--Pub-
         Mt. Hamilton, Calif.   licati ons

CMi   Loomis Museum Association
         Lassen Volcanic National Park
         Mineral, Calif.

COA   Oakland Art Museum
         Municipal Auditorium
         Tenth & Fallon
         Oakland 7, Calif.

CPA   Pasadena Art Museum   Mailing charge addi-
         46 Los Robles   tional
         Pasadena, Calif.

CPaM   Marineland of the Pacific
         Palos Verdes Estates, Calif.

CPal   Mount Wilson & Palomar Observatories
         California Institute of Technology
         Bookstore, 1201 E. California St.
         Pasadena, Calif.

CPs   Palm Springs Desert Museum
         135 E. Taquitz Dr.,
         Palm Springs, Calif.

CSC   Crocker, (E.B.) Art Gallery
         216 O St.
         Sacramento 14, Calif.

CSc   Saisset Art Gallery and Museum
         University of Santa Clara
         Santa Clara, Calif.

CSdF   San Diego Fine Arts Gallery
         PO Box 2107
         San Diego 12, Calif.

CSdSNH San Diego Natural History   Series listed:
        Museum   M--Memoirs
        San Diego Soc. of Natural   OP--Occasional Pa-
        History   pers
        Balboa Park,   T--Trails
        San Diego 1, Calif.   Trans--Transactions

CSdZ   San Diego Zoological Society
        P. O. Box 551
        San Diego 12, Calif.

CSfA   California Academy of   Series listed:
        Sciences   OP--Occasional Pa-
        Golden Gate Park   pers
        San Francisco 18, Calif.   P--Proceedings

CSfA-M Morrison Planetarium,   Mailing charge: $.10
        California Academy of   on ea. $1., or fraction
        Sciences   thereof, of price of ea.
        Golden Gate Park   order. Series listed:
        San Francisco 18, Calif.   B--Booklet

CSfDeY de Young, (M.H.), Memorial Museum
        Golden Gate Park
        San Francisco 18, Calif.

CSfMA   San Francisco Museum of Art
        Civic Center
        San Francisco 2, Calif.

CSfPL   California Palace of the   Mailing charge, all or-
        Legion of Honor   ders: $.15 minimum
        Lincoln Park
        San Francisco 21, Calif.

CStM   Stanford University Museum
        Stanford, Calif.

CStbMu Santa Barbara Museum of   Series listed:
        Natural History   DAB--Dept. of An-
        Santa Barbara, Calif.   thropology Bulletin
                                           DG--Dept. of Geology
                                           OP--Occasional Pa-
                                             pers
                                           SB--Spec. Bulletins

CYo   Yosemite Natural History   Mailing charge, all or-
          Association   ders: 5 percent of
          Yosemite National Park, Calif. order

CaACZ   Calgary Zoological Gardens
          St. George's Island, Calgary,
          Alberta, Canada

CaNBSM New Brunswick Museum   Series listed: G--
          Saint John, N.B.,   General Publica-
          Canada   tions
                                           M--History Mono-
                                            graphs
                                           NB--New Brunswick
                                            Ethnology
                                           SP--Spec. Publica.

CaOONG National Gallery of Canada
          Elgin and McLeod Streets
          Ottawa 4, Canada

CaOOO   Dominion Astrophysical Observatory
          Royal Oak, B.C.,
          Canada

CaOTAG Toronto Art Gallery
          Grange Park, Toronto 2B,
          Ontario, Canada

CaOTRM Royal Ontario Museum   Series listed:
          100 Queen's Park   B--Bulletins
          Toronto 5, Ontario   C--Contributions
          Canada   Ed--Educational Se-
                                            ries Handbook
                                           L--Leaflets
                                           OP--Occasional Pa-
                                            pers
                                          Add $.15 on each order
                                          for exchange of out-of-
                                          town checks

CoCF   Taylor Museum, Colorado   Mailing charge addi-
          Springs Fine Arts Center   tional
          West Dale St.,
          Colorado Springs, Colo.

CoDA   Denver Art Museum   Mailing charges: Orders
          1300 Logan St.   up to $.99--$.10; or-
          Denver 3, Colo.   ders $1. to $2.49--

                            xix

CoDMNH Denver Museum of Natural History
City Park
Denver 6, Colo.

$.20; $.10 ea. additional $2.50. Series listed: IL--Indian Leaflets--$.10 ea.; double numbers, $.20 ea. Series listed: MP--Museum Pictorial
P--Proceedings
PS--Popular Series

CoHi Colorado State Historical Society
318 State Museum
Denver 2, Colo.

CoU-Mu Colorado, University of, Museum
Hale Building,
Boulder, Colo.

Order from: Hugo G. Rodeck, Director
Series listed: ML--University of Colorado Museum Leaflets

CtHWA Wadsworth Atheneum
25 Atheneum Square
Hartford 3, Ct.

CtHi Connecticut Historical Society
1 Elizabeth St.,
Hartford 5, Ct.

CtL Litchfield Historical Society
Litchfield, Ct.

CtMy Mystic Seaport
Marine Historical Assoc.
Mystic, Ct.

Mailing charge, each publication: $.05

CtNlL Allyn, (Lyman), Museum
100 Mohegan Ave.
New London, Ct.

CtY-A Yale University Art Gallery
New Haven, 11, Ct.

CtY-PM Peabody Museum of Natural History
Yale University
New Haven, Ct.

Prices include postage; no disc. from listed prices. Series listed:
B--Bulletin
M--Memoir
P--Postilla

xx

DAMu   American Association of Museums
Smithsonian Institution
Washington 25, D.C.

DCGA   Corcoran Gallery of Art   Mailing charge, each
17th St. & New York Ave., NW publication: $.25
Washington 6, D.C.   Series listed: B--
                              Bulletin
                              CAA--Contemporary
                              American Artists

DDO   Dumbarton Oaks Research   Lists publications not
     Library & Collection   in PTLA
1703 32nd St., NW
Washington 7, D.C.

DFo   Folger Shakespeare Library   Mailing charge, orders
E. Capitol and 2nd, SE $.25-$1.: $.10; or-
Washington 3, D.C.   ders $1., and over:
                              $.25

DI-M   United States Dept. of the
     Interior Museum
Interior Building
Washington 25, D.C.

DN-HF Truxton-Decatur Naval Museum
Naval Historical Foundation
c/o U.S. Navy Department
Washington 25, D.C.

DPG   Phillips Gallery
1600 21st St., NW
Washington 9, D.C.

DSI   Smithsonian Institution   Lists only publications per
Washington 25, D.C.   taining to fine arts. See
                              also, listings for admini-
                              strative units of the Smith-
                              sonian Institution: Freer
                              Gallery of Art; National
                              Collection of Fine Arts;
                              National Gallery of Art

DSI-F	Freer Gallery of Art Washington 25, D.C.	Series listed: FOP-- Freer Occasional Papers
DSI-FA	National Collection of Fine Arts Washington 25, D.C.	
DSI-GA	National Gallery of Art Washington 25, D.C.	Series listed: NGA Book--National Gallery of Art Booklet
DTM	Textile Museum 2320 S St., NW Washington 8, D.C.	Series listed: WN-- Workshop Notes
De-Ar	Delaware State Museum, Public Archives Commission 316 S. Governors Ave. Dover, Del.	Series listed: B-- Bulletin Series
DeWS	Wilmington Society of the Fine Arts Delaware Art Center 2301 Kentmere Parkway Wilmington 6, Del.	
DeWint	du Pont, (Henry Francis), Winterthur Museum Winterthur, Del.	
FMS	Miami Seaquarium Rickenbacker Causeway Miami, Fla.	
FOC	Central Florida Museum P.O. Box 1763 Orlando, Fla.	
FSR	Ringling, (John & Mabel), Museum of Art P.O. Box 1690 Sarasota, Fla.	
FSi	Allen's, (Ross), Reptile Institute Silver Springs, Fla.	
FStA	St. Augustine Historical Society 22 St. Francis St. St. Augustine, Fla.	

GAHM   High Museum of Art
Atlanta Art Association
1280 Peachtree St., NE
Atlanta 9, Ga.

G-Ar   Georgia Department of Archives
      and History
1516 Peachtree St., NW
Atlanta 9, Ga.

HB   Bishop, (Bernice P.), Mu-   Series Listed:
      seum   B--Bulletins
Honolulu 17, Hawaii   M--Memoirs
                              OP--Occasional Papers
                              SP--Special Publica-
                                tions

HHo   Honolulu Academy of Arts   Series listed:
900 S. Beretania St.   SS--Special Studies
Honolulu 14, Hawaii

ICA   Art Institute of Chicago   Mailing charge, mini-
Michigan Ave & Adams St.   mum for ea. catalog &
Chicago 3, Ill.   handbook: $.20

ICAP   Adler Planetarium &   Series listed:
      Astronomical Museum   AB--Astronomical
900 E. Achsah Bond Dr.   Booklets
Grant Park, Chicago 5, Ill.

ICAS   Chicago Academy of Sciences   Order from: Office of
Lincoln Park,   the Director. Series
2001 N. Clark St.   listed: B--Bulletin
Chicago 14, Ill.   BNHS--Bulletin of the
                          Natural History Survey
                      NHM--Natural History
                        Miscellanea
                      PA--Program of Activi-
                      ties
                      SP--Special Publications

ICP   Chicago Natural History   Series listed: GMP-HV:
      Museum (Field Museum)   Genl. Mus. Pubns--
Roosevelt Rd. & Lakeshore   Histcl. Vol.
      Dr.   Anthropology
Chicago 5, Ill.   FA--Fieldiana: Anthro-
                      pology
                      A-M--Anthropology-

Memoirs
DS--Design Series
A-PS--Anthropology-
Popular Series
Botany
FB--Fieldiana: Botany
B-PS--Botany-Popular
Series
Geology
FG--Fieldiana: Geology
FGM--Fieldiana: Geol-
ogy Memoirs
G-SP--Geology-Special
Publications
G-PS--Geology-Popular
Series
Zoology
FZ--Fieldiana: Zoology
FZM--Fieldiana: Zool-
ogy Memoirs
OS--Ornithological Se-
ries
Z-SP--Zoology-Special
Publications
Z-PS--Zoology-Popular
Series
Also listed: FT--Field-
iana Technique
H--Handbooks
Museum Stories: 80
word pamphlets
Mailing chge additional

ICHi   Chicago Historical Soc.   Mailing chge, minimum,
        Clark St. at North Ave.   all publications: $.25
        Chicago 14, Ill.

ICS   Museum of Science and   Mailing charge, each
            Industry   publication: $.10
        E. 57th & S. South Shore Dr.
        Chicago 37, Ill.

ICZ   Chicago Zoological Park
        Brookfield, Ill.

IRi   Augustana Historical Society
        Augustana College
        Rock Island, Ill.

ISM	Illinois State Museum Springfield, Ill.	Series listed: B--Bulletins MS--Meaning of Scenery in Illinois State Parks PS--Popular Science Series R--Report of Investigations SI--Story of Illinois Series SP--Scientifica Paper Series Publications coded SI, are available only to scientific institutions
IdHi	Idaho Historical Society 610 Parkway Dr., Boise, Idaho	Service chge: $.50 all orders. Non-institutional orders must be accompanied by check. Series listed: MP-- Museum Pamphlets OP--Occasional Papers
InIJ	Herron, (John), Art Institute 110 E. 16th St. Indianapolis 2, Ind.	
KU-Mu	Kansas, University of, Museum of Natural History Lawrence, Kansas	Series listed: MP-- U of Kansas Museum of Nat. Hist. Miscellaneous Publications Pubns--U of Kansas Publications. Museum of Natural History Mailing chge, ea. publication: $.25
KyHi	Kentucky Historical Society Box 104 Frankfort, Ky.	
KyU-Mu	Kentucky, University of, Museum of Anthropology Lexington, Ky.	Order from: Director, Museum of Anthropology Series listed: RA--Reports on Anthropology

LNT-MA Middle American Research Institute
Tulane University
New Orleans 18, La.

Series listed: FIR--Foreign Influence on Native Religious Ideology
FIT--Foreign Influence on Native Technology
M--Miscellaneous Series
MARR--Middle American Research Records
P--Publications
PD--Philological and Documentary Studies
SSM--Synoptic studies of Mexican culture

MAnP-A Addison Gallery of American Art
Phillips Academy
Andover, Mass.

MB Boston Public Library
P. O. Box 286,
Boston 17, Mass.

Checks should be payable to: Trustees of the Boston Public Library

MBAt Boston Athenaeum
10-1/2 Beacon St.
Boston 8, Mass.

MBI Institute of Contemporary Art
Soldiers Field Road
Boston 34, Mass.

MBIMu Gardner, (Isabella Stewart), Museum
163 Worthington St.
Boston 15, Mass.

Mailing chge, all publications (except Museum Guide, which is postpaid): $.10 ea.

MBMu Museum of Fine Arts, Boston
479 Huntington Ave.
Boston 15, Mass.

Mailing chge, all publications, min. chge: $.25; larger orders, and orders to Middle and Far West: $.50

MH-A Arnold Arboretum
22 Divinity Ave.
Cambridge 38, Mass.

Order from: Librarian
Series listed:
C--Contributions
S--Sargentia

MH-FA	Fogg Art Museum, Harvard University Quincy St. & Broadway Cambridge 38, Mass.	Mailing chge additional
MH-O	Harvard Observatory Sky Publishing Corporation Cambridge 38, Mass.	
MH-P	Peabody Museum of Archae- ology & Ethnology, Harvard University 11 Divinity Ave., Cambridge 38, Mass.	Price chge 1961: $2. added to price of all clothbound Memoirs & Papers. Series listed: ASPR--American School of Prehistoric Re- search HA--Harvard African Studies M--Memoirs P--Papers RT--Russian Transla- tion Series
MH-Z	Museum of Comparative Zoology at Harvard College Cambridge 38, Mass.	Series listed: B--Bulletin Brev--Brevoria--$.25 ea CEL--Contributions from the Entomologi- cal Laboratory
MNBedfW	The Whaling Museum & Old Dartmouth His- torical Society 18 Johnny Cake Hill New Bedford, Mass.	Mailing chge additional
MNS-MA	Smith College Museum of Art Northampton, Mass.	
MP	Pilgrim Society Plymouth, Mass.	
MSMFA	Springfield Massachusetts Museum of Fine Arts 49 Chester St. Springfield 3, Mass.	

MSaE   Essex Institute
        132 Essex St.
        Salem, Mass.

MSaP   Peabody Museum of Salem
        East India Marine Hall
        161 Essex St.
        Salem, Mass.

MWA   American Antiquarian Soc.   Series listed: TC--
        Salisbury St. & Park Ave.   Transactions and Col-
        Worcester 9, Mass.   lections

MWM   Worcester Art Museum
        55 Salisbury St.
        Worcester 8, Mass.

MWelC-A Wellesley College. Dept. of
            Art. Jewett Arts Center
        Wellesley 81, Mass.

MdBMA   Baltimore Museum of Art   Mailing chge, ea. pub-
        Wyman Park   lication: $.25
        Baltimore 18, Md.

MdBPM   Peale Museum
        225 N. Holliday St.
        Baltimore 2, Md.

MdBWA   Walters Art Gallery
        600 N. Charles St.
        Baltimore 1, Md.

MdBZ   Baltimore Zoo
        Druid Hill Park
        Baltimore 17, Md.

MdHagM Washington County Museum of Fine Arts
            P. O. Box 423
        Hagerstown, Md.

MdHi   Maryland Historical Society
        201 W. Monument St.
        Baltimore 1, Md.

MeRF   Farnsworth, (William A.), Library & Art Museum
        Elm St.,
        Rockland, Maine

MiBloC	Cranbrook Institute of Science Bloomfield Hills, Mich.	Series listed: B--Bulletin G--Guide
MiDA	Detroit Institute of Arts 5200 Woodward Ave. Detroit 2, Mich.	Mailing chge, catalogs less than $1: $.15; $1. and over: $.20; books $1., and over: $.25 Series listed: B--Bulle- tin
MiDHi	Detroit Historical Museum Woodward at Kirby Detroit 2, Mich.	
MiDbFM	Ford, (Henry), Museum & Greenfield Village Dearborn, Mich.	Mailing chge additional
MiEM-Mu	Michigan State University. The Museum East Lansing, Mich.	Series listed: PB--Pub- lications of the Mu- seum--Biological Se- ries
MiLHi	Michigan Historical Commission Lewis Cass Building Lansing 13, Mich.	
MiU-A	Michigan, University of, Mu- seum of Anthropology, University Museums Bldg. Ann Arbor, Mich.	Series listed: AP-- Anthropological Papers OC--Occasional Contri- butions
MiU-P	Michigan, University of, Museum of Paleontology Ann Arbor, Mich.	Series listed: C--Con- tributions
MiU-Z	Michigan, University of, Museum of Zoology, University Museums Bldg. Ann Arbor, Mich.	Series listed: C--Circu- lars MH--Michigan Hand- books MP--Miscellaneous publications OP--Occasional Papers
MnHi	Minnesota Historical Society Cedar and Central St. Paul 1, Minn.	

MnMW   Walker Art Center
1710 Lyndale Ave., S.
Minneapolis, 3, Minn.

MnSSci   Science Museum of St. Paul   Mailing chge additional
       Institute
    51 University Ave.
    St. Paul 3, Minn.

MnU-M   Minnesota, University of,   Mailing chge, ea publi-
       Minnesota   cation: $.05.
    Museum of Natural History   Series listed: OP--Oc-
    Minneapolis 14, Minn.   casional Papers
                                  P--Pamphlet

MoHi   Missouri Historical Society
Jefferson Memorial Bldg.
St. Louis 12, Mo.

MoKNG   Nelson, (William Rockhill), Gallery
       of Art & Atkins Museum of Fine Arts
    4525 Oak St.
    Kansas City 11, Mo.

MoSCA   St. Louis City Art Museum   Mailing chge, ea order
    Forest Park   up to $1.75: $.10; or-
    St. Louis 5, Mo.   ders $1.75, and over:
                               $.25

MsLa   Rogers, (Lauren), Library &
       Museum of Art
    P.O. Box 1108
    Laurel, Miss.

NAlAI   Albany Institute of History & Art
125 Washington Ave.
Albany 10, N.Y.

NAlMu   New York State Museum   Checks should be pay-
    State Education Department   able to: New York State
    Albany 1, N.Y.   Education Department
                              Series listed:
                              B--Bulletin
                              C--Circular
                              H--Handbook
                              M--Memoir

NBB	Brooklyn Museum Eastern Parkway at Washington Ave. Brooklyn 38, N.Y.	Mailing chge additional, with minimum: $.10
NBG	Brooklyn Botanic Garden Brooklyn 25, N.Y.	
NBLiSt	Suffolk Museum at Stony Brook Long Island, N.Y.	Mailing chge additional
NBuA	Albright Art Gallery 1285 Elmwood Ave. Buffalo, N.Y.	
NBuHi	Buffalo & Erie County His- torical Society Delaware Park Buffalo 16, N.Y.	Series listed: B--Bulle- tin (Publications of Buffalo Soc. of Natur- al Sciences) F--Fascicles
NCooHi	New York State Historical Assoc. Farmers' Museum: Fenimore House Cooperstown, N.Y.	
NCooN	National Baseball Hall of of Fame & Museum Cooperstown, N.Y.	Mailing chge, orders under $1: $.20
NCorniC-M	Corning Museum of Glass Corning, N.Y.	Mailing chg, ea publi- cation: $.15
NElmH	Chemung County Historical Center 425 Market St. Elmira, N.Y.	
NGo	Hall of Fame of the Trotter Goshen, N.Y.	
NHi	New York Historical Society Central Park West at 77th St. New York 24, N.Y.	
NNAAA	Allied Artists of America 1083 Fifth Ave. New York 28, N.Y.	

NNAFA American Federation of Arts
       1083 Fifth Ave.
       New York 28, N. Y.

NNAIG American Institute of Graphic Arts
       5 E. 40th St.
       New York 16, N. Y.

NNCoo Cooper Union Museum for the   Series listed:
       Arts of Decoration   C--Catalog
       Cooper Square   MC--Museum Chroni-
       4th Ave at 7th St.   cles
       New York 3, N. Y.

NNFC Frick Collection   Mailing chge additional
       1 E. 70th St.
       New York 21, N. Y.

NNGu Guggenheim, (Solomon R.) Museum
       1071 Fifth Ave.
       New York 28, N. Y.

NNH Hispanic Society of America
       Museum and Library
       613 W. 155th St.
       New York 32, N. Y.

NNJ-Mu Jewish Museum under the auspices
       of Jewish Theological Seminary
       of America
       5th Ave. at 92nd St.
       New York 28, N. Y.

NNM American Museum of Natural   Popular publications
       History   Series listed: MN--Man
       Central Park West at 79th St.   and Nature Publica-
       New York 24, N. Y.   tions. SG--Science
                             Guide. Order from:
                             Man & Nature Publica-
                             tions. Technical publi-
                             cations Series listed:
                             AP--Anthropological
                              Papers
                             B--Bulletin
                             JNP--Jessup North Pa-
                             cific Expedition
                             M--Memoirs (Memoirs

marked * published by
E. J. Brill, Leiden,
The Netherlands, and
can be ordered from the
publisher or from Ste-
chert-Hafner, Inc., 31
E. 10th St., New York,
3, N. Y.)
N--American Museum
Novitates (Price: $.25
ea) Order from: Li-
brarian

NNM-H   Hayden Planetarium
81st St. & Central Park West
New York 24, N. Y.

NNMAI   Museum of the American
Indian
Heye Foundation
Broadway at 155th St.
New York 32, N. Y.

Series listed: C--Con-
tributions
INM--Indian Notes &
Monographs
INMM--Indian Notes &
Monographs Miscel-
laneous.
M--Miscellaneous
SA--Contributions to
So. Amn. Archeol.

NNMM   Metropolitan Museum of
of Art
5th Ave & 82nd St.
New York 28, N. Y.

Publications listed are
those not shown in Books
in Print, 1960. Series
listed: P--Met Mus of
Art Papers

NNMMA Museum of Modern Art
11 W. 53rd St.
New York 19, N. Y.

Publications listed are
those not shown in
Books in Print, 1960

NNMPA Museum of Primitive Art
15 W. 54th St.
New York 19, N. Y.

NNMus Museum of the City of New York
5th Ave. at 104th St.
New York 29, N. Y.

NNNBG	New York Botanical Garden Bronx Park New York 58, N. Y.	Lists only several publications, as books, and other monographs, and most serials (back issues and reprints) are distributed by Stechert-Hafner, Inc., 31 E. 10th St., New York 3, N. Y.
NNNSS	National Sculpture Society 1083 Fifth Ave. New York 28, N. Y.	
NNPM	Pierpont Morgan Library 29 E. 36th St. New York 16, N. Y.	Publications listed are those not shown in Books in Print, 1960
NNSI	Staten Island Historical Society Court & Center Sts., Richmondtown, Staten Island, N. Y.	
NNSM	Scalamandre Museum of Textiles 57 E. 57th St. New York 22, N. Y.	
NNSMu	Smith, (H. V.), Museum of the Home Insurance Co. 59 Maiden Lane New York 8, N. Y.	
NNW	Whitney Museum of American Art 22 W. 54th St. New York 19, N. Y.	Mailing chge, catalogs: Large--$.15 for one; $.05 for ea additional in order. Small annual catalogues--$.05 ea
NNZ	New York Zoological Society The Zoological Park New York 60, N. Y.	Popular publications Series listed: AK-- Animal Kingdom B--Bulletin PSB--Popular Series Booklets. Scientific Publications Series listed: Zool--Zoologica (listed to v 21, Apr 8, 1936, with this issue no longer available in

reprints, only in quar-
terly part)
Zoop--Zoopathologica

NOgR   REmington Art Memorial
        303 Washington St.
        Ogdensburg, N.Y.

NPV-A   Vassar College Art Gallery
        Poughkeepsie, N.Y.

NRM   Rochester Museum of Arts   Series listed: M--
          & Sciences   Museum Memoirs
        657 East Av.   RR--Research Records
        Rochester 7, N.Y.

NSyE   Everson Museum of Art (formerly
          Syracuse Museum of Fine Arts)
        State & James Sts.
        Syracuse 3, N.Y.

NTaS   Sleepy Hollow Restorations on
          the Tappan Zee
        Tarrytown, N.Y.

NUtM   Munson-Williams-Proctor Institute
        310 Genesee St.
        Utica, N.Y.

NbG   Oregon Trail Museum Assoc.   Mailing chge, ea order
        Scotts Bluff National Monu-   less than $1.25: $.12
          ment, Box 136
        Gering, Nebr.

NbHi   Nebraska State Historical   Series listed: AP--
          Society   Archeological Publica-
        1500 R St.   tions. PA--Publica-
        Lincoln 8, Nebr.   tions in Anthropology

NbU-Mu Nebraska, University of.   Mailing chge: $.25 first
          Nebraska State Museum   publication; $.10 for ea
        Morrill Hall   additional in order. Se-
        Lincoln 8, Nebr.   ries listed: B--Bulletin

NcRMA   North Carolina Museum of Art
        107 E. Morgan St.
        Raleigh, N.C.

NcRSM   North Carolina State Museum   Series listed: Info Circ
        Box 2281, State Agricultural   --Information Circulars
          Bldg.
        101 Halifax St.
        Raleigh, N. C.

NdHi   North Dakota State Historical Soc.
        Liberty Memorial Bldg.
        Bismark, N. D.

NjMonA Montclair Art Museum
        So. Mountain & Bloomfield Aves.
        Montclair, N. J.

NjNM   Newark Museum   Mailing chge, orders
        49 Washington St.   up to $. 75: $. 05; or-
        Newark 1, N. J.   ders $. 75 & over: $. 15
                                    Series listed: M--The
                                    Museum, New Series

NjP-A   Princeton University Art
          Museum
        Princeton, N. J.

NjPatM   Paterson Museum   Series listed: EP--Edu-
        268 Summer St.   cational Pamphlet (a-
        Paterson, 1, N. J.   vailable without chge
                                    for education purposes)

NjSom   Atlantic County Historical Soc.
        Somers Mansion
        Somers Point, N. J.

NjTM   New Jersey State Museum   Series listed: ANJ--
        Dept. of Education   Archaeology of New
        Trenton 25, N. J.   Jersey
                                    B--State Museum Bulle-
                                    tins
                                    L--Leaflets
                                    R--Research Series

NmRMA Roswell Museum & Art Center
        11th & Main Sts.
        Roswell, N. M.

NmSM-H New Mexico, Museum of   Series listed: P--Pub-
        Palace of the Governors,   lications
        P. O. Box 1727,
        Santa Fe, N. M.
        -- Historical Society of New Mexico

NmSM-L --Laboratory of Anthropology Series listed: B--
Bulletin; M--Memoir;
T--Technical Series

NmSM-S --School of American Research Series listed: M--
Monograph; P--Paper

NmSMI Museum of International Folk
Art, Museum of New Mexico
P.O. Box 4037
Santa Fe, N.M.

NmSMN Museum of Navajo Cere-   Series listed: B--Bulle-
monial Art   tin
P.O. Box 445
Santa Fe, N.M.

NvCN Nevada State Museum   Series listed: AP--
P.O. Box 495,   Anthropological Papers
Carson City, Nev.

OCA Cincinnati Art Museum
Eden Park
Cincinnati 6, Ohio

OCH-Mu Jewish Museum. Hebrew Union
College-Jewish Institute of
Religion
Clifton Ave.
Cincinnati 20, Ohio

OCMN Cincinnati Museum of Natural History
1720 Gilbert Ave.
Cincinnati 2, Ohio

OCT Taft Museum   Mailing chge additional
316 Pike St.
Cincinnati 2, Ohio

OClH Cleveland Health Museum   Mailing chge, ea pub-
8911 Euclid Ave.   lication: $.05
Cleveland 6, Ohio

CClMA Cleveland Museum of Art   Mailing chge, all orders:
11150 East Blvd.   min. $.15; add. on
Cleveland 6, Ohio   larger orders

OClMN   Cleveland Museum of   Series listed: PP--
           Natural History   Popular Publications
           10600 East Blvd.   SP--Scientific Publica-
           Cleveland 6, Ohio   tions

OHi   Ohio State historical Society
           Ohio State Museum
           15th Ave. & High St.
           Columbus 10, Ohio

OOxM-Mc McGuffey Museum
           Miami University
           Oxford, Ohio

OTM   Toledo Museum of Art   Mailing chge, orders
           Box 1013   less than $1: $.25; or-
           Toledo 1, Ohio   ders $1., or more:
                                      $.50

OYoB   Butler Institute of American Art
           524 Wick Ave.
           Youngstown 2, Ohio

OkA   Southern Plains Indians Exhibit
             & Crafts Center
           Box 447
           Anadarko, Okla.

OkB   Woolaroc Museum
           Bartlesville, Okla.

OkTG   Gilcrease, (Thomas), Institute of
             American History & Art
           2400 W. Newton St.
           Tulsa, Okla.

OkTP   Philbrook Art Center
           2727 S. Rockford Rd.
           Tulsa 14, Okla.

OkU-S   Stovall Museum of Science   Series listed: A--An-
            & History   thropological Papers
           University of Oklahoma   C--Information or Cir-
           Norman, Okla.   cular Series
                                   M--Museum Papers
                                   P--Paleontological Pa-
                                   pers
                                   TM--Treasure of the
                                   Month Series

OrK   Klamath County Museum   Series listed: RP--Re-
        3rd & Klamath   search Papers
        Klamath Falls, Ore.

OrPA   Portland Art Museum   Mailing chge, ea order:
        West Park & Madison $.25
        Portland 5, Ore.

OrPZ   Portland Zoo
        4001 S.W. Canyon Rd.
        Portland, Ore.

PDel   American Association of Botanical
          Gardens & Arboretums
        Box 216 Lima, Del. County,
        Pennsylvania

PDoHHi The Bucks County Historical Soc.
        Mercer Museum, Box 366
        Doylestown, Pa.

PHarH   Pennsylvania Historical &   Order from: State Bur-
          Museum Commission   eau of Publications,
        State Museum Bldg.   Publications Bldg.,
        Harrisburg, Pa.   Harrisburg, Pa.

PHi   Pennsylvania Historical Soc.
        1300 Locust St.
        Philadelphia 7, Pa.

PHoW   Wayne County Historical Soc.   Mailing chge, ea order:
        810 Main St. $.10. Bulletins listed
        Honesdale, Pa.   are available in volumes,
                        not as separate reprints

PJO   Old York Road Historical Soc.
        Abington Library
        Jenkintown, Pa.

PMeB   The Barnes Foundation
        Box 128, Merion Station
        Merion 1, Pa.

PNa   Moravian Historical Society
        Nazareth, Pa.

PPAN   Academy of Natural Sciences   Order from: Scientific
        of Philadelphia   Publications and Re-
        19th and the Parkway   prints. Series listed:
        Philadelphia 3, Pa.   M--Monograph
                                       N--Notulae Naturae
                                       Proceedings are indi-
                                       cated by date and num-
                                       ber, as 1957. 23, indi-
                                       cating the 23rd article
                                       in the Proceedings for
                                       the year 1957. Proceed-
                                       ings are listed from
                                       1923 on, as separate
                                       reprints are available
                                       only from that date.

PPComm Philadelphia Commercial
        Museum
        34th St. & Convention Ave.
        Philadelphia 4, Pa.

PPF   Fels Planetarium, Franklin Institute
        20th St. at Benjamin Franklin Pkwy.
        Philadelphia 3, Pa.

PPPM   Philadelphia Museum of Art,   Mailing chge, ea order:
        Benjamin Franklin Pkwy   25 percent of the sale
        at 26th St.   price of the order
        Philadelphia 1, Pa.

PPZ   Zoological Soc. of Philadelphia
        34th St. and Girard Ave.
        Philadelphia 4, Pa.

PPiCIA Carnegie Institute   Mailing chge, ea publi-
        Dept. of Fine Arts   cation order: $.25
        4400 Forbes St.
        Pittsburgh 13, Pa.

PPiCM   Carnegie Museum   Order from: Publica-
        4400 Forbes Ave.   tions Secretary
        Pittsburgh 13, Pa.   Series listed: A--Annals
                                       M--Memoirs

PRB   Berks County Historical Society
        940 Centre Ave.
        Reading, Pa.

xl

PRM	Reading Public Museum & Art Gallery 500 Museum Rd. Reading, Pa.	Series listed: B--Bulle-tins SP--Scientific Publica-tions
PU-Mu	The University Museum University of Pennsylvania 33rd & Spruce Sts. Philadelphia 4, Pa.	Series listed: AP--Anthropological Publi-cations B--University Museum Bulletin BE--Babylonian Expe-dition BFM--Bulletin of the Free Museum of Sci-ence & Art BS--Beth Shan Excava-tions CE--Eckley B. Coxe Expedition to Nubia CF--Eckley B. Coxe Foundation JP--Joint Publication MJ--Museum Journal MM--Museum Mono-graphs PBS(N) --Publications of the Babylonian Sec-tion (Nippur) T--Transactions of the Dept. of Archaeology Free Museum of Sci-ence & Art
RHi	Rhode Island Historical Society 52 Power St. Providence 6, R.I.	
RPD-M	Rhode Island School of Design Museum of Art Providence 3, R.I.	Series listed: B--Bulletin. Mailing chge, all orders: min. $.10; add. on larger orders
ScCG	Gibes Art Gallery Carolina Art Association 135 Meeting St. Charleston 5, S.C.	

ScCoM   Columbia Museum of Art
Senate and Bull Sts.
Columbia, S.C.

ScGB   Brookgreen Gardens Museum
Georgetown, S.C.

TxAl   West Texas Historical and
    Scientific Society
Big Bend Museum
Alpine, Tex.

TxAuM   Texas Memorial Museum   Series listed: B--
24th & Trinity Sts.   Bulletin
Austin 5, Tex.   IC--Information Circu-
    lar
    M--Mimeographed Se-
    ries

TxHM   Houston Museum of Fine Arts
1001 Bissonnet
Houston 5, Tex.

TxLT-Mu Texas Technological College
The Museum
Lubbock, Tex.

TxSaMc McNay, (Marion Koogler),
    Art Institute
755 Austin Highway
San Antonio, Tex.

TxSaW   Witte Memorial Museum   Series listed: BB--Big
Brackenridge Park   Bend Basket Maker Pa-
3801 Broadway   pers
San Antonio 9, Tex.

TxSaZ   San Antonio Zoo & Aquarium
3919 N. St. Mary's
San Antonio 12, Tex.

UV   Utah Field House of Natural History
Vernal, Utah

VWa   Mariners Museum
Newport News, Va.

ViMt   The Mount Vernon Ladies'
            Association of the Union
            Mount Vernon, Va.

ViRMu   Virginia Museum of Fine Arts Mailing chge additional
            Boulevard & Grove Ave.
            Richmond 20, Va.

ViRVM   Valentine Museum
            1015 E. Clay St.
            Richmond 19, Va.

ViWC   Colonial Williamsburg   Mailing chge, ea book
            Williamsburg, Va.   ordered: $.15

ViWR   Rockefeller, (Abby Aldrich),
            Folk Art Collection
            Williamsburg, Va.

VtHi   Vermont Historical Society   Mailing chge, orders
            Montpelier, Vt.   up to $5: $.25; ea ad-
                                              ditional $5: $.25
VtSM   Shelburne Museum
            Shelburne, Vt.

VtSpM   The Miller Art Center
            9 Elm St.
            Springfield, Vt.

WBB-Lo Logan Museum of Anthropol- Series listed:
            ogy   B--Bulletin
            Beloit College
            Beloit, Wis.

WiHi   Wisconsin State Historical Soc.
            816 State St.
            Madison 6, Wis.

WMA   Milwaukee Art Center
            750 N. Lincoln Memorial Dr.
            Milwaukee 2, Wis.

WMMMu Milwaukee Public Museum   Series listed:
            818 W. Wisconsin Ave.   B--Bulletin
            Milwaukee 3, Wis.   FG--Field Guides
                                              L--Leaflet Series
                                              PP--Popular Pamphlets
                                              (reprints from maga-

zine: Lore Leaves)
PSH--Popular Science
  Handbook Series
New Scientific Series:
PA--Publication in
  Anthropology
PB--Publications in
  Botany
PH--Publications in
  History
PO--Publications in
  Ornithology

WU-G   Wisconsin Union Gallery
        University of Wisconsin
        Madison 6, Wis.

WaSA   Seattle Art Museum
        Volunteer Park
        Seattle 2, Wash.

Mailing chge, ea pub-
lication: $.25 ea order
less than $2.50; $.50
ea order $2.50-$5. No
mailing chge on order
of $5., or more

WaSMu   Museum of History & Industry
        2720 Lake Washington Blvd, N.
        Seattle 2, Wash.

WvWA   American Association of Zoologi-
          cal Parks & Aquariums
        Oglebey Park
        Wheeling, W. Va.

WyY   Yellowstone National Parks Museums
        Box 117
        Yellowstone National Park, Wyo.

Abbreviations

For Museum symbols, see lists of Museums Distributing Publications.
For Series and Serial symbols, see Series listed, under Museum Symbol.

Ag	August
AIGA	American Institute of Graphic Arts
An	Annual
Anthrop	Anthropology; anthropological
Ap	April
art	article
B	Bulletin
BIP	Books in Print
book	booklet
brd	broadside
c	color
cat	catalog(s)
circ	circular
collect	collection(s)
cov	cover
D	December
Dept	Department
diagr	diagram(s)
drg	drawing(s)
ea	each
ed	edition; editor(s)
engrav	engraving(s)
ESSCO	Eastern Science Supply Company, Boston
etch	etching(s)
Exp	Expedition
Expl	Exploration
ext	extract
f	folder
F	February
facsim	facsimile
fasc	fascicle
fig	figure(s)
front	frontispiece
geol	geology
hdbk	handbook

il	illustration(s); illustrated
incl	including
Ja	January
Je	June
Jy	July
L	leaflet
mimeo	mimeographed
misc	miscellaneous
M	monograph
Mr	March
mss	manuscript(s)
multig	multigraphed
Mus	Museum
My	May
N	November
n sp	new species
nc	no charge
O	October
op	out of print
ornith	ornithology
p	page(s); paperbound
pam	pamphlet
PB	Picture Book
photog	photograph(s)
pl	plate(s)
pop	popular
port	portrait(s)
portf	portfolio
post	postage: handling and mailing, or shipping, charge
pt	part
ptg	printing
PTLA	Publishers' Trade List Annual
pubns	publications
repr	reprint
reprod	reproduction
rev	revised
S	September
sci	science
sect	section
ser	series
SI	Available only to Scientific Institutions
sigs	signatures only (unbound)
spec	special
suppl	supplement
tr	translator(s)
U	University
unbd	unbound

MUSEUM PUBLICATIONS

PART I

PUBLICATIONS IN ANTHROPOLOGY, ARCHAEOLOGY & ART

MUSEUMS AND MUSEUM WORK

American Association of Museums. Annual meeting report
(recent years avilable) apply DAMu   1
----. Annual report (recent years available) apply DAMu 2
----. Attendance at museums in the United States and Can-
ada, 1924-1928 14p 1929 p $.50 DAMu   3
----. Code of ethics for museum works apply DAMu   4
Collected papers on museum preparation and installation
(Pubns 3) 16p 1927 p $.50 DAMu   5
----. Constitution and by-laws, as amended May 28, 1952
2p apply DAMu   6
----. Index to publications of the American Association of
Museums (Completed serials: Proceedings of the Ameri-
can Association of Museums, 1907-1917; Museum Work,
1918-1926) (Pubns 52) 34p 1927 p. $.50 DAMu   7
----. Membership folder apply DAMu   8
----. Papers and reports read at the twenty-first annual
meeting (Pubns 1) 63p 1926 p $.50 DAMu   9
----. Inter-Museum Loans Committee. Report. Standard
procedure for inter-museum loans (repr. The Museum
News, May 15, 1950) 2p apply DAMu   10
----. Trustee-Employee Relations Committee. Report.
(repr. The Museum News, Sept. 1, 1955) 2p apply DAMu
     11
Bloomberg, Marguerite. An experiment in museum instruc-
tion (Pubns 8) 40p 1928 p $.50 DAMu   12
Coleman, Laurence Vail. City support of public museums
(repr, The Museum News, May 15, 1954) 5p apply DAMu
     13
----. College and university museums 73p 26 il 12 plan
1942 $1. DAMu   14
----. Museum buildings, a planning study v 1 298p 194 il
1950 $12.50 DAMu   15
Dana, John Cotton. A museum for everyday life (repr, The
Women's Home Companion, Jan 1925) 8p apply NjNM 16

47

----. The museum of service (repr, Survey Graphic, Feb
   1923) 8p il apply NjNM   17
Dudley, Dorothy H., et al. Museum registration methods
   225p 53 fig 1958 $7.50 DAMu   18
Frary, I.T. Museum membership and publicity (Pubns 13)
   35p 1935 p $.50 DAMu   19
Grundy, C. Reginald. Lessons from America in museum or-
   ganization and upkeep (repr, The Museums Journal, Lon-
   don, Dec 1926) 12p NjNM (op)   20
Guthe, Carl E. Museum salaries (repr, The Museum News,
   Oct 1, 1954) 4p apply DAMu   21
----. So you want a good museum, a guide to the manage-
   ment of small museums (Pubns 17) 37p 1957 p $.50
   DAMu   22
Howard, Richard Foster. Museum security (Pubns 18) 12p
   1958 p $.50 DAMu   23
Kingdon, Frank. John Cotton Dana: A life 175p front 1940
   $2. NjNM   24
Long, Charles J. Museum workers handbook 89p rev ed
   1960 $2. TxSaW   25
Lucas, Frederic A. Fifty years of museum work: autobi-
   ography, unpublished papers, and bibliography 81p 5 pl
   1933 p $1. NNM   26
Museum News. Index to special articles: The Museum News,
   volumes 1 to 30 (1924-1953), suppl to The Museum News
   19p 1953 $1. DAMu   27
The museum window (Bul 16) $.05 PRM   28
Museumobile exhibits, a teacher's guide p $.25 ISM   29
Porter, Mildred C.B. Behavior of the average visitor in the
   Peabody Museum of Natural History, Yale University
   (Pubns 16) 28p il 1938 p $.50 DAMu   30
Primer for preservation: A handbook for historic-house
   keeping (repr, Antiques, and New York History, July 1956),
   seven articles by experts based on Fall 1955 seminar 23p
   p $1. NCooHi   31
Pritchett, Henry S. Social philosophy of pensions (repr, The
   Museum News, May 15, 1930) 3p apply DAMu   32
Robinson, Edward S. The behavior of museum vistors
   (Pubns 5) 72p 1928 p $.50 DAMu   33
Smith, Ralph Clifton. A bibliography of museums and museum
   work 310p 1928 $5. DAMu   34
Woolford, Sam. Value of a museum as an auxiliary to a
   military historian 1954 apply TxSaW   35

--ART MUSEUMS See also Art

Creative projects; An instructor's handbook dealing with art

projects in different media p $1.   CoDA   36
Dana, John Cotton.   The Museum as an art patron (repr,
    Creative Art, March 1929) 7 p   apply NjNM   37
How to make objects of wood $2; p $1.50 MBI   38
Kennan, George F.   International exchange in the arts, an
    address at a symposium sponsored by the International
    Council of the Museum of Modern Art 8 p 1955 $.25
    NNMA   39
MacLeish, Archibald.   Art education and the creative pro-
    cess,   address delivered at Conference of Committee on
    Art Education 16p 1954 $.25 NNMMA   40
Melton, Arthur W.   Problems of installation in museums of
    art, edited by Edward S. Robinson (Pubns 14) 269 p.
    1935 p $2. DAMu   41
Munro, Thomas, and Jane Grimes.   Work of the Educational
    Department of the Cleveland Museum of Art p $1. OClMA
                                                           42
Paint and clay corner: A wartime service by the Newark
    Museum at Camp Kilmer, N.J. 32p il 1945 p $.25 NjNM
    (op)   43
Quandt, Russell J.   Reclamation of two paintings (B v 6, no
    3) 1953 p $.50 DCGA (op)   44
Sugden, Robert P.   Care and handling of art objects 32 p
    5 il 1946 p $.50 NNMM   45
----. Safeguarding works of art. Storage, packing, trans-
    portation, and insurance 80 p 12 il 1948 p $1.75 NNNM
                                                           46
Tuckerman, Lucy D. Suggestions for the library of a small
    museum of art (Pubns 6) 39 p 1928 p $.50 DAMu   47
Verhelst, Wilbert. Creative projects; a handbook for art
    teachers, describing art projects in various media 36 p
    $1. CoDA   48

--SCIENCE MUSEUMS See also Science

Arnold, Harold E. The capture and preservation of small
    mammals for study (SG 61) 54p 24 il p $.60; post $.10
    NNM   49
Aquaria and terraria (Info Circ) apply NcRSM   50
Burns, William A. Tan your own hide (SG 45; repr, Field
    and Stream, 1947) 2p il $.05; post, $.02 NNM   51
Chapin, James P. The preparation of birds for study (SG
    58) 48 p 26 il p $.40; post $.10 NNM   52
Cooke, Edmund. Nature trails in Cleveland (Pubns 10) 18p
    1930 p $.50 DAMu   53
Jonas, Louis. The mounting of an elephant group (Pubns
    11) 32p 1930 p $.50 DAMu   54

Lucas, Frederic A.   Preparation of rough skeletons (SG 59)
    15p 15 il p $.30; post $.10 NNM   55
Melton, Arthur W.   Experimental studies of the education of
    children in a museum of science (Pubns 15) 106p 1936 p
    $1. DAMu   56
Neal, Arminta. Cigar-box dioramas, handbook on 3-dimen-
    sional displays p $.75 IdHi   57
Pollard, Agnes L.   A book list for a small museum of natur-
    al sciences (Pubns 7) 28 p 1928 p $.50 DAMu   58
Reid, A.   Steps in making durable lightweight casts of latex
    5p $.25 CaOTRM   59
Stolper, Joel.   My trip to the zoo, drawings 32p $.20 NNZ
                                                                  60
Teaching conservation (Leaflet 5) p $.10 CaOTRM   61
Tunnel in the desert, an underground venture in education
    (ES 2) 34p 16 il p $.60 AzTu   62

--MUSEUM DIRECTORIES See also specific types of institu-
    tions, as Astronomy--Planetariums and Observatories;
    Zoology--Zoos and Aquariums

American Association of Museums.   Institution members,
    United States and Canada. Annual- (repr, The Museum
    News) $.50 DAMu   63
Coleman, Laurence Vail. Directory of museums in South
    America 133p 76 il 1929 $3. DAMu   64
Everard, L.C.   Zoological parks, aquariums, and botanical
    gardens (Pubns 12) 72p 1932 p $1. DAMu   65
A list of Michigan museums p apply MiLHi   66
Museum resources in the Detroit area p $.25 MiDHi   67
Museums of New York City.   Description of Museums, His-
    toric Houses, Botanical and Zoological Gardens in New
    York City 62p 1954 p $.35 NNPM   68
Treasure house of New York State--information about New
    York State museums p $.40 NBuM   69
Wyman, Donald, comp.   The Arboretums and botanical gar-
    dens of North America 69p il 1959 p $1.50 MH-A   70

--MUSEUMS--Catalogs, Guides, History   See also   Art--
    Museums and Galleries

Alaska. University. Museum.   Guide, giving history, com-
    ments on exhibits including those in anthropology and
    archaeology p $.10 AkU-Mu   71
American Museum of Natural History.   General guide (SG
    118) 248p $1.15 NNM   72
Arizona-Sonora Desert Museum.   The desert speaks--the

founding, building and objectives of the Arizona-Sonora
Desert Museum (ES 1) 49p 31 il p $.60 AzTu   73
----. Water Street, U.S.A., the Watershed Exposition of
the Arizona-Sonora Desert Museum (ES 3) 65p 43 il p
$.86 AzTu   74
Arnold Arboretum. Through the Arnold Arboretum, a guide-
book 44p 19 il (4 c) map 1949 p $.50 MH-A   75
Bishop (Bernice P.) Museum. Guide 1956 p $.25 HB   76
Boston Public Library. Handbook p $.50; post $.06 MB 77
Bucks County Historical Society Museum. Cummings, John.
Mercer Museum of the Bucks County Historical Society.
Guide book p $.50 PDoBHi   78
Buffalo Historical Society Museum. Severance, Frank H.,
ed. The book of the museum (Pubns v 25) 1921 p $1.
NBuHi   79
Buffalo Museum of Science. Clawson, H. Phelps. By their
works, based on archaeological and ethnological collections
in the Buffalo Museum of Science $4.20 NBuM   80
----. Cummings, Carlos E. A review of the work done by
the Buffalo Society of Natural Sciences in cooperation with
public schools (B v 8, no 4) p $.55 NBuM   81
----. Cummings, Virginia L. On the Indian trail in the
Buffalo Museum of Science p $.25 NBuM   82
----. Guide to the Hall of Civilization p $.20; Guide to the
Hall of Man p $.25; Guide to the Hall of Plant Life p
$.20 NBuM   83
----. Seventy-five years: A history of the Buffalo Society
of Natural Sciences, 1861-1936 (B v 18) $2.15 NBuM   84
Chicago Academy of Sciences. Centennial meeting (SP 13)
23p 8 pl 1958 p $.50 ICAS   85
Chicago Historical Society Museum. Angle, Paul M. The
Chicago Historical Society, 1856-1956; an unconventional
chronicle 275p il $7.50 ICHi   86
----. Descriptive tour of the Chicago Historical Society
Museum. il and in mailer $.10 ICHi   87
Chicago Natural History Museum. Colorama--museum ex-
hibits depicted in color with brief description opposite 87p
43 il c 6th ptg rev 1956 p $.75 ICM   88
----. General guide 48 p 39 il 38th ed 1959 p $.25 ICF 89
----. Gunsaulus, Helen C. The Japanese collections (A-
PS 3) 19 p 6 il 1922 p $.20 ICF   90
----. A historical and descriptive account of the Field
Columbian Museum (Historical Volume 1) 90 p 15 il 1894
p $2. ICF   91
Colonial Williamsburg. Official guidebook and map 126 p il
map c p $.50 ViWC   92
Colorado State Museum. Guidebook p $.50 CoHi   93

Corning Museum of Glass.   The Corning Glass Center; a
    visitor's guide to the Corning Museum of Glass, Hall of
    Science and Industry, and Steuben factory 63 p (10 c) 1958
    $.50 NCorniC-M   94
Cranbrook Institute of Science.   Guide to exhibits 65 p il 7th
    ed 1960 p $.50 MiBloC   95
----.   Cranbrook Institute of Science: a history of its found-
    ing and first twenty-five years (B 37) 158 p 33 pl 1959
    $5. MiBloC   96
Detroit Historical Museum.   Guide book p $.10 MiDHi   97
Dominican Astrophysical Observatory, Victoria, British Co-
    lumbia 34p il (Queen's Printer) 1951 p apply CaOOO   98
Essex Institute.   Essex Institute historical collections, July
    1958 (Special Hawthorne issue) p $2.   MSaE   99
----.   First half century of the Essex Institute 295p il 1898
    p $.50 MSaE   100
The Folger Shakespeare Library.   The Folger Shakespeare
    Library, a brief description p $.35 DFo   101
Franklin Institute.   Coulson, Thomas.   Story of the Franklin
    Institute p $.50 PPF   102
Hall of Fame.   Hilpert, Josef.   Hall of Fame booklet 32p
    35 il (7 c) p $1. CSc   103
Hispanic Society of America.   Museum and Library. Penney,
    C. L.   Catalogue of publications--bibliographical descrip-
    tions arranged chronologically beginning with the "Hunting-
    ton Reprints" 151p 55 il 1943 $2.50 NNH   104
Illinois State Museum.   Guide to the exhibits 22 p 6 il 1957
    p $.10 ISM   105
----.   Wright, A. Gilbert.   The Illinois State Museum,
    1877-1952, three quarters of a century of service (75th
    anniversary issue, The Living Museum, v 6, no 6, Oct
    1952) apply ISM   106
Kansas. University.   Museum of Natural History.   Moore,
    Roy R., and E. Raymond Hall.   Museum of Natural His-
    tory (MP no 19) 1959 p apply KU-Mu   107
Los Angeles County Museum.   Habitat groups of North
    America p $.35 CLCM   108
The Mariners Museum.   Mariners Museum--A history and
    guide 276p 275 il 1950 $3.50; post $.16 VWa   109
Michigan. University.   Ethnobotanical Laboratory.   Gilmore,
    Melvin R.   The Ethnobotanical Laboratory at the Univer-
    sity of Michigan (OC 1) 36 p 1 pl 1932 p $.50 MiU-A 110
Middle American Research Institute.   An inventory of the
    collections of the Middle American Research Institute, no.
    2.   Calendar of the Yucatan letters, 1778-1863 240p p
    1939 $2.50 LNT-MA   111
----.   Irvine, Marie Hunter.   Administrative papers: Copies

relating to New Spain. A collection of manuscripts in
Middle American Research Institute (M 5) 28 p 1948 p apply LNT-MA   112
Museum of Science and Industry. Chicago. Visitor's guide
p $.10 ICS   113
Museum of the American Indian. Guide to the Museum,
second floor 251 p 1922 p $.35; Guide to the collections
from the West Indies (M 32) 38 p 1922 p $.15 NNMAI
                                                          114
----. The Heye Collection (MJ v 1, no 1) 2p 1 il 1910 p
$.50 PU-Mu   115
----. History of the Museum. (M 55) rev ed 1960 p apply
NNMAI   116
Museum of the City of New York. Museum guide book il p
$.25; plus post NNMus   117
National Baseball Hall of Fame and Museum souvenir booklet
p $.50 NCooN   118
Nebraska State Historical Society. Museum pictorial tour p
$.25 NbHi   119
Nebraska State Museum. Barbour, Erwin H. A preliminary
report on the Nebraska State Museum (B 1:1) 1924 p
NbU-Mu   120
----. Barbour, Erwin H. Report of the progress of the
Nebraska State Museum (B 2:1) 1938 p NbU-Mu   121
Nevada State Museum. The Nevada State Museum, history
and exhibits of the museums (Information series) rev ed
p $.50 NvCM   122
New Brunswick Museum. Squires, W.A. History and de-
velopment of the New Brunswick Museum, 1842-1945 (Ad-
ministrative Series 2) 1945 $1. CaNBSM   123
New Jersey State Museum. Growth of the State Museum (B
1) 4 p 1 il 1946 p apply NjTM   124
New Mexico Museum. Museum of New Mexico: Its history
and functions (P ns 43) 27 p il rev ed 1953 p $.50
NmSM-S   125
----. Springer, Frank. Address of dedication of the New
Museum, Santa Fe, N.M., Nov 26, 1917 (P 42) 18 p 2
port 1917 p $.25 NmSM-S   126
----. Walter, Paul A.F. Twenty-five years of achieve-
ment (P ns 24) 25 p port 1932 p $.25 NmSM-S   127
New York Historical Society. Catalogue of books in the li-
brary of the New York Historical Society presented by
John Watts de Peyster, pt 1 Jan 1868 24 p $1. NHi   128
----. Catalogue of printed books in the library of the New
York Historical Society 653 p 1859 $5. NHi   129
----. Catalogue of the books, tracts, newspapers, maps,
charts, views, portraits, and manuscripts in the library

of the New York Historical Society 139 p 1813 $5; Cata-
logue...added to the library...since January 1839 32 p
1840 $2. MHi   130
----. Selected Americana exclusive of New York from the
library of the New York Historical Society. A short-title
list of rare and important books, pamphlets, and broad-
sides on exhibition at the Society, June 22-July 29, 1945
42p p $.20 NHi   131
----. Survey of the manuscript collections in the New York
Historical Society 96p 1941 $.65 NHi   132
New York State Historical Association. Jones, Louis C.
Cooperstown (Ostego County Historical Society)--The vil-
lage, surrounding area, museums, James Fenimore
Cooper 90 p 55 il 2nd ed 1953 $3; p $2 NCooHi   133
----. McFarlane, Janet. The Lippitt Homestead and the
Farmers' Museum (repr, Antiques, Aug 1953) il p $.25
NCooHi   134
New York State Museum. The People of the Longhouse, a
guide to the Iroquois Indian groups in the New York State
Museum 16 p 6 il p $.10 NAlMu   135
Newark Museum. The garden: Then--and now; the school-
house in the garden (The Museum, ns, v 9, no 2, Spring
1957) p $.75 NjNM   136
----. Newark Museum Planetarium (The Museum, ns, v 5,
no 2, Spring 1953) p $.50 NjNM   137
----. A survey: Fifty years of the Newark Museum (The
Museum, ns, v 11, nos 1-4, 1959) p $2. NjNM   138
North Carolina Museum of Art. Opening of the North Caro-
lina State Museum (special issue, Art News, April 1956)
$1. NcRMA   139
North Carolina State Museum. Guide leaflet (Information
Circular) apply NcRSM   140
Peabody Museum of Natural History. Yale University. A
pictorial book of some of the Museum exhibits 1956 $.25
CtY-PM   141
Peabody Museum of Salem. Goodspeed, Charles E. Nathaniel
Hawthorne and the Museum of the East India Marine So-
ciety, or the gathering of a virtuoso's collection 32p 6 pl
1946 $1. MSaP   142
----. Jenkins, Lawrence Waters, and Walter Muir White-
hill. The restoration of the East India Marine Hall 15 p
7 pl 3 fig 1948 $.50 MSaP   143
Peale's Museum. Faxon, Walter. Relics of Peale's Museum
(B v 49, no 3) 32 p 1915 p $.50 MH-Z   144
----. Hunter, Wilbur H., Jr., and Charles H. Elam.
Rendezvous for taste: Peale's Baltimore Museum, 1814-
1830 36 p 65 il $1. MdBPM   145

----. Story of America's oldest museum building 8 il p
   $.25 MdBPM   146
Philadelphia Academy of Natural Sciences. Phillips, M.E.
   A brief history of Academy publications (1948. 8) $1.20
   PPAN   147
Philadelphia Zoo. Official illustrated guide book p $.60
   PPZ   148
Pierpont Morgan Library. Review of activities and major
   aquisitions, 1941-1948, with a memoir of John Pierpont
   Morgan and the Pierpont Morgan Library, 1913-1943 108
   p 13 pl 1949 p $2. NMPM   149
Pilgrim Hall. Briggs. Pilgrim Hall, a museum of Pilgrim
   history. Catalogue p $.50 MP   150
Rancho Santa Ana Botanic Garden. Munz, P.A. History of
   Rancho Santa Ana Botanic Garden, 1928-1945 p $.60 CCR 151
Royal Ontario Museum. Dymond, J.R. History of the
   Royal Ontario Museum of Zoology (C 18) 52 p 1940 p
   $.40 CaOTRM   152
----. Frits, M.A. Outline of the history and development
   of the Royal Ontario Museum of Paleontology (C 1) 19 p
   1939 p $.25 CaOTRM   153
----. History of the collections of the Royal Ontario Mu-
   seum of Zoology (B 9) 1940 p $.10 CaOTRM   154
----. Royal Ontario Museum, a handbook 57 p il, floor
   plans p $.50 CaOTRM   155
San Diego Zoo. Official guide book p $.83 CSdZ   156
----. Wegeforth, Harry M., and Neil Morgan. It began
   with a roar--the story of the famous San Diego Zoo 1953
   p $2. CSdZ   157
Shelburne Museum. Hill, Ralph Nading, and Lilian Baker
   Carlisle. The story of Shelburne Museum $3. VtSM;VtHi 158
Southwest Museum. Handbook, an illustrated guide to the
   museum and its collections p $.15 CLSM   159
Steinhart Aquarium. Guide 39 p il 1943 p $.35 CSfA   160
Texas Memorial Museum. Guide p $.30 TxAuM   161
United States Department of the Interior Museum. Guide 9 il
   1 plan apply DI-M   162
University Museum. Goodale, J.C., and D. Perkins, Jr.
   The story of man, guide to the Hall of Man 28 p il 1953
   p $.15 PU-Mu   163
----. Griffin, C. The Museum library (B v 19, no 2) 6 p
   3 il 1955 p $.50 PU-Mu   164
----. Mason, J.A. The American collections of the Univer-
   sity Museum: The ancient civilizations of Middle America
   (B v 10, nos 1-2) 64 p 50 il $1. PU-Mu   165
----. Moore, E.M. The educational department of the University Museum (B v 12, nos 1-2) 52p 56 il1946 $1. PU-Mu   166

----. The new museum buildings, University Museum; with,
Rosenbach, A.S.W.   The Rittenhouse "Orrery" (BFM v 2,
no 2) 1899 p $.50 PU-Mu   167
----. The new North American Galleries (Tlingit) (B v 3,
no 1) 2 p 1 pl 1931 p $.35 PU-Mu   168
----. Illustrated guide 23 p 94 il 10 map 1956 $.65 Pu-Mu
169
Utah State Museum. Untermann.   Guide to Utah State Mu-
seum of Natural History and the unique Uinta County 1959
UV   170
Wadsworth Atheneum. Austin, A. Everett: A director's
taste and achievement. Cover design: Eugene Berman;
forword: Sir Osbert Sitwell; Essays: Edward W. Forbes,
R. Kirk Askew, James T. Soby, Julien Levy, Henry-Rus-
sel Hitchcock, Eugene Berman, T.H. Parker, Virgil
Thomson, Lincoln Kirstein 92 p 31 il 1958 p $2. CtHWA
171
----. Wadsworth Atheneum, Hartford. A brief guide: Colt,
Morgan, and Avery Memorials 4 p 20 il 1951 p $.10
CtHWA   172
----. Wadsworth Atheneum. Handbook 193 p 336 il (16 c)
1958 p $2.75; post $.25 CtHWA   173
----. Wadsworth Atheneum: 111 years, an exhibition re-
viewing the history of the Wadsworth Atheneum 1842-1952
16 p 1 pl c 1952 p $.35 CtHWA   174
Woolaroc Museum. KeMoHa. Indians, an illustrated book-
let of the Woolaroc Museum collections p $.25 OkB 175

ANTHROPOLOGY AND ARCHAEOLOGY

Braidwood, Robert J.   Prehistoric men (A-PS 37) 187 p 45
il 3rd ed 1957 p $1.25 ICF   176
Hewett, Edgar L.   Campfire and trail 165 p photog 1943 $2.
NmSM-S   177
----. From cave dwelling to Mount Olympus 143 p 1943
$1.50 NmSM-S   178
----. From culture to civilization (P ns 29) 10 p 1942 p
$.25 NmSM-S   179
----. Man and culture 146 p 1944 $2. NmSM-S   180
----. Man and the state 152 p 1944 $2. NmSM-S   181
----. What is man (P ns 30) 19 p 1942 p $.25 NmSM-S
182
McVaugh, Rogers, et al.   Farwelliana; an account of the life
and botanical work of Oliver Atkins Farwell, 1867-1944
(B 34) 107 p il 1953 p $1. MiBloC   183
Martin, Paul S. Digging into history (A PS 38) 157 p 64 il

   p $1. 50 ICF   184
Mason, J. Alden.   George G. Heye, 1874-1957 (L 6) 1957,
   privately distributed NNMAI   185
Rise of civilizations p $.10 MnSSci   186
Shapiro, Harry L.   A world full of people (SG 125;
   repr, Natural History) 9 p 10 il p $.15; post $.10 NNM
                                                               187

Anthropology--Material Culture

Bernstein, Morris M.   Edged weapons (EP 4) NjPatM   188
Ellsworth, Clarence.   Bows and arrows (leaflet 24) p $.25
   CLSM   189
Locke, L. Leland.   Supplementary notes on the quipus in
   the American Museum of Natural History (AP 30:2, p 39-
   73) 1 fig 1928 p $.35 NNM   190
Treskin, Andrew L.   Missiles (EP 21) NjPatM   191
Quimb, George I., and Alexander Spoehr.   Acculturation and
   material culture, Pt. 1 (FA 36:6) 41 p 29 il 1951 $1.
   ICF   192
Wieschoff, H.A.   Primitive money (B v 2, no 3) 43 p 16 il
   1945 p $.50 PU-Mu   193
Wolff, Eldon G.   Air guns (Publications in History, no 1)
   198 p 66 il 1958 p $5. WMMMu   194

Anthropology--Social Life and Customs

Allen, Hamilton Ford.   Two mummy labels in the Carnegie
   Museum (A v 8, no 2, p 218-21) 2 pl p $.10 PPiCM 195
Laufer, Berthold.   Geophagy (FA 18:2) 102 p 1930 $.50
   ICF   196
Martin, Richard A.   Mummies (A-PS 36) 43 p 20 il (1 c)
   1945 p $.50 ICF (op)   197
Miner, Horace M.   Culture and agriculture (OC 14) 96 p 2
   map 1949 p $1. MiU-A   198
Ritzenthaler, Robert E.   Shrunken heads (PP, Lore Leaves,
   no 4; repr, Lore) 7 il p $.15 WMMMu   199

Anthropology--Methodology

Colton, Harold S.   Field methods in archaeology, prepared
   for archaeological expeditions of the Museum of Northern
   Arizona (T 1) 30 p 1953 p $1. AzFM   200
----.   Potsherds: An introduction to the study of prehistoric
   Southwestern ceramics and their use in historic recon-
   struction (B 25) 86 p 1953 $3. AzFM   201
Culin, Stewart.   An archaeological application of the Rontgen
   rays (BFM v 1, no 4) 1 p 2 pl 1898 p $.50 PU-Mu   202

Deuel, Thorne. A new approach to studies of culture and
    society (repr, Trans Ill State Acad Sci, v 43, p 9-15,
    1950) p apply ISM   203
Difficulties of specimen identification, Pt. 1 (IL 86) CoDA
                                                             204
Excavating Indian sites, a description of methods p $.10
    CaOTRM   205
Griffin, James B., ed. Essays on archaeological methods.
    Proceedings of a conference held under the auspices of
    the Viking Fund (AP 8) 151 p 1951 p $1.50 MiU-A   206
March, Benjamin. Standards of pottery description (OC 3)
    55 p 4 pl 8 fig 1934 p $.75 MiU-A   207
Moodie, Roy L. Roentgenologic studies of Egyptian and Per-
    uvian mummies (AM 3) 66 p 76 photog 1931 $5. ICM 208
Stallings, William S., Jr. Dating prehistoric ruins by tree-
    rings (B 8) 1939 p $.50 NmSM-L   209
Swanson, Earl H. The archaeological survey system of the
    Museum (OP 1) 1938 p IdPI-Mu   210
Whiteford, Andrew H., ed. Teaching anthropology; papers
    presented at the Seminar on Teaching of Anthropology,
    33rd Annual Meeting of the Central States Anthropological
    Society, Madison, Wisconsin, 1957 (B 8) 66 p 1959 $1.
    WBB-Lo   211
Wendorf, Fred, ed. Highway salvage archaeology (Published
    by New Mexico State Highway Dept, and Museum of New
    Mexico) v 3 101 p map, chart, il 1957 p $1.25 NmSM-L
                                                             212
Wissler, Clark. The archaeologist at work (SG 116) 16 p
    38 il p $.65; post $.10 NNM   213

--Regional Anthropology

The Dixon memorial volume, studies in the anthropology of
    Oceania and Asia presented in memory of Roland B. Dixon
    by fourteen former students (P v 20) 220 p 20 pl 10 map
    7 il 1943 $7.25; p $4.25 MH-P   214
Ethnographical album of the north Pacific coasts of America
    and Asia, Pt 1, p 1-5 28 pl 1900 p $6. NNM   215
Nuttall, Zelia. The fundamental principles of Old and New
    World civilizations (P v 2) 602 p 7 pl 73 il 1901 $8; sig-
    natures $5.50 MH-P   216
Seder, T. Old World overtones in the New World (B v 16,
    no 4) 71 p 22 il 1952 p $.50 PU-Mu   217

-- Americas

Amsden, Charles Avery. America's earliest man (L 4)

Dockstader, Frederick J.   59

p $.15 CLSM   218
Dockstader, Frederick J.   The American Indian in graduate
studies, a bibliography of theses and dissertations (C v
15) 399 p 1957 p $5.   NNMAI   219
Fowke, Gerard.   Americans before Columbus 25 p 1930 p
$.25 OHi   220
Hewett, Edgar L.   The groundwork of American archaeology
(P 1) 5 p 1908 p $.25 NmSM-S   221

--Indians of North America

Ariss, Robert.   Indians of Western North America (AP 1)
28 p il 1955 p $.25 CLCM   222
Baerreis, David, ed.   The Indians in modern America, a
collection of three essays 70 p 1956 p $2.   WHi   223
Birchbark and the Indian (IL 102) CoDA   224
Copper and the Indian (IL 75/76) CoDA   225
Dunn, James Taylor.   The true, moral and diverting tale of
the Cardiff Giant (repr, New York History, July 1948) 10
p 1949 p $.20 NCooHi   226
Fisher, Reginald G.   The relations of North American pre-
history to Post-Glacial climatic fluctuation (M 3) published
with University of New Mexico 102 p map fig 1935 $2.
NmSM-S   227
Gallatin, Albert.   Indian tribes of North America (TC v 2)
1836 $25.   MWA   228
A guide to Texas Indians (M 1) p $.25 TxAuM   229
Hewett, Edgar L.   Two score years 146 p 1946 p $2.
NmSM-S   230
Indian culture areas in the United States (IL 107) CoDA   231
Indian life (Gallup Ceremonial Association) Annual, 1959-
p $.50 OkA   232
Indian reservations p apply MiLHi   233
Indians of the Old West il p $.50 NbG   234
Indians before history in the Upper Mississippi Valley 1957
$.60 MnSSci   235
Indians of western North America p $.25 CLCM   236
Mason, J.A.   Impressions of an ethnologist (B v 7, no 2)
3 p 1938 p $.50 PU-Mu   237
Mistaken ideas about the Indians (IL 112) CoDA   238
Peterson, C.A.   The Mound Building age in North America
(repr, Collections) 1902 p $3.   MoHi   239
Ritzenthaler, Robert E.   Famous American Indians (PP,
Lore Leaves no 7; repr, Lore) 16 il p $.25 WMMMu
                                                           240
Schuetz, Mardith K.   The Indians of Texas 25 p 1 il $.50
TxSaW   241

Shapiro, Harry L.   Americans--Yesterday, today, and to-
   morrow (SG 126; repr, Natural History) 10 p 10 il p
   $.30; post $.10 NNM   242
Tribal names, Pt 1 (IL 82); Pt 2 (IL 85); Pt 3 (IL 101)
   CoDA   243
Tschopik, Harry.   Indians of North America (SG 136) 64 p
   44 il p $1.15 NNM   244
Walker, Edwin F.   America's Indian background, an intro-
   duction to the subject of Indians in the United States area
   (L 18) p $.25; with tribal map, $.60 CLSM   245
Williams, Arthur B.   The Kirtland Society (Mormons) (PP
   3) 16 p 1943 p $.05 OClMN   246
Wormington, H.M.   Ancient man in North America (PS 4)
   322 p 71 il 1 map 4th ed 1957 $5.20 CoDMNH   247

--Indians of North America--Maps and Charts

Indians of North America, chart 24x32 c $1.10 NBuM   248
Kroeber, A.L.   Distribution of the Indian tribes of Northern
   America when they first came in contact with white
   people, map 21x28 $.35 CLSM   249
North American Indian tribes and culture areas, map (Map
   G) 15.5x17.5 $.15 NNM   250

--Indians of North America--Material Culture

American Indian material in the Newark Museum, and basketry of the Indians (Museum, ns, v 10, nos 3/4, Summer
   and Fall 1958) p $1.25 NjNM   251
Bryan, Kirk.   Flint quarries--the sources of tools and, at
   the same time, the factories of the American Indian (P v
   17, no 3) 40 p 1 pl 20 il 1950 p $2. MH-P   252
Indian foodstuffs p $.05 CLCM   253
Main types of Indian cradles (IL 115) CoDA   254
Mason, J.A.   Some unusual spearthrowers of Ancient America (Eskimo, Utah, Florida, Peru) (MJ v 19, no 3) 35 p
   14 il 1928 p $1. PU-Mu   255
Peterson, Harold.   Tomahawks and trade axes (C v 18) in
   press, to appear late 1960 NNMAI   256
Prehistoric objects classified and described (Dept. of Archae-
   ology, Bul 1) 32 p 14 pl 1913 p $.75 MoHi   257
Ritzenthaler, Robert E.   Indian cradles (PP, Lore Leaves
   no 1, repr Lore) 10 il p $.15 WMMMu   258
Snowshoes (MJ v 2, no 4) 13 p 17 il 1911 p $.50 PU-Mu
                                                               259
Speck, Frank G., and George G. Heye.   Hunting charms of
   the Montagnais and the Mistassini (M 13) 19 p il 1921 p

$.35 NNMAI

Totem poles (IL 79/80) CoDA   261
Wardle, H. N.   The Charles H. Stephens Collection (B v 3,
    no 5) 4 p 2 pl 1932 p $.35 PU-Mu   262
----.   The Franklin Peale Collection (B v 4, no 5) 2 p 2 pl
    1933 p $.35 PU-Mu   263
West, George A.   Exceptional prehistoric copper implements
    (B v 10, no 4) 26 p 31 pl 1932 p $.50 WMMMu   264
Wissler, Clark.   Harpoons and darts in the Stefansson Col-
    lection (AP 14:2, p 397-443) 44 fig 1916 p $.50 NNM
                                                                265

--Indians of North America--Social Life and Customs

American Indian tobacco varieties, cultivation and methods of
    use (IL 22) CoDA   266
The buffalo and the Indian (IL 7) CoDA   267
Culin, Stewart.   American Indian games (BFM v 1, no 3) 10
    p 9 il 1898 p $.50 PU-Mu   268
Harrington, M.R.   Mystery packs of the American Indian
    (MJ v 2, no 3) 3 p 1911 p $.50 PU-Mu   269
Indian symbols, folder giving origin and meaning p $.07
    NBuM   270
Jaeger, Ellsworth.   Indian calendar (BSNS) p $.15 NBuM
                                                                271
le Sueur, Jacques.   History of the calumet and the dance
    (C 12:5) 22 p il 1952 p $2.   NNMAI   272
The peyote cult (IL 105); --Ritual equipment (IL 106) CoDA
                                                                273
Skinner, Alanson.   Medicine ceremony of the Menomini,
    Iowa, and Wahpeton Dakota, with notes on the ceremony
    among the Ponca, Bungi Ojibwa, and Patawatomi (INM v 4)
    357 p 26 pl 1920 p $3.   NNMAI   274
Walker, Edwin F.   World crops derived from the Indians
    (Leaflet 17) p $.25 CLSM   275
Wissler, Clark.   General discussion of shaministic and danc-
    ing societies (AP 11:12, p 853-76) 1916 p $.25 NNM 276
Witthoft, John.   The American Indian as hunter 18 p 1953
    p $.25 PHarH   277
----.   A brief history of the Indian hunter 25 p 1954 p $.25
    PHarH   278

--Indians of North America--Eastern Woodlands

The Adena People, including a descriptive Adena trait list
    (Report on Anthropology v 6) p $3. KyU-Mu (op)   279
Archaeology in North Carolina (Info Circ) apply NcRSM 280
Archaic sites in McLean County, Kentucky (Report on An-

thropology v 7, no 1) p $.50 KyU-Mu   281
Archeological survey of Kentucky (Report on Anthropology v
    2) 463 p 65 fig 72 map $5. KyU-Mu   282
Barrett, S.A.   Ancient Aztalan (B 13) 602 p 100 pl 161 fig
    2 map 1933 p $7. WMMMu   283
----, and A. Skinner.   Certain mounds and village sites of
    Shawano and Oconto Counties, Wisconsin (B v 10, no 5)
    152 p 24 pl 30 fig 1932 p $1.50 WMMMu   284
Belknap, Jeremy, and Jedidiah Morse.   Report on the One-
    ida, Stockbridge, and Brotherton Indians--1796 (M 54) 39
    p facsim 1955 p $1.   NNMAI   285
Billington.   The vegetation of Cranbrook Lake bottom (B 11)
    20 p 1 pl 1 map 1938 p $.10 MiBloC   286
Bushnell, D.I., Jr.   The Cahokia and surrounding Mound
    Groups (P v 3, no 1) 20 p 5 pl map 7 il 1904 p $.50
    MH-P   287
Butler, Mary.   Archaeology in Western Pennsylvania (B v 6,
    no 5) 4 p 2 il 1936 p $.35 PU-Mu   288
The C. and O. Mounds at Paintsville, Sites Jo 2 and Jo 9,
    Johnson County, Kentucky (Reports on Anthropology v 5,
    no 4) p $.50 KyU-Mu   289
Callender, John M.   New light on Old Fort Snelling: An
    archaeological exploration, 1957-58 42 p il 1959 p $1.
    MnHi   290
The Carlos Annis Mound, Site 5, Butler County, Kentucky
    (Reports on Anthropology, v 7, no 4) p $.75 KyU-Mu 291
Chapin, Howard M.   Sachems of Narragansetts 117 p 1931
    $3.   RHi   292
The Chiggerville Site, Site 1, Ohio County, Kentucky (Reports
    on Anthropology v 4, no 1) p $.50 KyU-Mu   293
The Chilton Site in Henry County, Kentucky (Reports on An-
    thropology v 3, no 5) p $.50 KyU-Mu   294
The Chippewa or Ojibwa Indians (IL 36) CoDA   295
Claflin, William H., Jr.   The Stalling's Island mound, Col-
    umbia County, Georgia (P v 14, no 1) 60 p 72 pl 1931 p
    $2.75 MH-P   296
Cooper, L.R.   The Red Cedar River variant of Wisconsin
    Hopewell Culture (B v 16, no 2) 62 p 10 pl 4 fig 2 map
    $.75 WMMMu   297
----.   Indian Mounds Park Archeological site, Rice Lake,
    Wisconsin (Science Bul 6) 1959 $1.15 MnSSci   297a
The Crigler Mounds, Sites Be 20 and Be 27, and the Hart-
    man Mound, Site Be 32, Boone County, Kentucky (Reports
    on Anthropology v 5, no 6) p $.50 KyU-Mu   298
Cross, Dorothy.   The Indians of New Jersey (Archeological
    Society of New Jersey leaflet; repr, Jan 1952 Proceedings
    of the N J Historical Society) p $.25 NjTM   299

----. The Indians of New Jersey (Archeological Society of
New Jersey. 11 popular leaflets: Food; Shelter; Clothing;
Transportation; Trade and barter; Trails; Religion; Social
and political institutions; History; Contributions; Bibliog-
raphy) 16 p ea $.25 ea NjTM   300
Cunningham, Wilbur M. A study of the Glacial Kame culture
of Michigan, Ohio, and Indiana (OC 12) 51 p 11 pl 1948
p $1.50 MiU-A   301
Cypress Creek Villages, Sites 11 and 1a, McLean County,
Kentucky (Reports on Anthropology v 4, no 2) p $.50
KyU-Mu   302
Davidson, D.S. The Lock Haven (Pennsylvania) Expedition
(MJ v 20, no 3-4) 11 p 9 il 1929 p $2. PU-Mu   303
Densmore, Frances. A study of some Michigan Indians (AP
1) 41 p 1 fig 1949 p $.50 MiU-A   304
Douglass, John M. Indians of Wisconsin (PSH 6) 58 p 58 il
4 map 1954 p $.60 WMMMu   305
Dragoo, Don W. Archaic hunters of the Upper Ohio Valley
(Anthropological Series 3) (A v 35, no 10, p 139-246) il
1959 p $2; post $.19 PPiCM   306
Ehrich, Robert W. New Jersey's place in cultural history
from 16,000 B.C. to A.D. 1625, comparative exhibition
viewed and symbolized the cultural history of the world,
with the time periods of New Jersey Indian cultures serv-
ing as a means of organization 36 p 3 il 1957 p $.50
NjTM   307
Ferguson, Henry L. Archeological exploration of Fisher's
Island, New York (INM 11:1) 44 p il 1935 p $.75 NNMAI
                                                      308
The Fisher Site, Fayette County, Kentucky (Reports on Anthropology v 7, no 2) p $.50 Ky-Mu   309
Ford, James A. Greenhouse: A Troyville-Coles Creek period site in Avoyelles Parish, Louisiana (AP 44:1, p 1-132)
23 pl 49 fig 4 table 1951 p $2.50 NNM   310
----, and Clarence H. Webb. Poverty Point, a late archaic
site in Louisiana (AP 46:1, p 1-136) 6 pl 45 fig 9 table
1956 p $2. NNM   311
----, et al. The Jaketown site in west-central Mississippi
(AP 45:1, p 1-164) 8 pl 57 fig 15 table 1955 p $3. NNM
                                                      312
Fullen, Ripley P., and Frederick W. Sleight. Archaeological investigations of the Castle Windy Midden, Florida
(William L. Bryant Foundation American Studies, Report
no 1) p $.75 FOC   313
Gatschet, Albert S. The Karankawa Indians, the Coast
People of Texas (P v 1, no 2) 104 p map 1891, sigs $1.
MH-P   314

Greenman, Emerson F. Guide to Serpent Mound, Ohio 18 p
   rev ed 1950 p $.25 OHi   315
----. The Wolf and Furton Sites, Macomb County, Michigan
   (OC 8) 34 p 8 pl 4 fig 4 map 1939 p $.75 MiU-A   316
----. The Young Site: An archaeological record from
   Michigan (OC 6) 172 p 33 pl 9 fig 10 map 1937 p $2.25
   MiU-A   317
Griffin, James B. The chronological position of the Hope-
   wellian Culture in the Eastern United States (AP 12) 27 p
   2 chart 1958 p $1. MiU-A   318
----. The Fort Ancient Aspect 392 p 157 pl 18 fig 10 map
   1943 $6. MiU-A   319
----. The Hasinai Indians of east Texas as seen by Euro-
   peans, 1687-1772 (Pubns 12, PD v 2, no 3) 128 p 1953
   p $2.50 LNT-MA   320
Guthe, Alfred K. The late prehistoric occupation in Southwestern New York: An interpretive analysis (RR 11) $2.
   NRM   321
Harrington, J.E., et al. Archaeological excavations in
   courtyard of Castillos de San Marcos (repr, Florida His-
   torical Society Q, Oct 1955) 40 p il p $.25 FStA   322
Harrington, M.R. An ancient village site of Shinnecock Indi-
   ans (AP 22:5, p 227-83) 39 fig 1924 p $.50 NNM   323
----. Certain Caddo sites in Arkansas (M 10) 349 p 137 pl
   1920 $6. NNMAI   324
----. Cherokee and earlier remains on Upper Tennessee
   River (M 24) 321 p 86 pl 1922 p $4.50 NNMAI   325
Hawkes, E.W., and Ralph Linton. A Pre-Lenape site in
   New Jersey (AP v 6, no 3) 35 p 9 pl 1916 p $1.50 PU-
   Mu   326
Heye, George G. Certain mounds in Haywood County, North
   Carolina (C 5:3) (repr, Holmes Anniversary Volume,
   1916) 1919 p $.50 NNMAI   327
Hinsdale, W.B. Distribution of the aboriginal population of
   Michigan (OC 2) 35 p 2 pl 1 map 1932 p $.65 MiU-A 328
----. Primitive man in Michigan (Michigan Handbook Series
   1) unbound 1925 $1.50 MiU-A   329
A home group of Berks County Indians (B 1) $.05 PRM 330
Hooton, E.A. Indian village site and cemetery near Madi-
   sonville, Ohio (P v 8, no 1) 137 p 30 pl 5 il (with notes
   on artifacts by C.C. Willoughby) 1920 p $2.25 MH-P 331
Indian Knoll, Site Oh2, Ohio County, Kentucky, defining the
   shell mound culture complex including a trait list describing 156 traits (Reports on Anthropology, v 4, no 3, pt 1)
   p $1; Indian Knoll skeletons, of Site Oh 2, Ohio County,
   Kentucky (Report on Anthropology, v 4, no 3, pt 2) $1.
   KyU-Mu   332

Indian trails and villages of Chicago; Cook, DuPage and Will
    Counties, 1804 map 13.5x17 $.50; post $.25 ICHi   333
The Indians of Michigan p apply MiLHi   334
The Jonathan Creek Village, Site 4, Marshall County, Ken-
    tucky (Reports on Anthropology v 8, no 1) p $3. KyU-Mu
                                                                 335
The Lock Haven and Texas Expeditions (B v 1, no 1) 2 p 1
    il 1930 p $.35 PU-Mu   336
Long Island Indian culture (IL 50) CoDA   337
Long Island tribes (IL 49) CoDA   338
McKern, Will C.   Kletzien and Nitschke Mound groups (B v
    3, no 4) 156 p 24 pl 20 fig 2 map 1930 p $1. WMMMu
                                                                 339
----.   Neale and McClaughry Mound groups (B v 3, no 3)
    202 p 23 pl 31 fig 3 map 1928 p $1.75 WMMMu   340
----.   A Wisconsin variant of the Hopewell Culture (B v 10,
    no 2) 144 p 39 pl 14 fig 2 map 1931 p $2.75 WMMMu341
The McLeod Site in Hickman County, Kentucky (Reports on
    Anthropology v 3, no 1) p $.50 KyU-Mu   342
Manakee, Harold R.   Indians of early Maryland 47 p 16 il
    map p $1.80 MdHi   343
Mason, Ronald J.   Late Pleistocene geochronology and the
    Paleo-Indian penetration into the Lower Michigan Peninsula
    (AP 11) 49 p 9 pl 3 fig 5 map 7 table 1958 p $1. MiU-A
                                                                 344
Maxwell, Moreau S.   Woodland cultures of Southern Illinois
    (B 7) 287 p 49 il 1951 p $2. WBB-Lo   345
Mayer-Oakes, William J.   An archeological survey of the
    proposed Shenango river reservoir in Ohio and Pennsyl-
    vania (Anthropological ser 1) (A v 33, no 3, p 115-24)
    16 pl 1953 p $.75 PPiCM   346
----.   Prehistory of the Upper Ohio Valley; an introductory
archeological study (Anthropological ser 2) (A v 34) 296 p
    1955 $5; post $.25 PPiCM   347
Menomini Indians (IL 25) CoDA   348
Mills, William C.   Certain mounds and village sites in Ohio
    v 2 $10; unbd $6; v 4 $10; unbd $5. OHi   349
Miner, Horace.   Cave Hollow, and Ozark Bluff-Dweller Site
    (AP 3) 12 p 2 fig 1950 p $.50 MiU-A   350
Moore, Clarence B.   Additional mounds of Duval and Clay
    Counties, Florida (M 26) 71 p il 1922 p $.65 NNMAI 351
Moorehead, W. F.   The Hopewell Mound group of Ohio (FA
    6:5)   126 p 114 il 1922 $4; p $3 ICF   352
Moorehead, Warren King.   The Merrimack archaeological
    survey, a preliminary report 79 p 44 il 1931 $1.25 MSaP
                                                                 353
Morgan, Richard G.   Fort Ancient, Ohio 40 p 1950 p $.25

OHi   354
----, and Edward S. Thomas.   Fort Hill, Ohio 26 p 1950 p
    $.25 OHi   355
----, and James H. Rodabaugh.   Bibliography of Ohio ar-
    chaeology 189 p 1947 p $2.50 OHi   356
The Morgan stone mound, Site 15, Bath County, Kentucky
    (Reports on Anthropology v 5, no 3) p $.50 KyU-Mu (op)
                                                             357
Mt. Horeb earthworks, Site 1, and the Drake Mound, Site 11,
    Fayette County, Kentucky (Reports on Anthropology v 5,
    no 2) p $.50 KyU-Mu   358
Nelson, N.C.   Chronology in Florida (AP 22:2, p 75-103) 7
    fig 1918 p $.25 NNM   359
----.   Contributions to the archaeology of Mammoth Cave,
    and vicinity, Kentucky (AP 22:1, p 1-73) 18 fig 1917 p
    $.75 NNM   360
New England tribes, names and locations (IL 27/28) CoDA
                                                             361
Newcomb, William W.   The culture and acculturation of the
    Delaware Indians (AP 10) 141 p 4 fig 1 map 1956 p $2.
    MiU-A   362
The Parrish Village, Site 45, Hopkins County, Kentucky (Re-
    ports on Anthropology v 7, no 6) p $1. KyU-Mu   363
Peabody, Charles.   Exploration of mounds, Coahoma County,
    Mississippi (P v 3, no 2) 44 p 17 pl 1904 p $1. MH-P
                                                             364
Peeso, P.E.   The Cree Indians (MJ v 3, no 3) 7 p 6 il
    1912 p $.50 PU-Mu   365
Phillips, Philip, et al.   Archaeological survey in the Lower
    Mississippi alluvial valley, 1940-1947 (P v 25) 470 p 32
    pl 37 il 17 table 1951 $11.50; p $8.50 MH-P   366
Quimby, George I.   The Bayou Goula site, Iberville Parish,
    Louisiana (FA 47:2) 84 p 16 il 2 map 1957 $1.75 ICF367
----.   The Medora site, West Baton Rouge Parish, Louisiana
    (FA 24:2) 59 p 21 il 1951 $1.25 ICF   368
----, and Albert C. Spaulding.   The Old Copper Culture and
    the Keweenaw Waterway (FA 36:8) 13 p 7 il 1957 p $.40
    ICF   369
The Page Site, Logan County, Kentucky   (Reports on Anthro-
    pology v 1, no 3) p $.50 KyU-Mu (op)   370
The Read Shell Midden, Site 10, Butler County, Kentucky
    (Reports on Anthropology v 7, no 5) p $1. KyU-Mu   371
The Ricketts Site in Montgomery County, Kentucky (RA v 3,
    no 3) p $.50 KyU-Mu   372
Ricketts Site revisited, Site 3, Montgomery County, Kentucky
    (Reports on Anthropology v 3, no 6) p $.50 KyU-Mu 373
The Riley Mound, Site Be 15, and the Landing Mound, Site

Be 17, Boone County, Kentucky, with additional notes on
the Mt. Horeb Site, Site Fa 1, and Sites Fa 14 and Fa
15, Fayette County, Kentucky (Reports on Anthropology v
5, no 7) p $.50 KyU-Mu   374

Ritchie, William A.   An Algonkin village site at Levanna,
Cayuga County, New York (RR 1) $1. NRM   375

----. Certain recently explored mounds and their probable
relation to the Hopewell Culture (RR 4) $1. NRM   376

----. The chance horizon: An early state in the development of the Mohawk Iroquois culture (C 29) 53 p 9 pl 4
fig 1952 p $.50 NAlMu   377

----. An early site in Cayuga County, New York (RR 7)
$1.50 NRM   378

----. An introduction to Hudson Valley prehistory (B 367)
112 p 32 pl 1958 p $1.50 NalMu   379

----. A prehistoric fortified village site at Canandaigua,
Ontario County, New York (RR 3) $1.50 NRM   380

----. The Stony Brook Site and its relations to archair and
transitional cultures on Long Island (B 372) 169 p 53 pl
7 fig 1959 p $1. NAlMu   381

----. A stratified prehistoric site at Brewerton, New York
(RR 8) $1.50 NRM   382

----. Traces of early man in the Northeast (B 358) 91 p
18 pl map 1957 p $1.50 NAlMu   383

----. Two prehistoric village sites at Brewerton, New York
(RR 5) $1.50 NRM   384

----, et al. An early Owasco Sequence in eastern New York
(C 32) 93 p 7 fig 18 pl 1953 p $.75 NAlMu   385

Ritzenthaler, Robert E.   Oneida Indians of Wisconsin (B v
19, no 1) 52 p 17 pl 1950 p $1. WMMMu   386

----. Prehistoric Indians of Wisconsin (PSH 4) 44 p 111 il
1953 p $.60 WMMMu   387

----, and Frederick A. Peterson.   The Mexican Kickapoo
Indians (PA 2) 45 fig 1956 p $2. WMMMu   388

The Robbins Mounds, Sites Be 3 and Be 14.   Boone County,
Kentucky (Reports on Anthropology v 5, no 5) p $.50
KyU-Mu   389

Rowe, Chandler W.   The Effigy Mound Culture of Wisconsin
(PA 3) 103 p 36 fig 1956 p $2.25 WMMMu   390

Schwarze, W.N.   History of Moravian mission among the
Southern Indian tribes (Transactions, 2nd series, v 1) $5.
PNA   391

Shetrone, Henry C.   The Ohio aborigines (repr, History of
the State of Ohio, v 1, chapt 2, p 34-59) 1940 p $.25
OHi   392

----. Primer of Ohio archaeology: The Mound Builders and
the Indians 44 p 3rd ed 1938 p $.25 OHi   393

68   Sibley, John

Sibley, John. A report from Natchitoches in 1807, ed with
    an introduction by A.H. Abel (M 25) 102 p facsim 1922
    $1. NNMAI   394
Skinner, Alanson. The Indians of Manhattan Island and vi-
    cinity (SG 41) 64 p 27 il p $.50; post $.10 NNM   395
----. Notes on Iroquois archeology (M 18) 216 p 37 pl 1921
    p $3.25 NNMAI   396
----. Notes on Mahikan ethnology (B v 2, no 3) 30 p 5 pl
    1925 p $.40 WMMMu   397
Smith, Carlyle Shreeve. The archeology of coastal New
    York (AP 43:2, p 91-200) 8 pl 3 fig 5 table 1950 p $1.50
    NNM   398
Smith, Hale G. The Crable Site, Fulton County, Illinois, a
    Late Prehistoric Site in the Central Illinois Valley (AP 7)
    53 p 12 pl 1 map 1951 p $1. MiU-A   399
Smith, Harlan I. The prehistoric ethnology of a Kentucky
    site (AP 6:2, p 173-241) 45 pl 1 fig 1910 p $1. NNM
                                                         399a
Snow, C.E. Anthropological studies at Moundville. Pt 1.
    Indian skeletons from the museum burials at Moundville
    Pt 2. Possible evidence of scalping at Moundville (MP 15)
    57 p il p; post $.05 AU-Mu   400
South, Stanley A. Indians in North Carolina 69 p il 1959 p
    $.15 NcRNC   400a
Speck, Frank G. Chapters on the ethnology of the Powhatan
    Tribe of Virginia (INM 1:5) 228 p il 1928 p $.75 NNMAI
                                                         401
----. The Iroquois (B 23) 95 p 63 il 2nd ed 1955 p $1.
    MiBloC   402
----. The Rappahannock Indians of Virginia (INM 5:3) 83 p
    il 1925 p $.85 NNMAI   403
----. Territorial subdivisions and boundaries of the Wamp-
    noag, Massachusetts, and Nauset (M 44) 152 p il 1928 p
    $1.35 NNMAI   404
----. A visit to the Penobscot Indians (MJ v 2, no 1) 5 p
    5 il 1911 p $.50 PU-Mu   405
Spier, Leslie. The Tretnon argillite culture (AP 22:4, p
    167-226) 11 fig 1918 p $.50 NNM   406
Spring Lake Archeology. Pt 3. Sorg site; Pt 4. Vegetation of
    the Spring Lake Area $1.15 ea MnSSci   407
Stony Brook site and its relation to Archaic and Transitional
    Cultures on Long Island p $1.25 NBLiSt   408
Swauger, James L., and Arthur M. Hayes. Historic ar-
    cheology of Fort Pitt 1953 (Anthropological Series 4) (A
    v 35, no 4, p 247-74) 1959 $1. PPiCM   409
The Tolu site in Crittenden County, Kentucky (Reports on
    Anthropology v 1, no 5) il chart map p $.50 KyU-Mu 410

Town Creek Indian Mound, State historic site 6 p il 1958 ap-
    ply NcRNC   411
Tribes of the Great Lakes region (IL 81) CoDA   412
Virginia tribes of the 17th century (IL 57) CoDA   413
Volk, Ernest. The archaeology of the Delaware Valley (P
    v 5) 258 p 125 pl 26 il 2 map 1911 $8.75; p $5.75 MH-
    P   414
Wallace, Paul A.W. Historic Indian paths of Pennsylvania
    29 p 1952 p $.50 PHarH   415
Webb, William S., and D. L. DeJarnette. The Flint River
    site, Ma^O48 (MP 23) 87 p il 1948 p; post $.10 AU-Mu
                                                               415a
----, ----. Little Bear Creek site, Ct^O8 (MP 26) 64 p il
    1948 p; post $.10 AU-Mu   415b
----, ----. The Perry site (MP 25) 69 p il 1948 p; post
    $.10 AU-Mu   415c
Webb, William S., et al. Prehistoric Indians of the Ohio
    Valley 23 p 1952 p $.25 OHi   416
Werner, Ben. Indian archaeology of Long Island p $1.
    NBLiSt   417
Wichita, Waco, Towakoni and Kichai Indians (IL 40) CoDA
                                                               418
Willoughby, C.C. The Turner Group of earthworks, Hamilton
    County, Ohio, with notes on the skeletal remains by E.A.
    Hooton (P v 8, no 3) 132 p 27 pl 47 il 1922 p $2.25
    MH-P   419
Wimberly, S.B., and H.A. Tourtelot. McQuorquodale Mound,
    a manifestation of the Hopewellian phase in South Alabama
    (MP 19) 42 p il 1943 apply; post $.05 AU-Mu   420
Woolford, Sam. Types of archaeological sites in Bexar Coun-
    ty, Texas 14 p 11 il 1935 $.25 TxSaW   421

--Indians of North America--Eastern Woodland--Material Culture See also Art

Brown, A.P. Jade and similar green stones (BFM v 1, no
    3) 6 p 1898 p $.50 PU-Mu   422
Cresson, Hilborne T. Report upon pile-structures in Naa-
    man's Creek near Claymont, Delaware (P v 1, no 4) 24 p
    il 1892 sigs $.25 MH-P   423
Digging into the past, story of Indian artifacts found in Che-
    mung Valley, New York p $.25 NElmH   424
Dustin. Report on Indian earthworks in Ogemaw County,
    Michigan (S-1) 33 p 11 il 1932 p $.10 MiBloC   425
Gordon, G.B. Penobscot birchbark canoe (MJ v 1, no 1) 2
    p 1910 p $.50 PU-Mu   426
Hadlock, Wendell S., and Ernest S. Dodge. A canoe from

the Penobscot River 15 p 2 pl 4 fig 1948 $.50 MSaP 427
Harrington, M.R.   Sacred bundles of the Sac and Fox Indians
   (AP v 4, no 2) 142 p 21 pl 1914 p $3.50 PU-Mu   428
Iroquois foods (IL 26) CoDA   429
Mayer, Joseph R.   Flintlocks of the Iroquois, 1620-1687 (RR
   6) $1. NRM   430
Merrill, Robert S.   The calendar stick of Tshi-zun-hau-kau
   (B 24) 12 p il 1945 p $.25 MiBloC   431
Merwin, B.W.   Wampum (MJ v 7, no 2) 8 p 5 pl 1916 p
   $1.   PU-Mu   432
A new American Indian collection (Naskapi) (B v 1, no 3)
   2 p 1 pl 1930 p $.35 PU-Mu   433
Ritzenthaler, Robert E.   Building a Chippewa Indian birch-
   bark canoe (B v 19, no 2) 47 p 33 pl 1950 p $1. WMMMu
                                                         434
A rock shelter at Poplar Neck, Berks County, Pennsylvania
   (B 15) $.25 PRM   435
Rock shelters in Menifee County, Kentucky (RA v 3, no 4)
   p $.50 KyU-Mu (op)   436
Rock shelters of Wolfe and Powell Counties, Kentucky (RA
   v 1, no 4) p $.50 KyU-Mu (op)   437
Schuetz, Mardith K.   A report on Williamson County mound
   material 34 p 11 photog 1957 $1.10 TxSaW   438
Skinner, A.   Mascoutens or Prairie Potowatomi Indians. Pt
   2.   Notes on material culture (B v 6, no 2) 64 p 13 pl
   1926 p $.75 WMMMu   439
----.   Material culture of the Menomini (M 20) 478 p 107 pl
   1921 p $6. NNMAI   440
Speck, F.G.   Some uses of birchbark by our Eastern Indians
   (MJ v 1, no 2) 3 p 6 il 1910 p $.50 PU-Mu   441
----, et al.   Rappahannock taking devices: Traps, hunting,
   and fishing (JP 1) 28 p 30 il 1946 p $.50 PU-Mu   442
Wardle, H.N.   Chief Gabriel Paul's treasure (Penobscot)
   (B v 7, no 1) 3 p 3 pl 1937 p $.50 PU-Mu   443

--Indians of North America--Eastern Woodlands--Social Life
and Customs See also Folk Literature and Folk Lore

Barrett, S.A.   Dream dance of the Chippewa and Menominee
   Indians of Northern Wisconsin (B v 1, no 4) 156 p 17 pl
   1911 p $1.25 WMMMu   444
Caldwell, Joseph R.   Trend and tradition in the prehistory of
   the Eastern United States (SP v 10) 88 p il 1958 p $1.50
   ISM   445
Deserontyon, John.   A Mohawk form of ritual and condolence,
   1782, tr. with introduction by J.N.B. Hewitt (INM 10:8)
   23 p il 1928 p $.60 NNMAI   446

Farabee, W.C. Indian children's burial places in Western
   Pennsylvania (MJ v 10, no 3) 2 p 1919 p $1. PU-Mu 447
Faville, Foster H. A Montauk cemetery at Easthampton,
   Long Island (INM 2:3) 38 p il 1920 p $.60 NNMAI   448
Harrington, M.R. Some customs of the Delaware Indians
   (MJ v 1, no 3) 9 p 6 il 1910 p $.50 PU-Mu   449
Hatt, Robert T., et al. Sanilac petroglyphs (B 36) 158 p
   33 pl 1959 p $5. MiBloC   450
Johnson, Elden. Hopewell burial mounds p $.20 MnSSci
                                                      451
Kidd, Kenneth E. The excavation and historical identification
   of a Huron ossuary p $.35 CaOTRM   452
Ritchie, W.A. Recent discoveries suggesting an Early Wood-
   lands burial cult in the Northeast (C 40) 135 p 29 pl 4 fig
   1955 p $1.25 NAlMu   453
Ritzenthaler, E. Chippewa preoccupation with health (B v
   19, no 4) 84 p 13 pl 1954 p $1.25 WMMMu   454
Skinner, Alanson. Associations and ceremonies of the Meno-
   mini Indians (AP 13:2, p 167-215) 2 fig 1915 p $.40
   NNM   455
----. Social life and ceremonial bundles of the Menomini
   Indians (AP 13:1, p 1-165) 30 fig 1913 p $1.50 NNM 456
Slotkin, J.S. The Menomini powwow (PA 4) 166 p 19 il
   1957 p $4. WMMMu   457
Speck, F.G. Catawba hunting, trapping and fishing (JP 2)
   44 p 34 il 1946 p $.75 PU-Mu   458
----. The celestial bear comes down to earth, an account of
   the Bear Ceremony of the Delaware Indians 91 p 4 pl 9
   text figs 1945 $1.80 PRM   459
Tantaquidgeon, Gladys. A study of Delaware Indian medicine
   practice and folk belief 91 p p $1.50 PHarH   460
Trowbridge, C.C. Meearmeear traditions, edited by Vernon
   Kinietz 91 p 1 pl 1938 p $1. MiU-A   461
----. Shawnee traditions, edited by Vernon Kinietz and Er-
   minie Voegelin (OC 9) 71 p 1939 p $1. MiU-A   462
Willoughby, C.C. Indian burial place at Winthrop, Massa-
   chusetts (P v 11, no 1) 37 p 4 pl 20 il 1924 p $.75 MH-P
                                                      463
----. Prehistoric burial places in Maine (P v 1, no 6) 52 p
   4 pl 50 il 1898 p $.75 MH-P   464
Witthoft, John. Green corn ceremonialism in the Eastern
   Woodlands (OC 13) 91 p 1949 p $1.50 MiU-A   465

--Indians of North America--Plains and Plateau

Allison, Vernon C. The antiquity of the deposits in
   Jacob's Cavern (AP 19:6, p 293-335) 24 fig 1926 p $.75

NNM   466
Barreis, David A.   The preceramic horizons of Northeastern
    Oklahoma (AP 6) 121 p 3 pl 14 fig 2 map 1951 p $1.50
    MiU-A   467
Barbour, Erwin H., and C. Bertrand Schultz.   Paleontologic
    and geologic consideration of early man in Nebraska, with
    notice of a new bone bed in the Early Pleistocene of Mor-
    rill County, Nebraska (B 1:45) 1936 p NbU-Mu   468
Blackfoot Indians (IL 37/38) CoDA   469
Burnett, E.K.   The Spiro Mound collection in the Museum;
    with Clements, Forrest E.   Historical sketch of the Spiro
    Mound (C v 14) 68 p 94 pl 1945 p $3.50 NNMAI   470
Cooper, Paul.   The Historical Society Archeological Survey
    of 1938, a description of archeological work along the west
    bank of the Missouri River between Omaha and Homer,
    Nebraska (AP v 20, no 2) 1939 p $.50 NbHi   471
Culin, Stewart.   A summer trip among the Western Indians
    (The Wanamaker Expedition, 1900) Iowa, Wyoming (BFM
    v 3, no 1) 22 p 5 pl 1901 p $.50 PU-Mu   472
Deuel, Thorne.   Illinois records of 1000 A.D. (Reports 2;
    repr, Journal of the Ill State Hist Soc, v 61, no 3, Sept
    1948) 12 p p apply ISM (op)   473
----.   Man's venture in culture (Story of Illinois 6) 40 p 19
    il p $.25 ISM   474
----, ed.   Hopewellian communities in Illinois (SP 5) 272 p
    94 il 1952 p $3.50 ISM   475
Eifert, Virginia S.   The story of Illinois: Indian and pio-
    neer (Story of Ill 1) 24 p 12 il p $.25 ISM   476
Fowke, Gerard.   The Montezuma Mounds (repr, Collections)
    16 p il 1905 p $2. MoHi   477
Fowler, Melvin L.   Ferry Site, Hardin County, Illinois
    (Archaic) (SP v 8, no 1) 36 p 3 pl 1957 p $1.25 ISM 478
Gillin, John.   Archaeological investigations in Central Utah
    with an analysis of animal bones by Glover M. Allen (P
    v 17, no 2) 50p 9 pl 5 table 6 il 1941 p $1.50 MH-P   479
Goddard, Pliny Earle, et al.   Sun dance of the Plains Indi-
    ans--Notes on the Sun dance of the Sarsi (AP 16:4, p 271-
    385) 1919 p $1.50 NNM   480
Harrington, M.R.   Indians of the Plains (Leaflet 15) p $.30
    CLSM   481
----.   The Ozark bluff-dwellers (INM 12) 185 p 48 pl 16
    fig 1960 p $4.50 NNMAI   482
----.   A visit to the Otoe Indians (MJ v 4, no 3) 7 p 6 il
    1913 p $.50 PU-Mu   483
Hill, A.T., and George Metcalf.   A site of the Dismal River
    Aspect in Chase County, Nebraska (AP v 22, no 2, April-
    Je 1941) p $.50 NbHi   484

----, and Marvin Kivett. Woodland-like manifestations in
Nebraska (AP v 21, no 3, Jy-Sept 1940) p $.50 NbHi
                                                                  485
----, and Paul Cooper. The archeological field season of
1937: excavations in Cass, Sarpy, and Nemaha Counties
of Southeastern Nebraska (AP v 18, no 4, Oct-Dec 1937)
p $.50 NbHi   486
----, ----. The Schrader Site: A prehistoric village in
Lancaster County, Nebraska; the Champ Site: Excavations in a prehistoric village in Douglas County, Nebraska;
Fremont I: Prehistoric village in Sarpy County, Nebraska (AP v 17, no 4, Oct-Dec 1936) p $.50 NbHi   487
Hoebel, E. Adamson. The archaeology of Bone Cave, Mil-
ler County, Missouri (AP 40:2, p 135-58) 5 pl 5 fig 1946
p $.50 NNM   488
Indian villages of the Illinois Country (SP v 2). Pt. 1.
Tucker, Sara J. Atlas 12x16, portf, reproductions of old
maps 18 p 54 pl 1942 $3; Pt. 2. Temple, Wayne C. His-
toric Indians of Illinois Country p $3.50 ISM   489
Indians of Colorado 52 p 3rd ed 1960 $.50 CoHi   490
Indians of Eastern Oklahoma, illustrated by Charles Banks
Wilson $.50 OkTG   491
Indians of North Dakota p $1. NdHi   492
Irwin, H.J., and C.C. Irwin. Excavations at the LoDaisKa
Site (P 8) il p $2.50 CoDMNH   493
Jeske, John A. Grand River Mound group and camp site
(B v 3, no 2) 74 p 13 pl 17 fig 1927 p $1. WMMMu   494
KoMoHa. Sally, a story about the Oklahoma Basketmaker
culture 3000 years ago p $.25 OkB   495
Kivett, Marvin F. Woodland sites in Nebraska, excavations
in village and burial sites of the Woodland period in
Hitchcock, Hooker, and Platte Counties, Nebraska (PA 1)
1952 $2. NbHi   496
Lowie, Robert H. Notes on Shoshonean ethnography (AP 20:
3, p 185-314) 36 fig 1924 p $1. NNM   497
Mandelbaum, David G. The Plains Cree (AP 37:2, p 155-
316) 14 fig 1940 p $1.60 NNM   498
Martin, Paul S. Archaeological work in the Ackmen-Lowry
Area, Southwestern Colorado (FA 23:2) 88 p 67 pl 4 fig
1938 $2.25 ICF   499
----. Modified Basket Maker sites, Ackmen-Lowry Area,
Southwestern Colorado (FA 23:3) 196 p 86 fig 1 pl c 19
map 1939 $3. ICF   500
Moss, J.H., et al. Early man in the Eden Valley (MM)
124 p 34 fig 9 pl 1951 p $1.50 PU-Mu   501
Nash, Philleo. Excavation of Ross Mound Group No. 1 (B
v 16, no 1) 46 p 9 pl 8 fig 1 map 1933 p $.60 WMMMu502

Plains Indian tribes--location, population and culture (IL 23)
CoDA   503
Potter, W. B., and Edward Evers. Contributions to the
archaeology of Missouri 30 p 24 pl, containing 148 fig of
ancient pottery, 5 plan 1880 p $2.35 MH-P   504
Rinaldo, John B. An analysis of culture change in the Ackmen-Lowry Area (FA 36:5) 14 p 2 il 1950 ICF   505
Sakakawea p $.50 NdHi   506
Sioux or Dakota Indians (IL 41) CoDA   507
Skinner, A. Ethnology of Ioway Indians (B v 5, no 4) 174
p 29 pl 2 fig 1926 p $1.50 WMMMu   508
----. Observations on ethnology of Sauk Indians (B v 5, no
1) 57 p 1 pl 1923 p $.80; Pt. 2. War customs (B v 5,
no 2) 60 p 11 pl 1925 p $.80; Pt. 3. Material culture (B
v 5, no 3) 62 p 14 pl 1925 p $.90 WMMMu   509
Spaulding, Albert C. The Arzberger Site, Hughes County,
South Dakota (OC 16) 173 p 17 pl 7 fig 2 map 1956 p
$3.50 MiU-A   510
Swanson, Earl H., et al. Archaeological explorations in
Central and South Idaho--1958. Pt. 1. Types and distri-
butions of site features and stone tools (OP 2) 1959 p $1.
IdPI-Mu   511
Temple, Wayne. Shabbona, friend of the whites (R6; repr,
Outdoors in Illinois, Fall and Winter 1957, p 18-23) p
apply ISM (op)   512
Ute Indians (IL 10) CoDA   513
Wedel, Waldo R. Contributions to the archeology of the Up-
per Republican Valley, Nebraska. Minneapolis 1: A pre-
historic village site in Ottawa County, Kansas; Salina 1:
A protohistoric village site in McPherson County, Kansas
(AP v 15, no 3, Jy-Sept 1934) p $1. NbHi   514
Will, George F. Archaeology of the Missouri Valley (AP 22:
6, p 285- 344) 14 fig 1924 p $.50 NNM   515
Wissler, Clark. Changes in population profiles among the
northern Plains Indians (AP 36:1, p 1-67) 1936 p $.75
NNM   516
Wormington, H. M. A reappraisal of the Fremont Culture (P
1) 200 p 61 il 4 map 1955 p $3. CoDMNH   517
----, and Robert H. Lister. Archaeological investigations
of the Uncompahgre Plateau (P 2) 129 p 66 il 3 map p
$2.50 CoDMNH   518

--Indians of North America--Plains and Plateau--Material
Culture

Barbour, Erwin H., and C. Bertrand Schultz. The mounted
skeleton of Bison occidentalis and associated dart points

(B 1:33) 1932 p NbU-Mu   519
Coffin, Edwin F.   Archeological exploration of a rock shelter
    in Brewster County, Texas (M 48) 72 p il 1932 p $.75
    NNMAI   520
Densmore, Frances. A collection of specimens from the
    Teton Sioux (INM 11:3) 42 p il 1948 p $1.50 NNMAI 521
Dorsey, G.A.   An aboriginal quartzite quarrie in Eastern
    Wyoming (FA 2:4) 13 p 12 il 1900 $.50 ICF   522
Farabee, W.C.   Dress among Plains Indian women (MJ v 12,
    no 4) 13 p 5 il 1921 p $1. PU-Mu   523
Hall, H.U.   A buffalo robe biography (MJ v 17, no 1) 31 p
    17 il 1926 p $1. PU-Mu   524
----.   Some shields of the Plains and Southwest (MJ v 17,
    no 1) 26 p 16 pl 1926 p $1. PU-Mu   525
Harrington, M.R.   An archaic Iowa tomahawk (INM 10:6) 4
    p il 1920 p $.15 NNMAI   526
----.   A sacred warclub of the Oto (INM 10:2) 4 p il 1920
    p $.15 NNMAI   527
Lowie, Robert H.   The material culture of the Crow Indians
    (AP 21:3, p 201-70) 19 fig 1922 p $.75 NNM   528
Mason, J.A.   A collection from the Crow Indians (MJ v 17,
    no 4) 21 p 8 il 1926 p $1. PU-Mu   529
Meserve, F.G., and Erwin H. Barbour. Association of an
    arrow point with Bison occidentalis in Nebraska (B 1:27)
    1932 p NbU-Mu   530
Satterthwaite, Lincoln.   Stone artifacts at and near the Fin-
    ley Site, near Eden, Wyoming (MM) 22 p 5 fig 1947 $.75
    PU-Mu   531
Schultz, C. Bertrand.   Association of artifacts and extinct
    mammals in Nebraska (B 1:33) 1932 p NbU-Mu   532
Wardle, H.N.   Defensive and offensive power of the shield
    (Dakota) (B v 7, no 2) 3 p 1 pl $.50 PU-Mu   533
Wilson, Gilbert Livingstone. Hidatsa eagle trappings (AP
    30:4, p 99-245) 25 fig 1928 p $1.50 NNM   534
----.   The Hidatsa earth lodge, arranged and edited by Bella
    Weitzner (AP 33:5, p 341-420) 45 fig 1934 p $1. NNM
                                                       535
Winchell, N.H.   Weathering of aboriginal stone artifacts: A
    consideration of the paleoliths of Kansas (Collect v 16, pt
    1) 186 p 1913 unbd $1.15 MnHi   536

-- Indians of North America--Plains and Plateau--Social Life
and Customs

Deuel, Thorne.   American Indian ways of life, early Indian
    inhabitants of Illinois (Story of Ill 9) p $.25 ISM   537
Dorsey, George A.   The Arapaho sun dance; the ceremony

of the Offerings Lodge (FA 4) 228 p 137 il (10 c) 1903 $3.
ICF   538
----. The Cheyenne. Pt. 1. Ceremonial organization (FA
9:1) 55 p 23 il (17 c) 1905 $1.50; Pt. 2. The sun dance
(FA 9:2) 132 p 151 il 1905 $2.50 ICF   539
----. The Ponca sun dance (FA 6:2) 21 p 56 il (11 c) 1905
$1.50 ICF   540
----. Traditions of the Osage (FA 7:1) 60 p 1904 $.75
ICF   541
----, and A. L. Kroeber. Traditions of the Arapaho. Collected under the auspices of the Field Columbian Museum
and the American Museum of Natural History (FA 5) 476
p 1903 $3. ICF   542
----, and James R. Murie. Notes on Skiki Pawnee society,
prepared for publication by Alexander Spoehr (FA 27:2)
56 p 1 fig 1940 $.75 ICF   543
Goddard, Pliny Earle. Dancing societies of the Sarsi Indians
(AP 11:5, p 461-74) 1914 p $.25 NNM   544
Kroeber, A. L. The Arapaho. Pt. 3. Ceremonial organization (B 18:2, p 121-229) 6 pl 24 fig 1904 p $1.50 NNM
                                                           545
Linton, Ralph. Annual ceremony of the Pawnee medicine
man (A-PS 8) 20 p 2 il 1923 p $.10 ICF   546
----. Purification of the sacred bundles, a ceremony of the
Pawnee (A-PS 7) 11 p 1 il 1923 p $.10 ICF   547
----. The Thunder Ceremony of the Pawnee (A-PS 5) 19 p
4 il 1922 p $.20 ICF   548
Lowie, Robert H. Dance associations of the Eastern Dakota
(AP 11:2, p 101-42) 1913 p $.25 NNM   549
----. Dances and societies of the Plains Shoshone (AP 11:
10, p 803-35) 5 fig 1915 p $.25 NNM   550
----. Minor ceremonies of the Crow Indians (AP 21:5, p
323-65) 1924 p $.50 NNM   551
----. Notes on the social organization and customs of the
Mandan, Hidatsa, and Crow Indians (AP 21:1, p 1-99)
1917 p $1. NNM   552
----. Plains Indian age-societies: Historical and compara-
tive summary (AP 11:13, p 877-984) 1916 p $1. NNM
                                                           553
----. The religion of the Crow Indians (AP 25:2, p 309-
444) 7 fig 1922 p $1.25 NNM   554
----. Societies of the Arikara Indians (AP 11:8, p 645-78)
1915 p $.50 NNM   555
----. Societies of the Crow, Hidatsa, and Mandan Indians
(AP 11:3, p 143-358) 18 fig 1913 p $2. NNM   556
----. Societies of the Kiowa (AP 11:11, p 837-51) 1916 p
$.25 NNM   557

----. The sun dance of the Crow Indians (AP 16:1, p 1-50)
11 fig 1915 p $.50 NNM 558
----. Sun dance of the Shoshoni, Ute and Hidatsa (AP 16:5,
p 387-431) 4 fig 1919 p $.50 NNM 559
----. The Tobacco Society of the Crow Indians (AP 21:2,
p 101-200) 13 fig 1920 p $1.25 NNM 560
McClintock, Walter. Blackfoot medicine-pipe ceremony
(Leaflet 21) p $.25 CLSM 561
Meeker, L.I. Ogalala games (Teton Sioux) (BFM v 3, no 1)
24 p 25 il 1901 p $.50 PU-Mu 562
Murie, James R. Pawnee Indian societies (AP 11:7, p 543-
644) 18 fig 1914 p $1. NNM 563
Pepper, G.H. An Indian shrine (Hidatsa) (MJ v 4, no 3) 3
p 2 il 1913 p $.50 PU-Mu 564
Sebbelov, G. Osage war dance (MJ v 2, no 3) 4 p 1911 p
$.50 PU-Mu 565
Simms, S.C. Traditions of the Crows (FA 2:6) 44 p 1903
$.50 ICF 566
Skinner, Alanson. Political organization, cults and cere-
monies of the Plains-Ojibway and Plains-Cree Indians (AP
11:6, p 475-542) 10 fig 1914 p $.75 NNM 567
----. Societies of the Iowa, Kansa, and Ponca Indians (AP
11:9, p 679-801) 5 fig 1915 p $1. NNM 568
Spier, Leslie. Notes on the Kiowa sun dance (AP 16:6, p
433-50) 1 fig 1921 p $.25 NNM 569
----. The sun dance of the Plains Indians: Its development
and diffusion (AP 16:7, p 451-527) 1 fig 1921 p $1. NNM
570
Stoller, Marianne L. A sacred bundle of the Arapaho Indians
(A v 35, no 2, p 11-26) 1957 p $.50 PPiCM 571
The Thunder Ceremony of the Pawnee p $.20 NbHi 572
Walker, J.R. The sun dance and other ceremonies of the
Oglala division of the Teton Dakota (AP 16:2, p 51-221)
1917 p $1.50 NNM 573
Wildschut, William, and John C. Ewers. Medicine bundles
of the Crow Indians (C v 17) in press; to appear 1960
NNMAI 574
Wilson, Gilbert L. The horse and dog in Hidatsa culture
(AP 15:2, p 125-311) 127 fig 1924 p $1.75 NNM 575
Wissler, Clark. Societies and dance associations of the
Blackfoot Indians (AP 11:4, p 359-460) 29 fig 1913 p $1.
NNM 576
----. The sun dance of the Blackfoot Indians (AP 16:3, p
223-70) 1 fig 1918 p $.50 NNM 577

--Indians of North America--Southwest

Adams, William Y. Ninety years of Glen Canyon archaeology,
    1869-1959 29 p 3 map 1960 p $2.50 AzFM   578
----, and Neggie K. Adams. An inventory of prehistoric
    sites on Lower San Juan River (B 31) 53 p 1959 p $2.75
    AzFM   579
Alexander, Hubert G., and Paul Reiter. Report on the ex-
    cavation of the Jemez Cave, New Mexico (M 4--Publ with
    U of New Mexico) 72 p 22 pl 1935 $2. NmSM-S   580
Amsden, Charles Avery. The ancient Basketmakers (Leaflet
    11) p $.25 CLSM   581
----. Prehistoric Southwesterners, from Basketmakers to
    Pueblo, introduction by A.V. Kidder il $3.50 CLSM 582
Apache Indians (IL 16) CoDA   583
Ayer, Mart Y. The archaeological and faunal material from
    the Williams Cave, Guadelupe Mountains (P 1936.16) p
    $.65 PPAN   584
Bandelier, Adolph F. Documentary history of the Rio Grande
    pueblos of New Mexico, bibliographic introduction (P 13)
    28 p 1910 p $.25 NmSM-S   585
----. Hemenway Southwestern Expedition. Pt. 1. Contri-
    butions to the Southwestern portion of the United States
    (Pap of the Archaeological Institute of America, American
    Series, v 5) 1890 p $2.15; Pt. 2. An outline of the docu-
    mentary history of the Zuni tribe (J of American Ethnol-
    ogy and Archaeology, v 3, p 1-115) 1890 p $2. MH-P586
Betzinez, Jason. I fought with Geronimo $5. OkA   587
Bloom, Maude McFie. Tonita of the holy faith (P ns 5) 20
    p 1924 p $.25 NmSM-S   588
Bluhn, Elaine A. The Sawmill site. A Reserve phase vil-
    lage, Pine Lawn Valley, western New Mexico (FA 47:1)
    88 p 29 il 3 map 1947 $2.25 ICF   589
Bradfield, Wesley. Cameron Creek Village, a site in the
    Mimbres Area in Grant County, New Mexico (M 1) 127 p
    108 pl 1931 $5. NmSM-S   590
Breternitz, David A. Excavations at three sites in the Mid-
    dle Verde Valley (B 34) 29 p 1960 p $2.50 AzFM   591
Colton, Harold S. Pueblo II in the San Francisco Mountains,
    Arizona; with Hargrave, Lyndon L. Pueblo II houses of
    the San Francisco Mountains, Arizona (B 4) 75 p 1933 p
    $.75 AzFM   592
----. The Sinagua: A summary of the archaeology of the
    region of Flagstaff, Arizona (B 22) 328 p 1946 $9. AzFM
                                                              593
Cosgrove, C.B. Caves of the Upper Gila and Hueco areas,
    in New Mexico and Texas (P v 24, no 2) 182 p 122 pl 48
    il 1947 p $6.25 MH-P   594
Cosgrove, H.S., and C.B. Cosgrove. The Swartz Ruin: A

typical Mimbres site in Southwestern New Mexico, with a
section on the skeletal material by W.W. Howells (P v 15)
178 p 239 pl 17 il 1932 $8.85; p $5.85 MH-P   595
Daifuku, Hiroshi. Jeddito 264: A Basket Maker III--Pueblo
I site in Northeastern Arizona (P v 33) in prep MH-P
                                                     596

Danson, Edward Bridge. An archaeological survey of west
central New Mexico and east central Arizona (P v 44, no
133) 8 fig 10 il 23 table 1957 p $4.50 MH-P   597
DeJarnette, D. L., and S.B. Wimberly. The Bessemer site
(MP 17) 122 p il 1941 p; post $.05 AU-Mu   598
Ferdon, Edwin N., Jr. An excavation of Hermit's Cave,
New Mexico (M 10--Publ with U of New Mexico) 29 p 13
pl 1946 $2. NmSM-S   599
----. A trial survey of Mexican-Southwestern architectural
parallels (M 21) 36 p 3 fig 1955 $1.50 NmSM-S   600
Field work in the Southwest (B v 3, no 1) 2 p 1 pl 1931 p
$.35 PU-Mu   601
Fisher, Reginald G. The archaeological survey of the Pueb-
lo Plateau (Publ with U of New Mexico) 22 p map drg
1930 $.25 NmSM-S   602
Fleming, Henry Craig. Medical observations on the Zuni
Indians (C 7:2) 9 p il 1924 p $.35 NNMAI   603
Fulton, William Shirley. Archeological notes on Texas Can-
yon, Arizona (C v 12:1-3) 23 p il 1934 p 75; 23 p il 1934
p $1; 22 p il 1938 p $1. NNMAI   604
Guernsey, S.J. Explorations in northeastern Arizona (P v
12, no 1) 20 p 66 pl (1 c) 30 il 1931 p $3.50 MH-P 605
Hack, John T. The changing physical environment of the
Hopi Indians of Arizona (P v 35, no 1) 86 p front 12 pl
54 il 1942 p $1.75 MH-P   606
Hall, E.T., Jr. Archaeological survey of Walhalla Glades
(B 20) 32 p 1942 p $.60 AzFM   607
Henry, Emil W. The excavation of Los Muertos and neigh-
boring ruins in the Salt River Valley, southern Arizona
(P v 24, no 1) 224 p 90 pl front c 133 il 1945 p $5.85
MH-P   608
Havasupai Indians (IL 33) CoDA   609
Hawley, Florence M. The significance of the dated prehis-
tory of Chetro Ketl, Chaco Canyon, New Mexico (M 2--
Publ with U of Mexico) 92 p 18 pl 1934 $2. NmSM-S
                                                     610
Hewett, Edgar L. The excavations at El Rito de los Frijoles
in 1909 (P 10) 23 p il map 1909 p $.25 NmSM-S   611
----. The excavations at Tyuoni (Frijoles), New Mexico,
in 1908 (P 5) 22 p il map 1909 p $.25 NmSM-S   612
----. Letters on the Pueblo Indian situation (P ns 9) 18 p

1925 p $.25 NmSM-S   613
----. The Pajaritan culture (P 3) 11 p 1909 p $.25
NmSM-S   614
----. The Pajarito Plateau and its ancient people, 2nd ed
rev by Bertha P. Dutton (Publ with U of New Mexico) 174
p il 1954 $4.50 NmSM-S   615
----. Present condition of the Pueblo Indians (P ns 10) 8
p 1925 p $.25 NmSM-S   616
----. A proposed Indian Theater in Santa Fe (P ns 8) 14 p
il 1925 p $.25 NmSM-S   617
----. The proposed "National Park of the Cliff Cities" (P
34) 8 p il 1916 p $.25 NmSM-S   618
Hodge, Frederick Webb. The history of Hawikuh, New Mex-
ico, one of the so-called Cities of Cibola (Pubns Hodge I)
155 p 26 pl 2 map p $5. CLSM   619
Hopi history (R 2) 57 p p $1. AzFM   620
Hopi Indians (IL 13) CoDA   621
Howard, E.B. Excavations in New Mexico (B v 4, no 5) 4
p 1 pl 1933 p $.35 PU-Mu   622
----. The first Americans (B v 6, no 5) 3 p 1 pl 1936 p
$.35 PU-Mu   623
Kidder, A.V. The excavations at Pecos in 1925 (P ns 14)
34 p il 1926 p $.25 NmSM-S   624
----. Pecos exploration in 1924 (P ns 11) 12 p il 1925 p
$.25 NmSM-S   625
----. The story of the Pueblo of Pecos (P ns 44) 10 p il
1951 p $.15 NmSM-S   626
King, Dale S. Nalak ihu: Excavations at a Pueblo II site
on Wupatki National Monument, Arizona (B 25) 183 p
1949 p $4. AzFM   627
Lambert, Marjorie F. Paa-ko. Pt. 1-v. An archaeological and historical chronicle of an Anasazi Indian village
in north central New Mexico (M 19) 183 p il 1954 $6.
Rogers, Spencer L. Pt. VI. The physical type of the
Paa-ko population (M 19) 48 p il 1954 $3. NmSM-S 628
Leighton, Dorothea C., and Alexander H. Leighton. Gregorio, the hand-trembler: A psychobiological personality
study of a Navaho Indian (P v 40, no 1) 172 p 7 chart
1949 p $2.50 MH-P   629
Lockett, H. Clairborne, and Lyndon L. Hargrave. Wood-
chuck Cave: A Basketmaker II site in Tsegl Canyon,
Arizona (B 26) 33 p 1953 p $1. AzFM   630
McGregor, John C. Winona and Ridge Ruin, Pt. 1. Architecture and material culture (B 18) 313 p 1941 $5.25
AzFM   631
----. Winona village: A XIIth century settlement with a
ball court near Flagstaff, Arizona (B 12) 53 p 1937 p

$.75 AzFM (op)   632
Marriott, Alice. These are the People 1951 $3. NmSM-L
                                                       633
Martin, George C. Archaeological exploration of the Shum-
la Caves (BB 3) 96 p 60 photog and il 1933 $2. TxSaW
                                                       634
----. The Big Bend Basket Makers (BB 1) 14 p 5 photog
1931 $.35 TxSaW   635
Martin, Paul S. Higgins Flat Pueblo, western New Mexico
(FA 45) 218 p 85 il 1956 $4.50 ICF   636
----. The SU site. Excavations at a Mogollon village,
western New Mexico, 1939 (FA 32:1) 98 p 42 fig 11 map
1940 $2. ICF   637
----, and John B. Rinaldo. Sites of the Reserve Phase,
Pine Lawn Valley, western New Mexico (FA 38:3) 177 p
79 il 1940 $3. ICF   638
----, ----. Turkey Foot Ridge site, A Mogollon village,
Pine Lawn Valley, western New Mexico (FA 38:2) 162 p
65 il 1950 $2.75 ICF   639
----, et al. Caves of the Reserve area (FA 42) 227 p 102
il 1954 $5. ICF   640
----, ----. Cochise and Mogollon sites, Pine Lawn Valley,
western New Mexico (FA 38:1) 232 p 24 fig 1949 $3.50
ICF   641
----, ----. Late Mogollon communities (FA 49:1) 144 p
57 il 5 table 1957 $4. ICF   642
----, ----. Mogollon cultural continuity and change. The
stratigraphic analysis of the Tularos and Cordova Caves
(FA 40) 528 p 179 il 1952 $8. ICF   643
Mason, J.A. The Texas archaeological expedition (MJ v
20, no 3-4) 21 p 16 il 1929 p $2. PU-Mu   644
Mera, Harry P. Population changes in the Rio Grande
Glaze-paint area (T 9) 1940 p $2. NmSM-L   645
Mills, George. Navajo art and culture il 1959 $4.50; post
$.14 CoCF   646
Modern Pueblo Indian villages (IL 45/46) CoDA   647
Montgomery, Ross Gordon, et al. Franciscan Awatovi:
The excavation and conjectural reconstruction at a 17th
century Spanish mission establishment at a Hopi Indian
town in northeastern Arizona (P v 26) 362 p 18 pl (1 c)
45 il 1949 $8.85; p $5.85 MH-P   648
Morley, Sylvanus G. The excavation of the Cannonball
Ruins in southwestern Colorado (P 2) 15 p il map 1908
p $.25 NmSM-S   649
Morris, Earl H. Burials in the Aztec ruins (AP 26:3, p
139-225) 30 fig 1 chart 1 map; with The Aztec ruin an-
nex (AP 26:4, p 227-57) 9 fig 1924 p $1.25 NNM   650

82   Morss, Noel

----. Notes on excavations in the Aztec ruin (AP 26:5, p
   259-420) 27 fig 1928 p $1.50 NNM   651
Morss, Noel. The ancient culture of the Fremont River in
   Utah (P v 12, no 3) 112 p 43 pl 5 il 1931 p $2.80 MH-P
                                                        652
----. Notes on the archaeology of the Kaibito and Rainbow
   Plateaus in Arizona (P v 12, no 2) 29 p 7 pl 1931 p
   $.50 MH-P   653
Navaho Indians (IL 21) CoDA   654
Nesbitt, Paul H. The ancient Mimbrenos based on investi-
   gations at the Mattocks Ruin, Mimbres Valley, New Mexi-
   co (B 4) 105 p 43 il 1931 p $1.50 WBB-Lo   655
Neuman, Georg. A variation of Southwestern Pueblo culture
   (T 10) 1940 p $1.25 NmSM-L   656
Periods of Pueblo culture and history (IL 11) CoDA   657
Prehistoric finds in New Mexico (B v 4, no 1) 2 p 1932 p
   $.35 PU-Mu   658
Reagan, Albert B. Notes on the Indians of the Fort Apache
   region (AP 31:5, p 281-345) 1930 p $.50 NNM   659
Reiter, Paul. The Jemez Pueblo of Unshagi, New Mexico,
   with notes on the earlier excavations at "Amoxiumqua" and
   Giusewa, including appendices: Stallings, W.S., Jr.
   Tree Rings; Shepard, Anna O. Ceramic technology (M
   5-6-- Publ with U of New Mexico) 211 p 23 pl 1938 $3.
   NmSM-S   660
Rinaldo, John B. Foote Canyon Pueblo, eastern Arizona
   (FA 49:2) 154 p 62 il 3 table 1959 $4. ICF   661
Seltzer, Carl C. Racial prehistory of the Southwest and the
   Hawikuh Zunis (P v 23, no 1) 38 p 15 table 1933 p $.75
   MH-P   662
Simpson, Ruth DeEtte. The Hopi Indians (Leaflet 25) 91 p
   36 il p $1. CLSM   663
Sinclair, John L. The story of the Pueblo of Kuana (P ns
   45) 9 p il (2 c) 1951 p $.25 NmSM-S   664
Smith, Watson. Excavations in Big Hawk Valley, Wupatki
   National Monument, Arizona (B 24) 203 p 1932 p $4.50
   AzFM   665
Southwestern tribes--Names, locations and population (IL 55)
   CoDA   666
Spier, Leslie. Havasupai ethnography (AP 29:3, p 81-392)
   60 fig 2 chart 1928 p $3. NNM   667
Springer, Frank. Educational addresses, 1899-1902 (P n3
   17) 56 p port 1927 p $.25 NmSM-S   668
Stubbs, Stanley A., and Bruce T. Ellis. Archaeological in-
   vestigations at the Chapel of San Miguel and the site of
   La Castrense, Santa Fe, New Mexico (M 20) 21 p 3 fig
   map 1955 $.75 NmSM-S   669

----, et al. The excavations of Pindi Pueblo, New Mexico
    (M 18) 165 p il fig map 1954 $6. NmSM-S   670
A survey of prehistoric research (B v 5, no 3) 1 p 1934 p
    $.35 PU-Mu   671
Taylor, Walter W. Two archaeological studies in Northern
    Arizona--The Pueblo ecology study: Hail and Farewell
    and a brief survey through the Grand Canyon of the Colo-
    rado River (B 30) 30 p 1958 p $1. AzFM   672
Trowbridge, Lydia J. Zuni (P ns 19) 4 p folder 1927 $.10
    NmSM-S   673
Vogt, Evon Z. Navaho veterans: A study of changing value
    (P v 41, no 1) 224 p 3 table 11 chart 1951 p $3. MH-P
                                                       674
Voth, H.R. Brief miscellaneous Hopi papers (FA 11:2) 61
    p 24 il 1912 $.75 ICF   675
Watkins, Frances E. The Navaho (Leaflet 16) p $.30
    CLSM   676
Wendorf, Fred. Archaeological studies in the Petrified For-
    est National Monument (B 27) 203 p 1953 $2. AzFM 677
----. Salvage archaeology in the Chama Valley, New Mexi-
    co 124 p il fig map table 1953 $6. NmSM-S   678
----, et al, ed. Pipeline archaeology: Reports of salvage
    operations in the Southwest on El Paso Natural Gas Com-
    pany Projects 1950-1953 (Plateau) 410 p map chart 1956
    p $4. AzFM   679
Wormington, H.M. Prehistoric Indians of the Southwest
    (PS 7) 192 p 52 il 2nd ed 1951 $3.20; p $2.20 CoDMNH
                                                       680

--Indians of North America--Southwest--Material Culture

Bartlett, Katharine. The material culture of Pueblo II in
    the San Francisco Mountains, Arizona (B 7) 76 p p 1934
    p $.75 AzFM   681
----. Pueblo milling stones of the Flagstaff region (B 3)
    32 p 1933 p $.60 AzFM   682
Cushing, Frank Hamilton. Zuni breadstuff (INM v8) 673 p
    il 1920 p $5. NNMAI   683
Davenport, J. Walker. Painted pebbles from the Lower
    Pecos and Big Bend regions of Texas 41 p 17 il $2.
    TxSaW   684
Dixon, Keith A. Hidden House: A cliff ruin in Sycamore
    Canyon, central Arizona (B 29) 90 p 1956 p $3. AzFM
                                                       685
Dutton, Bertha P. Leyit Kin, a small house ruin, Chaco
    Canyon, New Mexico (M 7--Publ with U of New Mexico)
    101 p 21 pl 1938 $2. NmSM-S   686

Elmore, Francis H.   Ethnobotany of the Navajo (M 8--Publ
   with U of New Mexico) 136 p il table 1955 $2. NmSM-S
                                                            687

Gardner, Fletcher, and George C. Martin.   A new type of
   atlatl from a cave shelter on the Rio Grande near Shumla, Val Verde County, Texas (BB 2) 1932 $.25 TxSaW
                                                            688

Hack, John T.   Prehistoric coal mining in the Jeddito Valley, Arizona (P v 35, no 2) 24 p 5 pl 10 il 1942 p $.75
   MH-P   689

Harvest-time in Zuni (B 4) $.05 PRM   690

Hodge, Frederick Webb.   The age of the Zuni pueblo of
   Kechipauan (INM 3:2) 16 p il 1920 p $.40 NNMAI   691

----.   Circular kivas near Hawikuh, New Mexico (C 7:1) 37
   p il 1923 p $1.50 NNMAI   692

Hopi agriculture (R 5) 26 p $.75 AzFM   693

Howard, E.B.   Folsom points and Glacial Man (B v 4, no
   3) 4 p 1 pl 1933 p $.35 PU-Mu   694

Kelly, J.C., et al.   The association of archeological materials with geological deposits in the Big Bend Region of
   Texas 1940 $2.   TxAl   695

Kroeber, A.L.   Zuni potsherds (AP 18:1-37) 2 fig 1916 p
   $.30 NNM   696

Morris, Earl H.   An aboriginal salt mine at Camp Verde,
   Arizona (AP 31:3, p 75-97) 12 fig 1928 p $.30 NNM 697

----.   The house of the Great Kiva at the Aztec ruin (AP
   26:2, p 109-38) 5 fig 1921 p $.30 NNM   698

Nelson, N.M.   Pueblo ruins of the Galisteo Basin, New
   Mexico (AP 15:1, p 1-124) 4 pl 13 fig 1 map 7 plan 1914
   p $.75 NNM   699

Patrick, R.   The occurrence of flints and extinct animals
   in pluvial deposits near Clovis, New Mexico. Pt. 5. Di-
   atom evidence from the Mammoth Pit (1938.4) $.30
   PPAN   700

Pueblo Indian foods (IL 8) CoDA   701

Schuetz, Mardith K.   Analysis of Val Verde County cave material 27 p 8 il $1.40 1956 TxSaW   702

Spier, Leslie.   Mohave culture items (B 28) 35p 1955 p
   $1. AzFM   703

----.   Notes on some Little Colorado ruins (AP 13:4, p
   333-62) 5 fig 1918 p $.70 NNM   704

----.   An outline for a chronology of Zuni ruins (AP 18:3,
   p 207-331) 18 fig 1917 p $1. NNM   705

----.   Ruins in White Mountains, Arizona (AP 18:5, p 363-
   87) 3 fig 1919 p $.25 NNM   706

Vestal, Paul A.   Ethnobotany of the Ramah Navaho (P v 40,
   no 4) 94 p 1952 p $2.50 MH-P   707

Whiting, Alfred F. Ethnobotany of the Hopi (B 15) 120 p
  1950 p $2.25 AzFM   708
Woodbury, Richard B. Prehistoric stone implements of
  northeastern Arizona p $7.50 MH-P   709

--Indians of North America--Southwest--Social Life and
Customs

Bailey, Flora L. Some sex beliefs and practices in a Nav-
  aho community (Pv 40, no 2) 108 p 1950 p $3. MH-P
                                                            710
Davis, Edward H. The Papago ceremony of Vikita (INM 3:
  4) 19 p il 1921 p $.65 NNMAI   711
Dorsey, G.A., and H.R. Voth. The Oraibi Soyal ceremony
  (FA 3:1) 63 p 37 il 1901 $3. ICF   712
Harrington, M.R. Devil dance of the Apaches (MJ v 3, no
  1) 4 p 2 il 1912 p $.50 PU-Mu   713
Hopi customs, folklore and ceremonies (R 4) 79 p p $1.25
  AzFM (op)   714
Kroeber, A.L. Zuni kin and clan (AP 18:2, p 39-204) 3
  fig 9 map 1917 p $1.50 NNM   715
Landgraf, John L. Land-use in the Ramah area of New
  Mexico: an anthropological approach to areal study (P
  v 42, no 1) 98 p 18 il 1954 p $1.65 MH-P   716
Lowie, Robert H. Hopi kinship (AP 30:7, p 361-88) 1929
  p $.35 NNM   717
----. Notes on Hopi clans (AP 30:6, p 303-60) 1929 p
  $.50 NNM   718
Matthews, Washington. The night chant, a Navajo ceremony
  (M v 6) (Hyde Southwest Exp) 332 p 8 pl 19 fig 1902 p
  $5. NNM   719
Navaho customs (R 6) 105 p p $1.50 AzFM   720
Opler, M.E. Childhood and youth in Jicarilla Apache so-
  ciety (Pubns Hodge V) 170 p 2 pl 8 fig 1946 p $3. CLSM
                                                            721
Parsons, Elsie Clews. Laguna genealogies (AP 19:5, p
  133-292) 22 fig 1 map 1923 p $2. NNM   722
----. Notes on ceremonialism at Laguna (AP 19:4, p 85-
  131) 21 fig 1920 p $.50 NNM   723
Smith, Watson, and John M. Roberts. Zuni law: A field of
  values, with an appendix: Newman, Stanley. A practical Zuni orthography (P v 42, no 1) 176 p 1954 p $3.
  MH-P   724
Voth, H.R. The Oraibi Marau ceremony (FA 11:1) 88 p
  33 il 1912 $1. ICF   725
----. Oraibi natal customs and ceremonies (FA 6:2) 17 p 8
  il 1905 $.25 ICF   726

----. The Oraibi Oaqol ceremony (FA 6:1) 46 p 28 il (2
c) 1903 $1. ICF   727
----. The Oraibi summer Snake ceremony (FA 3:4) 97 p
72 il 1901 $1.50 ICF   728
----. Traditions of the Hopi (FA 8) 320 p 1905 $2. ICF
                                                                 729

--Indians of North America--California Area

Barrett, S.A. Washo Indians (B v 2, no 1) 52 p 13 pl 22
fig 1 map 1917 p $.50 WMMMu   730
----, and E.W. Gifford. Indian life of the Yellowstone re-
gion 277 p 50 il (earlier editions issued by Milwaukee
Public Museum) $2.95; p $1.95 CYo   731
Beal, Merrill D. The story of man in Yellowstone (Inter-
pretive Series 7) 320 p il rev ed 1956 $3.32 WyY   732
Dixon, Roland B. The Shasta (B 17:5, p 381-498) 14 pl 51
fig 1907 p $1.25 NNM   733
Godfrey. Indians, Yosemite--yesterday and today p $.35
CYo   734
Harrington, M.R. Ancient life among the Southern California
Indians (Leaflet 26) 38 p 11 il p $.50 CLSM   735
----. An ancient site at Borax Lake, California (P 16) 121
p 33 pl 45 fig 1947 p $3.50 CLSM   736
----. Gypsum Cave, Nevada (P 8) 206 p il 1933 p $4.
CLSM   737
----. A Pinto site, near Little Lake, California (P 17)
91 p 54 fig 1957 $5; p $3.75 CLSM   738
Kidder, Alfred V. Explorations in southwestern Utah (P 15)
23 p il map 1910 p $.25 NmSM-S   739
Klamath Indians (IL 48) CoDA   740
Merwin, B.W. The Patty Stuart Jewett Collection (Mainly
California basketry) (MJ v 9, no 3-4) 19 p 13 pl (4 c)
1918 p $2. PU-Mu   741
Orr, Phil C. Excavations in Moaning Cave (DAB 1) 19 p il
1952 p $.50 CStbMu   742
----. Radiocarbon dates from Santa Rosa Island, I (DAB 2)
10 p il 1956 p $.25 CStbMu   743
Heizer, Robert F. Notes on some Paviotso personalities
and material culture (AP 2) 1960 p $.35 NvCM   744
Roplogle, Wayne F. Yellowstone's Bannock Indian trails
(Interpretive Series 6) il p $.95 WyY   745
The Samuel A. Clarke papers, with an appendix compiled
from material in Clark's scrapbook (RP 2) 33 p 1960 p
$1.15 OrK   746
Schulz. Indians of Lassen Volcanic National Park p $.85
CMi   747
Simpson, George Gaylord. A Nevada fauna of Pleistocene

type and its probable association with man (N 667) 10 p 5
fig 1933 p NNM   748
Walker, E.F.   Five prehistoric archaeological sites in Los
Angeles County, California (Pubns Hodge VI) 116 p 50
pl 20 fig 1951 p $3.50 CLSM   749
----.   Indians of Southern California (Leaflet 10) p $.25
CLSM   750

--Indians of North America--California Area--Material
Culture

Barrett, S.A.   Material aspects of Pomo culture (B v 20)
508 p 62 pl 8 fig 1952 p $7. WMMMu   751
----, and E.W. Gifford.   Miwok material culture (B v 2,
no 4) 260 p 49 pl 65 fig 2 map 1933, repr 1956 p $1.95
WMMMu   752
Deuel, Thorne.   The Modoc shelter (R 7; repr Natural His-
tory, Oct 1957, p 400-5) p apply ISM (op)   753
Fowler, Melvin L.   Summary report of Modoc rock shelter,
1952-1956 (R 8) 72 p 1959 p $1.60 ISM   754
Heye, George G.   Certain aboriginal artifacts from San
Miguel Island, California (INM 7:4) 211 p 124 pl 1921 p
$4. NNMAI   755
Robinson, Eugene.   Shell fishhooks of the California coast
(OP 17:4) 1942 p $.25 HB   756
Wheat, Margaret M.   Notes on some Paviotso material cul-
ture: Making a tule and cattail boat; making a cattail
house (AP 1) 1959 p $.35 NvCM   757

--Indians of North America--California Area--Social Life
and Customs

Cleghorn, John C.   Historic water levels of Tule Lake,
California-Oregon and their relation to the petroglyphs
(RP 1) 10 p 4 pl 2 fig 1 map 1959 p $1. OrK   758
Davis, E.H.   The Diegueno ceremony of the death-images
(C 5:2) 27 p il 1919 p $.50 NNMAI   759
----.   Early cremation ceremonies of the Luiseno and Di-
egueno Indians of Southern California (INM 7:3) 20 p 1921
p $.20 NNMAI   760
Devereux, George.   Mohave etiquette (Leaflet 22) p $.25
CLSM   761
Orr, Phil C.   Customs of the Canalino (OP 6; repr from
OP 5) 26 p 6 pl 1956 p $.50 CStbMu   762
Taylor, Edith S., and William J. Wallace.   Mohave tattoo-
ing and face-painting (Leaflet 20) p $.25 CLSM   763
Wallace, William J.   Hupa warfare (Leaflet 23) p $.25

--Indians of North America--Northwest Coast

Boas, Franz. The Kwakiutl of Vancouver Island (M 8:2, p
   301-522) (JNP v 5) 26 pl 152 fig 1909 p $15. NNM* 765
Drucker, Philip. Indians of the Northwest Coast (SG 10)
   $5.75; post $.12 NNM   766
Giddings, J. L., Jr. Trace of early man on the North Ber-
   ing sea coast (B v 14, no 4) 12 p 5 il 1950 p $.50 PU-
   Mu   767
Harrington, M. R. The Northwest Coast Collection (MJ v 3,
   no 1) 6 p 3 il 1912 p $.50 PU-Mu   768
Indian tribes and languages of Old Oregon Territory, map
   22x33 c $1. OrHi   769
Indians of the Northwest (MJ v 4, no 3) 12 p 13 il 1913 p
   $.50 PU-Mu   770
Irvine, Albert. How the Makah obtained possession of Cape
   Flattery (M 6) 10 p 1921 p$.15 NNMAI   771
Northwest Coast Indians (IL 1) CoDA   772
Northwest Coast tribes--Names, locations and numbers (IL
   72) CoDA   773
Puget Sound Indians--Names, location and culture (IL 32)
   CoDA   774
Reagan, Albert B. Archaeological notes on western Wash-
   ington and adjacent British Columbia (P v 7, no 1, p 1-
   31) 6 pl 1917 p $.30 CSfA   775
Shotridge, L. My Northland revisited (MJ v 8, no 2) 11 p
   6 il 1917 p $1. PU-Mu   776
----. A visit to the Tsimshian Indians (MJ v 10, no 1-2)
   19 p 7 il 1919 p $2; (continued) (MJ v 10, no 3) 32 p
   10 pl 1919 p $1. PU-Mu   777
Smith, Harlan I. Archaeology of Lytton, British Columbia
   (M 2:3, p 129-62) (JNP v 1) 1 pl 117 fig 1899 p $2.
   NNM   778
----. Archaeology of the Gulf of Georgia and Puget Sound
   (M 4:6, p 301-441) (NJP v 2) 3 pl 99 fig 1907 p $4.50
   NNM*   779
----. Archaeology of the Thompson River region, British
   Columbia (M 2:6, p 301-42) (NJP v 1) 3 pl 51 fig 1900
   p $2. NNM   780
----. Shell-heaps of the lower Fraser River, British Col-
   umbia (M 4:4, p 133-91) (JNP v 2) 2 pl 50 fig 1903 p
   $1. NNM   781
Swanton, John R. Contributions to the ethnology of the Haida
   (of Queen Charlotte Islands) (M 8:1, p 1-300) (JNP v 5)
   26 pl 31 fig 10 map 1902 p $12. NNM*   782

Teit, James. The Lillooet Indians, edited by Franz Boas
(M 4:5, p 193-400) (JNP v 2) 2 pl 40 fig 1906 p $2.70
NNM*   783
----. The Shuswap, edited by Franz Boas (M 4:7, p 199-
281) (JNP v 2) 2 pl 82 fig 1909 p $8. NNM*   784
----. The Thompson Indians of British Columbia (M 2:4,
p 163-392) (JNP v 1) 7 pl 198 fig 1 map 1900 p $5.
NNM.   785

--Indians of North America--Northwest Coast--Material
Culture

de Laguna, F. Ceremonial paddle from the Eyak Indians,
Alaska (B v 5, no 2)3 p 1 pl 1934 p $.35 PU-Mu   786
Dorsey, G.A. The Dwarmish Indian spirit boat and its use
(BFM v 3, no 4) 11 p 5 pl 1902 p $.50 PU-Mu   787
Emmons, George T. Slate mirrors of the Tsimshian (M
15) 21 p il 1921 p $.35 NNMAI   788
----. The whale house of the Chilkat (AP 19:1, p 1-33) 4
pl 6 fig 1916 p $1. NNM   789
Shotridge, F. and L. Chilkat houses, house posts, and
screens and their heraldry (MJ v 4, no 3) 19 p 18 il
1913 p $.50 PU-Mu   790
Shotridge, L. The Kaguanton shark helmet (MJ v 20, no 3-
4) 5 p 2 pl 1929 p $2. PU-Mu   791
----. War helmets and clan hats of the Tlingit Indians
(MJ v 10, no 1-2) 6 p 6 pl c 1919 p $2. PU-Mu   792
Smith, Harlan I., and Gerard Fowke. Cains of British Columbia and Washington (M 4:2, p 55-75) (JNP v 2) 5 pl 9
fig 1 map 1901 p $1. NNM   793

--Indians of North America--Northwest Coast--Social Life
and Customs

Boas, Franz. Facial paintings of the Indians of northern
British Columbia (M 2:1, p 1-24) (JNP v 1) 6 pl 1898 p
$2. NNM   794
Davidson, D.S. Family hunting territories in northwestern
North America (M 46) 46 p map 1928 p $.30 NNMAI 795
Kahnweiler, W.S. Traditions of the Quinault Indians (M 4:
3, p 77-132) (JNP v 2) 1902 p $1. NNM   796
Leechman, J.D., and M.R. Harrington. String-records of
the Northwest (M 16) 64 p il 1921 p $.75 NNMAI   797
Shotridge, F. The life of a Chilkat Indian girl (MJ v 4, no
3) 3 p 1913 p $.50 PU-Mu   798
Shotridge, L. The bride of Tongass (A study of the Tlingit
bridal ceremony) (MJ v 20, no 2) 26 p 9 il 1929 p $1.

PU-Mu   799

--Indians of North Americas--Eskimo Area

Archaeological work in Alaska (B v 1, no 3) 3 p 1 pl 1930
    p $.35 PU-Mu   800
Boas, Franz. The Eskimo of Baffin Land and Hudson Bay.
    From notes collected by Capt. George Comer, Capt.
    James S. Mutch, and Rev. E.J. Peck (B 15:1, p 1-370)
    4 pl 172 fig 1901 p $3. NNM   801
Carpenter, Edmund. Eskimo $4.95 CaOTAG   802
de Laguna, F. The Alaskan expedition (B v 4, no 5) 2 p
    1933 p $.35 PU-Mu   803
----. Excavations in Alaska (B v 3, no 2) 3 p 1 pl 1931 p
    $.35 PU-Mu   804
Ford, James A. Eskimo prehistory in the vicinity of Point
    Barrow, Alaska (AP 47:1, 11-272) 13 pl 118 fig 28 table
    1959 NNM   805
Giddings, J.L., Jr. The arctic woodland culture of the Ko-
    buk River (MM) 143 p 46 pl 43 fig 1952 p $2.50 PU-Mu
                                                           806
----. Forest Eskimos, an ethnographic sketch of Kobuk
    River people in the 1880's (B v 20, no 2) 55 p 15 il 1956
    p $.50 PU-Mu   807
Gordon, G.B. Notes on the western Eskimo (T v 2, no 1)
    32 p 18 pl 23 fig 1906 p $1. PU-Mu   808
Merwin, B.W. The Copper Eskimo (MJ v 6, no 4) 6 p
    1915 p $1. PU-Mu   809
Rainey, Froelich G. Archaeology in central Alaska (AP 36:
    4, p 351-405) 12 fig 1939 p $.50 NNM   810
----. Eskimo prehistory: The Okvik site on the Punuk Is-
    lands (AP 37:4, p 453-569) 37 fig p $1.25 NNM   811
Shapiro, H.L. The Alaskan Eskimo. A study of the rela-
    tionship between Eskimo and the Chipewyan Indians of
    central Canada (AP 31:6, p 347-84) 5 fig 1931 p $.50
    NNM   812
Wissler, Clark. Archaeology of the polar Eskimo (AP 22:3,
    p 105-66) 33 fig 1 map 1918 p $.50 NNM   813

--Indians of North America--Eskimo Area--Material Culture

Cadzow, Donald A. Native copper objects of the Copper
    Eskimo (M 8) 22 p il 1920 p $.45 NNMAI   814
de Laguna, F. Eskimo dug-outs (B v 5, no 5) 4 p 1 pl
    1935 p $.35 PU-Mu   815
Jenness, Diamond. An archaeological collection from the
    Belcher Islands in Hudson Bay (A v 28, p 189-206) 9 pl

p $.60 PPiCM   816
Quimby, George I.   Toggle harpoon heads from the Aleutian
   Islands (FA 36:2) 10 p 9 fig 1946 $.35 ICF   817
Weyer, Edward Moffat, Jr.   Archaeological material from
   the village site at Hot Springs, Alaska (AP 31:4, p 239-
   79) 25 fig 1930 p $.50 NNM   818

--Indians of North America--Eskimo Area--Social Life and
Customs

An Eskimo hunting party (B 3) $.05 PRM   819
Hawkes, E.W.   The dance festivals of the Alaskan Eskimos
   (AP v 6, no 2) 41 p 5 pl 1914 p $1.50 PU-Mu   820
Larsen, Helge, and Froelich Rainey.   Ipiutak and Arctic
   whale hunting culture (AP 42:1, p 1-101) 4 table 1948 p
   $10. NNM   821
Rainey, Froelich G.   The whale hunters of Tigara (AP 41:
   2, p 227-84) 1947 p $.70 NNM   822
Weyer, Edward Moffat, Jr.   An Aleutian burial (AP 31:3,
   p 219-38) 7 fig 1929 p $.25 NNM   823

--Indians of North America--Canada   See also Indians of
North America--Eastern Woodlands; -- Eskimo Area;
--Northwest Coast

Bird, Junius.   Archaeology of the Hopedale area, Labrador
   (AP 39:2, p 117-88) 4 pl 40 fig 1945 p $.85 NNM   824
Farrand, Livinston.   Traditions of the Chilicotin Indians
   (M 4:1, p 1-54) (JNP v 2) 1900 p $1.50 NNM   824a
Goddard, Pliny Earle.   The Beaver Indians (AP 10:4, p
   201-93) 19 fig 1916 p $1. NNM   825
Greenman, Emerson F.   Old Birch Island cemetery and
   early historic trading route, Georgian Bay, Ontario (OC
   11) 69 p 26 pl 7 fig 4 map 1951 p $2. MiU-A   826
Ritchie, William A.   An archaeological survey of the Trent
   Waterway in Ontario, Canada, and its significance for
   New York State prehistory (RR 9) $1.50 NRM   827
Skinner, Alanson.   Notes on the Eastern Cree and Northern
   Saulteaux (AP 9:1, p 1-177) 2 pl 56 fig 1911 p $2. NNM
                                                        828
Speck, Frank G.   Beothuk and Micmac (M 22) 187 p 42 pl
   map 1921 p $3.25 NNMAI   829
Tushingham, A.D.   Archaeology and the Canadian p $.30
   CaOTRM   830
Wallis, Wilson D.   The Canadian Dakota (AP 4:1, p 1-226)
   1947 p $2.50 NNM   831

--Indians of North America--Canada--Material Culture

McIntosh, William. Chipped and flaked implements of New
   Brunswick (G 31; repr, Nat Hist Soc of New Brunswick
   Bul, no 31) 1913 $.25 CaNBSM   832
Skinner, Alanson. A native copper celt from Ontario (M 1)
   2 p il 1920 p $.15 NNMAI   833

--Indians of Mexico, Central and South America

The Amazon expedition (General) (MJ v 4, no 1) 12 p 12 il
   1913 p $.50 PU-Mu   834
Barratt, S.A. The Cayapa Indians of Ecuador (M 40) 2 v
   il 1925 p $8. NNMAI   835
Bennett, Wendell C. Archaeology of the north coast of
   Peru. An account of exploration and excavation in Viry
   and Lambayeque Valleys (AP 37:1, p 1-153) 22 fig 1939
   p $1.60 NNM   836
----. Excavations at La Mata, Maracay, Venezuela (AP 36:
   2, p 69-137) 17 fig 1937 p $.75 NNM   837
----. Excavations at Tiahuanaco (AP 34:3, p 359-494) 35
   fig 1934 p $1.50 NNM   838
----. Excavations in Bolivia (AP 35:4, p 329-507) 48 fig
   1936 p $1.75 NNM   839
----. The North Highlands of Peru. Excavations in the
   Callejon de Huaylas and at Chavin de Huantar (AP 39:1,
   p 1-116) 8 pl 33 fig 1944 p $1.75 NNM   840
Bennett, William C., and Junius B. Bird. Andean culture
   history (SG 15) revision in process NNM   841
Bird, Junius B. Excavations in northern Chile (AP 38:4,
   p 171-318) 46 fig 1943 p $1.75 NNM   842
Booy, Th. de. The People of the Myst (Macoa, Venezuela)
   (MB v 9, no 3-4) 42 p 19 pl 1918 p $1. PU-Mu   843
Borhegyi, Stephen F. de. Precolumbian culture connections.
   Mesoamerica and Ecuador (P 18; MARR v 2, no 6) 1959
   p $.75 LNT-MA   844
Brainerd, George W. The Maya civilization 97 p 25 il 2
   map $2.50 CLSM   845
Breton, Adela. Some notes on Xochicalco (T v 2, no 1) 17
   p 5 pl 14 fig 1906 p $1. PU-Mu   846
Burkitt, R. Excavations at Chocola and explorations in the
   Highlands of western Guatemala (MJ v 21, no 1) 68 p 30
   pl 1930 p $1. PU-Mu   847
Coe, W.R. Excavations in El Salvador (B v 19, no 2) 8 p
   3 il 1955 p $.50 PU-Mu   848
Collier, Donald. Survey and excavations in southern Ecua-
   dor (FA 35) 108 p 54 pl 18 fig 3 map 1943 $1.50 ICF 849

Cook, Lt. James. Remarks on a passage from the River
   Balise, in the Bay of Honduras, to Merida: The capital
   of the Province of Jucatan in the Spanish West Indies
   (Midameres Press, London) facsim of original of 1769,
   with perspective by Muriel Haas, limited ed 52 p $2.
   LNT-MA   850
Culin, S. The Indians of Cuba (BFM v 3, no 4) 41 p 11 pl
   1902 p $.50 PU-Mu   851
Dorsey, G.A. A bibliography of the anthropology of Peru
   (FA 2:2) 154 p 1898 $1.50 ICF   852
Drucker, Philip. Notes on an archaeological survey of the
   Chiapas coast (P 15; MARR v 1, no 11) 31 p 1948 p $1.
   LNT-MA   853
Dutton, Bertha P., and Hulda R. Hobbs. Excavations at
   Tajumulco, Guatemala, with appendices: T.D. Stewart
   on Skeletal remains; W.C. Root on Copper objects (M 9--
   Publ with U. of New Mexico) 121 p 101 il 6 map 2 table
   1943 $4. NmSM-S   854
Edmondson, Munro S. Los Manitos (P 25, no 1) 1957 p $2.
   LNT-MA   855
Ekholm, Gordon F. Excavations at Gussave, Sinaloa, Mexi-
   co (AP 38:2, p 23-139) 22 fig 1942 p $1.50 NNM   856
----. Excavations at Tampico and Panuco in the Huasteca,
   Mexico (AP 38:5, p 319-512) 57 fig 1944 p $2.25 NNM
                                                         857
Excavations at Piedras Negras (B v 3, no 6) 2 p 1932 p
   $.35 PU-Mu   858
Excerpts from Dr. Max Uhle's preliminary report on Pa-
   chacamac (Peru) (BFM v 1, no 1) 3 p 1897 p $.50 PU-
   Mu   859
The expedition to Piedras Negras (B v 4, no 3) 2 p 1933 p
   $.35; (B v 5, no 6) 6 il 1935 p $.35 PU-Mu   860
Farabee, W.C. The Amazon expedition (Guiana) (MJ v 6,
   no 1) 54 p 45 il 1915 p $1; (MJ v 7, no 4) 35 p 14 il
   1916 p $1; (Amazon Headwaters) (B v 8, no 1) 22 p 15
   il 1917 p $1; (Mundurucu) (B v 8, no 2) 19 p 6 il 1917
   p $1. PU-Mu   861
----. The Apalaii (MJ v 10, no 3) 15 p 8 il (1 c) 1919 p
   $1. PU-Mu   862
----. The Central Caribs (AP v 10) 282 p 1924 p $10.
   PU-Mu   863
----. Explorations at the mouth of the Amazon (MJ v 12,
   no 3) 20 p 11 il (1 c) 1921 p $1. PU-Mu   864
----. Indian tribes of eastern Peru (P v 10) 194 p 28 pl
   20 il 1922 $5.95; p $3.20 MH-P   865
Ferdon, Edwin N., Jr. Tonala, Mexico; an archaeological
   survey (M 16) 126 p il fig map 1953 $6. NmSM-S   866

Forsey, G.A.   Archaeological investigations in the island of
La Plata, Ecuador (FA 2:5) 36 p 73 il 1901 $3. ICF 867
Gillin, John.   The Barama River Caribs of British Guiana
(P v 14, no 2) 288 p 30 pl 13 il 1936 p $3.25 MH-P 868
Gordon, George Byron.   Researches in the Uloa Valley (M
v 1, no 4) 44 p il 12 pl map 1898; with --.   Caverns of
Copan (M v 1, no 5) 12 p 1 pl map 1898 p $2.25 MH-P
                                                    869
----.   Sucaneb (MJ v 6, no 4) 4 p 2 il 1915 p $1. PU-Mu
                                                    870
----.   A trip to Chichen Itza (MJ v 2, no 1) 12 p 8 il 1918
p $.50 PU-Mu   871
Harrington, M.R.   Cuba before Columbus. Pt. 1. 2 v. il
1921 p $8. NNMAI   872
Hatt, R.T.   Faunal and archaeological researches in Yuca-
tan caves (B 33) 119 p il 1953 p $1. MiBloC   872a
Hewett, Edgar L.   The third season's work in Guatemala
(P 22) 9 p il drg 1912 p $.25 NmSM-S   873
Kidder, Alfred II.   Archaeology of northwestern Venezuela
(P v 26, no 1) 178 p 18 pl 62 il 3 table 1944 p $3.75
MH-P   874
----.   Some early sites in the Northern Lake Titicaca Basin
(P v 27, no 1) (Research Project no 7 of the Institute of
Andean Research under sponsorship of the Co-ordinator
of Inter-American Affairs) 48 p front 7 pl 7 il 1943 p
$1.25 MH-P   875
King, Arden R.   Archaeological remains from the Cintlapa
region, Chiapas, Mexico (P 18; MARR v 2, no 4) 39 p
1955 p $1.25 LNT-MA   876
Kroeber, A.L.   Archaeological explorations in Peru. Pt. 1.
Ancient pottery from Trujillo (AM 2:1) 44 p 13 photog 4
etch 1926 $1.50; Pt. 2. The northern coast (AM 2:2) 72
p 17 photog 3 etch 1 map 1930 $1.50; Pt. 3. Textiles of
the early Nazca period (AM 2:3) 102 p 36 photog 2 pl c
1 fig 1937 $3.50, (op); Pt. 4. Canete Valley (AM 2:4)
56 p 22 photog 1937 $1.50 ICF   877
----.   Proto-Lima. A Middle Period Culture of Peru, with
an appendix: Wallace, Dwight T. Cloths (FA 44:1) 157 p
94 il 1954 $4. ICF   878
----.   The Seri (P 6) 60 p 12 il 1931 p $1.50 CLSM   879
Longyear, John M. III.   Archaeological investigations in El
Salvador (M v 9, no 2) 90 p 30 il 15 pl 1944 p $3.75
MH-P   880
Lothrop, Samuel K.   Archaeology of southern Veraguas,
Panama (M v 9, no 3) 116 p 150 il 10 table 1950 p $10.
MH-P   881
----.   Cocle: An archaeological study of central Panama.

Pt. 1. Historical background, excavations at the Sitio
Conte, artifacts and ornaments (M v 7) 327 p 271 il 4 pl
c map $15; p $10; Pt. 2. Pottery of the Sitio Conte and
other archaeological sites (M v 8) 292 p 491 il 3 pl c
map $15; p $10. MH-P   882
----. The Indians of Tierra del Fuego (C v 10) 244 p 19
pl 1928 p $3. NNMAI   883
Maler, Teobert. Explorations in the Department of Peten,
Guatemala, and adjacent region (M v 4, no 2) 74 p 30 pl
22 il 1908 p $4.50; (continued) (M v 4, no 3) 42 p 2 pl
1910 p $1.40 MH-P   884
----. Explorations in the Department of Peten, Guatemala.
Tikal (M v 5, no 1) 92 p 17 il 28 pl; with Tozzer, Al-
fred M. Prehistoric ruins of Tikal, Guatemala (M v 5,
no 2) 42 p 30 il 2 pl p $6.25 MH-P   885
----. Explorations of the Upper Usumatsintla and adjacent
regions (M v 4, no 1) 52 p 13 pl 8 il map 1908 p $2.50
MH-P   886
----. Researches in the central portion of the Usumatsintla
Valley (M v 2, no 1) 75 p 26 il 33 pl 1901 p $4.50; Pt.
2. (M v 2, no 2) 130 p 42 il 47 pl 1903 p $7.25 MH-P
                                                            888
Mason, J. Alden. The archaeology of Santa Marta, Colum-
bia. The Tairona Culture. Pt. 1. Report on field work
(FA 20:1) 130 p 64 pl 1 map 1931 $2.50; Pt. 2, sect 1.
Objects of stone, shell, bone, and metal (FA 20:2) 142 p
99 pl 1936 $3.50; Pt. 3. Objects of pottery, with an ap-
pendix on ceramic technology by Donald Horton (FA 20:3)
146 p 85 pl 26 fig 1939 $3.50 ICF   889
----. An exchange collection from Field Museum (Columbia)
(B v 3, no 2) 2 p 1 pl 1931 p $.35 PU-Mu   890
----. What we know about the Maya (MJ v 18, no 4) 33 p
18 il 1927 p $1. PU-Mu   891
The Matto Grosso expedition (B v 3, no 2) 3 p 1 pl 1931 p
35; (B v 4, no 4) 2 p 1 pl 1933 p $.35 PU-Mu   892
Means, Philip Ainsworth. History of the Spanish conquest of
Yucatan and of the Itzas (P v 7) 206 p 5 pl map 1917
$5.40; p $2.40 MH-P   893
Merwin, R.E., and George Clapp Valliant. The ruins of
Holmul, Guatemala (M v 3, no 2) 103 p 37 pl (1 c) 31 il
1932 p $5.25 MH-P   894
Middle American archaeology: The greater cultures (Rhode
Island School of Design. (B v 29, no 1-2) 1941 p $.50
RPD-M   895
Middle American Research Institute. Middle American Re-
search Records v 1 (P 15) 280 p il 1942-1950 p $6.
LNT-MA   896

Middle American Research Institute. Synoptic studies of
    Mexican culture (P 17) 200 p 1955 p $5.50 LNT-MA 897
Nimuendaju, Curt. The Serente, translated and edited by
    Robert H. Lowie (Pubns Hodge IV) 106 p 3 pl 4 fig map
    1942 p $1.75 CLSM   898
Nuttall, Zelia, trans and ed. Official reports on the towns
    of Tequizistlan, Tepechpan, Acolman, and San Juan Teo-
    tihuacan, sent by Francisco de Casteneda to His Majesty,
    Philip II, and the Council of the Indies in 1580 45 p 2 pl
    2 il 1926 p $.75 MH-P   899
Petrullo, V. M. The Guajiro expedition, 1935 (B v 6, no 3)
    2 p 10 il 1936 p $.35 PU-Mu   900
----. Primitive people of the Matto Grosso (MJ v 23, no
    2) 93 p 25 pl 1932 p $1. PU-Mu   901
----. Research in Venezuela (B v 5, no 3) 6 p 4 pl 1934
    pl 1934 p $.35 PU-Mu   902
The Piedras Negras expedition (B v 4, no 4) 2 p 1933 p
    $.35; (B v 5, no 3) 2 p 1935 p $.35 PU-Mu   903
Rainey, F.G. The Tikal project (B v 20, no 4) 22 p 25 il
    2 map 1956 p $.50 PU-Mu   904
Rowe, John H. An introduction to the archaeology of Cuzco
    (P v 27, no 2) (Research project no 7 of the Institute of
    Andean Research under the sponsorship of the Co-ordina-
    tor of Inter-American Affairs) 70 p 8 pl 19 il 1944 p
    $1.75 MH-P   905
Satterthwaite, L., Jr. The Piedras Negras expedition (B
    v 4, no 5) 4 p 3 pl 1933 p $.35 PU-Mu   906
----. Reconnaissance in British Honduras (B v 16, no 1)
    18 p 7 il 1951 p $.50 PU-Mu   907
Saville, Marshall H. Bibliographic notes on Palenque, Chia-
    pas (INM 6:5) 62 p 1928 p $.60 NNMAI   908
----. Bibliographic notes on Xochicalco, Mexico (INM 6:6)
    23 p 1928 p $.30 NNMAI   909
----. Tizoc, Great Lord of the Aztecs (C 7:4) 78 p il
    1929 p $1.60 NNMAI   910
Service, Elman R. Spanish-Guarani relations in early Colo-
    nial Paraguay (AP 9) 106 p 1 map 1954 p $1. MiU-A
                                                      911
Shook, Edwin M., et al. Tikal report numbers 1-41 (MM)
    150 p 26 fig 1958 $2.50 PU-Mu   912
Skinner, Alanson. Notes on the Bribri of Costa Rica (INM
    6:3) 107 p il 1920 p $1.50 NNMAI   913
Sorenson, John L. A chronological ordering of the Meso-
    american Pre-Classic (P 18; MARR v 2, no 3) 30 p 1955
    p $1. LNT-MA   914
Stone, Doris Z. The archaeology of central and southern
    Honduras (P v 49, no 3) 135 p front c 38 il 46 fig 1957

p $5. 85 MH-P   915
----. Archaeology of the north coast of Honduras (M v 9,
   no 1) 103 p 99 il 1941 p $3. MH-P   916
----. The Boruca of Costa Rica (P v 26, no 2) 50 p 8 pl
   2 il 1949 p $2. 50 MH-P   917
----. The Talamancan tribes of Costa Rica (P v 43, no 2)
   in prep MH-P   918
Surface survey of the Viru Valley, Peru. Pt. 1. Ford,
   James Alfred, and Gordon R. Wiley. Viru Valley: Back-
   ground and problems; Pt. 2. Ford, James Alfred. Culture dating of prehistoric sites in Viru Valley, Peru (AP
   43:1, p 1-90) 7 pl 9 fig 1949 p $1.50 NNM   919
Thompson, Edward H. A chaeological researches in Yuca-
   tan (M v 3, no 1) 20 p 9 pl (3 c) 11 il 1904 p $1.75
   MH-P   920
----. The Chultunes of Labna (M v 1, no 3) 20 p il 13 pl
   1897 p $1.50 MH-P   921
----. Explorations of the Cave of Loltun, Yucatan (M v 1,
   no 2) 22 p il 8 pl 1897 p $1.50 MH-P   922
----. Ruins of Xkichmook, Yucatan (FA 2:3) 22 p 30 il
   1898 p $1.50 ICF   923
Thompson, J. Eric. The civilization of the Mayas 98 p 36
   il 1 map 6th ed 1958 p $. 75 ICF (supply exhausted)   924
----. Ethnology of the Mayas of southern and central British Honduras (FA 17:2) 191 p 24 photog 1 map 1930 $3.
   ICF   925
Titiev, Mischa. Araucanian culture in transition (OC 15) 96
   p 2 map 1949 p $1. 50 MiU-A   926
Tozzer, Alfred M. Chichen Itza and its Cenote of Sacrifice;
   a comparative study of Maya and Toltec (M v 11, 12)
   316 p 710 il 27 table; Text (v 11); Reference material
   and illustrations (v 12) 1957 $35; p $25. MH-P   927
----, ed and trans. Landa's Relacion de las Cosas de Yucatan (P v 18) 400 p 1941 $8. 85; p $5. 85 MH-P   928
Tschopik, Harry, Jr. Indians of the Montaña (SG 135) 23 p
   30 il p $.65 NNM   929
Tschopik, Marion H. Some notes on the archaeology of the
   Department of Puno, Peru (P v 27, no 3) (Research project no 7 of the Institute of Andean Research under the
   sponsorship of the Co-ordinator of Inter-American Affairs) 58 p 10 pl 34 il 1946 p $1.65 MH-P   930
Valliant, George Clapp. Excavations at Ticoman (AP 32:2,
   p 199-439) 39 pl front 18 fig 6 map 1931 p $2. NNM 931
----. Excavations at Zacatenco (AP 32:1, p 1-197) 54 pl
   front 4 map 1930 p $2. NNM   932
Valliant, Suzannah B., and George Clapp Valliant. Excavations at Gualupita (AP 35:1, p 1-135) front 35 fig 1934 p

$1.25 NNM   933
von Hagen, Victor Wolfgang. The Jicaque Indians of Hon-
    duras (M 53) 112 p il 1943 p $2. NNMAI   934
----. The Tsatchela Indians of western Ecuador (M 51) 79
    p il 1939 p $1. NNMAI   935
Walde-Waldegg, H. von. An expedition to San Agustin and
    the Indian reservation of Tierradentro in southern Col-
    umbia (B v 6, no 6) 4 p 13 il 1937 p $.35 PU-Mu   936
Wauchope, Robert. Excavations at Zacualpa, Guatemala
    (P 14) 192 p 25 pl (folding front) 163 fig folding map
    table 1948 p $5.50 LNT-MA   937
----. Implications of radiocarbon dates from Middle and
    South America (P 18; MARR v 2, no 2) 24 p 1954 p $1.
    LNT-MA   938
----. Surface collection at Chiche, Guatemala (P 15; MARR
    v 1, no 10) 36 p 1948 p $1.25 LNT-MA   939
Willey, Gordon R., and Charles R. McGimsey. The Mona-
    grillo culture of Panama, with an appendix on Archaeo-
    logical marine shells by Robert E. Greengo (P v 49, no
    2) 158 p 34 il 20 fig 12 table 1954 p $4.65 MH-P   940

--Indians of Mexico, Central and South America--Material
Culture See also Art

Beyer, Hermann. Mexican bone rattles (P 5; Studies in
    Mid Am 7) 1934 p $1. LNT-MA   941
Blom, Frans, and Oliver La Farge. Tribes and temples,
    an archaeological and ethnological exploration of southern
    Mexico (P 1) 2 v 1926-27 $20. LNT-MA   942
Collier, Donald. Cultural chronology and change as re-
    flected in the ceramics of the Viru Valley, Peru (FA 43)
    226 p 73 il 1955 $5. ICF   943
de Booy, Theodoor. Certain kitchen-middens in Jamaica
    (C 3; repr, Amer Anthropol v 15, no 3, 1913) 10 p il
    1919 p $.50 NNMAI   944
Farabee, W.C. Ancient American gold (MJ v 11, no 3) 37
    p 22 il 1920 p $1. PU-Mu   945
----. The use of metals in Prehistoric America (MJ v 12,
    no 1) 8 p 2 il (1 c) 1921 p $1. PU-Mu   946
Gold in ancient America (B v 5, no 4) 3 p 2 il 1935 $.35
    PU-Mu   947
Holmes, W.H. Archeological studies among the ancient
    cities of Mexico. Pt. 1. Monuments of Yucatan (FA 1:
    1) 138 p 69 il 1895 $7; Pt. 2. Monuments of Chiapas,
    Oaxaca, and the Valley of Mexico (FA 1:2) 200 p 120 il
    1897 $6. ICF   948
Locke, L. Leland. The ancient quipu or Peruvian knot

record 84 p 59 pl front 17 fig 1 map 1923 p $3. NNM
                                                        949
----. A Peruvian quipu (C 7:5) 11 p il 1927 p $.30
NNMAI   950
Lothrop, Samuel K.   Archaeological remains in the Diquis
    Delta, Costa Rica (P v 51) in prep MH-P   951
----. Metals from the Cenote of Sacrifice, Pt. 2 (M v 10,
    no 2) 140 p 114 il 39 table 1952 p $10. MH-P   952
Nuttall, Zelia.   The atlatl, or spear-thrower of the ancient
    Mexicans (P v 1, no 3) 36 p 3 pl 1891 sigs $.55 MH-P
                                                        953
Prehistoric ruins of Copan, Honduras, a preliminary report
    of the explorations by the Museum, 1891-95 (Mv 1, no 1)
    48 p il 8 pl map 1896 p (photostat edition available) MH-
    P   954
Saville, Marshall H.   Bladed warclubs from British Guiana
    (M 14) 12 p il 1921 p $.25 NNMAI   955
----. The George G. Heye Expedition: Contributions to
    South American Archeology. The antiquities of Manabi,
    Ecuador: Final report (SA v 2) 284 p 114 pl 1910 $25.
    NNMAI   956
Tozzer, Alfred M. A preliminary study of the prehistoric
    ruins of Nakum, Guatemala (M v 5, no 3) 60 p 54 il 23
    pl 1913 p $4. MH-P   957
Uhle, Max. A modern kupu from Cutusuma, Bolivia (BFM
    v 1, no 2) 11 p 1 il 1897 p $.50 PU-Mu   958
----. The snuffing-tube from Tiahuanaco (BFM v 1, no 4)
    18 p 9 il 1898 p $.50 PU-Mu   959
Whitaker, Thomas W., and Junius B. Bird. Identification
    and significance of the cucurbit materials from Huaca
    Prieta, Peru (N 1426) 15 p 3 fig 1949 p NNM   960

--Indians of Mexico, Central and South America--Social Life
and Customs See also Folk Literature and Folk Lore

Adams, Richard, comp. Political changes in Guatemalan In-
    dian communities (P v 24, no 1) 1957 p $1.75 LNT-MA
                                                        961
Andrews, E. Wyllys. A revision of some dates on the hiero-
    glyphic stairway, Copan, Honduras (P v 26, no 1) 1958 p
    $.50 LNT-MA   962
Bandelier, Ad. F. On the relative antiquity of ancient Peru-
    vian burials (B 20:19, p 217-26) 1904 p $.10 NNM   963
Beyer, Hermann. Relation of the Synodial month and e-
    clipses, to the Maya correlation problem (P 5; Studies in
    Mid Am 6) 1934 p $.75 LNT-MA   964
Blom, Frans. The "negative batter" at Uxmal (P 4; Middle

American Pap 15) 1932 p $1. LNT-MA   965
Bowditch, Charles P.   A method which may have been used
   by the Maya in calculating time 1901 p $.50 MH-P   966
Burkitt, R.   The hills and the corn (AP v 8, no 2) 47 p 3
   pl 1920 p $2. PU-Mu   967
Correa, Gustavo.   Texto de un Baile de Diablos (P 27, no 2)
   1958 p $.25 LNT-MA   968
Farabee, W.C.   Mummified Jivaro heads (MJ v 10, no 4)
   11 p 3 il (1 c) 1919 p $1. PU-Mu   969
No entry   970
Fisher, Glen.   Directed culture change in Nayarit, Mexico:
   Analysis of a Mexican pilot project (P 17; SSM 2) 112 p
   1953 p $3. LNT-MA   971
Gillin, John.   The culture of security in San Carlos, a
   study of a Guatemalan community of Indians and ladinos
   (P 16) 128 p 1951 p $4. LNT-MA   972
Griffith, William J.   Attitudes toward foreign colonization in
   Guatemala, 1824-1868 (P23, Pt 2: Econmic-Political In-
   fluences 1) in press $1. LNT-MA   973
----.   A recent attempt at educational cooperation between
   the United States and Guatemala (P 15; MARR v 1, no 12)
   22 p 1949 p $1. LNT-MA   974
Harshberger, J.W.   The uses of plants among the ancient
   Peruvians (BFM v 1, no 3) 4 p 1898 p $.50 PU-Mu   975
Holmberg, Allan R.   Lizard hunts on the north coast of
   Peru (FA 36:9) 18 p 15 il 1957 $.75 ICF   976
Huckerby, Thomas.   Petroglyphs of Grenada and a recently
   discovered petroglyph in St. Vincent (INM 1:3) 22 p il
   1921 p $.50 NNMAI   977
La Farge, Oliver, and Douglas Byers.   The year bearer's
   people, a detailed study of the daily life and ceremonials
   of the Jacalteca Indians of the Guatemalan Highlands (P
   3) 380 p il 1931 $8. LNT-MA   978
Lewis, Oscar.   Aspects of land tenure and economics in a
   Mexican village (P 15; MARR v 1, no 13) 15 p 1949 p
   $.50 LNT-MA   979
Lothrop, Samuel K., and Joy Mahler.   A Chancay-style
   grave at Zapallan, Peru, an analysis of textiles, pottery
   and other furnishings (P v 50, no 1) 38 p 17 pl 10 il 9
   table 1957 p $2.50 MH-P   980
----, ----.   Late Nazca burials at Chavina, Peru (P v 50,
   no 2) 61 p 21 pl 14 il 5 table 1957 p $4.50 MH-P   981
Lumholtz, Carl.   Symbolism of the Huichol Indians (M 3:1,
   p 1-228) 4 pl 291 fig 2 map 1900 p $5. NNM   982
Martinez Hernandez, Juan.   Correlation of the Maya Venus
   calendar (P 4, Middle American Pap 6) 1932 p $.75
   LNT-MA   983

Mason, J.A.   The fiesta of Pinole at Azqueltan (MJ v 3, no
3) 7 p 3 il 1912 p $.50 PU-Mu   984
Molina, Cristobal.   War of the castes: Indian uprisings in
Chiapas, 1867-70, translated by Ernest Noyes and Dol-
ores Morgadanes (P 5; Studies in Mid Am 8) 1934 p $1.
LNT-MA   985
Morley, Sylvanus G.   The correlation of Maya and Christian
chronology (P 11) 12 p 1910 p $.25 NmSM-S   986
Munro, Edmonson.   Synthesis and remarks (on cultural
change in Mexico) (P 17; SSM 4) $1. LNT-MA   987
Nash, Ruth Cutter.   Calendrical interpretation of a golden
breastplate from Peru (M 52) 12 p il 1939 p $.30 NNMAI
                                                988
Palacios, Enrique Juan.   Maya-Christian synchronology or
calendrical correction (P 4; Mid Amer Pap 7) 1932 p
$1.50 LNT-MA   989
Rodriguez, Mario.   The Linginston codes and the Guatemalan
crisis of 1837-1838 (P23, Pt 1.   Intellectual and literary
influences 1) 32 p 1955 p $1. LNT-MA   990
Satterthwaite, L., Jr. Concepts and structures of Maya
calendrical arithmetic (JP 3) 168 p 1947 p $1. PU-Mu
                                                991
----.   Incense burning at Piedras Negras (B v 11, no 4) 7
p 4 il 1946 p $.50 PU-Mu   992
----.   Maya dates on stelae in Tikal "enclosures" (B v 20,
no 4) 17 p 12 il 1956 p $.50 PU-Mu   993
Silvert, Kalman H.   A study in government: Guatemala.
Pt. 1.   National and local government since 1944 (P 21)
104 p il 1954 p $3. LNT-MA   994
Spinden, Herbert J.   The reduction of Mayan dates (P v 6,
no 4) 286 p 4 pl 62 il 1925 p $3.50 MH-P   995
Thompson, J. Eric.   A correlation of Mayan and European
calendars (FA 17:1) 24 p 1927 $.25 ICF   996
Tschopik, Harry, Jr.   The Aymars of Chucuito, Peru. Pt.
1.   Magic (AP 44:2, p 133-308) 10 pl 11 fig 1 table
1951 p $3. NNM   997
Williams, George D.   Maya-Spanish crosses in Yucatan (P
v 13, no 1) 250 p 47 pl table 1931 p $3.50 MH-P 998
Willson, Robert E.   Astronomical notes on the Maya codices
(P v 6, no 3) 46 p 9 pl 6 il 1924 p $.75 MH-P   999
Wolf, Eric R.   The Mexican Bajio in the eighteenth century:
An analysis of cultural integration (P 17; SSM 3) 24 p
1955 p $1. LNT-MA   1000

--Europe

Ancient needles (Magdelenian) (B v9, no 1) 3 p 6 il 1941 p

$.50 PU-Mu   1001
Bonsor, George Edward. The archaeological expedition
  along the Guadalquivir, 1889-1901, tr from French by
  C. L. Penney 86 p 47 il 1931 $4.50 NNH   1002
Collie, George L. The Aurignacians and their culture (B 1)
  139 p 30 il 1928 p $.25 WBB-Lo   1003
History of Spain. Pt. 1. Old Stone Age; Pt. 2. New Stone
  Age il 1947 p $.25 ea NNH   1004
Laufer, Berthold. The introduction of tobacco into Europe
  (A-PS 19) 66 p 1924 p $.25 ICF   1005
Major movements of European population; vital changes in
  the population map of the world (1492-1942) (Map F)
  12.5x19 $.15 NNM   1006
Movius, Hallam L., Jr. comp. Old World bibliographies,
  recent publications mainly in Old World paleolithic archaeology and paleo-anthropology. No. 3 1950 p; No. 4
  1951 p; No. 5 1952 p $1. ea MH-P   1007
----, et al. The rock-shelter of La Colombiere (ASPR
  Bul 19) 176 p 52 il 1956 p $4.85 MH-P   1008

--Europe--Greece

Boyd, H.A. Excavations at Gournia, 1904 (T v 1, no 3) 12
  p 6 il 1905 p $1. PU-Mi   1009
Brinton, D.G. Note on the classical Murmex (BFM v 1, no
  2) 1 p 1897 p $.50 PU-Mu   1010
----. The so-called "Bow-Puller" identified as the Greek
  Murmex (BFM ▼ 1, no 1) 5 p 2 il 1897 p $.50 PU-Mu
                                                      1011
Cox, D.G. A third century hoard of Tetradrachms from
  Gordion (MM) 20 p 8 pl 1 map 1953 p $.75 PU-Mu 1012
The Cretan Expedition (MJ v 3, no 3) 5 p 4 il 1912 p $.50
  PU-Mu   1013
The Cyprus Expedition (B v 3, no 5) 3 p 3 il 1932 p $.35;
  (B v 4, no 1) 3 p 2 il 1932 p $.35; (B v 5, no 4) 2 p
  1 il 1935 p $.35 PU-Mu   1014
Daniel, J.F. Kourion 13 p 5 il; with Dikaios, P. Trial
  excavations at Sotira 8 p 5 il (B v 13, no 3) 1948 p $.50
  PU-Mu   1015
Dikaios, P. Excavations at Sotira--1951 (B v 17, no 1) 11
  p 16 il 1952 p $.50 PU-Mu   1016
Excavations at Kourion: The Basilica, the Palace and the
  Sanctuary of Apollo (B v 7, no 2) 14 p 13 il 1938 p $.50
  PU-Mu   1017
Exekias (B v 4, no 3) 2 p 3 il 1933 p $.35 PU-Mu   1018
Hall, E.H. Excavations in eastern Crete, Sphoungaras (AP
  v 3, no 2) 32 p 7 pl 25 fig 1912 p $1.50 PU-Mu   1019

----. Excavations in eastern Crete, Vrokastro (AP v 3, no 3) 108 p 62 fig 19 pl 1913 p $3.50 PU-Mu   1020
Kourion: The Late Bronze Age settlement (B v 7, no 1) 3 p 3 il 1937 p $.50; (B v 7, no 3) 3 p 4 il 1939 p $.50; --Sanctuary of Apollo at Kourion (B v 8, no 4) 7 p 5 il 1940 p $.50; --The Achaeans at Kourion (B v 8, no 1) 13 p 13 il 1940 p $.50 PU-Mu   1021
Luce, S.B. Greek jointed doll (MJ v 8, no 3) 2 p 1 il 1917 p $1. PU-Mu   1022
McFadden, G.H. Kourion, the Apollo Baths 13 p 5 il; with De Coursey, Fales, Jr. Kourion, the amusement area 11 p 6 il (B v 14, no 4) 1950 p $.50 PU-Mu   1023
Seager, R.B. The cemetery of Pachyammos, Crete (AP v 7, no 1) 30 p 21 pl (2 c) 1916 p $3.50 PU-Mu   1024
----. Excavations at Vasiliki, 1904 (T v 1, no 3) 8 il (1 c) 1905 p $1. PU-Mu   1025
Young, R.S. Gordion, 1950 (B v 16, no 1) 18 p 11 il 1951 p $.50 PU-Mu   1026
----. Progress at Gordion, 1951-1952 (B v 17, no 4) 37 p 35 il 1953 p $.50 PU-Mu   1027

--Europe--Italy

Bates, W.N. Casts from the Arch of Trajan at Beneventum (MJ v 1, no 1) 4 p 4 il 1910 p $.50 PU-Mu   1028
----. The Etruscan inscriptions in the Museum (T v 1, no 3) 3 p 5 il 1904 p $1. PU-Mu   1029
Excavations at Minturnae (B v 3, no 1) 4 p 3 il 1931 p $.35 PU-Mu   1030
Bonsor, George Edward. An archaeological sketch-book of the Roman Necropolis at Carmona, tr from French by C. L. Penney 94 pl (38 c) 159 p 1931 $6. NNH   1031
Edward, G. Roger. Italy and Rome (B v 22, no 2) 10 p 9 il 1958 p $.50 PU-Mu   1032
Johnson, Jotham. Inscriptions. Republican magistri (Excavations at Minturnae v 2, no 1) 138 p 35 fig 1933 p $3.50 PU-Mu   1033
----. Monuments of the Republican Forum (Excavations at Minturnae v 1) 122 p 45 fig 1 map 1935 $5. PU-Mu 1034
The Minturno expedition (B v 3, no 2) 2 p 2 il 1931 p $.35; (B v 3, no 3-4) 1 p 2 il 1932 p $.35 PU-Mu   1035
Progress at Minturno (B v 3, no 6) 1 p 1 il 1932 p $.35 PU-Mu   1036

--Europe--Russia, Central and Eastern Europe

Bororas, Waldemar. The Chukchee: Religion (M 11:2, p

277-536) (JNP v 7) 2 pl 100 fig 1907 p $6. NNM*   1037
----. The Chukchee: Social organization (M 11:3, p 537-
733) (JNP v 7) 1 pl 1 fig 1909 p $4.50 NNM*   1038
----. The Eskimo of Siberia (M 12:3, p 317-56) (JNP v 8)
1913 p $.90 NNM*   1039
Coon, Carleton S. The Mountains of the Giants: A racial
and cultural study of the North Albanian Mountain Ghegs
(P v 23, no 3) 106 p front 7 il 28 table 1950 p $4.75
MH-P   1040
The Czechoslovakian Expedition (B v 1, no 1) 2 p 1 pl 1930
p $.35 PU-Mu   1041
Development of the Russian project: Traces of a blond
race in Siberia (B v 4, no 2) 4 p 6 il 1933 p $.35 PU-
Mu   1042
Excavations in Russia (B v 5, no 1) 1 p 2 il 1934 p $.35
PU-Mu   1043
The Expedition to Central Europe (Czechoslovakia and Yugo-
slavia) (B v 3, no 2) 2 p 1 il 1931 p $.35 PU-Mu   1044
Field, Henry. Contributions to the anthropology of the Cau-
casus (P v 47, no 1) 156 p 24 fig 9 graph 235 table 1953
p $6.50 MH-P   1045
Gimbutas, Marija. The prehistory of Eastern Europe. Pt.
1. Mesolithic, Neolithic and Copper Age cultures in Russia and the Baltic Area (ASPR Bul 20) 241 p 176 il 1956
p $7.50; Pt. 2. Bronze Age cultures in Russia and the
Baltic area (ASPR Bul 21) in prep MH-P   1046
Hall, H.U. The Siberian Expedition (MJ v 7, no 1) 19 p
14 il 1916 p $1. PU-Mu   1047
Jochelson, Waldemar. Material culture and social organiza-
tion of the Koryak (M 10:2, p 383-811) (JNP v 6) 37 pl
193 fig 1908 p $18. NNM*   1048
----. Religion and myths of the Koryak (M 10:1, p 1-382)
(JNP v 6) 13 pl 58 fig 1 map 1905 p $15. NNM*   1049
----. The Yakut (AP 33:2, p 35-225) 107 fig 1933 p $2.
NNM   1050
----. The Yukaghir and Yukaghirized Tungus. Pt. 1. Social
organization (M 13:1, p 1-133) 7 pl 1 map 1910 p $5.25;
Pt. 2. Religion and folklore (M 13:2, p 135-342) 9 pl 26
fig 1924 p $10; Pt. 3. Material culture (M 13:3, p 343-
454) 10 pl 136 fig 1926 p $8.50 NNM*   1051
Mrs. Nuttall in Russia (BFM v 1, no 1) 1897 p $.50 PU-
Mu   1052
The Russian project (B v 3, no 3-4) 5 p 2 il 1932 p $.35;
(B v 4, no 5) 1 p 1933 p $.35 PU-Mu   1053

--Orient--Far East

Bartlett, Harley Harris.   The sacred edifices of the Batak
of Sumatra (OC 4) 31 p 31 pl 1934 p $1.75 MiU-A   1054
Bishop, C.W.   The Expedition to the Far East (China and
Japan) (MJ v 7, no 2) 27 p 36 il (11 c) 1916 p $1.
PU-Mu   1055
Coon, Carleton S.   Faces of Asia (B v 22, no 1) 7 p 40 il
1958 p $.50 PU-Mu   1056
Field, Henry.   Body markings in Southwestern Asia (P v 45,
no 1) 162 p 37 il 54 table 1958 p $6.50 MH-P   1057
Laufer, Berthold.   The domestication of the cormorant in
China and Japan (FA 18:3) 64 p 4 photog 1931 $.75 ICF
                                                                    1058
----.   Tobacco and its use in Asia (A-PS 18) 39 p 10 il
1924 p $.25 ICF   1059
----.   Use of human skulls and bones in Tibet (A-PS 10) 16
p 1 il 1923 p $.10 ICF   1060
Spock, Erskine L.   Petrology of stone artifacts from Mon-
golia (B 67:6, p 296-310) 8 pl 1934 p $.30 NNM   1061

--Orient--Far East--China

Bishop, C.W.   Shantung, China's Holy Land (MJ v 12, no 2)
31 p 12 il 1921 p $1. PU-Mu   1062
Laufer, Berthold.   Insect-musicians and cricket champions
of China (A-PS 22) 27 p 12 il 1927 p $.40 ICF   1063
Mickey, Margaret Portia.   The cowrie shell Miao of Kweichow (P v 32, no 1) 84 p 8 pl 12 il 1947 p $2.50 MH-P
                                                                    1064
Starr, Frederick.   Lolo objects in the Public Museum, Milwaukee (B v 1, no 2) 12 p 8 pl 19 il p $.25 WMMMu
                                                                    1065

--Orient--Far East--Japan

Furness, W.H.   Life in the Luchu Islands (BFM v 2, no 1)
28 p 5 il 1899 p $.50 PU-Mu   1066
Gunsaulus, Helen C.   The Japanese New Year's festival,
games and pastimes (A-PS 11) 18 p 8 il 1923 p $.15 ICF
                                                                    1067

--Orient--Near East

Bedouins in the Sahara Desert (B 9) $.05 PRM   1068
Distribution of tribes in Iraq (Map A) 19x24.5; Distribution
of tribes in Western Iran (Map B) 19x24.5; List of tribal
names appearing on Maps A and B (Maps designed to ac-
company FA 29 and FA 30) $.25 ICF   1069
Dupree, Louis B.   Shamshir Ghar: Historic cave site in
Kandahar Province, Afghanistan (AP 46:2, p 137-312) 32

pl 102 fig 32 table 1958 NNM   1070
Dyson, Robert H., Jr.   Iran (B v 21, no 1) 13 p 7 il 1957
p $.50 PU-Mu   1071
----. Iran, 1957:   Iron Age Hasanlu (B v 22, no 2) 8 p 8
il 1958 p $.50 PU-Mu   1072
Excavations in Mesopotamia and Western Iran (Sites of 4000-
500 B.C.) graphic analyses by Henry Ware Eliot; art
work by Theresa Garret Eliot portf of 32 charts 1950 p
$17.50 MH-P   1073
Fairservis, Walter A., Jr.   Excavations in the Quetta Valley, west Pakistan (AP 45:2, p 165-405) 27 pl 580 designs 71 fig 15 table 1956 p $4. NNM   1074
----. Preliminary report on the prehistoric archaeology of
the Afghan-Baluchi areas (N 1587) 40 p 5 fig 1952 p NNM
                                                               1075
Field, Henry.   An anthropological reconnaissance in the Near
East, 1950 (P v 48, no 2) 119 p 88 table 2 map 1956 p
$2.50 MH-P   1076
----. An anthropological reconnaissance in West Pakistan (P
v 52) 332 p 100 pl 44 il 118 table 9 map 1955 $12.75; p
$9.75 MH-P   1077
----. The anthropology of Iraq. The Lower Euphrates-
Tigris region (FA 30:2) 202 p 180 pl 4 fig 2 map 1949
$6.50 ICF   1078
----. The anthropology of Iraq. Pt. 1. The Northern
Jazira (P v 46, no 1) 116 p 49 pl 5 il 196 table 1951 p
$6.50; Pt. 2. Kurdistan, and conclusions (P v 46, no
2-3) 176 p 76 fig 9 chart 29 graph 187 table 1952 p $6.85
MH-P   1079
----. Arabs of Central Iraq. Their history, ethnology and
physical characters, with 66-page introduction by Sir Ar-
thur Keith (AM 4) 474 p 156 photog 43 fig 3 map 1935
$10. ICF   1080
----. Contribution to the anthropology of Iran (FA 29:1)
508 p 20 fig 1 map 1939 $7.50; Contributions to the an-
thropology of Iran (FA 29:2) 198 p 4 fig 144 pl 1939
$4.50 ICF (op)   1081
----. North Arabian desert archaeological survey, 1925-
1950 1960 p $8.25 MH-P   1082
Ingholt, Herald.   World famous cylinder seals (F 1) p $.20
NBuM   1083
Lehmann-Hartleben, Karl, and Erling C. Olsen. Dyonisiac
sarcophagi in Baltimore 104 p front 21 pl 1941 p $1.70
MdBWA   1084
Mackay, Ernest.   Report on excavations at Jemdet Nasr,
Iraq; with preface by Stephen Langdon (AM 1:3) 88 p 18
photog 1931 $2. ICF   1085

----. Report on the excavation of the "A" cemetery at
Kish, Mesopotamia; with preface by Stephen Langdon
(AM 1:1) 64 p 20 pl 1925 $1.50 ICF   1086
----. A Sumerian palace and the "A" cemetery at Kish,
Mesopotamia; with preface by Stephen Langdon (AM 1:2)
152 p 42 photog 1 map 1929 $3.50 ICF   1087
Seltzer, Carl C. Contributions to the racial anthropology
of the Near East, data collected by Henry M. Huxley (P
v 16, no 2) 72 p 8 pl table 1930 p $1. MH-P   1088
----. The racial characteristics of Syrians and Armenians
(P v 13, no 3) 77 p 2 map table 1936 p $1. MH-P 1089
Ure, Annie D. Boetian Orientalizing Lekanai. A studies
separate 21 p 30 il 1932 p $1. NNMM   1090
Yale excavations at Dura-Europos p $.25 CtY-A   1091
Yale excavations at Gerasa, City of the Decapolis p $.25
CtY-A   1092

--Orient--Near East--Africa

African tribal map and booklet (Map N) $2; post $.35 NNM
                                                    1093
Barringer, B. On the track of the black pit 17 p 3 il 2
map; with Goodenough, W. The pageant of death in Nakanai: A report of the 1954 expedition to New Britain 26
p 15 il 2 map (B v 19, no 1) 1955 p $.50 PU-Mu   1094
Briggs, L. Cabot. The living races of the Sahara Desert
(P v 28, no 2) 217 p front c 68 pl 5 il 103 table 1958 p
$7.85 MH-P   1095
----. The Stone Age races of Northwest Africa (ASPR Bul
18) 98 p 22 il 1955 p $3. MH-P   1096
Buell, Raymond L. Liberia: A century of survival, 1847-
1947 (African Hdbk 7) 140 p 1947 p $1.50 PU-Mu   1097
Coon, Carleton S. Tribes of the Rif (HA v 9) 1931 p $10.
MH-P   1098
Githens, Thomas S. Drug plants of Africa (African Hdbk 8)
125 p 1949 $2.25 PU-Mu   1099
----, and Carroll E. Wood, Jr. The food resources of
Africa (African Hdbk 3) 4 fig 1943 p $1.50 PU-Mu 1100
Hall, H.U. The African expedition (Sierra Leone) (B v 6,
no 6) 3 p 8 il 1937 p $.35 PU-Mu   1101
----. The Sherbro of Sierra Leone 15 p 35 il 1 map 1938
p $2. PU-Mu   1102
----. Twins in Upper Guinea (MJv 19, no 4) 22 p 4 il
1928 p $1.   1103
----. The West African expedition, November 1936-June
1937 (B v 7, no 1) 7 p 6 il 1937 p $.50 PU-Mu   1104
Hambly, Wilfrid D. Bibliography of African anthropology,

108   Hooton, Earnest Albert

1937-46, supplement to "Source Book of African Anthropology," 1937 op (FA 37:2) 142 p 1952 $1.50 ICF   1105
----. The Ovimbundu of Angola (FA 21:2) 276 p 84 photog
1934 $4. ICF   1106
Hooton, Earnest Albert. The ancient inhabitants of the Ca-
nary Islands (HA v 7) 1925 p $7.50 MH-P   1107
Howe, Bruce, and Hallam L. Movius, Jr. A stone age
cave site in Tangier (P v 28, no 1) 32 p 7 pl 1 il 1947
p $1. MH-P   1108
Laufer, Berthold, et al. Tobacco and its use in Africa (A-
PS 29) 45 p 6 il 1930 p $.25 ICF   1109
Lewin, Julius. Studies in African native law 1947 $2.50
PU-Mu   1110
Plass, Margaret. The king's day; a day in the life of an
African king 32 p 10 il 1 map 1956 p $.35 ICF   1111
Pond, Alonzo W. A contribution to the study of prehistoric
man in Algeria, North Africa; excavations at the site of
Mechta-el-Arbi, Constantine, Algeria; with supplementary
papers: Romer, Alfred S. Pleistocene mammal of Algeria (83 p); Cole, Fay-Cooper. Skeletal material from
Mechta-el-Arbi (23 p) (B 2) 189 p 31 il 1928 $1. WBB-
Lo   1112
----, and Louis Chapuis. Prehistoric habita-
tion sites in the Sahara and North Africa; a report on the
excavations and archaeological collections conducted under
the auspices of the museum between 1925 and 1930 at Ali
Bacha near Bougie, in the Aoulef region of the Sahara, in
the Commune Mixte of Canrobert and other areas of Algeria; with additional papers: Romer, Alfred S. Mamma-
lian remains from some Paleolithic stations in Algeria
(20 p); Baker, Frank Collins. The Molluscs of the shell
heaps or escargotieres of Northern Algeria, including
comparisons with the recent fauns of Algeria (40 p) (B 5)
224 p 110 il map 1938 $2. WBB-Lo   1113
Postel, A. Williams. The mineral resources of Africa (African Hdbk 2) 105 p 20 fig 15 table 1943 p $1.50 PU-Mu
                                                   1114
Reisner, George A. Excavations at Kerma, edited by E.A.
Hooton and Natica Bates. Pts. 1-3 (HA v 5) 1923 p $9;
Pts. 4-5 (HA v 6) 1923 p $9. MH-P   1115
Senyurek, Muzaffer Suleyman. Fossil man in Tangier, with
introduction by Carleton S. Coon (P v 16, no 3) 35 p 3
pl table 1940 p $.50 MH-P   1116
Some East African tribes (MJ v 2, no 2) 10 p 9 il 1911 p
$.50 PU-Mu   1117
Varia Africana. 5 v. v. 1 Bates, Oric, ed. (HA v 1) 1917
p $7; v. 2 Bates, Oric, ed. (HA v 2) 1918 p $7.50;

Wieschhoff, H.A.   109

v 3. Hooton, Earnest Albert, and Natica I. Bates, ed.
(HA v 3) 1922 p $6.50; v 4. Hooton, Earnest Albert,
and Natica I. Bates, ed. (HA v 8) 1928 p $9. v 5.
Hooton, Earnest Albert, and Natica I. Bates, ed. (HA 10)
1932 p $7. MH-P   1118
Wieschhoff, H.A. Colonial policies in Africa (African Hdbk
5) 138 p 1 map 1944 p $1.50 PU-Mu   1119
Wulsin, Frederick R. The prehistoric archaeology of North-
west Africa (P v 19, no 1) 173 p 92 il 1941 p $3.25
MH-P   1120

--Orient--Near East--Babylonia

The Assyrian expedition (B v 4, no 3) 1 p 1 il 1933 p $.35;
(B v 4, no 4) 1 p 1 il 1933 p $.35 PU-Mu   1121
Bache, Charles. The first Assyrian level at Tell Billa (MJ
v 24, no 1) 16 p 3 il 1935 p $1. PU-Mu   1122
A collection from Tell Billa and Tepe Gawra (B v 4, no 1)
2 p 1932 p $.35 PU-Mu   1123
Developments at Kirkuk (B v 2, no 6) 2 p 1931 p $.35 PU-
Mu   1124
Developments at Tell Billa and Tepe Gawra (B v 3, no 3-4)
1 p 1 il 1932 p $.35 PU-Mu   1125
Excavations at Tell Billa and Tepe Gawra (B v 3, no 5) 3 p
2 il 1932 p $.35; (B v 4, no 2) 2 p 1 il 1933 p $.35
PU-Mu   1126
Excavations at Ur (B v 2, no 6) 3 p 1 il 1931 $.35; (B v 3,
no 6) 1 p 1 il 1932 p $.35 PU-Mu   1127
The expedition at Fara (B v 2, no 6) 1 p 1 il 1931 p $.35
PU-Mu   1128
The expeditions to Tell Billa and Tepe Gawra (B v 3, no 2)
3 p 1 il 1931 p $.35 PU-Mu   1129
Gawra XII (B v 6, no 3) 2 p 5 il 1936 p $.35 PU-Mu 1130
Graham, A. Kenneth. Scientific notes on the finds from Ur
(MJ v 20, no 3-4) 12 p 13 il 1929 p $2. PU-Mu   1131
The Great Mound (Tepe Gawra) (B v 5, no 6) 5 p 4 il 1935
p $.35 PU-Mu   1132
Hilprecht, H.V. The new Babylonian expedition (BFM v 2,
no 1) 3 p 1899 p $.50 PU-Mu   1133
----. Note on the growth of the Babylonian Section (BFM
v 1, no 1) 5 p 1897 p $.50 PU-Mu   1134
The Joint Expedition to Ur (MJ v 16, no 3) 2 p 1925 p $1;
(B v 1, no 1) 1 p 1930 p $.35 (B v 1, no 3) 1 p 2 il
1930 p $.35; (B v 4, no 3) 2 p 1 il 1933 p $.35; (B v 4,
no 4) 1 p 1 il 1933 p $.35; (B v 5, no 2) 1 p 1 il 1934
p $.35; (B v 5, no 3) 1 p 1 il 1934 p $.35; PU-Mu 1135
Khafaje (B v 6, no 6) 2 p 8 il 1937 p $.35 PU-Mu   1136

The Kirkuk excavations (B v 1, no 3) 1 p 1 il 1930 p $.35
    PU-Mu   1137
Kramer, S. N.   A "Fullbright" in Turkey (B v 17, no 2) 52
    p 38 il 1952 p $.50 PU-Mu   1138
----.   Iraqui excavations during the war years (B v 13, no
    2) 32 p 20 il 1948 p $.50 PU-Mu   1139
Legrain, L.   Babylonian Collections of the University Mu-
    seum (B v 10, no 3-4) 78 p 55 il 2 map 1944 p $1. PU-
    Mu   1140
----.   Discovery of the Royal Tombs at Ur of the Chaldees
    (MJ v 18, no 4) 3 p 1927 p $1. PU-Mu   1141
----.   The Joint Expedition to Ur. of the Chaldees (MJ v
    16, no 2) 44 p 19 il 1925 p $1. PU-Mu   1142
----.   Nippur fifty years ago (B v 13, no 4) 36 p 11 il
    1948 p $.50 PU-Mu   1143
McCown, D.   Nippur: The Holy City (B v 16, no 2) 15 p
    7 il 1951 p $.50 PU-Mu   1144
Montgomery, J.A.   Abraham as the inventor of an improved
    plow (MJ v 4, no 2) 2 p 1913 p $.50 PU-Mu   1145
The Museum representative at Opis (B v 1, no 1) 1 p 1930
    p $.35 PU-Mu   1146
The Museum's Gudea (B v 6, no 6) 1 p 2 il 1937 p $.35
    PU-Mu   1147
The new Ur collection (B v 1, no 3) 1 p 1 il 1930 p $.35
    PU-Mu   1148
Nippur again (B v 9, no 1) 4 p 4 il 1941 p $.50 PU-Mu
                                                                 1149
Recent excavations of the University at Nippur (PFM v 2,
    no 2) 5 p 3 il 1899 p $.50 PU-Mu   1150
A report from Ur.   (B v 3, no 5) 2 p 2 il 1932 p $.35
    PU-Mu   1151
The Sally Crozer Hilprecht Collection (B v 1, no 1) 2 p 2
    il 1930 p $.35 PU-Mu   1152
Schmidt, Erich.   Excavations at Fara (MJ v 22, no 3-4) 54
    p 89 il 1931 p $2. PU-Mu   1153
Steele, F.R.   Nippur today (B v 14, no 1) 24 p 6 il 1949
    p $.50 PU-Mu   1154
Tepe Gawra excavations (B v 5, no 5) 1 p 4 il 1935 p $.35
    PU-Mu   1155
Tobler, A.J.   Excavations at Tepe Gawra, a Joint Expedi-
    tion of the Baghdad School and the University Museum to
    Mesopotamia, v 2 (MM) 260 p 182 pl $10. PU-Mu   1156
Woolley, C.L.   The excavations at Tell el-Obeid (MJ v 15,
    no 3) 15 p 1 il 1924 p $1. PU-Mu   1157
----.   Excavations at Ur, 1929-1930 (MJ v 21, no 2) 26 p
    47 il 1930 p $1; --, 1930-1931 (MJ v 22, no 3-4) 36 p
    25 il 1931 p $2; --, 1931-1932 (MJ v 23, no 3) 56 p 40

il 1932 p $1. PU-Mu   1158
----. The expedition to Ur (MJv 16, no 1) 30 p 15 il
1925 p $1. PU-Mu   1159

--Orient--Near East--Babylonia--Material Culture

Clay, A.T. An ancient plow (MJ v 1, no 1) 3 p 1 il 1910
p $.50 PU-Mu   1160
Hinkle, W.J. A new boundary stone of Nebuchadrezzar I
from Nippur (PBSN; Ser D--Researches and Treatises v
4) 323 p 52 il 1907 p $2.50 PU-Mu   1161
Nippur--Old drugstore (B v 8, no 1) 3 p 1 il 1940 p $.50
PU-Mu   1162
Objects from Ur (B v 2, no 6) 3 p 2 il 1931 p $.35; (B v
5, no 5) 2 p il c 1935 p $.35 PU-Mu   1163
Prince, J. Dyneley, and Robert Lau. An ancient Babyloni-
an axe-head (B 21:6, p 49-52) 1 pl 1 fig 1905 p $.10
NNM   1164
Tepe Gawra--the oldest acropolis (Bv 6, no 6) 3 p 5 il
1937 p $.35 PU-Mu   1165

--Orient--Near East--Babylonia--Social Life and Customs

Babylonian legal and business documents from the time of
the First Dynasty (PBSN; Ser A--Cuneiform Texts v 6)
Pt. 1. Ranke, Hermann. Chiefly from Sippar 90 p 84
pl 1906 p $4; Pt. 2. Poebel, Arno. Chiefly from Nippur
164 p 70 pl 1909 p $4. PU-Mu   1166
Barton, G.A. Sumerian business and administrative documents from the earliest times to the Dynasty of Agade
(PBS v 9, no 1) 33 p 74 pl 1915 p $3.50 PU-Mu   1167
----. The tablet of Enkhegal (MJ v 4, no 2) 5 p 1 il 1913
p $.50 PU-Mu   1168
Chiera, E. Legal and administrative documents from Nippur
chiefly from the Dynasty of Isin and Larsa (PBS v 8, no
1) 110 p 61 pl 1914 p $3.50 PU-Mu   1169
----. Old Babylonian contracts (PBS v 8, no 2) 115 p 98 pl
1922 p $3.50 PU-Mu   1170
Clay, A.T. Business documents of Murashu Sons of Nippur
dated in the reign of Darius II (PBS v 2, no 1) 54 p 123
pl 1912 p $3. PU-Mu   1171
----. Business documents of Murashu Sons of Nippur dated
in the reign of Darius II (424-404 B.C.) (PBSN; Ser A--
Cuneiform Texts v 10) 96 p 89 pl 1904 $4. PU-Mu 1172
----. Documents from the temple archives of Nippur dated
in the reigns of the Cassite rulers (PBS v 2, no 2) 92 p
31 pl 1912 p $2. PU-Mu   1173

----. Documénts from the temple archives of Nippur dated
in the reigns of the Cassite rulers (PBSN; Ser A--Cunei-
form Texts v 14-15). Pt. 1. With complete dates 86 p
87 pl 1906 p $4; Pt. 2. With incomplete dates 68 p 84
pl 1906 p $4. PU-Mu   1174
----. Legal and commercial transactions dated in the Assyrian, Neo-Babylonian and Persian periods chiefly from
Nippur (PBSN; Ser A--Cuneiform Texts v 8). Pt. 1. 85
p 81 pl 1908 p $4. PU-Mu   1175
----. Topographical map from Nippur (T v 1, no 3) 3 p 3
il 1905 p $1. PU-Mu   1176
Figulla, H.H. Business documents of the New Babylonian
period (Pubns of the Joint Expedition, Ur Excavations:
Texts v 4) 69 p 65 pl 1949 p $12.50 PU-Mu   1177
----, and W.J. Martin. Letters and documents of the Old
Babylonian period (Pubns of the Joint Expedition, Ur Excavation: Texts v 5) 80 p 142 pl 1953 p $11.80 (Order
from British Museum, London, W.C. 1, England)   1178
Galb, Ignace J. Old Akkadian inscriptions in Chicago Natur-
al History Museum (FA 44:2) 180 p 60 il 1955 $5. ICF
                                                      1179
Hilprecht, H.V., and A.T. Clay. Business documents of
Murashu Sons of Nippur dated in the reign of Artaxerxes I
(464-424 B.C.) (PBSN; Ser A--Cuneiform Texts v 9) 90
p 92 pl 1898 p $4. PU-Mu   1180
Holland, W.J. Proclamation of Nebuchadnezzer, King of
Babylon, inscribed upon a cylinder recently acquired by the
Carnegie Museum (A v 15, no 1, p 104-7) 1 pl p $.15
PPiCM   1181
Keiser, C.E. Tags and labels from Nippur (MJ v 3, no 2)
3 p 1 il 1912 p $.50 PU-Mu   1182
Kramer, S.N. Mercy, Wisdom, and Justice: Some new
documents from Nippur (B v 16, no 2) 1951 p $.50 PU-
Mu   1183
Kunz, Frederick George. On the ancient inscribed Sumerian
(Babylonian) axe-head from the Morgan collection in the
American Museum of Natural History, with translation by
Ira Maurice Price, and discussion by William Hayes Wark
(B 21:5, p 37-47) 1 pl 13 fig 1905 p $.20 NNM   1184
Langdon, S. An ancient Babylonian map (MJ v 7, no 4) 6 p
2 il 1916 p $1. PU-Mu   1185
----. A Babylonian tablet on the interpretation of dreams
(MJ v 8, no 2) 7 p 2 il 1917 p $1. PU-Mu   1186
----. A new tablet of the cult of deified kings in Ancient
Sumeria (MJ v 8, no 3) 15 p 2 il 1917 p $1. PU-Mu
                                                      1187

----. The ritual of atonement for a Babylonian king (MJ v
8, no 1) 6 p 1 il 1917 p $1. PU-Mu   1188
Legrain, L. Business documents of the third dynasty of Ur.
Pt. 1 207 pl; Pt. 2. Index, vocabulary, catalogue 288 p
(Pubns of Joint Expedition, Ur Excavations: Texts ▼ 3)
1937-1947 p $18.50 PU-Mu   1189
----. Horseback riding in Mesopotamia in the third millen-
nium B.C. (B v 11, no 4) 7 p 1 il 1946 p $.50 PU-Mu
1190
----. A new fragment of chronology. The Dynasty of Agade
(MJ v 12, no 1) 3 p 1 il 1921 p $1. PU-Mu   1191
----. Reconstructing ancient history. Pt. 1. Portrait of a
king who reigned 4130 years ago; Pt. 2. A new list of
kings who reigned from 3500 to 3000 B.C. (MJ v 11, no
4) 11 p 4 il 1920 p $1. PU-Mu   1192
----. Royal inscriptions and fragments from Nippur and
Babylon (PBS v 15) 50 p 36 pl 1926 p $5. PU-Mu   1193
Mellink, M.J. A Hittite cemetery at Gordion (MM) 60 p 30
pl 1 il 1956 $2.50 PU-Mu   1194
Radau, Hugo. Letters to Cassite kings from the temple ar-
chives of Nippur. Pt. 1. (PBSN; Ser A--Cuneiform Texts
v 17) 174 p 80 pl 1908 p $4. PU-Mu   1195
The royal tombs of Ur of the Chaldees, a descriptive hand-
book with reproductions and maps 28 p 15 pl 1929 p $.35
PU-Mu   1196
Sayce, A.H. The Museum collection of Cappadocian tablets
(MJ v 9, no 2) 3 p 1918 p $1. PU-Mu   1197
Ungnad, Arthur. Babylonian letters of the Hammurabi Peri-
od (PBS v 7) 50 p 104 pl 1915 p $3.50 PU-Mu   1198
Woolley, C.L. More royal tombs (MJ v 20, no 1) 29 p 18
il 1929 p $1. PU-Mu   1199
----. The Royal cemetery. Pt. 1. Text 634 p; P. 2. 274
pl (37 c) (Pubns of the Joint Expedition, Ur Excavations:
Archaeology, v 2) 1934 $9. PU-Mu (Crder from British
Museum, London, W.C. 1, England)   1200

--Orient--Near East--Egypt

Anthes, R. A first season of excavating in Memphis (B v
20, no 1) 24 p 9 il 1 map 1956 p $.50 PU-Mu   1201
----. Hermann Ranke, 1878-1953 (B v 17, no 4) 2 p 1 il
1953 p $.50 PU-Mu   1202
----. Memphis (Mit Rahineh) in 1956 (B v 21, no 2) 33 p
15 il 1957 p $.50 PU-Mu   1203
----, et al. Mit Rahineh 1955 (MM) 93 p 18 fig 45 pl map
1958 $4. PU-Mu   1204
A contemporary of Queen Hatshepsut (Amenemhet) (Nubia)

(B v 8, no 1) 2 p 1 il 1940 p $.50 PU-Mu   1205
The Coxe Egyptian Expedition (Meydum) (B v 3, no 5) 4 p 1
     il 1932 p $.35 PU-Mu   1206
Dimick, M.T.   Memphis, the city of the white wall 29 p 19
     il p 1956 $.50 PU-Mu   1207
The Director in Egypt (MJ v 10, no 4) 2 p 19 il 1919 p $1.
     PU-Mu   1208
The Eckley B. Coxe, Jr.   Expedition to Gizeh and Memphis
     (MJ v 6, no 2) 2 p 19 il 1915 p $1. PU-Mu   1209
The Egyptian Expedition (Meydum) (B v 1, no 1) 1 p 2 pl
     1920 p $.35; (B v 1, no 3) 2 p 1 il 1930 p $.35 PU-Mu
                                                    1210
Excavations at Meydum (B v 2, no 6) 5 p 3 il 1931 p $.35
     PU-Mu   1211
Fisher, C.S.   The Eckley B. Coxe, Jr. Expedition to Mem-
     phis and Dendereh (MJ v 8, no 4) 27 p 20 il 1916 p $1.
     PU-Mu   1212
----.   Excavations at Gizeh (MJ v 8, no 1) 7 p 5 il 1916
     p $1. PU-Mu   1213
Gordon, G.B.   Philae, the forsaken (MJ v 2, no 1) 6 p 7
     il 1911 p $.50 PU-Mu   1214
Jayne, H.H.F.   A new expedition to Egypt (Meydum) (MJ v
     20, no 2) 5 p 1929 p $1. PU-Mu   1215
The level of Seti I (Beisan) (B v 3, no 3-4) 3 p 1 il 1932
     p $.35 PU-Mu   1216
The Meydum excavations (B v 3, no 3-4) 4 p 3 il 1932 p
     $.35 PU-Mu   1217
Objects from Meydum (B v 4, no 3) 3 p 1 il 1933 p $.35
     PU-Mu   1218
Randall-MacIver, D.   The Eckley B. Coxe, Jr. Expedition
     to Nubia (MJ v 1, no 1) 1 p 1910 p $.50; (MJ v 1, no 2)
     6 p 7 il 1910 p $.50; (MJ v 1, no 3) 6 p 7 il 1910 p
     $.50 PU-Mu   1219
----, and Leonard Woolley.   Buhen (Coxe Expedition, v 7-
     8).   Pt. 1. Text 243 p drg front c; Pt. 2. 96 pl (7 plan)
     1911 $14. PU-Mu   1220
Riefstahl, Elizabeth, comp.   People of the Black Land--
     Egypt (Brooklyn Museum reading lists for students of an-
     cient history) Series I.   The country and the people. 1.
     The Nile and the sun; 2. What ancient Egyptians were
     like; 3. What ancient Egyptians wore; 4. How ancient
     Egyptians lived; 5. Ancient Egyptians at work; 6. Ancient
     Egyptians at play.   Series II.   Egyptian writing. 1. Do
     you want to learn Egyptian; 2. Hieroglyphics; 3. Ancient
     Egyptian writing materials; 4. The scribe p $.50 ea NBB
                                                    1221
Row, Alan.   The 1927 excavations at Beisan, final report

(Egyptian levels) (MJ v 19, no 2) 24 p 16 il 1928 p $1.
PU-Mu   1222
----.   The Palestine Expedition report of the 1928 season
(Egyptian levels at Beisan) (MJ v 20, no 1) 37 p 34 il
1929 p $1. PU-Mu   1223
Wilkins, E.P.   Napoleon's Egypt (MJ v 4, no 2) 7 p 2 il
1913 p $.50 PU-Mu   1224

--Orient--Near East--Egypt--Social Life and Customs

Allen, Thomas George.   Egyptian stelae in Field Museum of
Natural History (FA 24:1) 79 p 43 photog 43 copies of in-
scriptions in the text 1936 $1.50 ICF   1225
Egyptian mummies PB 16 p il p $.50 CaOTRM   1226
An Egyptian mummy cloth (B v 6, no 4) 2 p 1 il 1936 p
$.35 PU-Mu   1227
Fisher, Clarence S.   The Minor cemetery at Giza (Coxe
Foundation v 1) 170 p 55 pl (3 c) 3 plan 139 fig 1924 $10.
PU-Mu   1228
Griffith, F.L.   Karanog, the Meroitic inscriptions of Shablul
and Karanog (Coxe Expedition v 6) 181 p 30 pl $7. PU-
Mu   1229
How mummies were made (B v 5, no 4) 4 p 1 il 1935 p
$.35 PU-Mu   1230
The mummy case of Neb-Neteru (B v 1, no 3) 2 p il 1930 p
$.35 PU-Mu   1231
The new mummy room (B v 5, no 4) 5 p 4 il 1935 p $.35
PU-Mu   1232
Stela of Sisopduyenhab (Abydos) (B v 6, no 5) 4 p 5 il 1936
p $.35 PU-Mu   1233
Woolley, Leonard.   Karanog, the town (Coxe Expedition v 5)
51 p 30 pl 1911 $3.50 PU-Mu   1234
----, and D. Randall-MacIver.   Karanog, the Romano-Nubi-
an cemetery (Coxe Expedition v 3-4).   Pt. 1. Text 286
p drg; Pt. 2.   116 pl (14 c) 1910 $14. PU-Mu   1235

--Orient--Near East--India

Niehoff, Arthur.   Factory workers in India (PA 5) 115 p 11
il 1959 p $3. WMMMu   1236

--Orient--Near East--Palestine
The Beisan Expedition (B v 4, no 5) 2 p 1933 p $.35 (B v
5, no 1) 2 p 2 il 1934 p $.35; (B v 5, no 2) 4 p 2 il
1934 p $.35 PU-Mu   1237
The Beisan report (B v 3, no 3-4) 2 p 2 il 1932 p $.35 PU-
Mu   1238

The expedition to Palestine (B v 16, no 3) 2 p 1925 p $1.
  PU-Mu   1239
Fisher, C.S.   Beth-Shean (MJ v 13, no 1) 14 p 5 il 1922 p
  $1; (MJ v 14, no 4) 21 p 12 il 1923 p $1.   PU-Mu   1240
Fitzgerald, G.M.   Beth Shan excavations, 1921-1923: The
  Arab and Byzantine levels (Beth Shan Excav v 3) 64 p 52
  pl 2 map 1931 p $15.   PU-Mu   1241
----.   A sixth century monastary at Beth-Shan (Scythopolis)
  (Beth Shan Excav v 4) 19 p 23 pl 1939 p $7.50 PU-Mu
                                                                          1242
A new season at Beisan (B v 3, no 2) 2 p 2 il 1931 p $.35
  PU-Mu   1243
Objects from Beth Shemesh (B v 3, no 5) 1 p 1 il 1932 p
  $.35 PU-Mu   1244
Pritchard, James B.   Discovery of the biblical Gibeon (B v
  21, no 1) 25 p 22 il 1 map 1957 p $.50 PU-Mu   1245
----.   A second excavation at Gibeon (B v 22, no 2) 13 p
  10 il 1 map 1958 p $.50 PU-Mu   1246
Rowe, Alan.   Discovery of the temple of Ashtaroth (MJ v 16,
  no 4) 7 p 1925 p $1.   PU-Mu   1247
----.   The expedition at Beisan (MJ v 18, no 4) 31 p 26 il
  1927 p $1.   PU-Mu   1248
----.   The 1927 excavations at Beisan (MJ v 19, no 2) 26 p
  16 il 1928 p $1.   PU-Mu   1249
----.   Report of the 1928 season of the Palestine expedition
  (MJ v 20, no 1) 52 p 34 il 1929 p $1.   PU-Mu   1250

--Orient--Near East--Persia   See also additional listings under Orient--Near East

Coon, C.S.   Cave explorations in Iran (MM) 125 p 33 pl
  1951 p $1.50 PU-Mu   1251
Excavations at Rayy (B v 5, no 4) 1 p 1 il 1934 p $.35
  PU-Mu   1252
The Joint Expedition to Persia (Rayy) (B v 5, no 3) 2 p 2 il
  1934 p $.35 PU-Mu   1253
The Joint Expedition to Persia (Tepe Hissar) (B v 3, no 1)
  2 p 2 il 1931 p $.35; (B v 3, no 3-4) 1 p 2 il 1932 p
  $.35; (B v 3, no 5) 3 p 2 il 1932 p $.35 PU-Mu   1254
Mackay, Ernest J.H.   Chanhu-daro Excavations, 1935-1936,
  record of excavations sponsored by the Museum of Fine
  Arts and American School of Indic and Iranian Studies, at
  an Indus Valley site, dating from 3000 B.C.   338 p 97 pl,
  c front 1934 $3.   MBMu   1255
A new expedition to Persia (Rayy) (B v 4, no 5) 1 p 1 il
  1933 p $.35 PU-Mu   1256
Persepolis--1939 (B v 7, no 4) 8 il 1939 p $.50 PU-Mu 1257

The Persian Expedition (Rayy) (B v 5, no 5) 6 p 11 il 1935
    p $.35 PU-Mu   1258
The Persian Expedition (Tepe Hissar) (B v 4, no 1) 2 p 2
    il 1932 p $.35 PU-Mu   1259
Rayy research (B v 6, no 3) Pt. 1. 5 p 8 il 1936 p $.35
    PU-Mu   1260
Reconstruction of a burial from Persia (Tepe Hissar) (B v
    4, no 4) 2 p 1 il 1933 p $.35 PU-Mu   1261
Schmidt, Erich F.   Excavations at Tepe Hissar, Damghan
    478 p 79 pl 177 fig 1936 $15. PU-Mu   1262
----.   Tepe Hissar: Excavations of 1931 (MJ v 23, no 4)
    59 p 174 il p $1. PU-Mu   1263
Tol-E-Bakun; Prehistoric mound near Persepolis (B v 7, no
    1) 1 p 3 il 1937 p $.50 PU-Mu   1264

--Pacific Area

Aitken, Robert T.   Ethnology of Tubuai (Bayard Dominick
    Exp Pubn 19) (B 70) 169 p 13 pl 40 fig 1930 p $1.50 HB
                                                         1265
The Australian project (B v 1, no 1) 1 p 1930 p $.35 PU-
    Mu   1266
Beaglehole, Ernest, and Pearl Beaglehole.   Ethnology of
    Pukapuka (B 150) 419 p 6 pl 55 fig 1938 p $2. HB (op)
                                                         1267
Buck, Peter H.   Ethnology of Mangareva (B 157) 519 p 3 pl
    68 fig 1938 p $5. HB (op)   1268
----.   Ethnology of Manihiki and Rakahanga (B 99) 238 p 11
    pl 109 fig 1932 p $3. HB (op)   1269
----.   Explorers of the Pacific: European and American dis-
    coveries in Polynesia (SP 43) 125 p 13 il 1953 p $1.75
    HB   1270
Burrows, Edwin G.   Ethnology of Futuna (B 138) 239 p 11 pl
    37 fig 1936 p $2. HB   1271
----.   Ethnology of Uvea (Wallis Island) (B 145) 176 p 8 pl
    29 fig 1937 p $2. HB   1272
Cartwright, Bruce.   Some aliis of the migratory period (OP
    v 10, no 7) 1933 p $.50 HB   1273
Charlot, Jean.   Choris and Kamehameha 65 p 38 il 1958 p
    $2. HB   1274
Cole, Fay-Cooper.   The Bukidnon of Mindanao (FA 46) 142
    p 66 il 1 map 1956 $4. ICF   1275
----.   The wild tribes of Davao District, Mindanao (FA 12:
    2) 153 p 137 il 1 map c 1913 $2.50 ICF   1276
Drapkin, I.   Contribution to the demographic study of Easter
    Island (OP v 11, no 12) 1935 p $.50 HB   1277
East Indian and Fijian in Fiji: Their changing numerical re-

lation (SP 32) 14 p 9 graph 1938 p $.50 HB   1278
Emory, Kenneth P.   Additional notes on the archaeology of
    Fanning Island (OP v 15, no 17) 1939 p $.50 HB   1279
----. Archaeology of Mangareva and neighboring atolls (B
    163) 76 p 6 pl 28 fig 1939 p $1.50 HB   1280
----. Archaeology of the Pacific equatorial islands (Whip-
    poorwill Exp Pubn 4) (B 123) 43 p 5 pl 22 fig 1934 p
    $1.25 HB   1281
Fragments of Hawaiian history as recorded by John Papa I'i
    183 p 35 il 1959 $5.50; p $4. HB   1282
Goodenough, W.H.   Ethnological reconnaissance in New Guinea
    34 p 25 il 4 map; with Little, Keith.   My father, the
    crocodile (A Papuan legend) (B v 17, no 1) 1952 p $.50
    PU-Mu   1283
Hall, H.U.   The Bagobo (MJ v 7, no 3) 12 p 6 il 1916 p
    $1.   PU-Mu   1284
----. A book of Tapa (MJ v 12, no 1) 20 p 5 il (1 c) 1921
    p $1. PU-Mu   1285
----. A Marshall Island chart (MJ v 10, no 1-2) 7 p 2 il
    1919 p $1.   PU-Mu   1286
Holman, Lucia Ruggles.   Journal, letters descriptive of a
    voyage in 1819 to Hawaii (SP 17) 40 p 1931 p $1.50 HB
                                                     1287
Lewis, Albert B.   The Melanesians, people of the South Pa-
    cific (3rd ptg, rev, of "Ethnology of Melanesia") 259 p 60
    il 1951 p $1.75 ICF   1288
----. Use of sage in New Guinea (A-PS 9) 9 p 6 il 1923 p
    $.10 ICF   1289
Linton, Ralph.   Ethnology of Polynesia and Micronesia 191
    p 74 il 1926 p $2. ICF   1290
Luomala, Katharine.   Ethnobotany of the Gilbert Islands (B
    213) 129 p 1 map 1953 p $2.50 HB   1291
----. Specialized studies in Polynesian anthropology (B 193)
    88 p 1947 p $1.25 HB   1292
McAllister, J. Gilbert.   Archaeology of Kahoolawe (B 115)
    61 p 5 pl 25 fig 1933 p $1. HB   1293
Macgregor, Gordon.   Ethnology of Tokelau Islands (B 146)
    183 p 10 pl 25 fig 1937 p $2. HB   1294
----. Notes on the ethnology of Pukapuka (OP v 11, no 6)
    1935 p $.75 HB   1295
McKern, W.C.   Archaeology of Tonga (Bayard Dominick Exp
    Pubn 15) (B 60) 123 p 6 49 fig 1929 p $3.50 HB   1296
Malagan of New Ireland (B v 5, no 4) 2 p 1 il 1935 p $.35
    PU-Mu   1297
Malo, David.   Hawaiian antiquities (SP 2) 278 p 12 il 1903,
    reprint ed 1951 $5. HB   1298
Race and culture of the Pacific Islands p $.25 CLCM   1299

Sebbelov, G.   The E.W. Clark Collection (Polynesia) (MJ
   v 2, no 3) 7 p 10 il 1911 p $.50; --(New Caledonia)
   (MJ v 2, no 4) 4 p 5 il 1911 p $.50 PU-Mu   1300
Skinner, H.D., and William C. Baucke.   The Morioris (M
   v 9, no 5) 44 p 8 pl 1928 p $1.50 HB   1301
Spoehr, Alexander.   Marianas prehistory.   Archaeological
   survey and excavations on Saipan, Tinian and Rota (FA 48)
   187 p 89 il 1957 $4.50 ICF   1302
----.   Saipan: The ethnology of a war-devastated island
   (FA 41) 383 p 32 il 1954 $5. ICF   1303
Thompson, Laura.   Southern Lau, Fiji: An ethnography (B
   162) 228 p 5 pl 21 fig 1940 p $2.50 HB   1304
Whitcombe, J.D.   Notes on Tongan ethnology (OP v 9, no 9)
   1930 p $.50 HB   1305

--Pacific Area--Material Culture

Buck, Peter H.   Material culture of Kapingamarangi (B 200)
   291 p 167 fig 1950 p $6. HB   1306
Canoes of Oceania. v. 2.   Haddon, A.C.   The canoes of
   Melanesia, Queensland, and New Guinea (SP 28) 342 p 191
   fig 3 map 1937 p $5; v 3. Haddon, A.C., and James
   Hornell.   Definitions of terms, general survey, and con-
   clusions (SP 29) 88 p 39 fig 6 map 1938 p $1. (op- v.3)
   HB   1307
Cole, F.C.   The Philippine forge group (A-PS 2) 3 p 1 il
   1922 p $.10 ICF   1308
The E.W. Clark Collection (New Zealand) (MJ v 2, no 2)12
   p 15 il 1911 p $.50 PU-Mu   1309
Emory, Kenneth P., ed.   The canoe making profession of
   ancient times, translated by Mary Kawena Pukui, preface
   by Maude Jones (OP v 15, no 13) 1939 p $.50 HB   1310
----, et al.   Hawaiian archeology; Fishooks (SP 47) 45 p
   1959 p $2.50 HB   1311
----.   Stone remains in the Society Islands (B 116) 182 p 20
   pl 133 fig 1933 p $3. HB (op)   1312
----.   Tuamotuan stone structures (B 118) 78 p 10 pl 71 fig
   1934 p $2. HB   1313
Fowler, Henry W.   Archaeological fishbones collected byE.
   W. Gifford in Fiji (B 214) 51 p 13 fig 1955 p $1.50 HB
                                                      1314
Gudger, E.W.   Wooden hooks used for catching sharks and
   Ruvettus in the South Seas; a study of their variation and
   distribution (AP 28:3, p 199-348) 92 fig 1927 p $1. NNM
                                                      1315
Lewis, Albert B.   Melanesian shell money in the Field Mu-
   seum collection (FA 19) 36 p 25 photog 1939 $1.25

ICF   1316
Ritzenthaler, Robert E.   Native money in Palau (PA 1) 45 p
1 fig 1954 p $1. WMMMu   1317
Tinker, Spencer.   Some Marshall Islands fish traps (OP 20:
7) 1950 p $.25 HB   1318

--Pacific Area--Social Life and Customs   See also   Folk Literature and Folk Lore

Buck, Peter H.   Mangaian society (B 122) 207 p 1 fig 1934
p $3.50 HB   1319
Cole, F.C.   he Tinguian.   Social, religious and economic
life of a Philippine tribe (FA 14:2) 267 p 109 il 1922 $5;
p $4. ICF   1320
----.   Traditions of the Tinguian, a study in Philippine folklore (FA 14:1) 226 p 1915 $3. ICF   1321
Dorsey, G.A.   Observations on a collection of Papuan
crania, with notes on preservation and decorative features
by W.H. Holmes (FA 2:1) 48 p 11 photog 22 engrav 1897
$.75 ICF   1322
Emory, K.P.   Hawaiian tattooing (OP 18:17) 1946 p $.50
HB   1323
Goodenough, W.H.   Native astronomy in the Central Caro-
lines (MM) 46 p 5 il 1953 p $.75 PU-Mu   1324
Hambly, Wilfrid D.   Primitive hunters of Australia (A-PS
32) 59 p 13 il 1936 p $.30 ICF   1325
Hocard, A.M.   Lau Islands, Fiji, a description of the people
of the Lau Archipelago--social organization, beliefs, and
customs (B 62) 241 p 4 pl 11 fig 1929 p $2.50 HB 1326
Kroeber, A.L.   The history of Philippine civilization as re-
flected in religious nomenclature (AP 19:2, p 36-67) 1918
p $.25 NNM   1327
----.   Kinship in the Philippines (AP 19:3, 69-84) 1919 p
$.25 NNM   1328
Mead, Margaret.   Kinship in the Admiralty Islands (AP 34:2,
p 181-358) 17 fig 1934 p $1.75 NNM   1329
----.   The Mountain Arapesh. Pt. 1, An importing culture
(AP 36:3, p 139-349) 95 fig 1938 p $2; Pt. 2. Supernat-
uralism (AP 37:3, p 317-451) 1940 p $1.50; Pt. 3. So-
cio-economic life; with Pt. 4.   Diary of events in Alitos
(AP 40:4, p 159-420) 4 pl 1 fig 1947 p $2.50; Pt. 5.
The record of Unabelin with Rorschach analyses (AP 41:3,
p 285-390) 1 pl 1 fig 1949 p $1.50 NNM   1330
A new Guinea oracle (B v 5, no 1) 2 p 1 il 1934 p $.35
PU-Mu   1331
Oliver, Douglas L.   Studies in the anthropology of Bougain-
ville, Solomon Islands (P v 29, no 1-4) 1949 p $5.85. No.

1. The Peabody Museum Expedition to Bougainville,
Solomon Islands, 1938-1939 28 p 6 fig 9 il; no. 2. Hu-
man relations and language in a Papuan-speaking tribe of
Southern Bougainville, Solomon Islands 38 p 2 fig 1 il;
No. 3. Economic and social uses of domestic pigs in
Siuai, Southern Bougainville, Solomon Islands 30 p 4 fig
3 il; No. 4 Land tenure in Northeast Siuai, Southern Bou-
gainville, Solomon Islands 98 p 8 fig 7 il MH-P   1332
Pukui, Mary Kawena. Hawaiian beliefs and customs during
birth, infancy, and childhood (OP 16:17) 1942 p $.50
HB   1333
Sebbelov, G. Maori face tattoo (MJ v 3, no 1) 2 p 1 il 1912
p $.50 PU-Mu   1334
Tueting, Laura Thompson. Native trade in southeastern New
Guinea (OP v 11, no 15) 1935 p $.75 HB   1335
No entry   1336

--Physical Anthropology

Channing, Walter, and Clark Wissler. The hard palate in
normal and feeble-minded individuals (AP 1:5, p 283-349)
9 pl 8 fig 1908 p $.50 NNM   1337
Ewing, J. Franklin. Hyperbrachycephaly as influenced by
cultural conditions (P v 23, no 2) 100 p 2 pl 6 il 1950 p
$3.75 MH-P   1338
Farabee, W.C. Inheritance of digital malformation in man
(P v 3, no 3) 13 p 5 pl 1905 p $.35 MH-P   1339
Gregory, William K., and Milo Hellman. Further notes on
the molars of Hesperopithecus and of Pithecanthropus, with
an appendix "Notes on the casts of the Pithecanthropus
molars" by Gerrit S. Miller, Jr. (B 48:13, p 509-30) 15
fig 1923 p $.25 NNM   1340
Oetteking, Bruno. Declination of the Pars Basilaris in normal and in artificially deformed skulls (M 27) 25 p il
1924 p $.35 NNMAI   1341
Reynolds, Edward. The evolution of the human pelvis in relation to the mechanics of the erect posture (P v 11, no 5)
100 p 3 pl 100 il 1931 p $1.20 MH-P   1342
Shapiro, H.L. A correction for artificial deformation of
skulls (AP 30:1, p 1-38) 1928 p $.35 NNM   1343
Thieme, Frederick P. Lumber breakdown caused by erect
posture in man (AP 4) 44 p 1 fig 1950 p $.50 MiU-A
                                                     1344
Wissler, Clark. Comparative data on respiration and circulation among native and foreign born males and in New
York City (AP 23:5, p 259-307) 2 fig 1924 p $.50 NNM
                                                     1345

--Physical Anthropology--Methodology

Hambly, Wilfrid D.   Cranial capacities.   A study in methods
   (FA 36:3) 52 p 1947 $.75 ICF   1346
Jones, Frederic Wood.   Measurements and landmarks in
   physical anthropology; a handbook for students in physical
   anthropology (B 63) 67 p 9 fig 1929 p $.50 HB   1347

--Physical Anthropology--North America

Boas, Franz.   A.J. Stone's measurements of natives of the
   northwest territories (B 14:6, p 53-68) 5 pl 1901 p $.40
   NNM   1348
Cutler, F. Sanford.   The lady in the lake: The story of
   America's oldest skeleton (Educational Bul no 11) 10 p
   1931 mimeo p $.05 MnHi   1349
Fisher, A.K.   Dental pathology of the prehistoric Indians of
   Wisconsin (B v 10, no 3) 46 p 10 pl 3 fig 1931 p $1.
   WMMMu   1350
Gregory, William K., and Milo Mellman.   Notes on the type
   of Hesperopithecus haroldcooki Osborn (N 53) 16 p 6 fig
   1923 NNM   1351
Hrdlicka, Ales.   The crania of Trenton, New Jersey, and
   their bearing upon the antiquity of man in that region (B
   16:3, p 23-62) 22 pl 4 fig 3 table 1902 p $1.25 NNM
                                                             1352
Hinsdale, W.B., and Emerson F. Greenman.   Perforated
   Indian crania in Michigan (OC 5) 15 p 5 pl 2 fig 1 map
   1936 p $.50 MiU-A   1353
Howard, E.B.   Early human remains in the Southwest (P
   1935; repr, XVI International Geol Congress) p $.50
   PPAN   1354
Kelly, Arthur Randolph.   Physical anthropology of a Mexican
   population in Texas; a study in race-mixture (P 13) 118
   p 12 fig 104 table 1947 p $2. LNT-MA   1355
Matthews, D. Washington.   Human bones in Hemenway Col-
   lection (Southwestern Archaeological Expedition) repr,
   Memoirs of National Academy of Science v 6) 286 p 59 pl
   il 1890 p $3.25 MH-P   1356
Oetteking, Bruno.   Craniology of the north Pacific coast (M
   15:1, p 1-391) (JNP v 15) 11 p 107 fig 46 table 5 diagr
   1930 p $17. NNM*   1357
----.   Morphological and metrical variation in skulls from
   San Miguel Island, California. Pt. 2.   The Foramen
   Magnum (M 45) 54 p il 1928 p $.50 NNMAI   1358
----.   Skeletal remains from Santa Barbara, California (M
   39) 168 p 32 pl 1925 p $1.50 NNMAI   1359

----. The skeleton from Mesa House (P 5) 48 p 18 il 1930
p $1. CLSM   1360
Osborn, Henry Fairfield. Hesperopithecus, the first anthro-
poid primate found in America (N 37) 5 p 3 fig 1922 p
NNM   1361
The skeleton of Yellowhouse Canyon p $.20 TxAuM   1362
Snow, C.E. Condylo-Diaphysial angles of Indian humeri
from North Alabama (MP 16) 38 p 1940 apply; post $.05
AU-Mu   1363
----. Two prehistoric Indian dwarf skeletons from Mound-
ville (MP21) 99 p il 1943 apply; post $.05 AU-Mu   1364
Stewart, T. Dale. Anthropometric observations on the Eski-
mos and Indians of Labrador (FA 31) 164 p 16 pl 1 fig
1939 $1.75 ICF   1365
Sullivan, Louis R. Anthropometry of the Siouan tribes (AP
23:3, p 81-174) 7 fig 1920 p $1.25 NNM   1366
----. The frequency and distribution of some anatomical
variations in American crania (AP 23:5, p 203-58) 1 fig
1922 p $.50 NNM   1367
Wendorf, Fred, et al. The Midland discovery; A report on
the Pleistocene human remains from Midland, Texas (Publication by University of Texas Press) 139 p il map table
1955 $3.50 NmSM-L   1368
Wissler, Clark. Observations on the face and teeth of the
North American Indians (AP 33:1, p 1-33) 1931 p $.40
NNM   1369

--Physical Anthropology--Mexico, Central and South America

Blom, Frans. A Maya skull from the Uloa Valley, Honduras,
with notes on the teeth by S.S. Grosjean; comments on the
skull by Harold Cummins (P 5, Studies in Mid America 1)
1934 p $.75 LNT-MA   1370
Cummins, Harold. Dermatoglyphics in Indians of southern
Mexico and Central America (Sana Eulalia, Tzeltal, La-
candon, and Maya tribes) (P 4, Middle American Paper 8)
1932 p $.75 LNT-MA   1371
Gould, Harley N. Anthropometry of the Chol Indians of Chi-
apas, Mexico (P 15, MARR v 1, no 9) 32 p 1946 p $1.50
LNT-MA   1372
Hambly, Wilfrid D. Skeletal material from San Jose Ruin,
British Honduras (FA 25:1) 20 p 3 fig 1937 $.30 ICF
                                                           1373
Leche, Stella M. Dermatoglyphics and functional lateral
dominance in Mexican Indians (Mayas and Tarahumaras)
(P 5, Studies in Mid America 2) 1934 p $1.50 LNT-MA
                                                           1374

----, et al. Dermatoglyphics and functional lateral dominance in Mexican Indians (P 15, MARR v 1, no 6) 63 p
1944 p $1.50 LNT-MA   1375
Newman, Marshall T. Indian skeletal material from the Central Coast of Peru (P v 27, no 4) (Research project no 8
of the Institute of Andean Research, under the sponsorship of the Co-ordinator of Inter-American Affairs) 72 p
front 7 pl 26 table 1947 p $2.50 MH-P   1376
Sullivan, Louis R., and Milo Hellman. The Punin calvarium
(AP 23:7, p 309-37) 9 fig 1925 p $.40 NNM   1377

--Physical Anthropology--Europe

Gregory, William K., and Milo Hellman. The dentition of
Dryopithecus and the origin of man (AP 28:1, p 1-123) 25
pl 32 fig 1926 p $1.50 NNM   1378
Hooton, Earnest A., and C. Wesley Dupertuis. A physical
anthropology of Ireland (with a section on the West Coast
Irish Females by Helen Dawson) (P v 30) No 1. Text;
No. 2. Tables and halftones 304 p 38 il 47 pl 510 table
1955 $13; p $10. MH-P   1379
Sawtell, Ruth Otis. Azilian skeletal remains from Montardit
(Ariege), France (P v 11, no 3) 55 p 7 pl 1931 p $.75
MH-P   1380
Shapiro, H. L. Contributions to the craniology of central
Europe. Pt. 1. Crania from Greifenberg to Carinthia
(AP 31:1, p 1-120) 13 fig 1929 p $1.25 NNM   1381

--Physical Anthropology--Pacific Area

Chappell, H.G. Jaws and teeth of ancient Hawaiians (M v 9,
no 3) 18 p 4 pl 1927 p $1. HB   1382
Dunn, Leslie C. An anthropometric study of Hawaiians of
pure and mixed blood (P v 11, no 3) 122 p table 1928 p
$1.25 MH-P   1383
Hambly, Wilfrid D. Craniometry of Ambrym Island (FA 37:
1) 150 p 30 pl 7 fig 2 map 9 drg 1946 $2.75 ICF   1384
----. Craniometry of New Guinea (FA 25:3) 210 p 44 pl 15
fig 9 drg 1940 $2.50 ICF   1385
Howells, William W. Anthropometry and blood types in Fiji
and the Solomon Islands. Based upon data of Dr. William
L. Moss (AP 33:4, p 279-339) 1 fig 1933 p $.50 NNM
                                                            1386
Howells, W.M. Anthropometry of the natives of Arnheim
Land and the Australian race problem, data collected by
W. L. Warner (P v 16, no 1) 96 p front 2 map 1937 p
$1.25 MH-P   1387

Leigh, W.W.   Dental morphology and pathology of prehistoric
   Guam (M v 11, no 3) 19 p 3 pl 1929 p $.50 HB   1388
MacCurdy, G.G.   Human skulls from the Gazelle Peninsula
   (AP v 6, no 1) 21 p 10 pl 1914 p $1. PU-Mu   1389
Shapiro, H.L.   ¹he anthropometry of Pukapuka.   Based upon
   data collected by Ernest and Pearl Beaglehole (AP 38:3,
   p 141-69) 1942 p $.40 NNM   1390
----.   The physical characteristics of Ontong Javanese: A
   contribution to the study of non-Melanesian elements of
   Melanesia (AP 33:3, p 227-78) 7 fig 1933 $.50 NNM1391
----.   The physical characters of the Society Islanders;
   based on records by E.S. Craighill Handy and Willowdean
   C. Handy (M v 11, no 4) 39 p 4 pl 1930 p $1. HB   1392
----, and P.H. Buck.   The physical characters of the Cook
   Islanders (M v 12, no 1) 35 p 1 fig 1936 p $1. HB 1393
Sullivan, Louis R.   Marquesan somatology, with comparative
   notes on Somoa and Tonga; based on the field studies of
   E.S. Craighill Handy and Willowdean C. Handy (M v 9,
   no 2) 110 p 6 pl 1923 p $1. HB   1394
----.   Observations on Hawaiian somatology, prepared for
   publication by Clark Wissler (M v 9, no 4) 76 p 5 pl 1927
   p $1. HB   1395
Weidenreich, Franz.   Morphology of Solo man; with an introduction by G.H.R. von Koenigswald (AP 43:3, p 201-90)
   32 pl 26 fig 14 table 1951 p $2.50 NNM   1396
Wissler, Clark.   Growth of children in Hawaii; based on observations by Louis R. Sullivan (Bayard Dominick Expedition Pubn 17) (M v 11, no 2) 257 p 4 fig 1930 p $1. HB
                                                       1397

--Physical Anthropology--Africa and Asia

Broom, Robert.   The evidence afforded by the Boskop skull
   of a new species of primitive man (Homo capensis) (AP
   23:2, p 63-79) 5 fig 1918 p $.25 NNM   1398
Hambly, Wilfrid D.   Anthropometry of the Ovimbundu, Angola (FA 25:2) 60 p 30 pl 8 fig 1938 $1. ICF   1399
Koenigswald, G.H.R. von.   Gigantopithecus blacki von Koenigswald, a giant fossil hominoid from the Pleistocene of
   southern China (AP43:4, p 291-326) 2 pl 2 fig 10 table
   1952 p $.50 NNM   1400
Sullivan, Louis R.   A few Andamanese skulls with comparative notes on Negrito craniometry (AP 23:4, p 175-201) 1
   fig 1921 p $.30 NNM   1401
Swindler, D.R.   A study in cranial and skeletal material excavated at Nippur (MM) 40 p 8 pl 42 table 1956 $.75 PU-
   Mu   1402

Weidenreich, Franz. Giant early man from Java and South
   China (AP 40:1, p 1-134) 12 pl 28 fig 19 table 1945 p $2.
   NNM   1403

ART
--LANGUAGE ARTS-- Folk Literature and Folklore

Luomala, Katharine. Oceanic, American Indian and African
   myths of snaring the sun (B 168) 58 p 2 fig (map) 1940 p
   $1.25 HB   1404

--Folk Literature and Folklore--Americas--United States

Cutting, Edith E. Whistling girls and jumping sheep (with
   New York Folklore Society), New York State lore about the
   farm, livestock, the weather, planting, harvesting, and the
   year's special jobs. Drgs by Erwin H. Austin 86 p 1951
   p $1. NCooHi   1405
North Shore legends $2.75 NNSI   1406
Writers' Program, Nebraska. Nebraska folklore, no. 30.
   Pioneer schools 1940 $.25 NbHi   1407

--Folk Literature and Folk Lore--Indians of North America
See also Music--Indians of North America

Alexander, H.B.   The rain cloud in Indian myth (P ns 20)
   4 p folder 1927 $.10 NmSM-S   1408
Barrett, S.A. Pomo myths (B v 15) 608 p 1933 p $5.
   WMMMu   1409
Berard-Haile, Father.   Star lore among the Navajos 44 p
   7 pl 5 fig 1947 $6. NmSMN   1410
Big star (Sontso) and Coyote (Ma-ih) myths (B 2) p $.25
   NmSMN   1411
Boas, Franz. The mythology of the Bella Coola Indians (M
   2:2, p 25-128) (JNP v 1) 6 pl 1898 p $2. NNM   1412
Dixon, Roland B.   Maidu myths (B 17:2, p 33-118) 1902 p
   $.75 NNM   1413
Goddard, Pliny Earle. Myths and tales from the San Carlos
   Apache (AP 24:1, p 1-86) 1918 p $.75 NNM   1414
----. Myths and tales from the White Mountain Apache (AP
   24:2, p 87-139) 1919 p $.50 NNM   1415
Gordon, G.B. Legends of the Kit-Selas (MJ v 9, no 1) 12
   p 4 pl 1918 p $1. PU-Mu   1416
----. The trial of the Golden Dragon (MJ v 9, no 1) 10 p
   1918 p $1. PU-Mu   1417
Lowie, Robert H. Chipewyan tales (AP 10:3, p 171-200)
   1912 p $.25 NNM   1418

----. Myths and traditions of the Crow Indians (AP 25:1,
   p 1-308) 1918 p $3. NNM   1419
McLaughlin, Marie. Myths and legends of the Sioux $3.
   NdHi   1420
Mountain chant and Beauty chant myths (B 5) p $.25 NmSMN
                                                          1421
Nequatewa, Edmund. Truth of a Hopi and other clan stories
   of Shungopovi (B 8) 136 p 2nd ed 1947 $3. AzFM   1422
Night chant (Tleji or Yehbechai) myth (B 1) p $.25 NmSMN
                                                          1423
Parker, Arthur C. Seneca myths and folk tales (Pubns v
   27) 1923 p $5. NBuHi   1424
Powers, Mabel. Around an Iroquois story fire (BSNS)
   $3.35; p $2. NBuM   1425
Red ant and Shooting chant myths (B 7) p $.25 NmSMN 1426
Sapir, Edward. Two Paiute myths (MJ v 1, no 1) 4 p 1910
   p $.50 PU-Mu   1427
Shotridge, L. Ghost of courageous adventurer (A Tlingit
   legend) (MJ v 11, no 1) 17 p 11 il 1920 p $1. PU-Mu
                                                          1428
----. Land Otter-Man (A Tlingit myth) (MJ v 13, no 1) 5 p
   1 il 1922 p $1. PU-Mu   1429
Skinner, Alanson. Mascoutens or Prairie Potowatomi Indians.
   Pt. 3. Mythology and folklore (B v 6, no 3) 85 p 1927 p
   $.75 WMMMu   1430
----, and John V. Satterlee. Folklore of the Menomini In-
   dians (AP 13:3, p 217-546) 1915 p $1.60 NNM   1431
Speck, F.G. An Algonkian myth: The magic of the crooked
   stick (MJ v 1, no 3) 3 p 1910 p $.50 PU-Mu   1432
Stories and legends of Palm Springs Indians p $2. CPs 1433
Teit, James. Mythology of the Thompson Indians (M 12:2,
   p 199-416) (NJP v 8) 1912 p $4. NNM*   1434
Wheelwright, Mary C. Emergence myth according to the
   Hanethnlaye or upward-reaching rite, recorded by Father
   Berard-Haile (Navajo Religion Series v 3) 189 p 13 seri-
   graph pl c by Louie Ewing 1949 $20. NmSMN   1435
----. Great star chant and prayers, and Coyote chant (Nava-
   jo Religion Series v 4) 18 serigraph pl c by Louie Ewing
   1957 $20. NmSMN   1436
----. Navajo creation myth (Navajo Religion Series v 1) 238
   p 17 pl c 1942 $20. NmSMN   1437
----. Water and hail chants (Navajo Religion Series v 2)
   237 p 22 serigraph pl c by Louie Ewing 1946 $20.
   NmSMN   1438
Wind and feather myths (B 4) p $.25 NmSMN   1439
Wissler, Clark. Star legends among the American Indians
   (SG 91) 29 p 11 il p $.50; post $.10 NNM   1440

--Folk Literature and Folk Lore--Indians of South America

Burkitt, R.   The Hills and the Corn (MJ v 9, no 3-4) 16 p
    7 il 1918 p $2. PU-Mu   1441
Farabee, W.C.   The marriage of the electric eel (An Ama-
    zonian myth) (MJ v 9, no 1) 3 p 1918 p $1. PU-Mu
                                                           1442
Gordon, G.B.   Guatemala myths (MJ v 6, no 3) 42 p 5 il
    1915 p $1. PU-Mu   1443

--Folk Literature and Folk Lore--Europe

Bogoras, Waldemar.   Tales of Yakaghir, Lamut, and Rus-
    sianized natives of eastern Siberia (AP 20:1, p 1-148)
    1918 p $1.50 NNM   1444

--Folk Literature and Folk Lore--Orient--Near East

Bargon, G.A.   Kings before the flood (MJ v 6, no 1) 4 p
    1915 p $1.   PU-Mu   1445
Biblical parallels from Sumerian literature 1954 $.25 PU-Mu
                                                           1446
Hilprecht, H.V.   The earliest version of the Babylonian de-
    luge story and the temple library of Nippur. Pt. 1.
    (PBSN; Ser D--Researches and Treatises v 5) 65 p 4 il
    1910 p $.75 PU-Mu   1447
Kramer, S.N.   Ammerkar and the Lord of Aratta, a Sumeri-
    an epic tale of Iraq and Iran (MM) 55 p 28 pl 1952 p $1.
    PU-Mu   1448
----.   Tales of Sumer, man's oldest myths (B v 19, no 4)
    34 p 18 il (paintings by H. Schubert) 1955 p $.50 PU-Mu
                                                           1449
Langdon, S.   The epic of Gilgamesh (MJ v 8, no 1) 10 p 5
    il 1917 p $1. PU-Mu   1450
----.   The epic of Gilgamesh (PBS v 10, no 3) 23 p 8 pl
    $1.75 PU-Mu   1451
----.   Ishtar's journey to Hell (MJ v 7, no 3) 4 p 1 il 1916
    p $1. PU-Mu   1452
----.   A new Sumerian document (The Sumerian epic of para-
    dise, the flood and the fall of man) (MJ v 5, no 3) 4 p 1
    il 1914 p $1.   PU-Mu   1453
Montgomery, J.A.   The Lilith legend (MJ v 4, no 2) 4 p
    1913 p $.50 PU-Mu   1454
Poebel, Arno.   The Babylonian story of the Creation and the
    earliest history of the world (MJ v 4, no 2) 10 p 3 il
    1913 p $.50 PU-Mu   1455
Radau, Hugo.   Ninib, the determiner of fates from the Temple

library of Nippur. Pt. 2 (PBSN; Ser D--Researches and
Treatises v 5) 73 p 5 il 1910 p $1. PU-Mu   1456

--Folk Literature and Folk Lore--Pacific Area

Burrows, Edwin G. Sone of Uvea and Futuna (B 183) 121 p
60 fig 1945 p $1.50 HB   1457
Collocott, E.E.V. Tales and poems of Tonga (B 46) 169 p
1928 p $2.50 HB (op)   1458
Feher, Joseph. Portfolio: Tale-bearing winds 1956 p $4.
HB   1459
Handy, E.S. Craighill. Marquesan legends; English and
Marquesan versions, including a chapter on the Marquesan
language (B 69) (Bayard Dominick Expedition Pubns 18)
138 p 1 pl 1920 p $1.50 HB (op)   1460
Luomala, Katharine. Maui-of-a-thousand-tricks: His Ocean-
ic and European biographers (B 198) 300 p 8 fig (4 map)
1949 p $6. HB   1461
----. Menehune of Polynesia (B 203) 86 p 2 map 1951 p
$1.50 HB   1462
----. Voices on the wind: Polynesian myths and chants
191 p 9 il 1956 p $3. HB   1463
Norbeck, Edward. Folklore of the Atayal of Formosa and
the Mountain Tribes of Luzon (AP 5) 44 p 1 map 1950 p
$.50 MiU-A   1464
Stimson, J.F.   Legends of Maui and Tahaki (B 127) 100 p
7 fig 1934 p $1.25 HB   1465
----. Tuamotuan legends (Island of Anaa). Pt. 1. The
demigods (B 148) 147 p 1937 p $1. HB   1466

--LANGUAGE ARTS--Linguistics and Grammar

Mason, J.A. Linguistics research in the University Museum
(B v 19, no 2) 13 p 3 il 1955 p $.50 PU-Mu   1467
Middle American Research Institute. Philological and Docu-
mentary Studies. v 1 (P 11) 314 p il 1943-1948 p $6.
LNT-MA   1468
Thompson, J. Eric S. Pitfalls and stimuli in the interpreta-
tion of history through loan words (P 11; PD v 1, no 2)
11 p 1943 p $.75 LNT-MA   1469

--Linguistics and Grammar--Americas--United States

McArthur, L.A. Oregon geographic names 686 p 3rd ed
1952 $8. OrHi   1470
McCulloch, Walter F. Woods words: A comprehensive dictionary of loggers' terms 219 p 1958 $7.50 OrHi   1471

MacReynolds, George.   Place names in Bucks County Penn-
   sylvania 454 p index 2nd ed 1955 $5. PDoBHi   1472
Minnesota geographic names (Collect v 17). repr, Ramsey
   County and St. Paul p $.60; repr, Hennepin County and
   Minneapolis p $.60; repr, St. Louis County p $.60 MnHi
                                                         1473
New notes on the word, "Idaho" 4 p p $.10 IdHi   1474
The origin and meaning of the name, "Michigan" p apply
   MiLHi   1475
Rantoul, Robert S.   Origin of the name Beverly 35 p 1885 p
   $.50 MSaE   1476
Schulz.   Stories of Lassen's place names p $.40 CMi   1477

--Linguistics and Grammar--Americas--Indians of North
America

Boas, Franz.   Grammatical notes on the language of the
   Tlingit Indians (AP v 8, no 1) 179 p 1 pl 1917 p $2. PU-
   Mu   1478
Curtin, L.S.M.   Some plant names used by the Yuki Indians
   of Round Valley, Northern California (Leaflet 27)20 p 4
   il p $.25 CLSM   1479
Harrington, John P.   A brief description of the Tewa lan-
   guage (P 17) 8 p 1910 p $.25 NmSM-S   1480
----.   An introductory paper on the Tiwa language, Dialect
   of Taos, New Mexico (P 14) 38 p diagr 1910 p $.25
   NmSM-S   1481
----.   A key to the Navajo orthography employed by the
   Franciscan Fathers.   The numerals "two" and "three" in
   certain Indian languages of the Southwest (P 20) 4 p 1911
   p $.25 NmSM-S   1482
----.   On phonetic and lexic resemblances between Kiowan
   and Tanoan (P 12) 4 p 1910 p $.25 NmSM-S   1483
----.   The phonetic system of the Ute language (P 24) 24 p
   1911 p $.25 NmSM-S   1484
Huden, John C.   Indian place names in Vermont p $1. VtHi
                                                         1485
----.   Indian place-names of New England in prep; scheduled
   to appear 1961 NNMAI   1486
Indian linguistic stocks or families (IL 51/52) CoDA   1487
Lemoine, George.   Dictionnaire Francais-Montagnais, Gram-
   maire Montagnaise (W.B. Cabot and P. Cabot, Boston)
   346 p 1901 $3.25 MH-P   1488
McKenzie, Parker and John P. Harrington.   Popular account
   of the Kiowa Indian language (M 12, Publ with U of New
   Mexico) 21 p 1948 $2. NmSM-S   1489
Mason, J.A.   Language of the Papago of Arizona (MM) 84 p

1950 p $1. PU-Mu   1490
Sapir, Edward.   Notes on Chasta Costa phonology and mor-
    phology (AP v 2, no 2) 72 p 1914 p $1. PU-Mu   1491
Trumbull, J. Hammond.   Indian names of places...in and on
    the borders of Connecticut...93 p 1881 $12.50 CtHi 1492
Voth, H.R.   Hopi proper names (FA 6:3) 52 p 1905 $.75
    ICF   1493
Williams, Roger.   A key to the language of America (Collec-
    tions v 1) 163 p (the earliest English-Indian dictionary,
    originally published 1634) 1827 $10. RHi   1494

--Linguistics and Grammar--Americas--Indians of South
America

Brinton, Daniel G.   Catalogue of the Berendt Linguistic
    Collection (BFM v 2, no 4) 31 p 1 pl 1900 p $.50 PU-
    Mu   1495
Matos, Maldonado de.   Are dela lengua Szinca, Vocabulario
    dela lengua Szinca, Szinca grammar, with some critical
    reflections on the Kakchiquel grammar (Photostat reprod
    of old ms) v 1, 219 p $24; v 2. 91 p 1770 $12. MH-P
                                                          1496
Medina, Jose Toribio.   Bibliografia de las Lenguas Quecha
    y Aymaria (C 7:7) 117 p 1930 p $1.10 NNMAI   1497
Rendon, Sylvia.   Ordenanza del senor Cuauhtemoc; paleo-
    grafia, traduccion, y noticia introductoria (P 12; PD v 2,
    no 2) 26 p il 1952 p $1. LNT-MA   1498
Schuller, Rudolph R.   Discovery of a fragment of the
    printed copy of the work on the Millcayac language (of
    Chile) by Luis de Valdivia (P v 3, no 5) 37 p il 1913 p
    $.50 MH-P   1499
Tozzer, A.M.   A grammar of the Maya language including
    a bibliography, with an appraisal of the various works (P
    v 9) 301 p 1921 $6.25; p $3.25 MH-P   1500
Whorf, Benjamin Lee.   Loan words in ancient Mexico (P
    11; PD v 1, no 1) 12 p 1943 p $.75 LNT-MA   1501
----.   The phonetic value of certain characters in Maya
    writing (P v 13, no 2) 48 p front 13 il 1933 p $.75 MH-
    P   1502
Ydioma Zapoteco del Valle; including some common rules of
    grammar, a copious vocabulary, a confessionary (Photo-
    stat reprod of old ms) v 1.   286 p $33; v 2. 292 1793
    p $33 MH-P   1503

--Linguistics and Grammar--Europe--Spain

Espinosa, Aurelio M.   The Spanish language in New Mexico

and Southern Colorado (Pap 16) 37 p 1911 p $.25 NmSM-
H   1504
Kiddle, Lawrence B.   The Spanish word jicara (P 11; PD v
1, no 4) 39 p 1944 p $1. LNT-MA   1505
Lowe, S.K.   Paleographic guide for Spanish manuscripts,
fifteenth-seventeenth centuries: Roman numerals (P 12;
PD v 2, no 1) 12 p 1943 p $.75 LNT-MA   1506

--Linguistics and Grammar--Orient--Near East--Babylonia

Chiera, E.   Lists of personal names from the Temple school
of Nippur: Lists of Akkadian personal names (PBS v 11,
no 2) 85 p 33 pl 1916 p $3.50 PU-Mu   1507
----.   Lists of personal names from the Temple school of
Nippur: Lists of Sumerian personal names (PBS v 11, no
3) 103 p 34 pl 1919 p $3.50 PU-Mu   1508
----.   Lists of personal names from the Temple school of
Nippur: A syllabary of personal names (PBS v 11, no 1)
88 p 37 pl 1916 p $3.50 PU-Mu   1509
Poebel, Arno.   Grammatical texts (PBS v 6, no 1) 50 p 104
pl 1915 $3.50 PU-Mu   1510
Ranke, Hermann.   Early Babylonian personal names from the
published tablets of the so-called Hammurabi Dynasty
(2000 B.C.) (PBSN; Ser D--Researches and Treatises v 3)
255 p 1905 p $1.50 PU-Mu   1511

--Linguistics and Grammar--Pacific Area

Andrews, Edmund, and Irene D. Andrews.   A comparative
dictionary of the Tahitian language (SP 6) 253 p 1 table
1944 p $5. ICAS (op)   1512
Churchward, Spencer.   Traces of suffixed pronouns in Polynesian languages (OP v 9, no 22) 1932 p $.50 HB   1513
Gardner, Fletcher.   Philippine Indic studies 105 p 23 il 1943
$3.   TxSaW   1514
Grace, George W.   The position of the Polynesian languages
within the Austronesian (Malayo-Polynesian) language family (Indiana U Pubns Memoir 16, being suppl to International Journal of American Linguistics v 25, no 3, July
1959) (SP 46) p $2. HB   1515

--Linguistics and Grammar--Africa

Murray, G.W.   English-Nubian comparative dictionary, edited
by E.A. Hooton and Nitica I. Bates (HA v 4) 1923 p
$3.50 MH-P   1516

LANGUAGE ARTS--Literature   See also   Folk Literature and
Folk Lore; Music
-- Literature--English and American
Andrews, William P.   The life and services to literature of
    Jones Very 35 p 1891 p $.50 MSaE   1517
Angle, Paul M., comp.   The Lincoln-Douglas debates; rep-
    resentative selections 61 p p $.50 ICHi   1518
Austin, Mary.   Mary Austin--A memorial p $1. NmSM-L
                                                        1519
Austin, Mary.   When I am dead (poem) $.50 NmSM-L 1520
Butterfield, Lyman H., et al.   James Fenimore Cooper--A
    reappraisal 194 p 1954 $2.50 NCooHi   1521
Cater, Harold Dean.   Washington Irving and Sunnyside 40 p
    1957 p $.75 NTaS   1522
Clemens, Samuel L.   Mark Twain in Elmira p $.25 NElmH
                                                        1523
Crane, Hart.   Voyages--six poems, illus by Leonard Baskin
    (Gehenna Press, Northampton, Mass) 20 p 7 pl $12.
    NNMMA   1524
Dawson, Giles E.   The life of William Shakespeare il p $.75
    DFo   1525
Early Kentucky literature, 1750-1840 104 p 1931 p $2; 2nd
    ed 121 p 1932 p $4. KyHi   1526
Hansen, Harry.   North of Manhattan, descriptive and histori-
    cal accounts of Irving and the Philipses 181 p 1950 $3.50
    NTaS   1527
Hawthorne, Nathaniel.   Dedication of the Hawthorne memori-
    al 35 p il 1925 p $1.25 MSaE   1528
----.   Hawthorne centennial exercises 6 p etched port 1904
    p $.75 MSaE   1529
Huntington, Archer Milton.   Collected verse 1953 424 p $6;
    A flight of birds, including tr of Poem of the Cid 267 p
    1938 $1; Recuerdos 126 p 1949 $1; Rimas 203 p 1936 $1;
    Spain and Africa 169 p 1943 $1; The torch bearers 100 p
    1955 $2.50; Turning pages 75 p 1950 $1; Versos 98 p
    1952 $5.   NNH   1530
Irving, Washington.   Diary, Spain, 1828-1829, ed by C. L.
    Penney 142 p 7 il 1930 NNH   1531
Ives, Charles E.   Epilogue $3.   CtY-A   1532
Johnson, Samuel.   Samuel Johnson, LL.D.   An illustrated
    exhibition catalogue compiled by Herbert Cahoon 40 p 7 pl
    $5; $3.   NNPM   1533
Literary haunts and personalities of Old Frankfort, 1791-1941
    130 p il 1941 p $3. KyHi   1534
Little magazines p $.25 MnMW   1535
McVan, Alice Jane.   Tryst (poems) 93 p 1953 $1.50 NNH
                                                        1536

Minnesota Centennial Literature Group. Minnesota authors:
A selected bio-bibliography (Minn Statehood Centennial
Commission) 79 p 1958 p $1.35 MnHi   1537
Parker, Hedley. Miramichi poet, six poems edited by Louis
Manny (SP 5) 1948 $2. CaNBSM   1538
Perley, Sidney. Poets of Essex County 214 p 1889 $3.
MSaE   1539
Poems of Northwest poets, folders, set $1.50; $.25 ea
Or PA   1540
Rantoul, Robert S. Some personal reminiscences of Whittier
the poet 15 p il 1901 p $.50 MSaE   1541
Reynolds, Horace. A Providence episode in the Irish liter-
ary renaissance, an account of the Irish authors whose
works were published in the Providence Journal in the
1880's and 1890's (Providence Study Hall Club) 39 p 1929
$3. RHi   1542
Shakespeare, William. Anne Hathaway's cottage p $.30
DFo   1543
----. Shakespeare's birthplace p $.30 DFo   1544
Stratford-upon-Avon and Shakespeare country p $.60 DFo
                                                     1545
Stratford-upon-Avon in color p $.50 DFo   1546
Smart, Christopher. Jubilate Agno, a portion of a poem by
Christopher Smart (PB 8) 1957 p $.50 MH-FA   1547
Stowell, William H. H. Stowell genealogy $15.30 NBuM
                                                     1548
Swan, G.N. Swedish-American literary periodicals (P v 6)
1936 $1. IRi   1549
Tapley, Harriet S. Hawthorne's "Pot-8-o Club" at Bowdoin
College 8 p il 1931 p $1.75 MSaE   1550
----. John Greenleaf Whittier, Oak Knoll Collection in the
Essex Institute 6 p il 1931 p $1.75 MSaE   1551
Thackeray, William Makepeace. Mr. Thackeray in Richmond,
descriptive comments from a letter written by a young lady
in 1853, after meeting the distinguished British novelist
(Attic Press, Richmond) 7 p 1955 p $1. ViRVM   1552
Thompson, Craig R. The Bible in English, 1525-1611 il p
$.75 DFo   1553
Valentine, Benjamin B. Ole marster, and other verses, in-
terpretation, in dialect verse, of the philosophy and char-
acter of the Southern Negro of a century ago 117 p 1921 p
$1. CaOTAG   1554
Walser, Richard. Picture book of Tar Heel authors 38 p il
1957 p $.25 NcRNC   1555
Washington, George. The maxims of Washington, selections
from the writings 348 p $1.25 ViMt   1556
Wendell, Barrett. The influence of the Athenaeum on litera-

ture in America (in The Athenaeum Centenary) 1907 $3.
NBAt   1557

--Literature--French

Frank, Grace, and Dorothy Miner.   Proverbes en rimes 127
    p 186 pl 1937 $2.75 MdBWA   1558

--Literature--Indians of North America

Boas, Franz, ed.   Kwakiutl texts, recorded by George Hunt
    (M v 5; JNP v 3)   Pt. 1.   270 p 1902 p $3; Pt. 2.   p 271-
    402 1902 p $1.50; Pt. 3.   p 403-532 1905 p $2*; Second
    Series (M 14:1, p 1-269; JNP v 10) 1906 p $4. NNM*
                                                                           1559
Goddard, Pliny Earle.   Beaver texts; Beaver dialect (AP 10:
    5-6, p 295-546) 191 fig 1917 p $5. NNM   1560
----.   Chipewyan texts (AP 10:1, p 1-65); with Analysis of
    Cold Lake dialect Chipewyan (AP10:2, p 67-170) 249 fig
    1912 p $1. NNM   1561
----.   Jicarilla Apache texts (AP v 8, p 1-276) 1911 p
    $3.50 NNM   1562
----.   Navajo texts (AP 34:1, p 1-179) 1933 p $1.75 NNM
                                                                           1563
----.   San Carlos Apache texts (AP 24:3, p 141-367) 1919 p
    $2.50 NNM   1564
----.   White Mountain Apache texts (AP 24:4, p 369-527)
    1920 p $2. NNM   1565
Sapir, Edward.   Takelma texts (AP v 2, no 1) 268 p 1909 p
    $1.75 PU-Mu   1566
Swanton, John R.   Haida texts--Masset dialect (M 14:2, p
    271-812; JNP v 10) 1908 p $8. NNM*   1567

--Literature--Indians of South America

Anderson, Arthur J.O., and Charles E. Dibble.   Florentine
    Codex: General history of the things of New Spain, by
    Fray Bernardino de Sahagun, tr from the Aztec into Eng-
    lish, with notes and illustrations (M 14--Publ with U of
    Utah, with cooperation of the Museum of New Mexico) 8
    separates; more to be published.   1950 price for each
    separate $4 to $8; also sold as set NmSM-S   1568
Beyer, Hermann.   An incised Maya inscription in the Metro-
    politan Museum of Art, New York (P 15; MARR v 1, no 7)
    4 p 1945 p $.25 LNT-MA   1569
----.   The Maya hieroglyph chicchan derivative (P 15; MARR
    v 1, no 8) 3 p 1945 p $.25 LNT-MA   1570

The Book of Chilam Balam of Chumayel, with introd by G.
B. Gordon (U of Pennsylvania Museum, Philadelphia) 1913
photog reprod of the 107 p of the Book 1913 p $7.50 MH-
P   1571
Codex Nuttall, 84 p of facsim of the manuscript, in its orig-
inal colors--unbound sheets (explanatory notes op, but ob-
tainable on microfil,) small ed 1902 $20. MH-P   1572
Dibble, Charles E. Codex Hall: An ancient Mexican hieroglyphic picture manuscript, with silk screen facsim of the
codex by Louis H. Ewing (M 11) 16 p 17 il 4 pl 1947 $5.
NmSM-S   1573
d' Olwer, Luis Nicolau. English-Nahuatl edition of Sahagun:
General history of the things of New Spain, an essay from
Revista Interamericana de Bibliografia, v 5, no 3, 1955,
p 165-70, translated and republished with permission of
editor and author apply NmSM-S   1574
Forstemann, Ernst. Commentary on the Maya manuscript
in the Royal Public Library of Dresden (P v 4, no 2) 221
p 1 pl 10 il 1906 p $2.25, interleaved translation $3.35
MH-P   1575
Gates, William E. Commentary on the Maya-Tzental Codex
Perez (P v 6, no 1) 64 p 2 pl il 1910 p $.65 MH-P1576
Goodman, J.T. The archaic Maya inscriptions (Appendix to
Biologia Central-Americana). The archaic annual calen-
dar, with tables for 52 years; archaic chronological calen-
dar with 77 pages of tables; perpetual chronological calen-
dar with table; working chart 149 p 1897 p $4/25 MH-P
                                                         1577
Gordon, G.B. The book of Chilam Balam (AP v 5) 11 p 107
pl 1913 p $7.   PU-Mu   1578
----. The hieroglyphic stairway, ruins of Copan (M v 1, no
6) 38 p 26 il 18 pl 1902 p $2.75 MH-P   1579
Gropp, Arthur E. Guide to the libraries and archives in
Central America, the West Indies, Panama, Bermuda and
British Guiana 1941 p; Costa Rica $.35; Cuba $.50;
Dominican Republic $.15; France--Colonies $.25; Guate-
mala $2; Haiti $.15; Honduras $.20; Nicaragua $.20;
Panama $.20; El Salvador $.40; U.S.--Territories $.50;
LNT-MA   1580
----. Manuscripts in the Department of Middle American Re-
search (P 5; Studies in Mid America 5) 1934 p $1.50
LNT-MA   1581
Guthe, Carl E. A possible solution of the number series on
pages 51 to 58 of the Dresden Codex (P v 6, no 2) 31 p
1 pl 1921 $.50 MH-P   1582
Hewett, Edgar L. Fray Bernardino de Sahagun and the Great
Florentine Codex (P ns 36) 15 p 1944 p $.25 NmSM-S 1583

Hunter, William A. The Calderonian "Auto Sacramental,"
El Gran Teatro del Mundo (P 27, no 3) 1960 p $2.75
LNT-MA   1584
Landivar, Rafael. Rusticatio Mexicana, a mid-18th century
poem describing life in Mexico and Guatemala; the Latin
text with English translation by Graydon W. Regenos (P
11; PD v 1, no 5) 156 p il 1948 p $3.50 LNT-MA   1585
Morley, Sylvanus G. The historical value of the Books of
Chilam Balam (P 19) 20 p 1911 $.25 NmSM-S   1586
Spinden, Herbert J. Maya inscriptions dealing with Venus
and the Moon (B 14:1) p $.55 NBuM   1587
Tozzer, A.M., and G.M. Allen. The animal figures in the
Maya codices (P v 4, no 3) 100 p 39 pl 24 il 1910 p
$1.75 MH-P   1588

--Literature--Near East

Coomaraswamy, Ananda K. An Arabic treatise on Automata
(Communications to the Trustees v 4) 21 p 8 il 1924 p $1.
MBMu   1589
McLanathan, Richard B.K. Queen Tomyris and the head of
Cyrus: A short text (PB 6) c p $.50 MBMu   1590
Pritchard, James B. Hebrew inscriptions and stamps from
Gibeon (MM) 32 p 12 fig 1959 $1. PU-Mu   1591
The Song of Songs $1. PPComm   1592
Upton, Joseph M. A manuscript of the "Book of Fixed
Stars," by 'Abd Ar-Rahman As-Sufi. A studies separate
19 p 51 il 1933 p $.50 NNMM   1593

--Literature--Near East--Babylonian

Barton, G.A. One of the oldest Babylonian tablets in the
world (MJ v 3, no 1) 3 p 1 il 1912 p $.50 PU-Mu 1594
Burrows, Eric. Archaic texts (Publications of the Joint Ex-
ped, Ur Excav: Texts v 2) 63 p 55 pl 1935 p $10. PU-
Mu   1595
Hilprecht, H.V. Mathematical, meteorological and chrono-
logical tablets from the Temple library of Nippur (PBSN,
Ser A--Cuneiform texts v 20) 70 p 45 pl 1906 p $3.50
PU-Mu   1596
Hussey, Mary Inda. Babylonian tables in the Museum of the
Buffalo Society of Natural Sciences (B v 11, no 2) p $.55
NBuM   1597
Important historical documents found in the Museum's collec-
tion of ancient Babylonian clay tablets (MJ v 4, no 2) 5 p
3 il 1913 p $.50 PU-Mu   1598
Kramer, S.N. Schooldays: A Sumerian composition relating

to the education of a scribe (MM) 19 p 4 il 1949 p $.50
PU-Mu   1599
Langdon, S.   Historical and religious texts from Nippur (in
    Constantinople) (PBSN, Ser A--Cuneiform Texts v 31) 80
    p 54 pl 1914 p $5 PU-Mu (Order from: Rudolf Merkel,
    Universitäts-Buchhandlung, Erlangen (13a), Germany)1600
----.   Sumerian grammatical texts (PBS v 12, no 1) 44 p
    58 pl 1917 p $3.50 PU-Mu   1601
----.   Sumerian liturgical texts (PBS v 10, no 2) 105 p 56
    pl 1917 p $3.50 PU-Mu   1602
----.   Sumerian liturgies and psalms (PBS v 10, no 4) 124
    p 35 pl 1919 p $3.50 PU-Mu   1603
----.   A Sumerian liturgy containing an ode to the world
    (MJ v 9, no 2) 7 p 1 il 1918 p $1. PU-Mu   1604
Legrain, L.   Historical fragments (PBS v 13) 108 p 35 pl
    1 map 1922 p $3.50 PU-Mu   1605
----.   The tragic history of King Ibi-Sin (MJ v 17, no 4) 12
    p 1926 p $1. PU-Mu   1606
Lutz, Henry F.   Selected Sumerian and Babylonian texts
    (PBS v 1, no 2) 122 p 92 pl 1919 p $3.50 PU-Mu   1607
Montgomery, J.A.   Aramaic incantation texts from Nippur
    (PBS v 3) 326 p 41 pl 1913 p $3.50 PU-Mu   1608
----.   A love charm on an incantation bowl (MJ v 1, no 3)
    2 p 1910 p $.50 PU-Mu   1609
----.   The original script of the Manichaeans on texts in the
    Museum (MJ v 3, no 2) 5 pl 1 il 1912 p $.50 PU-Mu
                                                        1610
----.   The pronunciation of the "Ineffable Name" (MJ v 1, no
    2) 3 p 1 il 1910 p $.50 PU-Mu   1611
Myrhman, David W.   Babylonian hymns and prayers (PBS v
    1, pt 1) 12 p 47 pl 1911 p $2. PU-Mu   1612
Poebel, Arno.   Historical and grammatical texts (PBS v 5)
    125 pl 1914 p $7. PU-Mu   1613
----.   Historical texts (PBS v 4, no 1) 242 p 1914 p $3.50
    PU-Mu   1614
Radau, Hugo.   Sumerian hymns and prayers to God Dumuzi
    from the Temple library of Nippur, Pt. 1. (PBSN, Ser A--
    Cuneiform Texts v 30) 66 p 29 pl 1913 p $3.50 PU-Mu
    (Order from Rudolf Merkel, Universitäts-Buchhandlung,
    Erlangen (13 a), Germany)   1615
----.   Sumerian hymns and prayers to God Ninib from the
    Temple library of Nippur, Pt. 1. (PBSN, Ser A--Cunei-
    form Texts v 29) 88 p 21 pl 1911 p $2. PU-Mu   1616
Scheil, V.   The oldest written code (MJ v 11, no 3) 3 p 1920
    p $1. PU-Mu   1617
Steele, F.R.   Code of Lipit-Ishtar (MM) 28 p 7 il 1949 p
    $.50 PU-Mu   1618

----. Writing and history. The new tables from Nippur (B
v 16, no 2) 8 p 2 il 1951 p $.50 PU-Mu   1619

--Literature--Near East--Egypt

Conversations and calls recorded on the walls of the Tomb of
Kaipure (Saqqarah) (B v 7, no 3) 4 p 4 il 1939 p $.50
PU-Mu   1620
Hayes, William C., ed and tr. A papyrus in the Late Mid-
dle Kingdom in the Brooklyn Museum 165 p 14 il 1955 p
$10. NBB   1621
No entry   1622
--Literature--Spanish

Camoes, Luis de. The Lusiads, tr by Leonard Bacon, with
introduction and notes 435 p 3 maps 1950 $4.50 NNH1623
Cervantes Saavedra, Miguel de. The visionary gentleman
Don Quijote de la Mancha, tr by Robinson Smith, with a
life of Cervantes. Pt I, Pt II--2 v unbound, boxed $4;
bound $6. NNH   1624
El Cid Campeador. Poem of the Cid, reprinted from the
unique manuscript at Madrid; with tr and notes by A.M.
Huntington (reissue in 1 v of the 1907-1908 ed) 1942
$2.25 NNH   1625
Hartzenbusch, Juan Eugenio. The lovers of Teruel, tr by
Henry Thomas 72 p 1950 $.50 NNH   1626
Hernandez, Jose. A fragment from Martin Fierro (El Gau-
cho) tr by Joseph Auslander 13 p 1932 p $.25 NNH 1627
Historia de los amores de Bayad y Riyad; una chantefable
oriental en estilo persa (Vat Ar 368), ed with Spanish
translation by A.R. Nykl 50, 54 p 10 facsim (miniatures)
1941 $2. NNH   1628
Leguizamon, Mariniano. Calandria, a drama of Gaucho life,
tr from Spanish 65 p 1932 p $.25 NNH   1629
McVan, Alice Jane. Antonio Machado 256 p 6 il 1959 $5.
NNH   1630
Nykl, A.R. Hispano-Arabic poetry and its relations with the
old Provencal troubadours 416 p 1946 p $10. NNH 1631
Thomas, Sir. Henry. Monstruo y milagro; el gallo resuci-
tado 19 p 4 pl 1946 p $.50 NNH   1632
Translations from Hispanic poets (Selections from Spanish
and Portuguese poetry, 13th-20th century, and from verse
of 19th and 20th century poets in Hispanic-American countries) 271 p 1938 $1. NNH   1633

--LANGUAGE ARTS-- Theatre Arts

Costume design for the theatre 20 p il 1956 p $.50 CLCM
                                                          1634
Dramatic choice, the theater collects 38 p 25 il 1950 p $.50
    NBuA   1635
The theater in ancient art 36 p 56 il 1952 $.75 NjP-A 1636

--Theatre Arts--United States

The American Stage, an exhibition of designs for the Ameri-
    can Stage since 1915 52 p 5 il 1957 p $1. DCGA   1637
Berman, Eugene.   Eugene Berman's designs for Don Giovan-
    ni 1959 p $.50 TxSaMo   1638
Carson, William G.B.   St. Louis goes to the opera, 1837-
    1941 44 p il 1946 p $.75 MoHi   1639
Ernst, Alice Henson.   Theatrical trouping in the Oregon
    country il map 1959 $6. OrHi   1640
Griffith, Richard.   Fred Zinneman 20 p 10 pl p $.50 NNMMA
                                                          1641
Naeseth, Henriette C.K.   The Swedish theatre of Chicago
    1869-1950 (published with Augustana Library Pubns)
    (Pubns v 12) 1951 $3. IRi   1642
Robinson, Francis W.   Donald Oenslager, stage designer and
    teacher (C 33) 49 p 24 il 1956 p $.50 MiDA   1643
Three designers for the contemporary theatre: Robert Ed-
    mond Jones, Donald Oenslager, Lee Simonson 1950 p $.35
    MH-FA   1644

--Theatre Arts--Guatemala

Correa, Gustavo, and Calvin Cannon.   La loa en Guatemala:
    Contribucion al estudio del teatro popular hispanoamericana
    (P 27, no 1) 1958 p $2.   LNT-MA   1645
No entry   1646

--Theatre Arts--England

The Globe Playhouse, illustrations and descriptions of scale
    model by John Cranford Adams brd c $.05 DFo   1647
Wright, Louis B.   Shakespeare's Theatre and the dramatic
    tradition il p $.75 DFo   1648

--Theatre Arts--Oriental

Laufer, Berthold.   Oriental theatricals 59 p 11 il 1923 p
    $.25 ICF   1649

MUSIC

Barksdale, A.B.   Composer portraits and autograph scores
    --72 more important composers from the first half of the
    17th century to the present time 54 p 14 il 1954 p $1.
    OTM   1650
----.   Medieval and renaissance music manuscripts 65 p 12
    il 1953 p $1.   OTM   1651
----.   The printed note, 500 years of music printing and
    engraving 144 p il 1957 p $2.   OTM   1652
Mason, Leslie Lindsey, Collection.   Leslie Lindsey Mason
    Collection of musical instruments (repr, Bul no 91, Oct
    1917) 16 p 31 il p $.25 MBMu   1653
Musical instruments, a guide to the permanent collection
    1949 p $.50 OCA   1654
Musical instruments and their portrayal in art; an exhibition
    catalogue that "correlates the arts of music, painting and
    sculpture.   Adelyn D. Breeskin: foreword; Frederick P.
    Stieff: Essay "On the pianoforte."   Glossary of unusual
    instruments 48 p 12 il 1946 p $.75 MdBMA   1655

--Music--Americas--United States

The birth of the Star-Spangled Banner (Leaflet 14) p $.10
    MdHi   1656
Spell, Lota M.   Music teaching in New Mexico in the 17th
    century (repr, Hist Rev) 12 p 1927 $.25 NmSM-H   1657
The Star-Spangled Banner 26 p 5 il map p $.50 MdHi   1658
Stephen Foster: Maker of American songs (Leaflet 3) 4 p
    p $.05 PHarH   1659
Whipple, George M.   A sketch of the musical societies of
    Salem 30 p 1886 p $.50 MSaE   1660

--Music--Americas--Indians of North America

Alexander and Fletcher.   Indian music (P ns 18) 4 p folder
    1926 $.10 NmSM-S   1661
Densmore, Frances.   Cheyenne and Arapahoe music (P 10)
    111 p 8 il 72 songs 1936 p $2.50 CLSM   1662
----.   Music of the Maidu Indians (Pubns Hodge VII) 67 p 7
    fig 53 songs 1958 $5; p $3.75 CLSM   1663
----.   Music of the Santo Domingo Pueblo, New Mexico (P
    12)   songs with music 16 pl 18 fig 1938 p $3.50 CLSM
                                                          1664
Eells, Myron.   Hymns in the Chinook jargon language 40 p
    1889 p $3.   OrHi   1665
Indian musical and noise-making instruments (IL 29)

CoDA   1666
McAllester, David P.   Enemy way music: A study of social
  and esthetic values as seen in Navajo music (P v 41, no 3)
  96 p 52 pages of music 6 il 1954 p $2.65 MH-P   1667
Speck, F.G.   Ceremonial songs of the Creek and Yuchi Indians (AP v 1, no 2) 91 p 1911 p $1.75 PU-Mu   1668

--Music--Americas--Indians of Mexico, Central and South
America

Titiev, Mischa.   Social singing among the Mapuche (AP 2)
  17 p 1949 p $.25 MiU-A   1669
Mead, Charles W.   The musical instruments of the Inca
  (AP 15:3, p 313-47) 5 pl 8 fig 1924 p $.75 NNM   1670
Merwin, B.W.   A Voodoo drum from Haiti (MJ v 8, no 2)
  3 p 1917 p $1. PU-Mu   1671

--Music--Europe

Bessaraboff, Nicholas.   Ancient European musical instru-
  ments, an organological study of the musical instruments
  in the Leslie Lindsey Mason Collection at the Museum of
  Fine Arts 536 p 73 fig 16 pl 1941 $10. MBMu   1672
Mason, Dorothy E.   Music in Elizabethan England il p $.75
  DFo   1673

--Music--Orient

Dahomey songs (MJ v 2, no 2) 1911 p $.50 PU-Mu   1674
Fernald, H.E.   Ancient Chinese musical instruments (MJ v
  17, no 4) 46 p 43 il 1926 p $1. PU-Mu   1675

--Music--Pacific Area

Burrows, E.G.   Native music of the Tuamotus (B 109) 107
  p 1933 p $1. HB (op)   1676

VISUAL ARTS
--Aesthetics

Bingham, Lois A.   How to look at works of art; the search
  for line (NGA Hdbk 1) 40 p 36 il 1946 p $.35 DSI-GA
                                                     1677
Buermeyer, Laurence.   The aesthetic experience p $1.50
  PMeB   1678
Color, comprehensive treatment of the influence of color upon
  the various aspects of our world 23 p 22 il $.50

CoDA   1679
The contemporary scene: A symposium (includes: Sidney
    Hook--"The problem of the individual in a totalitarian so-
    ciety:" James P. Warburg--"The problems of the individu-
    al in a free society;" Henry A. Murrah--"Science in two
    societies;" Paul T. Tillich--"Religion in two socieities;"
    Lloyd Goodrich--"Art in democracies;" Hellmut Lehmann-
    Haupt. "Art under totalitarianism.") 74 p 8 il 1954 p
    $1.50 NNMM   1680
Dewey, John, et al. Art and education 330 p 2nd ed $4.
    PMeB   1681
Griswold, A. Whitney. On conversation chiefly academic
    $2.50 CtY-A   1682
Hayes, Bartlett H., Jr. The naked truth and personal vi-
    sion 117 il $3.75 MAnP-A   1683
Miner, Dorothy, ed. Studies in art and literature for Belle
    da Costa Greene 502 p 366 pl 1954 $25. MdBWA   1684
Rathbun, Mary C., and Bartlett H. Hayes, Jr. Layman's
    guide to modern art 112 p 117 il $2.75; p $1.95 MAnP-A
                                                        1685
Shapley, John. Comparisons in art--A companion to the Na-
    tional Gallery of Art 246 p 190 il 1957 $3.95 DSI-GA1686
Structure--Structure in nature as well as in man-made con-
    struction 24 p 30 il $.50 CoDA   1687
What is painting 40 p 32 il (2 c) 1953 p $.50 NBuA   1688

--Art Museums and Galleries--Catalogs, Guides, History
See also listings under country, as Art, United States

Albright Art Gallery. Catalogue of contemporary paintings
    and sculpture, The Room of Contemporary Art Collection
    (Albright Art Gallery) 214 p 80 il 1949 $2.50 NBuA 1689
----. Catalogue of paintings and sculpture in the permanent
    collection (of the Albright Art Gallery) 214 p 87 il 1949
    $2.50 NBuA   1690
----. Contemporary Art: Acquistions 1954-1957; gifts of
    Seymour H. Knox; Gallery purchases of contemporary
    sculpture; loans from Mr. and Mrs. Seymour H. Knox 55
    p 46 il (2 c) 1957 p $2. NBuA   1691
----. Contemporary Art: Acquistions 1957-1958 52 p 53 il
    1959 p $2. NBuA   1692
American Antiquarian Society. Catalogue of paintings il p $1.
    MWA   1693
Arizona, University of, Art Gallery. The Edward Joseph
    Gallagher III Memorial Collection--contemporary Americar
    and European p $1. AzU-A   1694
Art Institute of Chicago. Arthur Jerome Eddy Collection of

modern painting and sculpture 31 p il $.10 ICA (op) 1695
----. Masterpieces of painting-XV and XVI centuries 27 p
il 1946 p $.35 ICA   1696
----. Masterpieces of painting--XIX century 28 p il 1946 p
$.35 ICA   1697
----. Winterbotham Collection 45 il p $.25 ICA   1698
Athenaeum Gallery. Swan, Mabel Munson. The Athenaeum
Gallery, 1827-1873, The Boston Athenaeum as an early
patron of the arts $6. NBAt   1699
Baltimore Museum of Art. Handbook of the Cone Collection.
Introduction, Adelyn D. Breeskin; Essays, George Boas,
Adelyn D. Breeskin, Gertrude Rosenthal 55 p 53 il (12 c)
1955 p $2. MdBMA   1700
----. A picture book--200 objects in the Baltimore Museum
of Art; compiled by Gertrude Rosenthal, with notes on ma-
jor collections, introductions, Adelyn D. Breeskin 93 p
200 il 1955 p $2. MdBMA   1701
Butler Art Institute. Catalogue 120 p 126 il 1951 p $1. OYoB
                                                        1702
----. Catalogue--40th anniversary issue. Supplement to the
catalogue of the permanent collection 75 p 80 il p $1.
OYoB   1703
----. Catalogue--1954 supplement 59 p 42 il p $.50 1960
supplement 24 p 12 il p $.40 OYoB   1704
California Palace of the Legion of Honor. Illustrated hand-
book $2.40; mailing charge, $.35 CSfPL   1705
Cincinnati Art Museum. Guide to the collections; text and
floor plans 1956 107 il p $1. OCA   1706
----. The Lehman Collection. 800 years of Western art as-
sembled by Mr. Robert Lehman and his father, Mr. Phi-
lip Lehman--paintings, drawings, decorative arts $6.60
OCA   1707
Cleveland Museum of Art. Paintings, selected examples in
Museum's collection. No. 1. 57 il (3 c); No. 4 56 il (7
c) 1952 p $1. ea CClMA   1708
----. Bequest of Elisabeth Severance Prentiss--paintings,
sculpture, furniture, ceramics, prints 50 il (1 c) p $.75
CClMA   1709
----. Bequest of John L. Severance--paintings, sculpture,
furniture, ceramics and prints 39 il p $.75 OClMA 1710
----. Handbook 930 il 1958 p $2. OClMA   1711
----. Some contemporary works of art; foreword by Dr.
Lee; introduction by Dr. Munro 76 il 1958 p $1.50 OClMA
                                                        1712
Cooper Union Museum. An illustrated survey of the collec-
tions p $1. NNCoo   1713
----. Sixtieth anniversary jubilee, 1897-1957 (MC v 2, no 9)

    p $.25 NNCoo   1714
Corcoran Gallery of Art. Masterpieces of the Corcoran
    Gallery of Art p $1. DCGA   1715
Corning Museum of Glass. Guide to the collections--a chron-
    ology of glassmaking from Ancient Egypt to the beginning
    of the 20th century 96 p 106 il (19 c) 1958 p $1.50
    NCorniC-M   1716
Crocker (E.B.) Art Gallery. History of the collections of
    E.B. Crocker Art Gallery, catalogue of two galleries p
    $.20 CSC   1717
Delaware Public Archives Commission. de Valinger, Leon.
    Catalogue of Delaware portraits collected by the Delaware
    State Portrait Commission in the Capitol Buildings, Dover,
    Delaware (Delaware State Portrait Commission) 64 p 4 il
    1941 p apply De-Ar   1718
de Young (M.H.) Memorial Museum. Works of Art (Museum
    Handbook--M.H. de Young Memorial Museum) il p $1.55
    CSfDeY   1719
Detroit Institute of Arts. Favorite paintings from the De-
    troit Institute of Arts (B 3) 80 p 15 c il 1958 p $.75
    MiDA   1720
----. Guide (G 6) rev ed 1959 p $.15 MiDA   1721
----. Richardson, Edgar P. Paintings and sculpture given
    by Edgar B. Whitcomb and Anna Scripps Whitcomb to the
    Detroit Institute of Arts (B 8) 134 p 71 il (6 c) 1954 $5.
    MiDA   1722
----. Twentieth century painting (G 2) 58 p 30 il 4th ed
    1947 p $.50 MiDA   1723
duPont (Henry Francis) Winterthur Museum. Museum and
    garden guide to Winterthur in the spring 40 p 50 il (6 c)
    1957 p $1.10 DeWint   1724
Essex Institute. Foote, Henry W. Catalog of portraits in
    the Essex Institute 295 p 100 il 1936 $12.50 MSaE   1725
----. Jackson, Russell L. Catalog of portraits in the Essex
    Institute, additions 28 p il 1950 p $2. MSaE   1726
Fogg Art Museum. Huntsinger, Laura M., comp; Alan
    Burroughs, ed. Harvard portraits: A catalogue of por-
    trait paintings at Harvard University 1936 p $2. MH-FA
                                              1727
----. Modern painting, drawing and sculpture collected by
    Louise and Joseph Pulitzer, jr., V. 1, 1957 $2.50; v. 2
    1958 $3; 2 v 1958 p $5. MH-FA   1728
Freer Gallery of Art (Smithsonian Institute, pubn 4185) 16 p
    8 il, 3 plans 1958 p $.15 DSI-F   1729
----. Stubbs, B.A. Paintings, pastels, drawings, prints
    and copper plates by and attributed to American and Euro-
    pean artists, together with a list of original Whistleriana

in the Freer Gallery of Art (FOP v 1, no 2; Smithsonian
Institute, pubn 3905) 152 p 20 pl 1948 p $.50 DSI-F
                                                      1730
Frick Collection.   Frick Collection paintings, check list p
    $.15 NNFC   1731
Gardner (Isabella Stewart) Museum.   Carter, Morris. Isa-
    bella Stewart Gardner and Fenway Court $3.50; $.16 post
    MBIMu   1732
----.   The Gardner Collection il $3; $.65 post MBIMu 1733
----.   Hendy, Philip.   Catalogue of the exhibited paintings
    and drawings (Isabella Stewart Gardner Museum) il p
    $2.50; $.24 post MBIMu   1734
----.   Longstreet, Gilbert W.   General catalogue 32 il p
    $2; $.14 post MBIMu   1735
----.   Museum guide p $.75; $.09 post MBIMu   1736
Guggenheim (Solomon R.) Museum.   The Solomon R. Guggen-
    heim Museum.   Foreword by James Johnson Sweeney;
    trilingual: English, French, German 81 il p $.75 NNGu
                                                      1737

----.   Svendsen, Louise Averill, and James Johnson
    Sweeney.   Solomon R. Guggenheim Museum Collection.
    Handbook (Published by the Solomon R. Guggenheim Found-
    ation).   Preface by Harry F. Guggenheim 248 pl 1959
    $9.75 NNGu   1738
Herron (John) Art Institute.   Marmon Memorial Collection of
    paintings p $.75 InIJ   1739
----.   105 paintings, John Herron Art Museum p $.50 InIJ
                                                      1740
Hispanic Society of American Museum. Handbook: Museum
    and library collections 443 p 597 il 1938 $1.50 NNH 1741
----.   Hispanic Society of America, Museum and Library 72
    p 77 il 1954 p $.50 NNH   1742
----.   History of the Hispanic Society of America, Museum
    and Library, 1904-1954, with a survey of the collections
    569 p 432 il 1954 $6.50 NNH   1743
Houston Museum of Fine Arts.   Baffer Memorial Collection
    p $.25 TxHM   1744
Los Angeles County Museum.   Mr. and Mrs. George Gard de
    Sylva Collection of French Impressionists and modern
    painting and sculpture 78 p il 1950 p $.78 CLCM   1745
McNay (Marion Koogler) Collection.   Catalogue p $2.50
    TxSaMc   1746
Metropolitan Museum of Art.   Howe, Winifred E.   A history
    of the Metropolitan Museum of Art. v 1 (1869-1912) 361 p
    front 63 il 1913; v 2 (1905-1941) 269 p front 11 il (Co-
    lumbia University Press) 1946 $3. ea; set, $5. NNMM
                                                      1747

----. The Lewisohn Collection. A catalogue; foreword by
Francis Henry Taylor; introduction by Theodore Rousseau,
Jr. 86 p 61 il (4 c) 1951 p $2.50 NNMM   1748
----. Rousseau, Theodore, Jr. The picture galleries. A
picture book 56 p 73 il 1954 p $.50 NNMM   1749
Milwaukee Art Center. The Zadok Collection p $.50 WMA
                                                          1750
Montclair Art Museum. Your Montclair Art Museum p $.50
NjMonA   1751
Museum of Fine Arts, Boston. A catalogue of paintings and
drawings in water color--acquired by the Museum before
January 1948; with indexes for places, portraits and per-
sons, saints and sacred subjects, secular subjects, artists
by schools and date of birth, donors and collections,
paintings in order of acquisition 310 p 679 il p $2.
MBMu   1752
----. Gilman, Benjamin Gives. Museum of Fine Arts,
1870-1920 40 p 25 il 1920 p $.25 MBMu (op)   1753
----. Handbook of the Museum 193 p 162 il and plans
$1.25 MBMu   1754
----. Leaflet guide 16 p p $.10 MBMu (op)   1755
----. The Niarchos Collection, paintings and sculpture 61 il
(14 c) 1958 p $3. MBMu   1756
Museum of Modern Art. Barr, Alfred H., Jr. The Museum
of Modern Art--Painting and sculpture collection. Tri-
lingual text: English, French, German (Published by
Braun & Cie, Paris) 64 p 58 pl p $.60 NNMMA   1757
National Academy of Design. Cowdrey, Bartlett, comp. Ex-
hibition records: National Academy of Design, 1826-1860
2 v. v 1. A-L 300 p; v 2. M-Z 365 p $6. American
Academy of Fine Arts (1816-1835) and of the American
Art Union (1839-1851) 2 v. v. 1 Introduction 311 p; v. 2
Exhibition Record 504 p il index set, 2 v. $7.50 NHi1758
National Collection of Fine Art. Beggs, Thomas M. Cata-
log of American and European paintings in the Gellatly
Collection (Smithsonian Institute, pubn 4143) 13 il 4th ed
1954 p $.35 DSI-FA   1759
----, ----. Harriet Lane Johnston and the National Collec-
tion of Fine Arts (repr, Smithsonian Report, 1954, p 443-
8; Smithsonian Institute, pubn 4208) 8 pl 1955 p apply
DSI-FA   1760
----. Check list of works of art from the Widener Collection, with a foreword by David E. Finlay and John Walker
24 p 1942 p apply DSI-FA   1761
----. Holmes, William H. National Collection of Fine Art.
Catalogue of Collections. Pt. 2. (Title, "National Gallery
of Art," former title of the Collection) 118 p 45 il 1926

$1.65 (Government Printing Office) **DSI-FA**   1761a

----. The opening of the Adams-Clement collection, 1951
(Smithsonian Special pubn; pubn 4055) 23 p il 1951 p apply
DSI-FA   1762

National Gallery of Art. Cairns, Huntington, and John
Walker. Great paintings from the National Gallery of Art
85 color plates, with "relevant passages from the world's
literature" 1952 $12.50 **DSI-GA**   1763

----, ----, ----. Masterpieces of painting from the National
Gallery of Art 85 color plates, with "interpretive passages
from the world's literature" 1943 $12.50 **DSI-GA**   1764

----. Favorite paintings from the National Gallery of Art 80
p 15 il c 1946 p $.75 **DSI-GA**   1765

----. Painting and sculpture from the Widener Collection,
with foreword by David E. Finley and introduction by John
Walker 172 p 141 il 1947 p $1.25 **DSI-GA**   1766

----. Paintings and sculpture from the Mellon Collection,
with foreword by David E. Finley, and introduction by John
Walker 196 p 157 il 1949 p $1.25 **DSI-GA**   1767

----. Recent additions to the Ralph and Mary Booth Collection 1948 p apply **DSI-GA**   1768

----. Walker, John. National Gallery of Art, Washington
62 p 85 il (24 c) 1956 p $7.95 **DSI-GA**   1769

National Gallery of Canada. Engagement calendar. Annual
1961, spiral bd $2.50 **CaOONG**   1770

----. Hubbard, R.H., ed. The National Gallery of Canada,
Catalogue of paintings and sculpture. v 1. Older schools
$4.95; p $1.50; v 2. Modern European schools $10; p
$4.25 **CaOONG** (Distributed by: University of Toronto
Press)   1771

Nelson (William Rockhill) Gallery of Art, and Atkins Museum
of Fine Arts. Gallery handbook p $3; $.25 post **MoKNG**
                                                       1772

New York Historical Society. Catalogue of the museum and
gallery of art of the New York Historical Society, 1862
39 p 1866 61 p; 1873 74 p; 1881 78 p; il p $.60 ea **NHi**
                                                       1773

----. Catalogue of the Stuart Collection (now at the New
York Historical Society), New York Public Library 60 p
1941 p $.50 **NHi**   1774

Newark Museum. Additions to the Museum's collections of
paintings and sculpture: European, American, since 1950
(The Museum, ns, v 8, no 2-3, Spring-Summer 1956) p
$.75 **NjNM**   1775

----. Bamberger Memorial book 36 p front 1944 p $1.50
NjNM (op)   1776

----. Eighteenth-20th century paintings and sculpture ac-

quired since 1944 (The Museum, ns, v 2, no 3-4, Summer-Fall 1950) p $.75 NjNM 1777
----. Four significant paintings: Acquisitions and re-atributions (The Museum, ns, v 10, no 1, Winter 1958) p $.75 NjNM 1778
----. The Herman A.E., and Paul C. Jaehne Collections (The Museum, ns, v 2, no 1, Winter 1950) p $.50 NjNM 1779
----. Louis Bamberger: A record of his benefaction to his community and his country 27 p il p $1. NjNM 1780
----. The Marcus L. Ward bequest (The Museum, ns, v 1, no 3, July 1949) p $.40 NjNM 1781
North Carolina Museum of Art. Valentiner, W.R. Catalog of paintings, including three sets of tapestries 90 p 151 il p $1.50 NcRMA 1782
Oakland Art Museum. Early paintings of California in the Robert E. Honeyman, Jr. Collection p $1.50 COA 1783
Pennsylvania Historical Society. Sawitzky, William. Catalogue descriptive and critical of the paintings and miniatures in the Historical Society of Pennsylvania 285 p 1942 unbd $2.50 PHi 1784
Philadelphia Museum of Art. Benson, E.M. Masterpieces of the Philadelphia Museum of Art (Metropolitan Museum of Art Minieatures, Album LP) 31 p 24 il c 1952 p $1.25 PPPM 1785
----. Canaday, John. Twentieth century paintings in the Philadelphia Museum of Art (Metropolitan Museum of Art Mineatures, Album ME) 28 p 24 il c 1955 p $1.25 PPPM 1786
----. Gallatin, A.E., et al. A.E. Gallatin Collection-- Museum of living art, a modern painting collection 153 p 179 pl (10 c) 1954 $5. PPPM 1786a
----. Handbook: Floor plans, general information, historical sketch, explanation of each section 30 p il p $.50 PPPM 1787
----. Louise and Walter Arensberg Collection. v 1. Twentieth century painting and sculpture; foreword by Fiske Kimball, introduction by Henry Clifford 218 p 220 pl (8 c) 1954 $5; v 2. Pre-Columbian sculpture, classified and annotated by George Kubler; foreword by Fiske Kimball 224 p 162 pl 1954 $5. PPPM 1788
Philbrook Art Center. Guide p $.50 OkTP 1789
Phillips Gallery. Catalogue 310 il (10 c) $3.50 DPG 1790
Phoenix Art Museum. Rubel Collection catalogue il $2.50 AzPhA 1791
Princeton University Art Museum. The Carl Otto von Kienbusch, Jr. Memorial Collection 32 p 30 il 1956 $.75

NjP-A   1792
Reading Public Museum and Art Gallery.   Catalog of oil
    paintings (B 24) $1.   PRM   1793
Rhode Island School of Design Museum.   Treasures, picture
    book of important objects in the Museum 1956 p $.35
    RPD-M   1794
Ringling (John and Mabel) Museum of Art.   Catalogue of
    paintings il $2.50 FSR   1795
----.   Fifty masterpieces in the Museum il p 1961 $.25
    FSR   1796
Rockefeller (Abby Aldrich) Folk Art Collection.   Little, Nina
    Fletcher.   The Abby Aldrich Rockefeller folk art collec-
    tion 420 p 165 il c boxed $11.95   ViWC   1797
Rogers (Lauren) Library and Museum of Art.   Lauren
    Rogers Library and Museum of Art 14 il p $.25 MsLA
                                                              1798
Roswell Museum and Art Center.   Bob Crosby Collection p
    $.10 NmRMA   1799
----.   The permanent collection of the Roswell Museum p
    $.25 NmRMA   1800
St. Louis City Art Museum.   City Art Museum, St. Louis.
    Handbook of the collection 282 p 505 il (3 c) rev ed $3;
    p $2; post $.25 MoSCA   1801
----.   Forty masterpieces, catalogue of the 40th anniversary
    exhibition 95 p 40 il p $1.50; $.10 post MoSCA   1802
----.   Modern art in the Washington University Collection
    (Art Bulletin) 48 p 30 il p $.75; $.10 post MoSCA   1803
Seattle Art Museum.   Handbook of the permanent collection
    127 il p $1.50 WaSA   1804
----.   The Le Roy M. Backus Collection 16 p il p $.50
    WaSA   1805
----.   Picture book of 100 objects in the permanent collec-
    tion 100 p spiral $1.   WaSA   1806
----.   Seattle Art Museum; introduction by Richard E.
    Fuller 30 p il p $.50 WaSA   1807
Springfield Museum of Fine Arts Handbook 1948 p $1; 1958
    p $2.50 MSMFA   1808
Stanford Museum.   General catalog p $.25 CStM   1809
Taft Museum Collection.   Catalog p $2. OCT   1810
Toledo Museum of Art.   Godwin, Molly Ohl.   Masterworks,
    survey of best known works in the Toledo Museum of Art
    46 p 22 il (10 c) 1952 p $1.25 OTM   1811
----.   Guide, including the Egyptian Gallery, Classic Court,
    Stevens Gallery (printing and books), Gothic Hall, Cloister,
    French Gallery, Great Gallery, and others 23 p 28 il
    1958 p $.25 OTM   1812
Vassar College Art Gallery.   Catalogue 1939 p $.50 NPV-A 1813

----. Centennial catalogue 1961 (in prep) NPV-A   1814
Virginia Museum of Fine Art. The Aldrich Collection--
   paintings and sculpture collected by Mr. and Mrs. Larry
   Aldrich 61 il p $1.50 ViRMu   1815
----. The collection of paintings of the Virginia Museum 44
   il 1938 p $1. ViRMu   1816
----. T. Catesby Jones Collection--drawings and paintings,
   predominantly French 62 p 22 il p $1. ViRMu   1817
Wadsworth Atheneum. Josef and Anni Albers: Paintings,
   tapestries and woven textiles; introduction by Charles E.
   Buckley 11 p 5 il 1953 p $.35 CtHWA   1818
Walter Art Center. John and Dorothy Rood Collection p
   $.35 MnMW   1819
----. Lowenthal Collection p $.50 MnMW   1820
----. Neuberger Collection p $.50 MnMW   1821
----. Zacks Collection p $1. MnMW   1822
Walters Art Gallery. Masterpieces in the Walters Art Gal-
   lery, a picture book (in prep) MdBWA   1823
The Washington County Museum of Fine Arts. Catalogue p
   $.10 MdHagM   1824
Wellesley College. Department of Art. McAndrew, John,
   and Curtis Shell. European and American sculpture,
   paintings and drawings at Wellesley College 1958 p $1.50
   MWelC-A   1825
Yale University Art Gallery. A guide to the collections p
   $.25 CtY-A   1826
----. Hamilton, George Heard, ed. Collection of the So-
   ciete Anonyme, a definitive catalogue of the collection at
   Yale given in 1941 by Katherine S. Dreier and Marcel Duchamp il 1950 $10; p $7.50 CtY-A   1827

--Art Exhibitions, Private Collections, etc.

Alexis Paul Arapoff Memorial Exhibition catalog; foreword by
   Constantin A. Pertzoff, biographical notes and catalogue by
   Catherine Green Arapoff 54 p 13 il (cover c) 1952 p $1.50
   MBMu (op)   1828
Alvin T. Fuller Memorial Exhibition 40 il (1 c) 1959 p $2.25
   MBMu   1829
Allied Artist of America. Annual Exhibition catalog (National
   Academy Galleries, New York). List of exhibits--oil
   painting, water color, sculpture il 48th annual, 1961 $.50
   NNAAA   1830
The art collection of Billy Pearson p $.50 COA   1831
Art exhibition by merchant seamen of the United Nations,
   sponsored by the United Seamen's Service and War Shipping
   Administration. Annual--1943, 1946 $.10 ea DCGA   1832

Art through fifty centuries. p $1. MWM   1833
Barrodas, Jose Peziz de.   80 masterpieces from the Gold
  Museum; foreword by Henry Francis Taylor 99 p 79 il
  (4 c) 1954 p $1.50 NNMM   1834
Batz, Georges de.   Chinese ceramics and European drawings
  34 p 145 pl 1953 p $4. MBMu   1835
Behold the Child--Exhibition catalog of paintings and sculp-
  ture of children from the Renaissance to Matisse 20 p 9
  il 1950 p $.50 MdBMA   1836
Byrnes, James E.   Masterpieces of art: Catalogue of the
  W.R. Valentiner Memorial Exhibition, including two unpublished manuscripts by Dr. Valentiner, and a bibliogra-
  phy of his writings 324 p 200 il $3.75 NcRMA   1837
Carl Gaertner Memorial Exhibition, selected examples from
  exhibition in Museum 1953 37 il p $.25 OClMA   1838
Carnegie Institute.   1958 retrospective exhibition of paintings
  from previous internationals p $1. PPiCIA   1839
The Crystal Palace, by Henry-Russell Hitchcock 39 p 2 pl
  2nd ed 1952 p $.25 MNS-MA   1840
The Dial, and the Dial Collections p $1.75 MWM   1841
Exhibition of paintings, prints and models lent by the President of the United States (Franklin D. Roosevelt) 16 p
  1936 p $1. DCGA   1842
The first Hartford Festival, program with notes 31 p 17 il
  1936 p $1. CtHWA   1843
4000 years of modern art 32 p il 1953 p $.15 MdBWA 1844
Great collector: Dr. William S. Disbrow 54 p il 1925 p
  $.35 NjNM   1845
Guggenheim International Award 1958, checklist of work of
  116 artists from 27 countries il (1 c) p $1. NNGu 1846
Haddon, A.C.   Evolution in art (BFM v 3, no 4) 9 p 1902 p
  $.50 PU-Mu   1847
In freedom's search, exhibition catalogue 1950 p $.25
  MSMFA   1848
In memory of Katherine S. Dreier, 1877-1952, a memorial
  exhibition of works belonging to Katherine S. Drier 12 il
  1952 p $.50 CtY-A   1849
J. Hall Pleasants--A memorial exhibition; catalogue of ex-
  hibition of early Maryland silver and painting in honor of
  the Maryland historian; foreword by J.G.D. Paul, notes
  by James W. Foster 24 p 5 il 1958 p $.50 MdBWA 1850
Hanna, Leonard C., Jr.   In memoriam 107 il (4 c) 1958 p
  $1. OClMA   1851
Lucas, E. Louise.   Guides to the Harvard Libraries, No. 2
  Fine Arts 1949 p $.50 MH-FA   1852
----.   The Harvard list of books on art 1952 p $2.25 MH-
  FA   1853

Mary and Vincent Price Collection; introduction by Vincent
    Price 19 il p $.50 CLMA   1854
Masterpieces from Detroit private collections (C 14) 16 p 11
    il (2 c) 1949 p $.25 MiDA   1855
Masterpieces from the Cook Collection of Richmond, England
    il 1944 p $.25 OTM   1856
Masterpieces of art from the two World's Fairs 1941 p $.25
    OCA   1857
New York-Paris, exhibition assembled with the Houston Mu-
    seum of Fine Arts 1959 p $.50 TxSaMc   1858
Owned in New Jersey: Paintings and decorative arts from
    New Jersey homes 21 p 1946 p $.15 NjNM (op)   1859
A picture book: Small in size; great in art (PB 3) 24 p 24
    il 1946 p $.25 MiDA   1860
Privately owned, a selection of works of art from collections
    in the Washington area 64 p 59 il 1952 p $1. DCGA 1861
St. Louis Collections, exhibitions of 20th century art 1948 p
    $.50; $.10 post MoSCA   1862
St. Louis Collects, exhibition selected from private collec-
    tions p $1; $.10 post MoSCA   1863
Silsbee, Edward A. An informal talk on architectural and
    art topics 20 p 1880 p $.25 MSaE   1864
Sommer, William. William Sommer Memorial exhibition,
    selected examples from an exhibition in Museum 1950 68
    il p $.50 OClMA   1865
Themes and variations in painting and sculpture--a compara-
    tive exhibition catalog emphasizing artists' approach from
    early Chinese bronzes to the present; foreword by Adelyn
    D. Breeskin, introduction by E.M. Benson, comments by
    Gertrude Rosenthal; bibliography 72 p 42 il 1948 p $1.
    MdBMA   1866
A tribute to Curt Valentin, an exhibition of 20th century art
    selected from St. Louis collections 24 p 19 il 1955 p $.75;
    $.10 post MoSCA   1867
Vanguard 1955 p $.50 MnMW   1868
The Vladimir Golschmann Collection--a catalogue of French
    paintings, drawings, and prints with emphasis on Picasso's
    work; ancient bronzes, African and Oceanic sculpture 23
    p 8 il 1958 p $.50 MdBMA   1869
The Whitney Annual exhibition of contemporary American
    paintings and sculpture, watercolors and drawings. Annu-
    al-- il $.50 NNW   1870
Wisconsin Salon of Art. Annual -- p WU-G   1871
Works of art collected and painted by James N. Rosenberg
    1950 p $.20 MH-FA   1872

--Art Exhibitions, Private Collections--Specific Subjects

and Themes

Animal kingdom, illustrated catalogue of an exhibition of
    manuscript illuminations, book illustrations, drawings,
    cylinder seals, and bindings 70 p front and 12 pl 1930 p
    $1. NNPM   1873
Art in Asia and the West; introduction by Grace L. McCann
    Morley 38 p 75 il 1957 p $2. CSfMA   1874
Botanical books, prints, and drawings from the collection of
    Mrs. Roy Arthur Hunt, catalog 1952 p $1. PPiCIA   1875
Children in art 20 p il 1948 p $.25 OTM   1876
East-West (B, Division of Art and Archaeology 19) 42 p pl
    1952 p $.75 CaOTRM   1877
Harlequin and the arts, handbook for a special exhibition re-
    lating to Commedia dell' Arte and its influence on the arts
    20 p 22 il $.50 CoDA   1878
Laufer, Berthold.   The giraffe in history and art (A-PS 27)
    100 p 32 il 1928 p $.60 ICF   1879
Life of Christ (PC 7) 43 p 20 il (4 c) 1951 p $1. MiDA
                                                                 1880
The life of Christ: A loan exhibition of works of art illus-
    trating episodes in the life of Christ; introduction by
    Esther I Seaver   36 p 16 il 1948 p $.75 CtHWA   1881
Man at Work--the history of occupations illustrated through
    paintings and sculpture 19 p 21 il $.25 CoDA   1882
Masterpieces of religious art 62 p il 1954 p $1. ICA   1883
The medicine man: Medicine in art, a special exhibition in
    honor of the centennial of the Hartford Hospital; foreword
    by Charles C. Cunningham, introduction by A. Hyatt
    Mayor   62 p 18 il 1954 p $1. CtHWA   1884
Mississippi panorama, life and landscape of the Father of
    Waters and its tributary, the Missouri, depicted in paint-
    ings, drawings, prints, photographs, and river boat
    models 228 p 181 il (5 c) p $1.95; rev ed clothbound
    $3.95; $.25 post MoSCA   1885
Nine lives: The cat in history and art (Catalog 10) il p
    $.25 NNCoo   1886
Parker, Helen.   The Christmas story 47 p il 1949 p $.25
    ICA (op)   1887
Richards, Edgar P., and Paul L. Grigaut.   Venice, 1700-
    1800 (C 27) 111 p 98 il 1952 p $1.25 MiDA   1888
Shooting and fishing in art; foreword by George W. Constable
    8 p 6 il 1958 p $.50 MdBMA   1889
Sports and pastimes from the fourteenth through the eight-
    eenth century, illustrated guide to an exhibition 47 p 1946
    p $.25 NNPM   1890
Vail, R.W.G.   Gold fever: A catalogue of the California

gold rush centennial exhibition at the New York Historical
Society, October 19, 1948-December 24, 1949 (repr,
Quarterly, Oct 1949) 28 p 18 il p $1. NHi   1891
Venice, 1700-1800 il p 1952 $1. InIJ   1892
A visit to Rome in 1764 (PB 5) 1956 p $.50 MH-FA   1893
West-East (B, Division of Art and Archaeology 21) 60 p pl
    1953 p $.75 CaOTRM   1894

--Painting, Drawing and Graphic Arts--Catalogs, Guides,
Collections

Avinoff, Andrew. An exhibition of Andrew Avinoff: The
    man, catalog 1953-4 p $1. PPiCIA   1895
Carnegie Institute. International exhibition of contemporary
    painting. Annual-1952- (1958 op) p $1. ea PPiCIA 1896
The cities collect--paintings from the Toledo Museum of Art
    and the Art Gallery of Toronto 34 p il 1948 p $1. OTM
                                                     1897
The collection of John Rewald--loan exhibition of paintings,
    drawings, and prints; introduction by John Rewald 17 il p
    $.50 CLMA (op)   1898
Feininger-Villon. Lyonel Feininger and Jacques Villon p
    $1.25 MBI   1899
Fifteen paintings, 15th anniversary exhibition 1948 p $.25
    MSMFA   1900
Fifty paintings taken from fifty Texas collections 1957 p $.25
    TxSaMc   1901
Fourteen painter-printmakers 20 p 28 il 1956 p $.50 NBB
                                                     1902
From the Collection of Mrs. C. Suydam Cutting: Catalogue
    of an exhibition of paintings, drawings and prints 18 p pl
    1954 p $.75 NjNM   1903
International watercolor exhibition biennial 1939- p $.25 ea
    NBB   1904
Modern paintings. Helen Birch Bartlett memorial 63 p il
    1946 p $.10 ICA   1905
1900-1925, Paintings and prints 1951, work by 60 interna-
    tional artist p $.15 OCA   1906
Oakland Art Museum California Painters' exhibition 1950 p
    $.15 COA   1907
Old and New England, an exhibition of American paintings of
    Colonial and early Republican days together with English
    paintings from the same time il 1945 p $.50 RPD-M
                                                     1908
Onslow-Ford, Gordon. Toward a new subject in painting--
    Max Ernst, Joan Miro, Roberto Matta Eschaurren, Ives
    Tanguy, and Jean Varda 56 p 41 il 1948 p $2. CSfMA 1909

Painters' painters, 16th century to 20th century 67 p 45 il
    1954 p $1. NBuA   1910
Paintings from the Collection of Paul Magriel 2 p 1 il 1957
    p $.10 DCGA   1911
Paintings from Smith Alumnae Collections by Robert D.
    Parks, with a foreword by Herbert Davis 108 p 45 fig
    1959 p $.50 MNS-MA   1912
Paintings from the collections of the Honourable and Mrs.
    Francis Biddle 2 p 1 il 1957 p $.10 DCGA   1913
Paintings from the Stedalije Museum, Amsterdam p $1.50
    WMA   1914
Paintings in Hartford Collections; foreword by Henry Tracy
    Kneeland 26 p front 1936 p $.25 CtHWA   1915
Pictures collected by Yale alumni, 250 paintings and drawings
    from private collections il 1956 $5; p $2.50 CtY-A 1916
Pictures for a picture of Gertrude Stein--a partial reassem-
    bling of Gertrude Stein's collection of modern art, with
    excerpts from her writings (Yale University Press) il
    1951 p $1. CtY-A   1917
Thirty-five paintings p $.75 CLCM   1918
Trends in painting, 17th century to 19th century 64 p 35 il
    1957 p $1.50 NBuA   1919
Trends in watercolors today: Italy, United States (Catalog of
    1957 International Watercolor Exhibition Biennial) 21 p 10
    il p $.25 NBB   1920
Twenty contemporary painters from the Philippe Dotremont
    Collection, Brussels--an illustrated checklist 4 il p $.25
    NNGu   1921
Walker Art Center Biennial of paintings and prints 1949
    (2nd) - 2nd and 3rd $.25 ea; 4th, 1954, $.50; 5th, 1956,
    $.65; 6th, 1958, $.75 MnMW   1922

--Painting, Drawing, and Graphic Arts--Catalogs, Guides,
Collections--Specific Subjects and Themes

Baur, John I.H.   Nature in abstraction 57 il (16 c) p $1.75
    NNW (op)   1923
Bolton, Charles Knowles.   Portraits of the Founders, en-
    gravings and photographs of persons born abroad who came
    to the North American colonies before 1701, with brief
    biographical sketches. v 3. 1926 $6. MBAt   1924
Chase, A. Elizabeth.   Famous paintings for young people
    1951 $3.50 CtY-A   1925
The development of flower painting from the 17th century to
    the present (Art Bul) 32 p 21 il p $.75; $.10 post
    MoSCA   1926
Early American portraits: An exhibition 13 p il 1947 p

$.35 NjNM (op) 1927

Fifty painters of architecture; introduction by Charles C.
Cunningham 28 p 14 il p $.50 CtHWA 1928

Five centuries of marine paintings W.R. Valentiner: Flemish,
Dutch, English, French and Italian sections; Francis W.
Robinson: American sect (C 3) 40 p 32 il p 1942 $.50 MiDA
1929

Flowers: Variations on a theme; introduction by Charles C.
Cunningham 11 p 1953 p $.10 CtHWA 1930

Four centuries of miniature paintings from the collection of
A. Jay Fink Foundation and of A.J. Fink Co--subjects:
residents of Europe and America; introduction by Harry
B. Wehle; foreword by Adelyn D. Breeskin 69 p 77 il
$1.50 MdBMA 1931

Four centuries of portrait miniatures from the Heckett Collection, catalog 1954 p $1. PPiCIA 1932

Hendy, Philip. Tercentenary Exhibition: One hundred Colonial portraits 100 il 1930 p $1. MBMu 1933

Ide, John Jay. The portraits of John Jay (1745-1829) (v 10,
Jones Fund) 69 p 25 il $2.50 NHi 1934

Illusionism and tromp l'oeil, the history of painting which
fools the eye 1949 p $2. CSfPL 1935

McLanathan, Richard B.K. Great Americans from the Revolution to the Civil War: Reproductions of a series of 30
portraits from the Athenaeum Washington to a unique
photograph of Lincoln (PB 1) p $.50 MBMu 1936

Man and his years; exhibition catalog of aged as models and
painters; foreword by Adelyn D. Breeskin, essay by Gertrude Rosenthal 40 p 38 il p $1.25 MdBMA 1937

National Society of the Colonial Dames in the State of Delaware, comp. Portraits in Delaware, 1700-1850--a listing
of 295 portraits owned in Delaware, including 43 now in
the Winterthur Collection, giving subject, size, artist,
owner, and including portraits and biographical notes on
artists $5. DeWint 1938

Nature's bounty and Man's delight: Still life exhibition 12 p
11 il 1958 p $.50 NjNM 1939

Neustatter, Otto. Mice in plague pictures 10 p il p $.20
MdBWA 1940

Off for the holidays: A loan exhibition of holiday travel,
sites, pastimes, sports and pleasures; introduction by
Charles C. Cunningham 16 p 16 il 1955 p $.50 CtHWA
1941

Pictures within pictures; introduction by Charles C. Cunningham 33 p 16 il 1949 p $.75 CtHWA 1942

Portrait miniatures, Edward B. Greene Collection in Museum
91 il (12 c) 1951 p $1. OClMA 1943

Richmond portraits in an exhibition of Makers of Richmond,
    1737-1860 286 p 156 il 1949 $6. ViRVM   1944
Scenes from everyday life, 16th-18th century paintings 1 il
    1956 p $.35 NSyE   1945
Scenes from the life of Jesus. A picture book arranged by
    Albert Ten Eyck Gardner 40 p 34 il 1944 p $1. NNMM
                                                             1946

Still life and flower paintings, exhibition catalog from the
    17th to 20th centuries; foreword by Adelyn D. Breeskin
    32 p 14 il 1945 p $.15 MdBMA   1947
Still life painting since 1470 1956 p $1. OCA; $1.25 WMA
                                                             1948

--Drawings and Graphic Arts--Catalogs, Guides, Collections

The Albert P. Strietmann Collection of color lithographs
    1954 p $.25 OCA   1949
Art of lithography, catalog 61 il 1949 p $.50 OClMA   1950
Contemporary drawings from twelve countries: 1945-1952
    48 p 39 il p $.25 ICA   1951
Cooper Union Museum. Collection of engravings and etch-
    ings formed by the late George Campbell Cooper and pre-
    sented by him to the Cooper Union Museum, catalogue (C
    1) p $.15 NNCoo   1952
----. Engravings and etchings presented by George A.
    Hearn to the Cooper Union Museum, catalog (C 2) p $.10
    NNCoo   1953
----. Etchings and lithographs presented by Samuel P.
    Avery to the Cooper Union Museum, catalog (C 3) 3 p
    $.10 NNCoo   1954
----. An introduction to the collection of drawings (MC v 2,
    no 4) 4 il p $.15 NNCoo   1955
Drawings from the Collection of Curtis O. Baer 1958 p
    $1.50 MH-FA   1956
Exhibition of prints of the 15th, 16th, 17th, and 18th centu-
    ries from the collection of Herbert Greer French 1941 p
    $.75 OCA   1957
Handbook on drawings of the masters 66 il p $.50 CSC 1958
International Biennial of contemporary color lithography.
    Annual, 1950- p $.50 ea OCA   1959
The Laura P. Hall Memorial Collection of prints and draw-
    ings 32 p 1947 p $.75 NjP-A   1960
National Serigraph Society International Exhibition. Annual-,
    19th, 1958; 20th, 1959 il p NNNSer   1961
150 years of lithography 1947 p $.25 OCA   1962
Prints, 1400-1800. Loan exhibition sponsored by Minne-
    apolis Institute of Art, Art Institute of Chicago, and

Cleveland Museum of Art, 1956-1957 49 il p $1.75
CClMA   1963
Prints and drawings from the Yale Collections, 1400-1900,
Twentieth Century, Americana, Japanese Prints 14 loose
il 1957 p $1.50 CtY-A   1964
Rosenwald Collection, an exhibition of recent acquisitions,
with foreword by Rosenwald, and descriptive text by
Elizabeth Mongan 126 p 92 il 1950 p $2. DSI-GA   1965
A selection from the First International Exhibition of Prints,
assembled by the Modern Gallery, Ljubljana, Yugoslavia
1956 p $.25 OCA   1966
Seventy master drawings 1948 p $.25 MH-FA   1967
Twentieth century biblical and religious prints, Collection of
Mr. and Mrs. Ross W. Sloniker, 1954 p $.25; Pt. 2. p
$.25 OCA   1968
Twentieth century graphic art: The Ernest Steefel Collec-
tion; foreword by Andrew Carnduff Ritchie 32 il (cover c)
1959 p $1. CtY-A   1969
Vincent Price collects drawings p $.50 COA   1970
Wick, Peter A. Modern prints: 32 reproductions of con-
temporary works (PB 4) c p $.50 MBMu   1971
Zigrosser, Carl. Ars medica, a collection of medical
prints presented to the Museum of Smith, Kline and French
48 p 14 il 1955 p $.50 PPPM   1972

--Photography

Hartford International Exhibition of Photography. Annual-
(1949-1951, 1953-1954) p $.25 ea CtHWA   1973
International Salon of Photographic Art. 2nd, 1950 (B v 3,
no 2) p $.50 DCGA   1974
Leonard, Harold, ed. The film index--The film as art 723
p 44 pl $10. NNMMA   1975

--Sculpture

Brookgreen Gardens. History p $.10 ScGB   1976
----. Map of Museum of Small Sculpture p $.05 ScGB 1977
----. Verses in the Gardens p $.10 ScGB   1978
Buckley, Charles E. Alexander Calder (mobiles) and Naum
Gabo (kinetic constructions and constructions in space) 27
p 17 il 1953 p $.75 CtHWA   1979
Modern sculpture (PB 6) 44 p 18 il 1949 p $.50 MiDA 1980
Outdoor sculpture il 1950 p $.50 NNNSS   1981
Proske, Beatrice Gilman. Catalogue sculpture (13th to 15th
centuries) in the collection 269 p 67 il 1932 $1. NNH
                                                      1982

----. Catalogue sculpture (16th to 18th centuries) in the
collection 260 p 168 il 1930 $1. NNH   1983
Sculpture festival il 1940 p $.40 NNNSS   1984
Sculpture in our time: Collected by Joseph H. Hirshborn
(C 36) 96 p 74 il 1959 p $1.50 MiDA   1985
Sculptures and drawings from seven sculptors, an illustrated
checklist of sculptures by: Chillada, Hajdu, Lakakis,
Etienne-Martin, Paolozzi, Penalba, Tsuji 7 il p $.25
NNGu   1986
Seymour, Charles. Masterpieces of sculpture from the Na-
tional Gallery of Art 142 il 1949 $5.95 DSI-GA   1987
Small sculptures in bronze. A picture book; introduction by
Angela Bowlin and Beatrice Farwell 32 p 60 il 1950 p
$.50 NNMM   1988

--Sculpture--Masks

Masks, 32 pages of illustrations with commentary (B v 13, no
1) 1947 p $.50 PU-Mu   1989
Masks: The faces of man 80 p 250 pl p $2. CaOTRM 1990
Wissler, Clark. Masks (SG 96) 32 p 64 il (1 c) p $.45;
$.10 post NNM   1991

--Decorative Arts

American and European decorative arts 39 p il 1951 p $1.
ICA   1992
Color--all phases of color, as influence in business world,
medicine il p $.50 CoDA   1993
Craftsmanship, catalogue p $.96 CLCM   1994
Culin, S. The origin of ornament (BFM v 2, no 4) 8 p
1900 p $.50 PU-Mu   1995
Design for Christmas. Annual- (1951, 1953, 1955-6) p $.25
ea MBI   1996
Design in industry p $.35 MBI   1997
Edward B. Aldrich Collection: Furniture, ceramics, and
glass il 1958 p $.35 RPD-M   1998
An exhibition of contemporary crafts; foreword by Belle Boas
32 p 13 il 1944 p $1. MdBMA   1999
Folkwandering art, catalogue 1961 (in press) MdBWA   2000
For modern living (C 16) 120 p 140 il 1949 p $1. MiDA
2001
International exhibition of contemporary glass and rugs; in-
troduction by Charles R. Richards (Published by American
Federation of Arts) 125 p 51 il 1930 p $.50 MdBMA 2002
Lustig, Alvin. Collected writings on design $4.50 CtY-A
2003

Modern design: A survey at the Newark Museum (The Museum, ns, v 4, no 1-2, Winter & Spring 1952) p $.75 NjNM   2004
Structure--The human body, nature, ancient and modern construction p $.50 CoDA   2005
Useful objects today $2.95 MBI   2006
Watkins, C. Law. The language of design 176 p 146 pl 43 il $7.50 DPG   2007

--Gems

Gems (The Museum, ns, v 7, no 2, Spring 1955) p $.50 NjNM (op)   2008
Gems and precious stones (Mimeo Ser no 26) p $.10 TxAuM
2009
Kris, Ernst. Catalogue of postclassical cameos in the Milton Weil Collection 49 p 123 il 40 pl 1932 p $.50 NNMM
2010
Slawson, et al. Opals 16 p il (cov c) p $.40 MiBloC   2011
Vermeule, C.C. Cameo and intaglio, engraved gems from the Sommerville Collection 35 p 2 il 1956 $.25 PU-Mu
2012

--Ceramics

Ceramic International exhibition catalogue, 19th, 1956 40 p 33 il p $.75; 20th, 1958 41 p 32 il p $1. NSyE   2013
Sykes, Edith. Ceramics (EP 8) NJPatM   2014
European and American ceramics (The Museum, ns, v 4, no 4, Fall 1952) p $.50 NjNM   2015
Glossary of ceramics terms 13 p 1952 p $.35 NjNM   2016
An introduction to ceramics: Catalogue of an exhibition 29 p 1953 p $.25 NjNM   2017

--Glass

Ancient glass in the Eugene Schaefer Collection (The Museum, ns, v 3, no 1, Winter 1951) p $.50 NjNM   2018
Art in crystal: A short history of the Libbey Glass Company 8 p 9 il 1951 p $.25 OTM   2019
European and American glass in the Newark Museum's collections (The Museum, ns, v 7, no 3-4, Summer & Fall 1955) p $.75 NjNM   2020
Glass, 1959; catalog of a special summer exhibition of 292 objects from glass makers and designers from 21 countries 329 p 292 il $3; $.35 post NCorniC-M   2021
Glass from the ancient world; special summer exhibition

catalogue of Ray W. Smith Collection 298 p 455 il 1957
p $3; $.20 post NCorniC-M   2022
Handbook of glass; exhibition handbook: "Glass through
time;" essay on glass making 28 p 12 il 2 map 1 chart
1933 p $.75 MdBMA   2023
McKearin, Helen. American historical flasks; describing
315 objects from the George S. McKearin Collection 70
p 96 il (92 drg) 1953 p $1. NCorniC-M   2024
Strauss, Jerome. Glass drinking vessels; exhibition catalogue of collections of Jerome Strauss and Ruth Bryan
Strauss Memorial Foundation; descriptions of 361 objects
142 p 70 il (3 c) 1955 p $1. NCorniC-M   2025
2500 Degrees F: The art and technique of modern glass (C
14) p $.15 NNCoo   2026

--Textiles

Art of the weaver 24 p il 1954 p $.50 CLCM   2027
Bellinger, Louisa. Craft habits. Pt. 1. Loom types sug-
gested by weaving details; Pt. 2. Spinning and fibers in
warp yarns (Workshop notes no 19, 20) p $1.25 ea DTM
                                                       2028
Brett, K. Bouquets in textiles, an introduction to the tex-
tile arts 18 p pl p $.75 CaOTRM   2029
Children at the textile show, 1916 16 p il p $.25 NjNM (op)
                                                       2030
Comparisons in lace design (MC v 1, no 11) il p $.15
NNCoo   2031
Cooper Union Museum. Some observations on the textile de-
signs in the Museum (MC v 2, no 8) il p $.25 NNCoo
                                                       2032
----. Trimmings in the Museum's collection: Fringes,
tassels, gimps and galloons (MC v 1, no 9) il p $.15
NNCoo   2033
Crawford, M.D.C. 5000 years of fibers and fabrics; hand-
book of an exhibition 34 p 8 il p $.35 NBB   2034
Development of the modern in textile design p $.25 NNSM
                                                       2035
Emery, Irene. Notes on some of the basic requirements for
a terminology of ancient and primitive fabrics (Workshop
notes no 11) p $1.25 DTM   2036
----. The primary structure of fabrics: An illustrated
classification (in prep) DTM   2037
Greene, Francina S. Cleaning and mounting procedures for
wool textiles (Workshop notes no 1) p $1.25 DTM   2038
Hispanic Society of America Museum. May, Florence Lewis.
Catalogue of laces and embroideries in the collection 147

p 120 il 1936 $1. NNH   2039
----. Modern bobbin lace in the collection, with compara-
tive material 24 p 37 il $.05 NNH   2040
History of silk and sericulture p $.25 NNSM   2041
Howell, C.-J. Warp and woof (B v 14, no 3) 24 p 16 il
1949 p $.50 PU-Mu   2042
The human story in needlework 8 il p $.50 ViRMu   2043
Hunter, Nancy E. Rug analysis: Discussion of method
(Workshop notes no 7) p $1.25 DTM   2044
McMahon, Margaret M. Jacquard weaving (EP 23) NJPatM
                                                          2045
The lace with the delicate air 18 p 18 il 1956 p $.50 NBB
                                                          2046
Macdonald, Dorothy K. Fibres, spindles and spinning-
wheels, an introductory history of spinning from earliest
times 49 p il p $.50 CaOTRM   2047
Myers, George Hewitt. Rugs: Preservation, display and
storage (Workshop notes no 5) p $1.25 DTM   2048
Notes on floor coverings: 950 B.C. to 1930 A.D., a read-
ing list 19 p 1930 p $.10 NjNM (op)   2049
Stitches in time: Embroidery and needlework technique (C
13) p $.10 NNCoo   2050
Textile Museum. Preparation Department. Principles and
practical cleaning for old and fragile textiles (Workshop
notes no 14) p $1.25 DTM   2051
Textiles, from the Hobart and Edward Small Moore Memorial
Collection (Picture Book 2) 43 il p $.50 CtY-A   2052
Touceda, Elena. Procedures for cleaning cotton textiles
(Workshop notes no 4) p $1.25 DTM   2053
Two hundred years of textile designs p $.25 NNSM   2054
Two thousand years of silk weaving--a survey of silk weaving
from 296 B.C. to 1860 A.D.; selected from an exhibition
in the Museum 63 p 87 il (1 c) p 1944 $1.56 OClMA
                                                          2055
Weaving techniques p $.25 CtY-A   2056
Weibel, Adele C. Two thousand years of silk weaving; use-
ful textbook of history of silk weaving, 296 B.C. to 1850
A.D. (C 5) 150 p 87 il 1944 $2.50 MiDA   2057
Why textiles (MC v 2, no 7) il p $.15 NNCoo   2058

--Leather

Leather in the decorative arts (C 9) il p $.20 NNCoo 2059
Nothing takes the place of leather 32 p il 1926 p $.25
NjNM   2060

--Tapestry

Tapestries bulletin (B v 9, no 2) 1957 p $.50 DCGA   2061
Wrought with the needle (The Museum, ns, v 10, no 2,
    Spring 1958) p $.75 NjNM (op)   2062
2000 years of tapestry weaving, a loan exhibition; foreword
    by Adelyn D. Breeskin and Charles C. Cunningham; in-
    troduction by Adele Coulin Weibel 86 p 50 il 1952 p $1.50
    CtHWA   2063

--Costume and Adornment   See also Theatre Arts

No entry   2064
The costume collection in the Wadsworth Atheneum; intro-
    duction by Florence Paull Berger 129 il 1947 p $.25
    CtHWA   2065
Costumes from the Elizabeth Day McCormick Collection 16 p
    15 il p $.20 MBMu   2066
Niehoff, Arthur. For beauty's sake (Primitive head orna-
    mentation) (PP, Lore Leaves no 3; repr, Lore) 14 il p
    $.15 WMMMu   2067
Shapiro, Harry L. From the neck up (SG 131; repr, Natur-
    al History) 12 p 31 il p $.50; $.10 post NNM   2068
Taylor, Emily. The glass of fashion 13 p il 1958 p $.30
    MdBWA   2069
What's a hat (The Museum, ns, v 8, no 1, Winter 1956) p
    $.50 NjNM   2070

--Metal Work

All that glistens: Thirty centuries of golden deception (C 4)
    il p $.25 NNCoo   2071
Chicago Natural History Museum. Tarbell, F.B. Catalogue
    of bronzes, etc., in the Field Museum of Natural History
    (FA 7:3) 54 p 300 il 1909 $3. ICF   2072
European and American silver (The Museum, ns v 5, no 3-
    4, Summer & Fall 1953) p $.75 NjNM   2073
An introduction to silver: Catalogue of an exhibition 59 p
    pl 1954 p $.75 NjNM   2074
Milliken, William M. Art of the goldsmith p $.25 OClMA
                                                      2075
Nichols, Henry W. Restoration of ancient bronzes and cure
    of malignant patina, with foreword by Berthold Laufer
    (FT 3) 52 p 11 il 1930 p $.50 ICF   2076

--Arms and Armor

Cleveland Museum of Art. Severance Collection of Arms and
    Armor; including a short history of arms and armor, and

7 pages of armorers' marks 33 il p $.75 OClMA   2077
Detroit Institute of Arts. Robinson, Francis W. Arms and
    armor from the William Randolph Hearst Collection of
    Arms and Armor in the Detroit Institute of Arts (PB 8)
    36 p 34 il (1 c) 1954 p $.75 MiDA   2078
Historical armor. A Picture Book; introduction by Stephen
    V. Granscay 32 p 25 il rev ed 1951 p $.50 NNMM   2079
Medieval and Renaissance arms and armor from the Metro-
    politan Museum of Art 1953 p $1.20 CLCM; $1. CSfPL,
    MdHagM; $2. PPiCIA   2080
Morse, Edward S. Additional notes on arrow release 48 p
    5 pl 43 text figs 1922 $1. MSaP   2081
New Mexico Museum. School of American Research. Curtis,
    F.S., Jr. Catalog of the Borrowdale Collection of Weap-
    ons (P ns 3) 26 p 1921 p $.25 NmSM-S   2082
St. Louis City Art Museum. Arms and armor; a guide to
    the collection 56 p 60 il p $.75; $.10 post MoSCA   2083

--Clocks and Watches

Carnegie Museum. Stewart, Douglas, et al. Catalog of the
    collection of watches belonging to H.J. Heinz in the Car-
    negie Museum (A v 12, no 1, p 1-32) 33 pl $.50; p $.30
    PPiCM   2084
Henry P. Strause Collection of Clocks 46 il p $.50 ViRMu
                                                        2085
Holtz, Frederick C., and Frances S. Ridgley. Clocks from
    the Hunter Collection (SP v 9) 64 p 14 pl 1957 p $2. ISM
                                                        2086
Time and man--An exhibition of horological devices and re-
    lated material from the sixteenth century through the nine-
    teenth century; prints of the same period, works by con-
    temporary artists 1952 p $1. CSfPL   2087

--Coins, Medals, etc.

Ancient coins (PB 4) 1956 p $.75 MH-FA   2088
Index to Emilio Collection of military buttons 22 p 1880 p
    $.25 MSaE   2089
Mosher, Stuart. Story of money as told by the Knox Collec-
    tion (B 17:2) p $1.15 NBuM   2090
Outerbridge, A.E., Jr. Curiosities of American coinage
    (BFM v 1, no 4) 20 p 2 pl 1898 p $.50 PU-Mu   2091

--Toys, Dolls, Ships, etc.

Colleen Moore's doll house p $.50 ICS   2092

Make-believe and whimsey: European and American dolls in
the collection (The Museum, ns, v 7, no 1.   Winter
1955) p $.50 NjNM   2093
Paper dolls and other cut-out toys 28 p il 1932 p $.75
NjNM   2094
Sentimental valentines: A showing...from the collection of
Lillian Newton Stone 12 p front 1931 p $.10 NjNM   2095

--Book Arts

The art of fine printing and its influence upon the Bible in
print, an historical introduction 51 p 1956 p $.50 CaOTRM
                                                           2096
Boyce, G.K.   Modern literary manuscripts in the Morgan Library (repr, from PMLA, v 17, February 1952) 33 p
$.25 NNPM   2097
Calligraphy: The golden age and its modern revival 50 p
60 pl 1958 $2.50 OrPA   2098
Guild of Book Workers Exhibition, 1959:   Hand bookbinding,
protective cases, restoration calligraphy, illumination,
hand decorated papers il p $1. NNAIG   2099
History of bookbinding, 525-1950 A.D.   275 p 106 pl 1957
$10.50; p $7. MdBWA   2100
Illuminated manuscripts and incunabula p $.35 ViRMu   2101
International book illustration, checklist, illustrations in-
serted, 1935-1945 1945 p $.50 NNAIG   2102
List of books printed before 1601 in the Library--Brief line-
listing, with references to detailed bibliographical descriptions, including over 250 incunabula and 2500 books of
Hispanic provenance or interest, many having been printed
in Portugal, Mexico, Peru, Italy, and the Netherlands.
Offset reissue, with additions to date 305 p front (facsim)
1955 $1.50 NNH   2103
Livengood, W.W.   Our textbooks, yesterday and today; foreword by Arthur Thompson 1953 p $.50 NNAIG   2104
Manuscripts from the William S. Glazier Collection; an illustrated catalogue compiled by John Plummer 34 p 37 pl
(6 c) 1959 p $3. NNPM   2105
Penney, Clara Louise.   List of books printed 1601-1700 in
the Library--about 5800 entries, including the Cervantes
Collection, and a check list of Hispanic printing sites and
printers (1468?-1700) 972 p front 1938 $2. NNH   2106
Religious symbolism in illuminated manuscripts.   A picture
book issued as a handbook to an exhibition 16 p 16 pl
1940 p $.25 NNPM   2107
Sanborn, Herbert W.   Modern art influences on printing design (published by Washington, D.C. Chapter AIGA) 1956

p (free with orders on request) NNAIG   2108
Two thousand years of science; description and checklist of
   an exhibition 19 p 1952 p $.25 NNPM   2109
The world econompassed; catalogue of an exhibition of the
   history of maps 140 p 60 pl 1952 p $4.75 MdBWA   2110

--Gardens

Gardens as illustrated in prints. A picture book; introduction by Margaret Harrington Daniels 32 p 30 il 2nd ed
   1949 p $.50 NNMM   2111
Nelson, Boris Erich. Flower prints and garden books from
   the 16th to the early 19th centuries 15 p 1 il 1942 p $.25
   NjTM   2112

--Interior Decoration

Thorne, Narcissa. Miniature rooms: Architectural models
   32 p il 1942 $.25 NjNM   2113
Some gilt bronze furniture mounts in the Museum (MC v 2,
   no 2) il p $.15 NNCoo   2114

--Art, American

Morley, Sylvanus G., et al. The Morley Collection of Spanish Colonial Ecclesiastical art (P ns 39) 36 p il 1945 p
   $.50 NmSM-S   2115

--Art, Canadian

Arts of French Canada, 1613-1870, loan exhibition in Museum
   1946 p $.25 OClMA   2116
Aspects of contemporary painting in Canada, 1942 63 p 37 il
   p $1.50 MAnP-A   2117
Barbeau, Marius. Painters of Quebec 40 p il $1. CaOTAG
                                                    2118
Brett, K.B. Ontario handwoven textiles; an introduction to
   handweaving in Ontario in the nineteenth century 18 p 10
   pl p $1. CaOTRM   2119
Canada. Department of Citizenship and Immigration. Arts
   in Canada (Queen's Printer) p $.75 CaOONG; CaOTAG
                                                    2120
Canadian abstract painters (Smithsonian Traveling Exhibition
   Catalog) il 1956 p DSI-FA   2121
Canadian art il 1944 p $.25 CtY-A   2122
Canadian painters (Phaidon Edition) 91 pl (4 c) 1945 p $6.
   CaOONG   2123

Canadian painting 1950 p $.50 CaOONG   2124
Canadian portraits of the 18th century p $.50 CaOONG 2125
Canadian water colours and graphics today p $.25 CaOONG
                                                       2126
Comfort, Charles. The artist at war $4.95 CaOTAG   2127
Early Canadian glass--The Edith Choun Pierce and Gerald
    Stevens Collection il p $.50 CaOTRM   2128
Fitzgerald Memorial Exhibition 1958 p $1. CaOONG   2129
Forty years of Canadian painting from Tom Thomson and the
    Group of Seven to the present day 36 p 15 il 1949 p $.50
    MBMu   2130
Gowans, Allan. Looking at architecture in Canada $7.95
    CaOTAG   2131
MacDonald, Thoreau. The group of seven 40 p il p $1.
    CaOTAG   2132
Painting in Canada, a historical survey 1946 p $1.50 NAlAI
                                                       2133
Ross, Malcolm. The arts in Canada $10. CaOTAG   2134
Spendlove, F. St. George. The face of early Canada $8.50
    CaOTAG   2135
----. The furniture of French Canada p $.50 CaOTRM2136

--Art, Canadian--Individual Artists

Beatty, J.W. Hoover, Dorothy. J.W. Beatty 40 p il $1.25
    CaOTAG   2137
Cockburn, James Pattison. Spendlove, F. St. George. The
    Canadian watercolors of James Pattison Cockburn (1779-
    1847) p $.25 CaOTRM   2138
Gagnon, Clarence A. Robson, Albert H. Clarence A. Gag-
    non 40 p il $1.25 CaOTAG   2139
Harris, Lawren. Lawren Harris, paintings, 1910-1948 p
    $.50 CaOONG   2140
Jackson, A.Y. A painter's country, the autobiography $5.
    CaOTAG   2141
----. A.Y. Jackson, paintings, 1902-1953 p $.50 CaOONG
                                                       2142
----. Jackson exhibition catalogue p $.25 CaOTAG   2143
Jefferys, C.W. Colgate, William. C.W. Jefferys 40 p il
    $1. CaOTAG   2144
Julien, Henri. Barbeau, Marius. Henri Julien 40 p il p $1.
    CaOTAG   2145
Krieghoff, Cornelius. Robson, Albert H. Cornelius Krieg-
    hoff 40 p il p $1. CaOTAG   2146
Lismer, Arthur. Arthur Lismer, paintings, 1913-1949 p
    $.50 CaOONG   2147
MacDonald, J.E.H. Robson, Albert H. J.E.H. MacDonald

40 p il $1.25 CaOTAG   2148
Milne, David.   David Milne 1955 p $1. CaOONG   2149
Morrice, J.W.   Buchanan, Donald W.   J.W. Morrice 40 p
    il p $1. CaOTAG   2150
Phillips, Walter J.   Scott, Duncan Campbell.   Walter J.
    Phillips 40 p il $1.25 CaOTAG   2151
Robinson, A.H.   Lee, Thomas R.   A.H. Robinson 40 p il p
    $1. CaOTAG   2152
Russell, Edward John.   Ryder, Huia.   Edward John Russell,
    marine artist, with a catalogue of the artist's marine
    paintings compiled by George McBeath (SP 6) 1953 $.50
    CaNBSM   2153
Spickett and Caiserman p $.10 CaOONG   2154
Varley, F.H.   F.H. Varley, paintings, 1915-1954 p $.50
    CaOONG   2155
----.   Varley exhibition catalogue p $.25 CaOTAG   2156
Wolfe, James.   Webster, J.C.   A study of the portraiture
    of James Wolfe (G 14; repr, Trans of the Royal Society
    of Canada) 1925 $1. CaNBSM   2157

--Art, United States

Addison Gallery of American Art.   Handbook 133 p 122 il p
    $1.50 MAnP-A   2158
American art: Four exhibitions in the American Pavilion at
    the Brussels World's Fair.   Trilingual text: English,
    French, Dutch il 1958 p $1.25 CtY-A   2159
American art in San Antonio collections 1958 p $.25 TxSaMc
                                                                       2160
American folk art, a collection of paintings presented in 1958
    by Edward Duff Balken 16 p 17 il $.50 NjP-A   2161
American painting and sculpture: Catalogue of an exhibition
    ...from the Museum's collection, with an introduction by
    Holger Cahill 191 p il 1944 p $1.25 NjNM   2162
American paintings from the collection of Stephen C. Clark
    15 p 15 il p $.25 MAnP-A   2163
American primitive paintings from the collection of Edgar
    William and Bernice Chrysler Garbisch, with foreword by
    David E. Finley and introduction by John Walker.   Pt. 1.
    120 p 100 il 1954 p $1.25; Pt. 2. with foreword by John
    Walker, and introduction by William Campbell 120 p 100
    il 1957 p $1.25 DSI-GA   2164
American primitive painting from the collection of the Chi-
    cago Historical Society 24 p il p $.50 ICHi   2165
American Processional, 1492-1900 270 p 208 il (1 c) 1950
    p $5.   DCGA (op)   2166
Art in New England, catalogues of five exhibitions held

throughout New England in connection with the New York
World's Fair 1939 p $3.   CtY-A   2167
Art in New England: Paintings, drawings, and prints from
   private collections in New England 134 p 191 il 1939 p $1.
   MBMu   2168
Art of the Americas, selected examples from an exhibition in
   Museum, 1945-1946 46 il (5 c) p $.75 OClMA   2169
Barker, Virgil.   A critical introduction to American paintings
   $.60 NNW   2170
Brooklyn Bridge--75th anniversary exhibition 44 p 10 il p
   $.25 NBB   2171
The coast and the sea, a survey of American marine painting
   36 p 11 il 1948 p $.50 NBB   2172
Collection in progress, selections from the Lawrence and
   Barbara Fleischman Collection of American Art (C 32) 48
   p 52 il (2 c) 1955 p $2.50 MiDA   2173
Commager, Henry Steele.   The artist in American history
   (B v 4, no 2) 1951 p $.50 DCGA   2174
----, Edgar P. Richardson, and Lloyd Goodrich.   Art and
   history in America, 3 Corcoran Gallery of Art Bulletins,
   1952 $1. DCGA (op)   2175
Corcoran Gallery of Art.   American paintings in the Corcor-
   an Gallery 96 p 26 il 1947 p $.50 DCGA   2176
Country style 43 p 27 il 1956 p $.75 NBB   2177
Dana, John Cotton.   American art: How it can be made to
   flourish 32 p 1929 p $1. NjNM   2178
De Gustibus: An exhibition of American paintings illustrating
   a century of taste and criticism 23 il 1949 p $1. DCGA
                                                      2179
Descriptive catalogue of the Historical monument of the
   American republic p $.50 MSMFA   2180
Early New Jersey artists, 18th and 19th centuries 30 p il
   1957 p $1.25 NjNM   2181
Expressionism in American painting, a selective exhibition to
   define Expressionism and its origins 64 p 61 il 1952 p $1.
   NBuA   2182
Face of America 56 p 47 il 1957 p $1.50 NBB   2183
From Colony to Nation: An exhibition of American painting,
   silver, and architecture from 1650 to 1812 140 p il 1949
   p $.50 ICA   2184
Gordon, John.   American painting in the Brooklyn Museum
   Collection (PB) 49 p 74 il 1953 p $1. NBB   2185
King, Edward S., and Marvin C. Ross.   Catalogue of the
   American works of art in the Walters Art Gallery, includ-
   ing French medals made for America 63 p 2 pl 1956 p
   $1.75 MdBWA   2186
Little, Nina Fletcher.   Itinerant painting in America, 1750-

1850 (repr, New York History, April 1949)16 p il p $.25
NCooHi   2187
Los Angeles County Museum.   American painting, Karolik
Collection p $1.20 CLCM   2188
McLanathan, Richard B.K.   American marine painting, from
John Singleton Copley to the present day (PB 7) c p $.50
MBMu   2189
Main currents in the development of American painting 54 il
p $1. ViRMu   2190
National Gallery of Art.   American painting in the National
Gallery of Art (NGA Book 1) 1959 p $.25 DSI-GA   2191
New England miniatures 56 il (11 c) 1957 p $1.50 MBMu
                                                                2192
Osgood, Samuel.   Thomas Crawford and art in America 40
p 1875 p $.60 NHi   2193
A picture book of an exhibition of American birds and their
painters and sculptors (C 7) 24 p 20 il 1945 p$.25 MiDA
                                                                2194
Portraits of Americans (B v 6, no 1) 1953 p $.50 DCGA
                                                                2195
Portraits of Americans by Americans, exhibition of the National Association of portrait painters, April 1-May 5,
1945 129 p 80 il $1; p $.50 NHi   2196
The Presidents and their wives, from Washington to Eisen-
hower 53 p il p $.35 MBMu   2197
Reality and fantasy p $.75 MnMW   2198
Rediscovered artists of Upstate New York, paintins gathered
by five Upstate New York museums (Published: Cooperstown) il 1958 $2. NSyE   2199
Rediscoveries in American painting 1955 p $.25 OCA   2200
Richardson, Edgar Preston.   Art aspects of American Processional (B v 4, no 4) 1951 p $.50 DCGA   2201
----.   Painting in America, the story of 450 years (C 31)
32 p 21 il 1957 p $1. MiDA   2202
Rockefeller (Abby Aldrich) Folk Art Collection.   American
folk art from the Abby Aldrich Rockefeller Folk Art Collection, travelling exhibition catalogue 48 p 15 bw il 8 c pl
$3.95; p $1.50 ViWR   2203
----.   Gallery book, including a brief statement on the Collection and the background of American folk art 16 p 8 c
pl p $.25 ViWR   2204
Shelley, Donald A.   A catalogue of American portraits in
the New York Historical Society 374 p 430 il 1941 $1.50
NHi   2205
Sport in art, presented by Sports Illustrated and the Ameri-
can Federation of Arts 64 p 46 il 1956 p $1. DCGA 2206
Survey of American painting, catalogue 1940 p $1.

PPiCIA   2207
Ten primitives in the James E. Roberts Collection of paint-
    ings p $.10 InIJ   2208
"This is our city" 11 il p $.50 NNW   2209
Three early New England portraits in the Museum's collec-
    tion (The Museum, ns, v 1, no 1, Feb 1949) p $.40
    NjNM   2210
Time in New England $6. MBI   2211
Two hundred and fifty years of painting in Maryland; exhibi-
    tion catalogue of a survey of painting in Maryland from
    Justus E. Kuhn to Thomas C. Corner; foreword by Adelyn
    D. Breeskin, essay by J. Hall Pleasants 78 p 44 il, map
    1945 p $2. MdBMA   2212
Two Indian costumes; with American folk art; Paul Revere,
    silversmith; the architecture of Thomas Tefft (B 28, no
    2, Nov 1940) p $.50 RPD-M   2213
Whitney Museum of American Art. Sara Roby Foundation
    Collection 34 il (4 c) p $1.25 NNW   2214
----. The Whitney Museum and its collection, history, pur-
    pose and activities; catalogue of the collection 8 il p $.75
    NNW   2215
Work in painting the portraits of distinguished contemporary
    Americans for the art gallery of the New York Historical
    Society on the occasion of the 129th anniversary of the
    founding of the Society, Monday, November 20, 1933 26 p
    14 il 1934 p $.25 NHi   2216

--Art, United States--17th and 18th centuries

Early American painting and its European background p $.25
    CtY-A   2217
Early American painting, portraits by outstanding artists in
    America in the 18th and early 19th centuries; introduction
    by Albert Rosenthal 13 p 1931 p $.25 NjTM   2218
Goodrich, Lloyd. Pioneers of modern art in America 34 il
    1946 p $1. NNW   2219
Hudson Valley painting, 1700-1750 1959 $2. NAlAI   2220
Jenkins, Lawrence Waters. A catalogue of the Charles H.
    Taylor Collection of ship portraits in the Peabody Museum
    of Salem, with an appreciation of Charles H. Taylor by
    Stephen W. Phillips 36 p 9 pl 1949 $1. MSaP   2221
Kelby, William. Notes on American artists, 1754-1820 (from
    advertisements in newspapers of the day (v 5, Jones Fund)
    80 p 6 il 1922 $2.50 NHi   2222
Late 18th and early 19th century portraits by Vermont artists
    Horace Bundy, Zedekiah Belknap, Asahel Powers, Aaron
    Dean Fletcher, and by John Brewster, Abraham Tuthill,

John L. Harding, William M. Prior and several unknown
    artists folder 1958 p VtSM   2223
Naval actions in the American Revolution (Published by U.S.
    Naval Institute) (PB) 59 il p $.50 DN-HF   2224
Portraits of George Washington and his associates; catalogue
    68 p 3 il 1932 p $2. DCGA   2225
Portraits of the shipmasters and merchants in the Peabody
    Museum of Salem; introduction by Walter Muir Whitehill
    185 p 32 pl 1939 $5. MSaP   2226
Two early American portraits (B v 1, no 1) 1947 p $.50
    DCGA   2227

--Art, United States--17th and 18th Centuries--Individual
Artists

Copley, John Singleton. Catalogue of a loan exhibition of
    Copley paintings, pastles, miniatures and drawings 34 p 1
    il 1938 p $.25 MBMu   2228
----. Parker, Barbara Neville, and Anne Bolling Wheeler.
    John Singleton Copley: American portraits in oil, pastel
    and miniature, with biographical sketches 284 p 210 il
    1938 p $7.50 MBMu   2229
Earl, Ralph. Sawitsky, William. Ralph Earl, 1751-1801 16
    il p $1. NNW   2230
Feke, Robert. Goodrich, Lloyd. Robert Feke 12 il 1946 p
    $1. NNW   2231
----. Robert Feke 36 p 13 il 1946 p $.50 MBMu   2232
Greenwood, John. Burroughs, Alan. John Greenwood in
    America, 1727-92 87 p 52 il 1943 p $2. MAnP-A   2233
Lechford, Thomas. Note-book, 1638-1641 (TC v 7) 1885
    $5. MWA   2234
Pratt, Matthew. Sawitzky, William. Matthew Pratt (1734-
    1805), a study of his work 103 p 44 il 1942 $5. NHi
                                                                2235
Ramage, John. Morgan, John Hill. A sketch of the life of
    John Ramage, miniature painter (v 8 Jones Fund) 55 p 22
    il 1930 $2.50 NHi   2236
Smibert, John. Phillips, John Marshall. The Smibert tra-
    dition 1949 p $.50 CtY-A   2237
Stuart, Gilbert. Gilbert Stuart il 1942 p $.50 InIJ   2238
----. Morgan, John Hill. What was Gilbert Stuart's name
    (repr, R.I. Historical Society Collections, April 1941) 12
    p 1941 p $1. RHi   2239
Trumbull, John. John Trumbull, painter-patriot, an exhibi-
    tion organized to honor the bicentennial of the artist's
    birth; preface by Evan H. Turner 10 il 1956 p $1. CtHWA
                                                                2240

----. The life and works of John Trumbull p $.25 CtY-A
                                                        2241
Vanderlyn, Pieter. Harris, Charles X.   Pieter Vanderlyn,
   portrait painter (repr, Quarterly Bulletin, Oct 1921) 14 p
   4 il p $.50 NHi   2242
Williams, William. Sawitzky, William. Further light on
   the work of William Williams (repr, Quarterly Bulletin,
   July 1941) 14 p 4 il p $.60 NHi   2243

--Art, United States--19th Century to 1925

Admiral Dewey and the Manila Campaign $3. DN-HF   2244
American classics of the 19th century; catalogue of an exhibition of the paintings of the chief masters of the 19th
   century; foreword by George Bailey Washburn 44 p 17 il
   1957 p $1.   PPiCIA; also MdBMA   2245
American painting, 1815-1865 (Karolik Collection of Museum
   of Fine Arts, Boston) p $1.50 WMA   2246
American painting in the nineteenth century 1954 p $.15
   NNW   2247
American primitives: An exhibition of the paintings of 19th
   century folk artists 79 p 21 pl 1930 p $1.25 NjNM   2248
Beggs, Thomas M.   Profiles of the time of James Monro,
   an exhibition commemorating the 200th anniversary of the
   birth of the fifth President of the U.S. (Smithsonian Pubn
   4348) port 1955 p apply DSI-FA   2249
Boyd, E.   Popular arts of Colonial New Mexico 51 p 13 il
   (6 c) 1951 p $1.75 NmSMI   2250
Building the West, panorama of a special exhibition of Western American art 32 p 48 il $.50 CoDA   2251
Catalogue of the M. and M. Karolik Collection of American
   paintings, 1815-1865; foreword by G.H. Edgell; letter to
   the director by Maxim Karolik; "Trends in American paint-
   ing" by John I. H. Baur 544 p 233 pl 1949 $25. MBMu
                                                        2252
Corbitt, D. L.   Pictures of the Civil War period in North
   Carolina 82 p 68 il, map 1958 p $.25 NcRNC   2253
The Eight, memorial exhibition 26 p 17 il 1958 p $1. NSyE
                                                        2254
An exhibition of paintings and bronzes by Frederic Remington
   and Charles M. Russell p $.25 OkTG   2255
Fiftieth anniversary exhibition of the Independents of 1910 il
   p $2. DeWS   2256
Frank W. Benson--Edmund C. Tarbell, exhibition of paint-
   ings, drawings, and prints, with an introduction by Lucien
   Price and Frederick W. Coburn 40 p 8 il 1938 p $.10
   MBMu   2257

Hipkiss, Edwin J.   Karolik Collection--American arts of the
    eighteenth century (repr, Bul no 236, Dec 1941) 10 p 24
    il p $.15 MBMu   2258
Hipkiss, Edwin J. M. and M. Karolik Collection of eighteenth
    century American arts: Painting, drawings, engravings,
    furniture, silver, needlework, and incidental objects
    gathered to illustrate the achievements of American artists
    and craftsmen of the period from 1720 to 1820; with notes
    on drawings and prints by Henry P. Rossiter, comments
    on the Collection by Maxim Karolik 408 p 171 il 1950 p
    $10. MBMu   2259
The Hudson River School and the early American landscape
    tradition 123 p il 1945 $2.50 ICA (op)   2260
Jones, Agnes Halsey. Rediscovered painters of Upstate New
    York, 1700-1875 (Munson-Williams-Proctor Institute,
    Utica, New York) 80 p 76 il c 1958 p $2. NCooHi   2261
Newark portraits by Rembrandt Peale and Oliver Tarbell
    Eddy (The Museum, ns, v 1, no 4, Oct 1949) p $.40
    NjNM   2262
Nineteenth century Virginia genre painting 10 il p $.50
    ViRMu   2263
Of other days (Scenes of everyday life): An exhibition of
    19th century genre painting 4 p 1957 p $.25 NjNM   2264
Old favorites revisited--a loan exhibition of paintings popular
    during the turn-of-the-century; introduction by Carl Shep-
    ard 29 il (1 c) p $.50 CLMA   2265
Rathbone, Perry T. M. and M. Karolik Collection (American
    painting 1815-1865) 98 il (3 c) 1957 p $1.25 NNW   2266
Santos, New Mexican folk art; foreword by Thomas W.
    Leavitt, introduction by Lawrence P. Frank 19 p il 1960
    p $1.50 CPA   2267
Santos of the Southwest: Bultos and retablos. A survey and
    catalogue of the Denver Art Museum's collection of Span-
    ish-American liturgical art 32 p 33 il $.50 CoDA   2268
Sweet, Frederick A. Sargent, Whistler and Mary Cassatt
    104 p 92 il (3 c) 1954 p $1.50 ICA (op) also NNMM 2269
Travelers in Arcadia, a survey of American artists and their
    work in Italy from 1830-1875; introduction by E. P. Rich-
    ardson, and Otto Wittmann, Jr. 68 p il 1951 p $1.25 OTM
                                                             2270
Virginia miniatures prior to 1850 36 il p $.50 ViRMu 2271
Westward the way, pioneering of the West from the Mississip-
    pi to the Rockies 200 p 255 il (4 c) $3.95 MnMW; $3.95;
    $.25 post; MoSCA   2272
The world of the romantic artist, a survey of American cul-
    ture from 1800 to 1875 (C 8) 35 p 28 il 1945 p $.50
    MiDA   2273

--Art, United States, 19th Century to 1925--Individual
Artists

Abbey, Edwin Austin. A description of Abbey's "Quest of the
   Holy Grail," Boston Public Library Mural p $1.50; $.06
   post MB   2274
----. Paintings, drawings and pastels by Edwin Austin Ab-
   bey; foreword by Royal Cortissoz, introduction by George
   Heart Hamilton 16 il 1939 p $.25 CtY-A   2275
Allston, Washington. Richardson, Edgar P. Washington
   Allston (B 6) 300 p 60 il (front c) 1948 $5. MiDA   2276
----. Washington Allston (C 11) 36 p 27 il p $.50 MiDA
                                                        2277
Bard, James and John. Sniffen, Harold S. James and John
   Bard: Painters of steamboat portraits (ext, Art in Amer-
   ica, April 1949), with a checklist of over 300 Bard paint-
   ings done between 1830-90, compiled by Alexander C.
   Brown 32 p 19 il p $1.95; $.05 post VWa   2278
Barney, Alice Pike. Beggs, Thomas M. Alice Pike Barney:
   Paintings in oil and pastel (Smithsonian pubn 4291) 99 pl
   (front c) 1957 p $1.50 DSI-FA   2279
Bellows, George. Paintings, drawings, and prints 92 p il
   1946 p $1. ICA   2280
----. George Bellows: Prints and drawings (Smithsonian
   Traveling Exhibition Catalog) il 1957 p DSI-FA   2281
----. George Bellows--A retrospective exhibition, with fore-
   word by John Walker, and introduction by Henry McBride
   128 p 90 il 1957 p $1.50 DSI-GA   2282
Blakelock, Ralph Albert. Goodrich, Lloyd. Ralph Albert
   Blakelock, 1847-1919 16 il 1947 p $1. NNW   2283
Butler, Howard Russell. Oliver, Frances E. Appreciation
   of the paintings of Howard Russell Butler p $.10 NBuM
                                                        2284
Catlin, George. Quimby, George I. Indians of the western
   frontier. Paintings of George Catlin 78 p 35 il 2nd ptg
   1958 p $.60 ICF   2285
Chase, William Merritt. Chase centennial exhibition il 1949
   p $1. InIJ   2286
Cole, Thomas. Thomas Cole, 1801-1848: One hundred
   years later; introduction by Esther I. Seaver 60 p 38 il
   1949 p $1. CtHWA   2287
Corinth, Lovis. Lovis Corinth p $.35 MBI   2288
Cox, Jacob. Jacob Cox, early Indianapolis artist il 1941 p
   $.25 InIJ   2289
Dickinson, Anson. Kidder, Mary Helen, ed. List of miniatures painted by Anson Dickinson, 1803-1851 75 p front
   1937 $3.50 CtHI   2290

Dunlap, William. The diary of William Dunlap (1766-1839),
the memoirs of a dramatist, theatrical manager,' painter,
critic, novelist, and historian 1929-31 3 v 40 il $12. NHi
                                                                          2291
Durrie, George Henry. Cowdrey, Bartlett. George Henry
Durrie, 1820-1863; Connecticut painter of American life
23 p 44 il 1947 p $1. CtHWA   2292
Duveneck, Frank. Exhibition of the work of Frank Duveneck, 1936 p $.75 OCA   2293
Eddy, Oliver Tarbell. Oliver Tarbell Eddy, 1799-1868: A
catalogue of his works compiled by Edith Bishop 68 p 28
pl 1950 p $1.25 NjNM   2294
Elder, John Adams. A retrospective exhibition of the work
of John Adams Elder 10 il p $.50 ViRMu   2295
Fraser, Charles. A Charleston sketchbook, 1796-1806--
forty watercolors of the city and surroundings include
plantation and parish churches; introduction and notes by
Alice R. Huger Smith 2nd ed 1940 $3.75 ScCG   2296
Gibson, Charles Dana. Charles Dana Gibson: Exhibition of
drawings and paintings 16 p 2 il 1943 p $.25 MBMu 2297
Glackens, William James. William Glackens memorial ex-
hibition, 1938-39 27 il p $.25 NNW (op)   2298
Hart, George Overbury ('"Pop"). "Pop" Hart (George Over-
bury Hart): Catalogue of an exhibition of oils, water-
colors, drawings and prints 63 p 19 pl 1935 p $1. NjNM
                                                                          2299
Heade, Martin J. McLanathan, Richard B.K. Martin J.
Heade: A biography of this versatile nineteenth century
American artist, and reproductions of his works from the
Museum's M. and M. Karolik Collection of American
paintings, 1815-1865 (PB 5) c p $.50 MBMu   2300
Healy, George Peter Alexander. Healy's sitters--A comprehensive collection of the likenesses of some of the most
important personages of Europe and America as portrayed
by George P.A. Healy between the years 1837-1899 94 p
100 il p $3. ViRMu   2301
Hewins, Amasa. Journal, 1830-1833 (Boston portrait painter
in Italy), edited by Francis H. Allen 1931 $1.50 MBAt
                                                                          2302
Homer, Winslow. Winslow Homer, a retrospective exhibition
132 p 103 il (2 c) 1958 p $2.95 DSI-GA   2303
----. Winslow Homer, oils and watercolors 66 il (6 c)
1959 $3.50; p $2.25 MBMu   2304
Hubard, William James, 1807-1862 (English-born artist living
in Virginia mid-19th century); biographical introduction by
Helen G. McCormack 35 p 25 il 1948 p $1. ViRMu;
ViRVM   2305

Jarvis, John Wesley. Dickson, Harold E. John Wesley
Jarvis, American painter, 1780-1840 (v 12 Jones Fund)
548 p 105 il 1949 $10. NHi   2306
Keith, William. An introduction to the art of William Keith,
1829-1919 p $.25 OCA   2307
Kern, Edward M. Heffernan, William. Edward M. Kern
--travels of an artist explorer (Pubn 15) 1953 $2.50
CBakHi   2308
Lane, FitzHugh. McLanathan, Richard B.K. FitzHugh Lane,
a biographical sketch of this gifted American painter, with
reproductions of his work (PB 8) c p $.50 MBMu   2309
Lawson, Thomas Bayley. Coburn, Frederick W. Thomas
Bayley Lawson, portrait painter of Newburyport and Lo-
well 59 p il 1947 p $1.75 MSaE   2310
Lehn, Joseph. Poole, Earl L. Joseph Lehn, driven to de-
sign (19th century Pennsylvania Dutch folk artist) (B 20)
il $.05 PRM   2311
Luks, George Benjamin. George Luks: Catalogue of an ex-
hibition of the work of George Benjamin Luks 57 p 1934 p
$1. NjNM   2312
Magoun, Thatcher. French, Hollis. Thatcher Magoun 57 p
8 il $3.50 MAnP-A   2313
Miller, Alfred Jacob. Ross, Marvin C. The West of Alfred
Jacob Miller 448 p front c il 1951 $10.30 MdBWA   2314
Morse, Samuel F.B. Samuel F.B. Morse, paintings,
models il 1956 p $.25 NSyE   2315
Myers, Jerome. Jerome Myers memorial exhibition 1941 p
$.15 NNW   2316
Newman, Robert Loftin. Robert Loftin Newman 17 il p $.50
ViRMu   2317
Paxton, William McGregor. Catalogue of a memorial exhibi-
tion of paintings by William McGregor Paxton; introduction
by Frank W. Buston and R.H. Ives Gammell 36 p 6 il
1941 p $.10 MBMu   2318
Peale, Raphaelle. Raphaelle Peale, still lifes and portraits
p $.75 WMA   2319
Peale Family. Paintings by the Peale Family (Cincinnati Art
Museum) 28 p 31 il 1954 p $.25 OCA; also $.75 MdBPM
2320
Peto, John F. John F. Peto, catalog of the exhibition with
a critical biography by Alfred Frankenstein 50 p 23 il 1950
p $.75 NNB   2321
Prendergast, Maurice. Boston water-color sketchbook, 1899.
Full color facsimile. 96 p 89 il (52 wc, 37 pencil drg);
descriptive text by Peter A. Wick 1960 $15. MBMu 2321a
----. Rhys, Hedley H. Maurice Prendergast; foreword by
Perry T. Rathbone, and catalogue of Prendergast Centen-

nial Exhibition 156 p 148 il (36 c) 1960 $7.50; p $2.75
MBMu   2321b
Pyle, Howard.   Catalog Raisonne of the work of Howard
  Pyle $5. DeWS   2322
----.   Howard Pyle Collection p $.25 DeWS   2323
Quidor, John.   Baur, John I.H.   John Quidor, 1801-1881 57
  p 27 il 1942 p $.75 NBB   2324
Ranger, Henry Ward.   Beggs, Thomas M.   Henry Ward
  Ranger centennial exhibition, 1858-1958 (Smithsonian pubn
  4349) 30 p port 1958 p apply DSI-FA   2325
Remington, Frederic.   Frederic Remington, leaflet, port
  $.10 NOgR   2326
----.   Frederic Remington Memorial Collection.   Catalogue,
  with chronology and notes by Dr. Harold McCracken il
  (2 c) $7.50 NOgR   2327
----.   McKown, Robin.   Painter of the Wild West--Frederic
  Remington $2.95 NOgR   2328
----.   Remington Art Memorial, Ogdensberg, New York,
  leaflet il $.10 NOgR   2329
----.   Vail, R.W.G.   Frederic Remington--Chronicler of the
  vanished West (New York Public Library) p $.50 NOgR
                                                    2330

Rimmer, William.   Kirstein, Lincoln.   William Rimmer,
  1816-1879 16 il 1946 p $1. NNW   2331
Sargent, John Singer.   McKibbin, David.   Sargent's Boston,
  with an essay and a biographical summary and a complete
  check list of Sargent's portraits; catalogue of the Centennial Exhibition at the Museum; foreword by Perry T.
  Rathbone 132 p 53 il (front, 1 c) 1956 $3.25; p $2.
  MBMu   2332
----.   Sargent decorations of the rotunda; including a gener-
  al description by Thomas Fox, and the decorations in de-
  tail 28 p 18 il 1921 p $.25 MBMu   2333
----.   Sargent decorations over the main stairway and Li-
  brary; 12 paintings and 6 reliefs 24 p 18 il 1925 p $.25
  MBMu   2334
Singer, William Henry, Jr.   De Vries, R.W.P., Jr.   Wil-
  liam Henry Singer, Jr.--The man and the artist $7.50
  MdHagM   2335
Sloan, John.   John Sloan, retrospective exhibition, 1938 95 p
  39 il p $1. MAnP-A   2336
----.   John Sloan, Whitney Museum of Art 87 p 47 il (3 c)
  1949 $1. DCGA   2337
Sohon, Gustavus.   Ewers, John C.   Gustavus Sohon's por-
  traits of Flathead and Pend d'Oreille Indians, 1854 (Smithsonian MC 110:7; pubn 3941) 1948 p $1.15 DSI   2338
Vanderlyn, John.   John Vanderlyn's panoramic view of the

Palace and Gardens of Versailles, introduction by Marshall B. Davidson; with articles by Albert Ten Eyck Gardner and Lawrence J. Majewski 12 p 13 il (1 c, 1 fold out)
1956 p $.50 NNMM   2339
Waugh, Alfred S.   Travels in search of the elephant: The
wanderings of Alfred S. Waugh, artist in Louisiana, Missouri, and Santa Fe, in 1845-46; John Frances McDermott, ed 153 p 1951 $3.75 MoHi   2340
Weir, John Ferguson.   Sizer, Theodore, ed.   Recollections
of John Ferguson Weir (repr, three issues, New York
Historical Society Bul) $2. CtY-A   2341
Whistler, James McNeill. Stubbs, B.A.   James McNeill
Whistler, a biographical outline illustrated from the Collections of the Freer Gallery of Art (Freer Occas Pap v
1, no 4; Smithsonian pubn 3994) 29 p 29 pl 1950 p $1.
DSI-F   2342
----.   Whistler exhibition catalogue p $.25 CaOTAG   2343
Wimar, Charles.   Charles Wimar, catalogue of the Wimar
exhibition 77 p 35 il p $1; $.10 post MoSCA   2344
Winter, George.   George Winter, pioneer artist of Indiana
il 1939 p InIJ   2345

--Art, United States--Contemporary (1925-   )

American artists paint the city; catalogue of the American
pavilion at the Venice Biennale 47 p 33 il, some c 1956 p
$.25 ICA   2346
American painting 21 il 1954 p $.65 25 il 1958 p $.25
ViRMu   2347
American painting in our century p $2.50 CLCM   2348
An American show: Paintings by Bouche, Hopper, Kuhn,
Kuniyoshi, Marin, and Weber 1948 p $.25 OCA   2349
American water colors, drawings, and prints; foreword by
Robert Berly Hale and Roland J. McKinney 88 p 56 il
1952 p $2. NNMM   2350
Arizona, University of, Art Gallery. The American Collec-
tion, contemporary p $1. AzU-A   2351
Art in the 20th century--Commemorating the tenth anniver-
sary of the signing of the United Nations Charter; introduction by E. Morris Cox and Grace L. McCann Morley
20 il (1 c) 1955 p $1. CSfMA   2352
Artists of Central New York. Regional Exhibition 6th, 1958
12 p 2 il p $.50 NSyE   2353
Artists of Cincinnati and Vicinity. Annual, 1946- p $.25
ea OCA   2354
Artists of Los Angeles and Vicinity. Annual, 1954 p $.48;
1957 36 il p $.75; 1958 36 p il p $.75; 1959 36 p il $.75;

1960 32 p il p $1. CLCM   2355
Artists of Washington. Annual exhibition of works 4th, 1949-
    (some op) p $.50 ea DCGA   2356
Bailey, Vernon Howe. Special exhibition of Naval defense
    activities: Drawings and watercolors by Vernon Howe
    Bailey made under the authorization of the Navy Depart-
    ment il 1942 p $.10 DCGA   2357
Baur, John I.H., ed. Young America 53 il 1957 p $1.
    NNW (op)   2358
Biennial exhibition of contemporary American paintings il
    1938- p $.60 ea ViRMu   2359
Biennial of American artists, first p $1.44 CLCM   2360
Brooklyn Society of Artists. Biennial catalog, 1950, 1952,
    1954, 1958 p $.25 ea NBB   2361
Byrnes, James B. Panel's choice: Loan exhibition of paint-
    ings and sculpture by artists of the New York School il p
    $.20 NcRMA   2362
California Water Color Society. National exhibition 24 p il
    38th, 1958; 40th, 1960 p $1. CLCM   2363
Carnegie Institute. Painting in the United States. Annual,
    catalog 1941-1949 (1942 op) p $1. ea PPiCIA   2364
Contemporary American painting, catalogue of a special ex-
    hibition 32 p 13 il 1951 p $1; $.10 post MoSCA   2365
Contemporary fine arts exhibit of the American Jewish Ter-
    centery 13 p 9 il 1955 p $.50 DCGA   2366
Contemporary painters of Japanese origin in America p $1.
    MBI   2367
Corcoran Gallery. Biennial exhibition of contemporary Amer-
    ican oil painting 1907- 1st through 20th, 1907-1947 $1;
    21st through 24th, 1949-1955 $.25; 25th through 26th
    1957-1959 $.50 ea DCGA   2368
Crawford--Cutler; works by Ralston Crawford, painter and
    Charles Cutler, sculptor 1949 p $.25 OCA   2369
Critics choice of American painting 1945 p $.25 OCA   2370
Dynation, 1951--the work and statements of Wolfgang Paalen,
    Gordon Onslow-Ford, and Lee Mullican 66 p 22 il (3 c)
    p $2.50 CSfMA   2371
Four abstract classicists, loan exhibition of four California
    painters: Karl Benjamin; Lorser Feitelson; Frederick
    Hammersley; John McLaughlin 72 p il (4 c) 1959 p $1.92
    CLCM   2372
Goodrich, Lloyd, and Hermon More. Juliana Force and
    American art; survey of American art 1909-1948 40 il
    1949 p $1. NNW   2373
----, and John I.H. Baur. Four American expressionists:
    Doris Caesar; Chaim Gross; Karl Knaths, and Abraham
    Rattner 54 il (12 c) p $1.75 NNW   2374

The Hallmark Art Award 87 p 113 il (2 c) 1949 p $1. DCGA
                                                       2375
Indiana art, John Herron Art Museum p $.25 InIJ   2376
Levine, Reminick, Shikler (3-man show) fold 1 il 1956 $.15
    NSyE   2377
Lucille Evans and Barbara Ferrell (CCA 10) 1951 p $.10
    DCGA   2378
Mackay, William Andrew, and A.A. Canfield. Murals in the
    Roosevelt Memorial (American Museum of Natural History)
    (SG 119) 12 il p $.50 NNM   2379
Morley, Grace L. McCann. Pacific Coast art--the United
    States' representation at the third Biennial of Sao Paulo
    24 p 50 il 1956 p $1. CSfMA   2380
National Exhibition of Art by the Public Works Art Project
    30 p 1934 p $1. DCGA   2381
The Negro artist comes of age, a national survey of con-
    temporary American artists il 1945 p $1. NAlAI   2382
North Carolina Artists' Exhibition. Annual, 1956- 58 $.10
    ea; 1959 $.25 NcRMA   2383
Oklahoma Artists Competition. Annual - p $.25 OkTP 2384
100 American painters of the 20th century; introduction by
    Robert Beverly Hale 111 p 8 pl c 102 il 1950 p $3. NNMM
                                                       2385
Paintings and sculptures of the Pacific Northwest 72 p 60 il
    (8 c) 1959 $1. OrPA   2386
Paintings of naval aviation p $.35 MBI   2387
Reginald Marsh, and Jacques Maroger (2 one-man shows)
    fold 2 il 1956 $.15 NSyE   2388
Robert Osborn--Mischa Richter; essay on Osborn by Charles
    C. Cunningham, essay on Richter by Evan H. Turner 28 p
    14 il p $.75 CtHWA   2389
A selection of American painters of the present day, includ-
    ing one-man exhibitions for Arbit Blatas, and Lawrence
    Lebdusca il 1944 p $.25 RPD-M   2390
Significant war scenes by battlefront artists, Chrysler Cor-
    poration 16 il p $.50 DCGA   2391
Southern States Art League. Annual exhibition 27th 8 il p
    $.25 ViRMu   2392
Three Americans, one-man shows: William Thon; John
    Helliker; James Suzuki 6 p 3 il 1958 p $.25 NSyE 2393
Toledo Museum of Art. Catalogue of contemporary American
    oil paintings acquired by the Museum, 1901-1951 20 p p
    $.25 OTM   2394
----. Contemporary American paintings--(Elizabeth C. Mau
    Collection) 20 p il 1950 p $.25 OTM   2395
Twentieth century painting from three cities: New York, New
    Haven, Hartford; foreword by Charles C. Cunningham, in-

troduction by Belle Krasne Ribicoff 18 p 12 il 1955 p $1.
CtHWA   2396
Whitney Museum of American Art. The Museum and its
friends--18 living American artists selected by the Friends
of the Whitney 36 il 1959 p $1.25 NNW   2397
----. The Museum and its Friends--20th century American
art from collections of the Friends of the Whitney 38 p il
(6 c) 1958 p $1.50 NNW   2398
Wight, Frederick S. American painting in our century, selected examples from an exhibit in Museum, 1949 50 il
(21 c) p $1. OClMA   2399
Wisconsin painters and sculptors Annual, 42nd, 1956; 45th,
1959; 46th, 1960 p $.50 ea WMA   2400
Work by New Jersey artists: An exhibit 12 p 7 il 1955 p;
p 1958; p 1961 apply NjNM   2401
Young Connecticut talent, 1957; foreword by Charles C. Cun-
ningham 12 p 9 il p $.25 CtHWA   2402
Younger American painters; foreword by James Johnson
Sweeney 57 il p $2. NNGu   2403

--Art, United States--Contemporary (1925-   )--Individual
Artists

Acheson, Alice. Alice Acheson (CAA 18) 1954 p $.10
DCGA   2404
Albers, Josef. Poems and drawings $5. CtY-A   2405
----. Josef Albers 1949 p $.15 OCA   2406
Ascher, Mary G. Ascher squares p $.35 MBI   2407
Avery, Milton. Milton Avery p $1.50 MBI   2408
Barnett, Herbert Phillip. Herbert Phillip Barnett, paintings
and drawings 1951 p $.15 OCA   2409
Bengtz, Ture. Ture Bengtz, one-man show fold 1 il 1957
$.15 NSyE   2410
Ben-Zion, 1933-1959, a retrospect 32 p 29 il 1959 p apply
NNJ-Mu   2411
Bloom, Hyman. Hyman Bloom p $.35 MBI   2412
----. Wight, Frederick S. Hyman Bloom retrospective
exhibition 9 il (2 c) 1955 p $.50 NNW   2413
Bookatz, Samuel. Samuel Bookatz (CCA 3) 1948 p $.10
DCGA   2414
Calder, Alexander. Alexander Calder (CAA 27) 1958 p $.10
DCGA   2415
Clark, Horace. Horace Clark, recent painting fold 1 il 1957
p $.25 NSyE   2416
Crawford, Ralston. Ralston Crawford exhibition p $.75
WMA   2417
Davis, Stuart. Arnason, H.H. Stuart Davis retrospective

exhibition 40 il (4 c) 1957 p $1. NNW   2418
Dove, Arthur G. Wight, Frederick S. Arthur G. Dove 59
   il (23 c) 1958 p $2. NNW   2419
Embry, Morris. Morris Embry p $.35 MBI   2420
Feininger, Lyonel. Lyonel Feininger, selected examples
   from an exhibition in Museum 31 il 1951 p $1. OClMA
                                                     2421
Fogel, Seymour. Seymour Fogel paintings and drawings
   1958 p $.25 TxSaMc   2422
Folinsbee, John Fulton. Paintings by John Folinsbee 23 p il
   p MeRF   2423
Frankenthaler, Helen. Helen Frankenthaler paintings 12 il
   (cover c) 1960 p apply NNJ-Mu   2424
Fuller, Sue. Sue Fuller (CAA 11) 1951 p $.10 DCGA 2425
Gates, Margaret.   Margaret Gates (CAA 1) 1948 p $.10
   DCGA   2426
Gates, Robert. Robert Gates (CAA 20) 1954 p $.10 DCGA
                                                     2427
Gath, Ethel Robertson. Ethel Robertson Gath (CAA 2) 1948
   p $.10 DCGA   2428
Gil, Alvar Carrillo. Paintings and collages by Dr. Alvar
   Carrillo Gil 1958 p $.25 TxSaMc   2429
Gorky, Arshile. Gorky p $.75 MnMW   2430
Gwathmey, Robert. Robert Gwathmey p $.50 MBI   2431
Hartley, Marsden. Marsden Hartley p $2.50 CLCM   2432
Hofmann, Hans. Hans Hofmann p $1.50 MnMW   2433
Huhn, Rudolf von. Rudolf von Huhn (CAA 12) 1952 p $.10
   DCGA   2434
Hurd, Peter. Fresco mural, rotunda, Texas Technological
   College (Journal v 1) $5. TxLT-Mu   2435
James, Alexander R. Alexander James, 1890-1946 20 p 16
   il 1947 p $.50 DCGA   2436
Kainen, Jacob. Jacob Kainen (CAA 7) 1949 p $.10 DCGA
                                                     2437
Karp, Leon. Leon Karp exhibition; foreword by Fiske Kim-
   ball, comments by Joseph T. Frazer, Leo Lionni, Andre
   Girard, and Leon Kelly 50 p 47 il 1952 p $1. PPPM2438
Keller, Henry George. Henry G. Keller, memorial exhibi-
   tion, 1950 75 il (1 c) p $.50 OClMA   2439
Kempton, Greta. Portraits by Greta Kempton 2 il 1949 p
   $.10 DCGA   2440
Kent, Frank. Frank Kent, one-man show fold 1 il 1957
   $.15 NSyE   2441
Kingman, Dong. Dong Kingman (CAA 23) 1955 p $.10
   DCGA   2442
Lahey, Richard. Richard Lahey (CAA 17) 1953 p $.10
   DCGA   2443

Levine, Jack. Wight, Frederick S. Jack Levine retrospective exhibition 9 il 1955 p $.50 NNW   2444
McManus, James Goodwin. James Goodwin McManus, retrospective exhibition; introduction by Charles C. Cunningham 8 p 8 il 1954 p $.50 CtHWA   2445
McKnight, Dodge. Dodge McKnight, catalogue of a loan exhibition of water-colors held at the Museum, with introduction by Dorothy Adlow 48 p 17 il (cover c) 1950 p $1.
MBMu   2446
McMillan, Mary. Mary McMillan, memorial exhibition 1 il
1957 p $.25 NSyE   2447
Marin, John. John Marin, selected examples from memorial
exhibition 40 il (12 c) p $1.50 OClMA   2448
Masselink, Eugen. Studies, abstractions and executed work
by Eugene Masselink (murals, screens, wall hangings) il
1959 p WU-G   2449
Maurer, Albert H. Albert H. Maurer p $1. MBI; MnMW
                                                        2450
----. McCausland, Elizabeth. Alfred Maurer, 1868-1932
17 il 1949 p $1. NNW   2451
Maurer, Leonard. Leonard Maurer (CAA 16) 1953 p $.10
DCGA   2452
Meltsner, Paul Raphael. Paul Meltsner, one-man show fold
1 il 1956 $.15 NSyE   2453
Myers, Jerome. Jerome Myers 12 il p $.50 ViRMu   2454
Paulsen, Esther Erika. Esther Erika Paulsen, one-man
show fold 1 il 1956 $.15 NSyE   2455
Pereira, I. Rice. I. Rice Pereira (CAA 24) 1956 p $.10
DCGA   2456
Perlmutter, Jack. Jack Perlmutter (CAA 25) 1956 p $.10
DCGA   2457
Phillips, Marjorie. Marjorie Phillips (CAA 22) 1955 p $.10
DCGA   2458
Price, Clayton S. Clayton S. Price p $.50 MnMW   2459
Rabinovits, Harold. Harold Rabinovits, memorial exhibition
1952 p $.25 MSMFA   2460
Rattner, Abraham. Abraham Rattner (CAA 28) 1958 p $.10
DCGA   2461
Robus, Hugo. Hugo Robus (CAA 29) 1958 p $.10 DCGA
                                                        2462
Roszak, Theodore. Arnason, H.H. Theodore Roszak ret-
rospective exhibition 40 il (5 c) 1956 p $1. NNW   2463
Salemme, Attilio. Attilio Salemme p $1. MBI; MnMW
                                                        2464
----. Attilio Salemme retrospective exhibition 11 il (8 c) p
$.75 NNW   2465
Shahn, Ben. Ben Shahn p $1.25 MBI   2466

Sluis, George Vander. George Vander Sluis, one-man show
  fold 1 il 1956 $.15 NSyE   2468
Smith, Samuel David. Samuel David Smith (CAA 6) 1949 p
  $.10 DCGA   2469
Speicher, Eugene. Eugene Speicher 16 p 23 il 1950 p $.50
  NBuA   2470
Stella, Joseph. Joseph Stella: Catalogue of paintings and
  drawings in a retrospective exhibition 13 p 8 pl 1939 p
  $.25 NjNM   2471
Still, Clifford E. Paintings by Clifford Still 71 p 38 il (4 c)
  1959 p $2.75 NBuA   2472
Takal, Peter. Peter Takal, selected examples from an ex-
  hibition in Museum, 1958 25 il (1 c) p $1. OClMA   2473
Tobey, Mark. Thomas, Edward B. Mark Tobey, catalog of
  retrospective exhibition; foreword by Richard E. Fuller 51
  il 1959 p $1.25 WaSA   2474
Tomlin, Bradley Walker. Baur, John I.H. Bradley Walker
  Tomlin memorial exhibition 36 il (5 c) 1957 p $1.25 NNW
                                                           2475
Toney, Anthony. Anthony Toney, one-man show fold 1956
  $.15 NSyE   2476
Turnbull, Grace H. Grace H. Turnbull (CAA 5) 1949 p $.10
  DCGA   2477
Warneke, Heinz. Heinz Warneke (CAA 26) 1957 p $.10
  DCGA   2478
Weisz, Eugen. Eugen Weisz (CAA 21) 1954 p $.10 DCGA
                                                           2479
Wingren, Dan. Dan Wingren, paintings 1958 p apply
  TxSaMc   2480
Wright, S. MacDonald. S(tanton) MacDonald Wright, retro-
  spective exhibition paintings 28 p il 1956 p $1.50 CLCM
                                                           2481
Wyeth, Henriette. Paintings of Henriette Wyeth p $.10
  NmRMA   2482
Young, Mahonri M. Mahonri Young, retrospective exhibition
  1940 57 p 47 il p $1. MAnP-A   2483
Zerega, Andrea. Andrea Zerega (CAA 15) 1952 p $.10
  DCGA   2484

--Art, United States--Graphic Arts and Drawing

American prints today p $1.25 MnMW   2485
Bay Printmakers' Society. National exhibition fifth p $.15
  COA   2486
Brooklyn Museum. National Print Annual 1948- p $.25 ea
  NBB   2487
California Prints and Drawings, loan exhibition from Robert

B. Honeyman, Jr.   Collection 44 p il 1954 p $.75 CLCM
        2488
Corcoran Gallery of Art.   American prints in the Corcoran
    Gallery of Art (B v 2, no 3) 1949 p $.50 DCGA   2489
Early prints of California p $.75 CLCM   2490
Drawings by three Wisconsin artists: John Wilde; Dorothy
    Zupancich; and Harold Altman p $.25 WMA   2491
An exhibition of American drawings (C 5) p $.05 NNCoo
        2492

Hart, Charles H.   An etched portrait of Washington 5 p
    1879 p $.75 MSaE   2493
Hayes, Bartlett H., Jr.   The American line--100 years of
    drawing $2.50; p $1.50 MAnP-A   2494
Johnson, Una E.   American woodcuts, 1670-1750, a survey
    of woodcuts and wood-engravings in the United States 55 p
    44 il p $1. NBB   2495
----.   Golden years of American drawings, 1905-1956 42 p
    36 il 1957 p $.75 NBB   2496
----.   What is a modern print (former title: "Ten years of
    American prints, 1947-1956"), with Brooklyn Museum 10th
    National Print Annual, and Brooklyn Museum Print Annual
    Purchase Awards, 1947-1956 48 p 47 il 1959 p $1.25 NBB
        2497
Richter, Emil H.   Early engraving in America 151 p 1904
    $1; p $.50 MBMu   2498
Wisconsin Printmakers Exhibition.   Annual p WU-G   2499

--Art, United States--Graphic Arts and Drawing--Individual
Artists

Bloom, Hyman.   Drawings of Hyman Bloom; introduction by
    Bernice Davidson 14 p 5 il 1958 p $.25 CtHWA   2500
Burchfield, Charles.   Selected examples from a drawing ex-
    hibition in Museum 20 il 1953 p $1. OClMA   2501
Corinth, Lovis.   Prints by Lovis Corinth, loan exhibition
    from the Mr. and Mrs. Sigbert H. Marcy Collection 28 p
    il 1956 p $.50 CLCM   2502
Erickson, Carl Oscar August.   Eric: Portraits and places;
    Carl Oscar August Erickson--100 drawings, 1913-1958, a
    memorial exhibition il 1959 p $.15 NNB   2503
Frasconi, Antonio.   Antonio Frasconi, selected examples
    from an exhibition in Museum 10 il 1952 p $.75 OClMA
        2504
----.   Frasconi woodcuts p $.48 CLCM   2505
Friedlaender, Johnny.   Etchings by Johnny Friedlaender
    1956 p $.25 CCA   2506
Goldthwaite, Anne.   Anne Goldthwaite--a memorial exhibi-

tion; foreword by Harry B. Wehle, biography by Holger
Cahill, essay "The Graphic Artist," by Adelyn D. Brees-
kin 24 p 12 il 1945 P $.50 MdBMA   2507
Mayer, Frank Blackwell.   With pen and pencil on the fron-
tier in 1851:   The diary and sketches of Frank Blackwell
Mayer; edited by Bertha L. Heilbron 214 p il 1932 $3.25
MnHi   2508
Peterdi, Gabor.   Johnson, Una E.   Gabor Peterdi: Twenty-
five years of his prints, 1934-1959 45 p 33 il 1959 p $1.
NBB   2509
Pozzatti, Rudy.   Pozzatti, selected examples of an exhibition
of prints in Museum 22 il (1 c) p $.75 OClMA   2510
Weir, Julian Alden.   Zimmermann, Agnes.   An essay to-
wards a catalogue raissone of the etchings, drypoints and
lithographs of Julian Alden Weir (P 3) 54 p front 5 pl
1923 p $.25 NNMM   2511

--Art, United States--Photography--Individual Artists

MacDonald, Pirie.   List of 500 portraits of men made in
New York City, 1900-1942 by Pirie MacDonald, photog-
rapher-of-men 23 p il 1943 p $.20 NHi   2512
Steichen, Edward.   Family of man 192 p 503 pl p $.95
NNMMA   2513
Stieglitz, Alfred.   Exhibition of photographs by Alfred Stieg-
litz, with a foreword by John Walker, and interpretive
notes by Doris Bry 60 p 17 il 1958 p $1.75 DSI-GA 2514

--Art, United States--Sculpture

American folk sculpture: The work of the 18th and 19th
century craftsmen 108 p il 1931 p $1.25 NjNM   2515
American sculpture 1951; foreword by Robert Beverly Hale
84 p front 49 il 1951 p $2. NNMM   2516
Boyd, E.   New Mexican santos (L 1) 4 p il 1953 p $.10
NmSM-S   2517
Brookgreen Gardens.   Proske, Beatrice Gilman.   Catalogue
of sculpture p $1.25 ScGB   2518
Brown, Alexander C.   Paddle box decorations of American
sound steamboats (ext, American Neptune, v 3 1943) 15 p
16 pl 23 il p $.75; $.04 post VWa
Kachinas and saints; cultures of Pueblo Indians and Spanish-
Americans of the Southwest compared 48 p il p $1.25
CoCF   2520
Parks, Robert C., and Gloria Seaman.   New sculpture now,
with an essay by Daniel Aaron 36 p 6 fig 1960 $.25
MNS-MA   2521

New Jersey clay 16 p il 1915 p $.25 NjNM (op)   2522
New Mexican santos il p $.25 CoCF   2523
The Oakland Art Museum. California Sculptors' Annual Ex-
    hibition, 1959 p $.25 COA   2524
Pease, Z.W. Scrimshaw (Sketches no 50) p $.25 MNBedfW
                                                       2525
Recent sculpture, U.S.A. il p $.75 CoDA   2526
Sculptors of Maryland, Washington, Virginia 3 il 1948 p
    $.10 DCGA   2527
Six American sculptors: Baskin, Farr, Glasco, Lipton,
    Schmidt, and Schor p $.50 WMA   2528
Sniffen, Harold S. Figureheads and their subjects (repr,
    Antiques Magazine, July 1954) 4 p 7 il p $.10; $.04
    post VWa   2529
Stackpole, Edouard Alexander. Scrimshaw at Mystic Seaport
    $2. CtMy   2529a
Walker Art Center Sculpture Exhibition, 5th p $.50 MnMW
                                                       2530

--Art, United States--Sculpture--Individual Artists See also
Art, United States

Albert, Calvin. Sculpture fold 2 il 1960 apply NNJ-Mu 2531
Baillie, Robert A. Proske, Beatrice Gilman. Robert A.
    Baillie, carver of stone p $.25 ScGB   2532
Barnhard, Raymond. Collage-constructions of Raymond
    Barnhart 1959 p apply TxSaMc   2533
Flannagan, John. The sculpture of John Flannagan 4 il p
    $.25 ViRMu   2534
Haseltine, Herbert. Sculptures of champion domestic ani-
    mals of Great Britain (Z-PS 13) 45 p il 1934 p $.25 ICF
                                                      2535
Huntington, Anna Hyatt. Animals sculptured by Anna Hyatt
    Huntington p $.15 ScGB   2536
----. Exhibition of sculpture by Anna Hyatt Huntington 2 il
    1938 p $.20 DCGA   2537
----. Sculpture of Anna Hyatt Huntington...exhibited at The
    Hispanic Society of America; introduction by B.G. Proske
    24 p 15 il 1957 p $.35 NNH   2538
Hutzler, Elsa W. Memorial sculpture exhibition; foreword
    by Adelyn D. Breeskin 14 p 10 il 1953 p $.50 MdBMA
                                                      2539
Manship, Paul. Beggs, Thomas M. A retrospective exhibi-
    tion of sculpture by Paul Manship (Smithsonian pubn 4336)
    31 p il 1958 p $.75 DSI-FA   2540
----. Paul Manship p $.35 MnMW   2541
Rinehart, William Henry. Ross, Marvin C., and Anna W.

Rutledge.   A catalogue of the work of William Henry Rinehart, Maryland sculptor, 1825-1874 124 p 49 pl 1949
$6.15; p $3.90 MdBWA   2542
Rush, William.   Marceau, Henry.   William Rush, the first
native American sculptor; introduction by William Rush
Dunton, Jr. 114 p 28 pl 1937 p $.50 PPPM   2543
Townley, Hugh.   Hugh Townley, American, one-man sculpture exhibition p $.25 WMA   2544
Whitney, Gertrude V.   Memorial exhibition 23 il 1943 p
$.50 NNW   2545

--Art--United States--Decorative Arts and Design

American arts and crafts il p $.15 CtY-A   2546
American decorative arts 10 p il p $.25 ICA   2547
Carlisle, Lilian B.   Hat boxes and bandboxes 212 p 1960
$4.25 VtSM   2548
Decoys at Shelburne Museum (in prep) VtSM   2549
Designer-craftsmen of the West, 1957 34 p 32 il p $.50
CSfDeY   2550
Gottesman, Rita Susswein, comp.   The arts and crafts in
New York, 1726-1776, advertisements and news items
from New York City newspapers 450 p 1938 $4. NHi 2551
Johnston, Elma Lawson.   Early domestic furnishings, Early
American furniture, silver, glass, china, and portraits
19 p 5 il by George A. Bradshaw 1929 p $.25 NjTM 2552
Life in the Colchester Reef lighthouse $1.50 VtSM   2553
Shaker handcrafts 1935 p $.15 NNW   2554
Twentieth century design; U.S.A. 96 p 154 il 1959 p $2.75
NBuA   2555
Twentieth century design, U.S.A., a survey exhibition, co-
sponsored by eight museums, 1959-1960 37 il p $2.25
OClMA   2556
Williams, Carl M.   Early arts and crafts of New Jersey
(series). Furniture, pewter, samplers, 1695-1840 18 p 1
il 1953 p $.25 NjTM   2557
----, ----.   Paintings, silver, glass, 1750-1850 24 p 1952
p $.25 NjTM   2558
Wisconsin Designer-Craftsmen, Annual, 38th, 1958; 40th,
1960 $.50 ea WMA   2559

--Art, United States--Decorative Arts and Design--Trans-
portation

Callaway, E. B.   The Stourbridge Lion: America's first loco-
motive 1956 p $.15 PHoW   2560
Carlisle, Lilian Baker.   The carriages at Shelburne Museum

(Museum Pamphlet Series, no 1) $2.50 VtSM; also VtHi
                                                          2561
Carriage catalogues p $1. ea NBLiSt   2562
The Conestoga wagon (Leaflet 5) 4 p p $.05 PHarH   2563
Fire engines on parade--The H.V. Smith Museum Collection
   il c 1956 p apply NNSMu   2564
Zoref, F.V. First Holland submarine (EP 12) NjPatM 2565
Holland, W.J. The "Vigilant" fire engine (A v 13, no 3-4,
   p 319-24) 1 pl p $.15 PPiCM   2566
Mount catalogues p $1. ea NBLiSt   2567
Ox carts and covered wagons p $.05 CLCM   2568
Rigs of the nine principal types of American sailing vessels
   10 p il in silhouette by Charles G. Davis $.25 MSaP
                                                          2569
Ship models PB 46 il p $1. MBMu   2570
The ship "Tyre" p $2. PPComm   2571
Story of the U-505 p $.50 ICS   2572
Yachting then and now (Marine RM Pubn no 3) 12 p 24 il
   1950 p $1. CtHWA   2573

--Art, United States--Decorative Arts and Design--Jewelry
and Gems

North Carolina gemstones (Info Circular) apply NcRSM 2574
Smith, Julia B. Jewelry industry in Newark 12 p 1929 p
   $.25 NjNM   2575

--Art, United States--Decorative Arts and Design--Ceramics

Barrett, Richard. Bennington pottery and porcelain $7.50
   VtHi   2576
Mercer, Henry C. Guide book to the tiled pavement in the
   Capitol of Pennsylvania 420 designs $1. PDoBHi   2577
The Mount Vernon china, illustrated catalog of chinaware
   used by General and Mrs. Washington in domestic life 52
   p $.50 ViMt   2578
Nelson, Boris Erich. Early arts and crafts of New Jersey
   (series). Potter's art in New Jersey, 1688-1900 56 p 2
   il 1956 p $.50 NjTM   2579
Pottery and porcelain of New Jersey, prior to 1876: Catalogue of an exhibition 32 p 1915 p $.25; -- , 1688-1900:
   Catalogue of an exhibition 100 p il 1947 p $1.25 NjNM
   (op)   2580
Stieglitz Collection: Dr. Wall Worcester porcelain 52 p il
   1947 p $1. ICA   2582
Tucker China, 1825-1839; introduction by Horace H.F. Jayne
   36 p 24 pl (4 c) (Including working drawings, marks and

inscriptions) 1957 p $2.   PPPM   2583

--Art, United States--Decorative Arts and Design--Glass

Davidson, Marshall B.   American glass revised by Joan Wilson 32 p 30 il 3rd ed 1949 p $.50 NNMM   2584
Rose, James H.   American pressed glass of the lacy period,
1825-1850; exhibition catalogue describing 955 objects
from 47 public and private collections 163 p 33 il, mold
diagrams 1954 p $1. NCorniC-M   2585
Suydam, Frederick Dorflinger.   Christian Dorflinger, 1828-
1915, founder of the Dorflinger Glass Works (1865-1921)
1956 p $1. PHoW   2586

--Art, United States--Decorative Arts and Design--Textiles

Carlisle, Lilian Baker.   Pieced work and applique quilts at
Shelburne Museum (Museum pam series no 2) $2.50
VtSM; also VtHi   2587
Early American hand-woven coverlets 15 p il 1946 p $.35
ICA   2588
Handwoven coverlets in the Newark Museum 83 p il 1947 p
$1. NjNM   2589
Historic fabrics as used in restored Williamsburg p $.25
NNSM   2590
Holloway, H.M.   American scenes and events on textiles--
an exhibition of printed cottons, linens, and silks from
1777 to 1941 32 p 1941 p $.25 NHi   2591
MacFarlane, Janet, and Virginia Parslow.   Hand processing
wool in America (repr, The Chronicle, Oct 1954) il p
$.20 NCooHi   2592
Parslow, Virginia.   The story of flax, illustrated brochure
describing the flax process as demonstrated at the
Farmers' Museum 1956 p $.20 NCooHi   2593
----.   Weaving and dyeing processes in early New York 20
p il 1949 p $.35 NCooHi   2594
Quilts and counterpains in the Newark Museum 90 p il 1948
p $1.25 NjNM   2595

--Art, United States--Decorative Arts and Design--Textiles--
Individual Artists

Alexander, James.   Parslow, Virginia.   James Alexander,
weaver (repr, Antiques Magazine, April 1956) il p $.25
NCooHi   2596
Kramer, Helen Kroll.   Helen Kroll Kramer, textile art.
Studies in color and texture, wall-textures ('paintings in

yarn"). folder il 1960 apply NNJ-Mu   2597

--Art, United States--Decorative Arts and Design--Textiles
--Costume

Bridal gowns in the Museum's collection (The Museum, ns,
   v 2, no 2, Spring 1950) p $.50 NjNM   2598
California leather jackets of 1769 p $.05 CLCM   2599
Clothes make the man, a special exhibition of the history of
   costume (Denver Art Museum Quarterly) 32 p 35 il $.25
   CoDA   2600
Colonial dress and travel (Leaflet 6) p $.10 MdHi 2601
Crawford, M.D.C. Philosophy in clothing 20 p 10 il 1940 p
   $.35 NBB   2602
Frary, I.T. Ohio in homespun and calico $2. OClMA 2603
While fashion is at full: Costumes from the 1790's to 1837
   (The Museum, ns, v 6, no 2, Spring 1954) p $.50 NjNM
                                                    2604

--Art, United States--Decorative Arts and Crafts--Metal
Work

American church silver of the XVII and XVIII centuries with
   a few pieces of domestic plate; catalogue listing 1,033
   pieces arranged alphabetically by names of makers, giving
   an index of American silversmiths and of unidentified
   marks 163 p 38 pl 1911 p $2. MBMu (op)   2605
Boyd, E. New Mexico tinwork (Leaflet 2) 4 p il 1953 p
   $.10 NmSM-S   2606
Buck, John H. Early church plate of Salem 17 p il 1907 p
   $.75 MSaE   2607
Buhler, Kathryn C. Colonial silversmiths--masters and ap-
   prentices 152 p 127 il 1956 $3.50; p $2.50 MBMu (op)
                                                    2608
----. Mount Vernon silver, an illustrated booklet of silver-
   ware used by General and Mrs. Washington in domestic
   life 76 p $1.50; p $1. ViMt   2609
Dudley, Dorothy H. Medals made in Newark 24 p il 1928 p
   $.25 NjNM   2610
Early New England silver lent from the Mark Bortman Col-
   lection, by Robert O. Parks 24 p 7 fig 1958 p $.50 MNS-
   MA   2611
Early American silver--a picture book; introduction by Vin-
   cent D. Anrus 26 p 28 il 1955 p $.50 NNMM   2612
An exhibition of early American silver 25 p 21 il 1945 p
   $.50 CtHWA   2613
Fales, Martha Gandy. American silver in the Henry Francis

du Pont Winterthur Museum 58 p 171 il 1958 $3; p $2.
DeWint   2614
Graham, John M.   American pewter--handbook based on the
collections in the Brooklyn Museum 36 p 33 il 1949 p
$.75 NBB   2615
Grigaut, Paul L.   The French in America, 1520-1880, with
sections on silver by Francis W. Robinson (C 22) 208 p
114 il 1951 p $1.75 MiDA   2616
Masterpieces of New England silver, 1650-1800 35 il 1939 p
$1. CtY-A   2617
Mercer, Henry C.   The Bible in iron--pictured stoves and
stove plates of the Pennsylvania Germans 3rd ed 1961
PDoBHi   2618
Nelson, Boris Erich.   Early arts and crafts of New Jersey
(series).   New Jersey iron, 1674-1850 42 p 2 il 1954 p
$.50 NjTM   2619
Pelletreau, Elias.   Elias Pellatreau: Long Island silver-
smith and his source of design; with articles by Marvin D.
Schwartz, and Arthur J. Pulos 48 p 29 il 1959 p $.50
NBB   2620
Philadelphia silver, 1682-1800; preface by Phoebe Phillips
Prime 32 p 26 pl 1956 p $1. PPPM   2621
Rantoul, Robert S.   The Pickman Silver 23 p il 1903 p $.75
MSaE   2622
Wildung, Frank H.   Woodworking tools at Shelburn Museum
(Museum pam ser no 3) $2.50 VtSM   2623

--Art, United States--Decorative Arts and Design--Metal
Work--Arms and Armor

Hanson, Charles.   The Northwest gun (PA 2) 1955 $3.
NbHi   2624
The Pennsylvania rifle (Leaflet 4) 4 p p $.05 PHarH   2625
Peterson.   Arms and armor of the Pilgrims p $.50 MP
                                                            2626

--Art, United States--Decorative Arts and Design--Book Arts

American type designers, il, ports 1948 p; with What types
do we need?   An inquiry 1947 p $.50 NNAIG   2627
Annual Textbook Show.   Annual 1952-5, 1957-9, $.50 ea;
1961 (Fall) $1.50 NNAIG   2628
The Children's Book Show--, 1955-1957 il 1958 p $1.00,
1958-60 1961 (Fall) $1.50 NNAIG   2629
Conrad, Joseph.   The Tremolino, designed by Bruce Rogers,
color woodcuts by Edward A. Wilson $1.   NNAIG   2630
Design and printing for commerce and 50 advertisements of

the year Annual, 1950- checklists, no illustrations 1956,
1958-60 $1. ea; il p 1961 (Fall) $1.50 NNAIG   2631
Design award booklet, 1957-1958 p $.25 CaOONG   2632
Fifty books of the year Annual, 1937, 1944, 1947-51 $.50
ea; 1954-60 $1. ea; 1961 $1.50 NNAIG   2633
Fifty packages of the year 1957, with 50 record album covers
of the year p $.50; 1959-60 $1; 1961 (Fall) $1.50
NNAIG   2634
Graphics in packaging, 1959 il p $1.50 NNAIG   2635
A joint exhibition: Fritz Kredel, woodcutter and book illus-
trator, and Herman Zapf, calligrapher and type designer
(Catalog 8) il p apply NNCoo   2636
The magazine show 1950, 1952, 1953 il p $1. ea NNAIG
2637

Thomas, Isaiah. Diary, 1805-1828. v. 1. (TC v 9) 1909
$4; v 2. (TC v 10) 1909 $4. MWA   2638
----. History of printing in America v 1. (TC v 5) 1874
$10.; v 6. 1874 $10. MWA   2639

--Art, United States--Decorative Arts and Design--Interior
Design and Furniture

American Antiquarian Society. Antiquities of the Western
States (TC v 1) 1820 $6. MWA   2640
Baltimore furniture; the work of Baltimore and Annapolis
cabinetmakers from 1760 to 1810; foreword by Adelyn D.
Breeskin; introduction by J.G.D. Paul; essays: Hepple-
white-Sheraton Period, Chippendale Period, Baltimore
Painted Furniture 195 p 131 il 1947 $6; to museums and
libraries $5. MdBMA   2641
Bissell, Charles S. Antique furniture in Suffield, 1670-1835
144 p il $8.75 CtHi   2642
Burnap Collection (repr, Antiques Magazine) p $.50 MoKNG
2643
Burnap Collection catalogue $3.50 MoKNG   2644
Connecticut chairs in the collection of the Connecticut His-
torical Society; foreword by Newton C. Brainard (Catalog
1) 57 p 1956 p $1. CtHi   2645
Cooperstown. Durant, John and Alice. A century of Coop-
erstown (repr, American Heritage, Dec 1958) il p $.25
NCooHi   2646
----. New York State Historical Association (repr, Antiques
Magazine, Feb 1959, special issue on the collections in
Fenimore House and in the Farmers' Museum) il p $1.
NCooHi   2647
Early furniture made in New Jersey, 1690-1870 89 p 22 il p
$1.75 NjNM   2648

Ford (Henry) Museum. Antiques at the Henry Ford Museum
    p $1. MiDbFM   2649
Luther, Clair Franklin. The Hadley Chest (Thankfull Taylor
    Chest) 144 p il 1935 $5. CtHi   2650
McIntire, Samuel. Hipkiss, Edwin J. Three McIntire rooms
    from Peabody, Massachusetts; describes three rooms
    from "Oak Hill," built 1800-1801 for Elizabeth Derby West
    25 p 34 il, 7 drg 1931 p $1. MBMu (op)   2651
----. Samuel McIntire. A bicentennial symposium, 1757-
    1957 65 il $4. MSaE   2652
----. Swan, Mabel M. Samuel McIntire and the Sander-
    sons, Salem cabinet makers 44 p il 1934 $2. MSaE
                                                         2653
Merrill, Walter M. New England treasury of American be-
    ginnings, Essex Institute (Newcomen Society of North
    America) 8 il 1957 p $.75 MSaE   2654
Rantoul, Robert S. A historic ball room 19 p 1894 p $.50
    MSaE   2655
Sanderson, Elijah and Jacob. Swan, Mable M. Elijah and
    Jacob Sanderson, early Salem cabinetmakers 41 p il 1934
    p $1.75 MSaE   2656
Sunnyside and its furnishings (issue of The American Col-
    lector magazine, Oct 1947) $.15 NTaS   2657
Thorne, Narcissa. Thorne rooms: American rooms in
    miniature 78 p 37 pl 1941 p $1. ICA; 1945 p InIJ 2657a
Whistler, James A. McNeill. The Whistler Peacock Room,
    an illustrated pamphlet containing a brief description and
    history of the Peacock Room decorated by James A. Mc-
    Neill Whistler (Smithsonian pubn 4024) 22 p 8 pl 1951 p
    DSI-F   2658
Williamsburg. Antiques at Williamsburg, compiled by edi-
    tors of Antiques Magazine 68 p 200 il $4. ViWC   2659
Wingfield, Virginia. New-England's rarieties, etc (TC v 4)
    1860 $5. MWA   2660

--Art, United States--Architecture

Architecture in America, 100 years 106 il (6 c) p $1.75
    MBMu   2661
Architecture of the Detroit Institute of Arts; forty photo-
    graphs of interior and exterior views with special empha-
    sis on architectural details. Floor plans of ground and
    main floors, as well as longitudinal and transverse sec-
    tions of the building 102 p 44 il (B 1) 1928 p $1. MiDA
                                                         2662
Armstrong, Moses K. Early Empire buildings of the Great
    West $3. NdHi   2663

Beale, Marie. Decatur House and its inhabitants $4.50
DN-HF   2664
Blueprint for tomorrow: A survey of Baltimore's architec-
tural future 34 il p $.50 MdBPM   2665
Dickson, Harold E. One hundred Pennsylvania buildings
1946 $6.50 PHarH   2666
Domestic architecture in the San Francisco Bay region; arti-
cles by: Lewis Mumford, William W. Wurster, Elizabeth
K. Thompson, and Gardner Dailey 1949 p $1.50 CSfMA
2667

Fenimore House (Art in America, April 1950 special issue)
il p $.75 NCooHi   2668
Frary, I.T. They built the Capitol $2.50 OC1MA   2669
Gebhard, David. The contemporary house p $.10 NmRMA
2670

How Maryland Colonists built homes (Leaflet 2) p $.10
MdHi   2671
Hunter, Wilbur H., Jr., and Charles H. Elam. Century of
Baltimore architecture, an illustrated guide to buildings
designed in the past century by members of the Baltimore
Chapter, AIA, with an introduction by Eleanor P. Spencer,
and an Index to Baltimore Architecture 48 p 83 p $1.
MdBPM   2672
Kimball, Fiske. Mansion of Elias Hasket Derby in Salem
20 p il plan 1924 p $1.50 MSaE   2673
The Liberty Pole on the commons (repr, Quarterly Bulletin,
Jan 1920) 20 p 6 il p $.60 NHi   2674
Nichols, Frederick D., and William B. O'Neal. Architec-
ture in Virginia, 1776-1958: The Old Dominion's twelve
best buildings, a survey p $1.50 ViRMu   2675
One hundred years of American architecture p $1.92 CLCM
2676
Overly, Charles. Philipsburg Manor, Upper Mills, a picture
story book p $.50 NTaS   2677
The Park Houses, Fairmont Park 24 p il 1956 p $.50 PPPM
2678

Pease, Z.W. The Arnold mansion, and its traditions
(Sketches 51) 38 p p $.25 MNBedfW   2679
Peare, Catherine Owens. William Penn's dream house, the
Founder's country home in Pennsbury 6 p il c 1957 p
$.15 PHarH   2680
Perley, Sidney. Dwellings at Boxford, Massachusetts 275
p il 1893 p $4. MSaE   2681
Purcell and Elmslie il, port p $.35 MnMW   2682
Quakers and their meeting house at Apponegansett (Sketches
80) 32 p p $.25 MNBedfW   2683
Ravenel, Beatrice St. Julien. Architects of Charleston;

stories of houses, churches, and public buildings of
Charleston; with an introduction by William Watts Ball,
and photographs by Carl Julien 329 p 1945 p $3. ScCG
2684

Roots of California contemporary architecture--a photographic
exhibition; introduction by Esther McCoy 19 il p $.50
CLMA   2685

Rounds, Ruby M.   Octagonal buildings of New York State;
compiled from information supplied by Stephen R. Leonard; foreword by Carl Carmer 22 p il rev ed 1954 p
$.35 NCooHi   2686

Scott, Mary Wingfield, and Louise F. Catterall.   Virginia's
capitol square, its buildings and its monuments 35 p 15
il 1957 p $1. ViRVM   2687

Seckel, Haryy W.   Hawaiian residential architecture: Contemporary Hawaiian architecture 17 p 12 il 1954 p $.50
HB   2688

Stoney, Samuel Gaillard.   Plantations of the Carolina low
country; edited by Albert Simons and Samuel Lapham,
Jr., with introduction by John Mead Howells 247 p 147
photog 3 map 20 plan 25 drg 4th ed 1955 boxed $12.50
ScCG   2689

----.   This is Charleston; analysis and list of 1168 buildings
141 p 571 photog 1944 p $2.50 ScCG   2690

Sunnyside, home of Washington Irving, a picture story book
1957 p $.50 NTaS   2691

Sweeney, John A.H.   Grandeur on the Appoquinimink: The
house of William Corbit at Odessa, Delaware--a detailed
account of the building of a colonial mansion, including an
appendix with reproductions of documents relating to the
construction, and photographs of 18th and early 19th century furniture (Published by New York University Press)
146 p 1959 $6.   DeWint   2692

Tripp, Thomas A.   Apponagansett meeting houses (Sketches
57) 16 p p $.25 MNBedfW   2693

Upham, Charles W.   Authenticity of the First Meeting House
(Salem) 15 p 1904 p $.50 MSaE   2694

----.   First houses in Salem 47 p 1859 p $1.25 MSaE 2695

Waters, Henry F.   Some Old Ipswich houses 45 p 1898 p
$1.25 MSaE   2696

Whiffen, Marcus.   The public buildings of Williamsburg 286
p il $12.50 ViWC   2697

Williamsburg.   Kocher, A. L., and Howard Dearstyne.   Colonial Williamsburg, its buildings and gardens 112 p phtog
$2.50 ViWC   2698

Zabriskie, George A.   The New York obelisk--"Cleopatra's
Needle" from Egypt to Central Park (repr, Quarterly Bul,

Oct 1940) 10 p 3 il p $.25 NHi   2699

--Art, United States--Architecture--Individual Architects

Gill, Irving. Irving Gill, photographs of his architecture
    60 p 1958 il $1. CLCM   2700
Neutra, Richard. Wight, Frederick S. Richard Neutra--is
    planning possible; Can destiny be designed 1958 p $1.
    CLU-A   2701
Sullivan, Louis. Louis Sullivan: Architect of free enter-
    prise 45 p il 1956 $1. ICA   2702

--Art, United States--Architecture--Spanish Colonial

Anderson, Clinton P. The Adobe Palace (repr, Hist Rev)
    26 p 3 map 1944 $.50 NmSM-H   2703
Casa de Adobe handbook, an illustrated guide to the replica
    of an early California ranch-house p $.15 CLSM 2704
Cullimore, C. Old adobes of forgotten Fort Tejon (Pubn 11)
    rev ed 1949 $2. CBakHi   2705
Fenyes, Eva Scott. Thirty-two adobe houses of Old Cali-
    fornia, reproductions of water colors, with descriptive
    text by Isabel Lopez de Fages 80 p 32 pl (1 c) $2.50
    CLSM   2706
Harrington, M.R. How to build a California adobe (Ander-
    son-Ritchie Press, with cooperation of Southwest Museum)
    63 p 32 il $2.50 CLSM   2707
Hewett, Edgar L. Hispanic monuments (P ns 28) 16 p il
    1938 p $.25 NmSM-S   2708
----, and Reginald Fisher. Mission monuments of New Mex-
    ico (Pub with U of New Mexico) 269 p il 2nd ptg 1946 $4.
    NmSM-S (op)   2709
----, and William Templeton Johnson. Architecture of the
    Panama-California International exposition (P 32) 7 p il
    1916 p $.25 NmSM-S   2710
Kidder, A.V. Early Pecos ruins on the Forked Lightning
    Ranch (P ns 16) 8 p 1926 p $.25 NmSM-S   2711
----. The Old North Pueblo of Pecos 10 p il; with The
    condition of the Main Pecos ruins (P 38) 2 p 1917 p $.25
    NmSM-S   2712
Mission Santa Clara 19 il c, cover c p $.50 CSc   2713
Mission trails p $.50 CLCM   2714
Old Santa Fe and vicinity (P 36) 36 p il 1930 rev ed $.35
    NmSM-H   2715
Toulouse, Joseph H., Jr. The Mission of San Gregorio de
    Abo: A report of the excavation and repair of a seven-
    teenth-century New Mexican mission; including appendices

on Mexican Majolica ware; notes on some organic remains from Abo Mission by Volney H. Jones, and Mission
of San Gregorio de Abo trait list (Salinas Focus) (M 13)
42 p 1949 $3.   NmSM-S   2716
Wuthenau, A. von.   Spanish military chapels in Santa Fe and
the Reredos of Our Lady of Light (repr, Hist Rev) 20 p
il 1935 $.25 NmSM-H   2717

--Art, United States--Architecture--Gardens and Gardening

Little, R. Burton, ed.   Landscape architecture--Bay Region
work 1958 p 55 il p $2.50 CSfMA   2718

--Art, Indians of North America

American Indian Painting Competition.   Annual p $.25 OkTP
                                                         2719
Blackfoot crafts p $.50 OkA   2720
Colors in Indian Art--Sources and uses (IL 56) CoDA   2721
Davidson, D.S.   Decorative art of the Tetes de Boule of
Quebec (INM 10:9) 38 p il 1928 p $1.15 NNMAI   2722
Denver Art Museum.   The native craftsmen, a review of
American Indian art in the Denver Art Museum's collec-
tion 9 p 15 il $.25 CoDA   2723
Design areas in Indian art (IL 62) CoDA   2724
Dewdney, Selwyn.   The Quetico pictographs p $.25 CaOTRM
                                                         2725
Dutton, Bertha P.   Indian artistry in wood and other media
(P ns 47) 28 p il (cover c) 1957 p $.35 NmSM-S   2726
Ewers, John C.   Early white influence upon the Plains Indian
paintings: George Catlin and Carl Bodmer among the
Mandan, 1832-34 (Smithsonian MC 134: 7; pubn 4292) p
$.50 DSI   2727
The Exposition of Indian Tribal Arts, Inc. Introduction to
American Indian art.   Pt.1. 59 p 33 il (many c) $2.
NmSM-S   2728
Farabee, W.C.   Indian cradles (MJ v 11, no 4) 22 p 26 il
(2 c) 1920 p $1.   PU-Mu   2729
Ford, James A.   Measurements of some prehistoric design
developments in the southeastern states (AP 44:3, p 309-
84) 23 fig 3 table 1952 p $2. NNM   2730
Gordon, G.B.   The double axe and some other symbols (MJ
v 7, no 1) 23 p 81 il 1911 p $1. PU-Mu   2731
Hewett, Edgar L.   Pre-Hispanic frescoes in the Rio Grande
Valley (P ns 27) 14 p il 1938 p $.25 NmSM-S   2732
Hopi Indian arts and crafts (Repr 3) 102 p p $1.50 AzFM
                                                         2733

Indian art of the Great Plains, a survey of the decorative
  arts of the Plains Indians 16 p 13 il $.25 CoDA   2734
Indian crafts and lore by Ben Hunt $1.95 OkA   2735
Indian sand paintings--Tribes, techniques and uses (IL 43/44)
  CoDA   2736
Iroquois crafts p $.50 OkA   2737
Jayne, H.H.F. American Indian portraits (B v 7, no 2) 2
  p 3 pl 1938 p $.50 PU-Mu   2738
Keithahn, E.L. Alaskan native art, a catalogue of the
  Alaska Historical Library and Museum's collection of na-
  tive art 80 p 126 il 1959 $1.50 AkHi   2739
No entry   2740
Lowie, Robert H. Crow Indian art (AP 21:4, p 271-322)
  23 fig 1922 p $.60 NNM   2741
Mason, J.A. Eskimo pictorial art (MJ v 18, no 3) 36 p 15
  il 1927 p $1. PU-Mu   2742
Mera, Harry P. The rain bird: A study in Pueblo design
  (M 2) 1938 $5. NmSM-L   2743
Native arts of the Pacific Northwest $7.50 OrPA   2744
Nute, Grace Lee. The picture rock of Crooked Lake (repr,
  Minnesota History, v 29) 1 il c p $.20 MnHi   2745
Ojibwa crafts p $.50 OkA   2746
Praus, Alexis A. A new pictographic autobiography of Sit-
  tin Bull (Smithsonian MC 123:6; pubn 4180) 1955 p $.35
  DSI   2747
Prehistoric and indigenous art of Southern California p $1.
  CPs   2748
Putnam, Fred W. Conventionalism in ancient American art 13
  p il 1887 p $.50 MSaE   2749
Quimby, George I. Prehistoric art of the Aleutian Islands
  (FA 36:4) 16 p 7 fig 1948 $.30 ICF   2750
Red-Dark-Light in designs (IL 114) CoDA   2751
Shotridge, L. The emblems of the Tlingit culture (MJ v 19,
  no 4) 28 p 7 pl 1928 p $1. PU-Mu   2752
----. Keyt-Gooshe "Killer Whale's Dorsal Fin" (a Tlingit
  dance baton) (MJ v 10, no 4) 4 p 1 pl c 1919 p $1.
  PU-Mu   2753
Skinner, Alanson. An antique tobacco-pouch of the Iroquois
  (INM 2:4) 2 p il 1920 p $.15 NNMAI   2754
Smith, Watson. Kiva mural decoration at Awatovi and Ka-
  waika-a: With a survey of other wall paintings in the
  Pueblo Southwest (P v 37) 384 p 64 fig 9 pl c 28 il 1952
  $10.50; p $7.50 MH-P   2755
Speck, F.G. Concerning iconology and masking complex in
  Eastern North America (B v 15, no 1) 60 p 15 il 1950 p
  $.50 PU-Mu   2756
----. Montagnais art in birch bark, a circumpolar trait

(INM 11:2) 157 p il 1937 p $1.50 NNMAI   2757
Speck, Frank G.   Symbolism in Penobscot art (AP 29:2, p
    25-80) 44 fig 1927 p $.50 NNM   2758
Stirling, Matthew W.   Three pictographic autobiographies of
    Sitting Bull 1938 (Smithsonian MC 97:5; pubn 3482) p
    $.75 DSI   2759
A study of Navajo symbolism.   Pt. 1.   Newcomb, Frank
    Johnson.   Navajo symbols in sandpaintings and ritual ob-
    jects; Pt. 2.   Fishler, Stanley A.   Navajo picture writing;
    Pt. 3.   Wheelwright, Mary C.   Notes on corresponding
    symbols in various parts of the world (P v 32, no 3) 100
    p 16 pl (12 c) 87 il 1956 p $5.   MH-P   2760
Symbolism in Indian art and the difficulty of its interpreta-
    tion (IL 61) CoDA   2761
Wardle, H.N.   Attu treasure (B v 11, no 4) 4 p 2 il 1946
    p $.50 PU-Mu   2762
Wauchope, Robert, and Arden R. King.   Exhibit of native
    American arts and crafts (M 8)16 p 1953 p apply LNT-
    MA   2763

--Art, Indians of North America--Sculpture

Boas, Franz.   A bronze figurine from British Columbia (B
    14:5, p 51-2) 1 pl 1901 p $.20 NNM   2764
Burnett, E.K.   Inlaid stone and bone artifacts from Southern
    California (C v 13) 60 p 71 pl 1944 p $3.50 NNMAI 2765
de Laguna, F.   An Alaskan stone lamp (B v 4, no 1) 3 p 1
    pl 1932 p $.35 PU-Mu   2766
----.   Three carvings from Cook Inlet, Alaska (B v 4, no
    2) 3 p 1 pl 1933 p $.35 PU-Mu   2767
Gordon, G.B.   An engraved bone from Ohio (T v 2, no 1)
    2 p 3 pl 1906 p $1.   PU-Mu   2768
Heye, George G.   A Mahican wooden cup (INM 5:2) 4 p il
    1921 p $.20 NNMAI   2769
Hodge, F.W.   Hawikuh bonework (INM 3:3) 151 p 56 pl 1920
    p $2.   NNMAI   2770
No entry   2771
No entry   2772
Mason, J. Alden.   A remarkable stone lamp from Alaska (MJ
    v 19, no 2) 25 p 6 il 1928 p $1.   PU-Mu   2773
Pepper, George H.   A stone effigy pipe from Kentucky (INM
    10:1) 20 p il 1920 p $.25 NNMAI   2774
----.   A wooden image from Kentucky (INM 10:7) 20 p il
    1921 p $.30 NNMAI   2775
Ritzenthaler, Robert E.   Totem poles (Popular Pam, Lore
    Leaves no 6; repr Lore) 16 il p $.15 WMMMu   2776
Skinner, Alanson.   An Iroquois antler figurine (INM 2:5) 2 p

il 1920 p $.15 NNMAI   2777
----. Two antler spoons from Ontario (M 2) 2 p il 1920
  p $.15 NNMAI   2778

--Art, Indians of North America--Sculpture---Masks

Keppler, Joseph. Comments on certain Iroquois masks (C
  12:4) 40 p il 1941 p $1.50 NNMAI   2779
Ritzenthaler, Robert E. Masks of North American Indians
  (Popular Pam, Lore Leaves no 200; repr Lore) 17 il p
  $.15 WMMMu   2780
Skinner, Alanson. Two Lenape stone masks from Pennsyl-
  vania and New Jersey (M 3) 3 p il 1920 p $.20 NNMAI
                                                                  2781
Types of Indian masks (IL 65/66) CoDA   2782
Wardle, H.N. Eskimoe Tun-Ghat mask (B v 6, no 6) 2 p l
  pl c 1937 p $.35 PU-Mu   2783

--Art, Indians of North America--Decorative Arts and De-
sign--Jewelry and Gems

Camman, S. Carbings in walrus ivory 31 p 14 il; with
  Emerick, D. The Havasupais, people of Cataract Canyon
  16 p 12 il (B v 18, no 3) 1954 p $.50 PU-Mu   2784
Ferdon, Edwin N., Jr. Characteristic figurines from Es-
  meraldas (P ns 40) 25 p il 1945 p $.25 NmSM-S   2785
Hodge, F.W. Turquoise work of Hawikuh (L 2) 30 p il
  1921 p $3. NNMAI   2786
Main types of Indian metal jewelry (IL 104) CoDA   2787
Mera, Harry P. Indian silverwork of the Southwest--
  Bridles (B 17) 1944 p $.75;--Band bracelets, embossed
  (B 19) 1945 p $.75 NmSM-L   2788
Navaho silversmithing (IL 15) CoDA   2789
Woodward, Arthur. A brief history of Navajo silversmithing
  (B 14) 84 p 1946 $2. AzFM   2790

--Art, Indians of North America--Decorative Arts and De-
sign--Ceramics

American Indian pottery p $.50 OkTP   2791
Chapman, Kenneth M. The pottery of Santo Domingo: A de-
  tailed study of its decoration (M 1) 192 p pl drg 2nd ed
  1953 $6.50 NmSM-L   2792
Colton, Harold S. Check list of Southwestern pottery types
  (Ceramic 2) 43 p 1955 loose $1. AzFM   2793
----. Pottery types of the Arizona Strip and adjacent areas
  in Utah and Nevada (Ceramic 1) 98 p 1952 loose $2.

AzFM   2795

Designs of the Membrenos, an exhibition of zoomorphic decor-
    ations on Indian pottery from the Mimbres River Valley,
    New Mexico il 1956 p $.50 CtY-A   2796
Dutton, Bertha P. A history of plumbate ware (Pns 31) 50
    p il 1943 p $1.50 NmSM-S   2797
Heimlich, Marion D. Guntersville basin pottery (MP 32)
    63 p il 1952 apply; $.06 post AU-Mu   2798
Hoerler, Alice. Selected pottery from the excavations of the
    Indian site survey of New Jersey (ASNL 6) 1939 p $.25
    NjTM   2799
Hopi Indian pottery (IL 47) CoDA   2800
Indian pottery folder, brief descriptions of pottery from vari-
    ous tribes p $.07 NBuM   2801
Martin, Paul S., and Elizabeth S. Willis. Anasazi painted
    pottery in Field Museum of Natural History (AM 5) 284 p
    125 pl 1 map 1940 $6. ICF (op)   2802
Modern Pueblo pottery types (IL 53/54) CoDA   2803
Morris, Earl H. The beginnings of pottery making in the
    San Juan area; unfired prototypes and the wares of the
    earliest ceramic period (AP 28:2, p 125-98) 43 fig 1927
    p $1. NNM   2804
Morrs, Noel. Clay figurines in the American Southwest,
    with a description of a new Pillings find in northeastern
    Utah and a comparison with certain other North American
    figurines (P v 49, no 1) 74 p 18 fig 13 il 2 map 1954 p
    $3.50 MH-P   2805
Pottery of the Southwestern tribes (IL 69/70) CoDA   2806
Pottery types of the Southwest (Ceramic 3). Pt. a. Colton,
    Harold S. Wares 8A, 8B, 9A, 9B (Tusayan Gray, Tusayan
    White, Little Colorado Gray, Little Colorado White) 98 p
    1955 p $2; Pt. b. Abel, Leland J. Wares 5A, 10A, 10B,
    12A (San Juan Red, Mesa Verde Gray, Mesa Verde White,
    San Juan White) 66 p 1955 p $1.75; Pt. c. Colton, Har-
    old S. Wares 5A, 5B, 6A, 6B, 7A, 7B, 7C (San Juan
    Red, Tsegi Orange, Homolovi Orange, Winslow Orange,
    Awatovi Yellow, Jeddito Yellow, Sichomovi Red) 1956 $2;
    Pt. d. Colton, Harold S., et al. Wares 14, 15, 16, 17,
    18 (revised descriptions Alameda Brown Ware, Tizon
    Brown Ware, Lower Colorado Buff Ware, Prescott Gray
    Ware, San Francisco Mt. Gray Ware) 105 p 1958 p $1.75
    AzFM   2807
Pueblo Indian pottery making (IL 6) CoDA   2808
Quimby, George I. Pottery from the Aleutian Islands (FA
    36:1) 14 p 1945 $.20 ICG   2809
Rinaldo, John B., and Elaine A. Bluhm. Late Mogollon

pottery types of the Reserve Area (FA 36:7) 39 p 33 il
1 map 1956 $1.25 ICF   2810
Santa Clara and San Juan pottery (IL 35) CoDA   2811
Schmidt, Erich F. Time-relations of prehistoric pottery
types in southern Arizona (AP 30:5, p 247-302) 36 fig
1928 p $.75 NNM   2812
Schoolcraft, Henry R. Notices of some antique earthern
vessels found in the low tumuli of Florida and in the
caves and burial places of the Indian tribes north of these
latitudes. An address 15 p 2 il 1847 $1. NHi   2813
Tschopik, Harry, Jr. Navaho pottery markings (P v 17, no
1) 85 p 16 pl 7 il 1941 p $1.75 MH-P   2814
Utterback, Martha, and Mardith Schuetz. Indian pottery of
the Southwest 17 p 5 il 1954 $.75 TxSaW   2815
Wormington, H.M., and Arminta Neal. The story of Pueblo
pottery (MP 2) 64 p 54 il p CoDMNH   2816

--Art, Indians of North America--Decorative Arts and De-
sign--Textiles

Heye, George G., and William C. Orchard. A rare Salish
blanket (L 5) 15 p il 1926 p $1.75 NNMAI   2817
Hopi Indian weaving (IL 18) CoDA   2818
Indian cloth making (IL 59/60) CoDA   2819
Indian vegetable dyes. Pt. 1. (IL 63); Pt. 2. (IL 71)
CoDA   2820
Main types of Pueblo cotton textiles (IL 92/93) CoDA 2821
Main types of Pueblo woolen textiles (IL 94/95) CoDA 2822
Mera, Harry P. Navajo blankets of the "Classic Period" (B
3) 1945 p $.25 NmSM-L   2823
----. Navajo textile arts 1947 $2.75 NmSM-L (op)   2824
----. Navajo twilled weaving (B 14) 1945 p $.25 NmSM-L
                                                        2825
----. Pictorial blankets (B 6) 1945 p $.25 NmSM-L   2826
----. Pueblo Indian embroidery (M 4) 1943 $5. NmSM-L
                                                        2827
----. The slave blanket (B 5) 1945 p $.25 NmSM-L   2828
----. The so-called "chief blanket" (B 2) 1945 p $.25
NmSM-L   2829
Merwin, B.W. Some Ojibway Buffalo robes (MJ v 7, no 2)
4 p 8 pl c 1916 p $1. PU-Mu   2830
Navaho spinning, dyeing and weaving (IL 3) CoDA   2831
Navaho weaving--blankets (IL 113) CoDA   2832
Orchard, William C. Sandals and other fabrics from Ken-
tucky Caves (M 4) 20 p il 1920 p $.30 NNMAI   2833
Parfleches and other rawhide articles (IL 77/78) CoDA 2834
Plains Indian hide dressing and bead sewing techniques (IL 2)

CoDA   2835
Pueblo weaving--Acoma (IL 89); --Tewa Village (IL 90);
    --Keres, Tiwa, and Jemez Villages (IL 91); -- Zuni (IL
    96/97) CoDA   2836
Schuetz, Mardith K.   The Navajo and the art of weaving 2 p
    1959 $.15 TxSaW   2837
Southwestern weaving materials (IL 116) CoDA   2838
Whitford, A.C.   Textile fibres used in eastern aboriginal
    America (AP 38:1, p 1-22) 1942 p $.25 NNM   2839

--Art, Indians of North America--Decorative Arts and De-
sign--Textiles--Costume

Basic type of Indian women's clothing (IL 108) CoDA   2840
Brinton, D.G.   Note on the criteria of wampum (BFM v 1,
    no 4) 2 p 1898 p $.50 PU-Mu   2841
Farabee, W.C.   A newly acquired wampum belt (MJ v 11,
    no 1) 4 p 1 pl 1920 p $1. PU-Mu   2842
----.   Recent discovery of ancient wampum belt (MJ v 13,
    no 1) 9 p 3 il 1922 p $1. PU-Mu   2843
Indian costumes p $.05 CLCM   2844
Indian women's clothing--fashion and function (IL 109) CoDA
                                                                   2845
Plains Indian clothing (IL 24) CoDA   2846
Pueblo Indian clothing (IL 4) CoDA   2847
Speck, F.G.   Huron treaty belts (MJ v 2, no 1) 2 p il 1911
    p $.50 PU-Mu   2848
----, and William C. Orchard.   The Penn wampum belts
    (L 4) 20 p il 1925 p $3.75 NNMAI   2849
War bonnets (IL 110) CoDA   2850
Wissler, Clark.   Distribution of moccasin decorations among
    the Plains tribes (AP 29:1, p 1-23) 4 fig 1927 p $.25
    NNM   2851

--Art, Indians of North America--Decorative Arts and De-
sign--Basketry

American Indian basketry p $.50 OkTP   2852
Apache Indian coiled basketry (L 64) CoDA   2853
Baketry construction techniques (IL 67) CoDA   2854
Basketry decoration techniques (IL 68) CoDA   2855
Basketry east of the Rockies (IL 87) CoDA   2856
Basketry of Washington and Northwest Oregon (IL 98) CoDA
                                                                   2857
Farrand, Livingston.   Basketry of the Salish Indians (M 2:5,
    p 393-400; JNP v 1) 3 pl 15 fig 1900 p $.75 NNM   2858
Gordon, G.B.   The Richard Waln Meirs Collection (mainly

California basketry) (MJ v 10, no 1-2) 3 p 2 il 1919 p
    $2. PU-Mu   2859
Hopi Indian basketry (IL 17) CoDA   2860
Indian basketry--Types, techniques and distribution (IL 58)
    CoDA   2861
Indian baskets p $.20 TxAuM   2862
Kissell, Mary Lois. Basketry of the Papago and Pima (AP
    17:4, p 115-264) 81 fig 1916 p $1.50 NNM   2863
Kroeber, A.L. Basketry designs of the Mission Indians (SG
    55) 19 p 9 il p $.30; $.10 post NNM   2864
----. Basket designs of the Mission Indians of California
    (AP 20:1, p 149-83) 6 pl 97 fig 1922 p $.50 NNM   2865
Main divisions of California Indian basketry (IL 83/84) CoDA
                                                                 2866

Main types of Southwestern twined, wicker and plaited basket-
    ry (IL 99/100) CoDA   2867
Merwin, B.W. Basketry of Chitimacha Indians (MJ v 10,
    no 1-2) 6 p 4 pl 1919 p $2. PU-Mu   2868
Pima Indian close coiled basketry (IL 5) CoDA   2869
Roberts, Helen H. Basketry of the San Carlos Apache (AP
    31:2, p 121-218) 27 fig 1929 p $1. NNM   2870
Sapir, E. An Apache basket (MJ v 1, no 1) 3 p 1 il 1910
    p $.50 PU-Mu   2871
Shotridge, L. Tlingit woman's root basket (MJ v 12, no 3)
    17 p 7 il (1 c) 1921 p $1. PU-Mu   2872
Southwestern coiled basketry (IL 88) CoDA   2873
Spruce root basketry of the Alaskan Tlingit p $.50 OkA 2874
Wardle, H.N. American Indian baskets (B v 7, no 3) 1 p 1
    pl 1939 p $.50 PU-Mu   2875
----. The Brock Collection of baskets (B v 3, no 3-4) 3 p
    1 pl 1932 p $.35 PU-Mu   2876
----. A Datsolalee basket (B v 7, no 3) 2 p 2 il 1939 p
    $.50 PU-Mu   2877

--Art, Indians of North America--Decorative Arts and De-
sign--Quill and Beadwork

Beadwork--history and techniques (IL 117) CoDA   2878
Hall, H.U. A souvenir of the great explorers (on a Tahitian
    featherwork breastplate found on Admiralty Island, believed
    brought there by Captain Cook or George Vancouver (MJ
    v 16, no 3) 18 p 4 pl 1925 p $1. PU-Mu   2879
Harrington, M.R. A bird-quill belt of the Sauk and Fox
    (INM 10:5) 4 p il 1920 p $.15 NNMAI   2880
----. Old Sauk and Fox beaded garters (INM 10:4) 3 p il
    1920 p $.15 NNMAI   2881
Indian beadmaking p $.05 CLCM   2882

Main types of sewn beadwork (IL 118/119) CoDA   2883
Merwin, B.W.   The art of quillwork (MJ v 9, no 1) 6 p 6
    il (1 c) 1918 p $1. PU-Mu   2884
Orchard, William C.   Beads and beadwork of the American
    Indians (C v 11) 140 p 31 pl 1929 p $2.50 NNMAI   2885
Plains beads and beadwork designs (IL 73/74) CoDA   2886
Porcupine quill work (IL 103) CoDA   2887
Pueblo shell beads and inlay--manufacture and uses (IL 30)
    CoDA   2888
Quill and beadwork of the Western Sioux p $.50 OkA   2889
Skinner, Alanson.   An Illinois quilled necklace (INM 10:3)
    2 p il 1920 p $.15 NNMAI   2890
A study of Indian beadwork p $.40 MnSSci (op)   2891
Wildschut, William, and John C. Ewers.   Crow Indian bead-
    work, a descriptive and historical study (C v 24) 55 p 47
    pl (3 c) 1959 p $3.50 NNMAI   2892

--Art, Indians of North America--Decorative Arts and De-
sign--Toys, Dolls, etc.

Indian dolls (for the younger reader) (B v 5, no 2) 2 p 2 il
    1934 p $.35 PU-Mu   2893
Kachinas and Kachina dolls (IL 111) CoDA   2894
Hunt, W. Ben.   Kachina dolls (PSH 7) 32 p 12 il (7 c) 1958
    p $1. WMMMu   2895
Wardle, H.N.   Hopi kachinas (B v 9, no 1) 5 p 2 pl 1941
    p $.50 PU-Mu   2896
Watkins, Frances E.   Hopi toys (Leaflet 19) p $.20 CLCM
                                                       2897

--Art, Indians of North America--Architecture

Dakota bark house p $.60 MnSSci   2898
The grass house of the Caddo and the Wichita (IL 42) CoDA
                                                       2899
Indian houses p $.05 CLCM   2900
Iroquois longhouse (IL 12) CoDA   2901
Jaeger, Ellsworth.   Plains Indian tepee, story of tepee and
    pattern for making a miniature tepee (BSNS) p $.15
    NBuM   2902
New England houses, forts and villages (IL 39) CoDA   2903
Plains Indian earthlodge (IL 20)   CoDA   2904
Plains Indian tipi (IL 19) CoDA   2905
Puget Sound Indian houses (IL 34) CoDA   2906
Southwest Indian dwellings (IL 9) CoDA   2907
Waterman, T.T., and Ruth Greiner.   Indian houses of Puget
    Sound (Misc 9) 61 p il 1921 p $.70 NNMAI   2908

----, etal. Native houses of western North America (Misc
   11) 97 p il 1921 p $1.50 NNMAI   2909

--Art, Central and South America   See also Indians of
Mexico, Central and South America under Primitive Art

Art in Colonial Mexico il 1951 p $.50 InIJ   2910
Chilean contemporary art; introduction by Molly Ohl Godwin;
   articles by Eugenio Pereira Salas, Corlos Humeres Solar
   169 p 50 il p $1. OTM   2911
Latin American collection paintins p $.25 CSfMA   2912
Mexican collection, Modern Mexican school since 1920 p
   $.25 CSfMA   2913
Mexican popular arts today 64 p p $1.50 CoCF   2914
Twentieth century Mexican paintings 1958 p $.25 TxSaMc
                                                           2915
Velde, Paul Van de, and Henrietta Romeike Van de Velde.
   The black pottery of Coyotepec, Oaxaca, Mexico (Paper
   13) 43 p 15 pl 1939 p $2.50 CLSM   2916
Foster, George M. Contemporary pottery techniques in
   southern and central Mexico (P 22; FIT 1) 48 p il 1955 p
   $2. LNT-MA   2917
Rendon, Silvia. Modern pottery of Riotenco San Lorenzo,
   Cuauhtitlan (P 15; MARR v 1, no 15) 18 p 1950 p $.75
   LNT-MA   2918
Stone, Doris. Notes on present-day pottery making and its
   economy in the ancient Chorotegan area (P 15; MARR v 1,
   no 16) 12 p 1950 p $.50 LNT-MA   2919

--Art, Central and South American--Individual Artists

Matta Eschurren, Roberto. Matta p $1. MnMW   2920
Orozco, Jose Clemente. Jose Clemente Orozco p $.25 MBI
                                                           2921
----. Orozco 1959 p $.25 TxSaMc   2922
Rivera, Diego. Frescoes of Detroit by Diego Rivera (G 7)
   16 p 18 il (cover c) 1956 p $.25 MiDA   2923
Velasco, Jose Maria. Jose Maria Velasco--Mexican land-
   scapist; introduction by Henry Clifford and Carlos Pellicer
   80 p 52 pl 1944 p $1. PPPM   2924

--Art, European

Age of elegance: The Rococo and its effect--a catalogue of
   an exhibition of rococo art assembled from American collections; foreword by Adelyn D. Breeskin; essays by
   George Boas, "Intellectual currents of the 18th century,"

and James D. Breckenridge, "The rococo and its effect"
91 p 90 il 1959 p $2. MdBMA   2925
Arizona, University of, Art Gallery. Samuel H. Kress Col-
lection--Renaissance art p $1. AzU-A   2926
Art Institute of Chicago. The Lucy Maud Buckingham Medieval Collection Handbook 80 p il p $.75 ICA   2927
Art treasures from the Vienna Collection; introduction by
Ernst H. Buschbeck, Erich V. Strohmer 112 p il 1949 p
$.75 OTM   2928
Berlin Museums. Masterpieces from Berlin Museums, se-
lected examples from an exhibition in Museum, 1948 113
p 98 il p $.75 OClMA; OTM   2929
----. Paintings from the Berlin Museums exhibited in co-
operation with the Department of Army of the United
States of America 72 p front c 52 pl1948 p $1. NNMM;
$.50 PPPM   2930
Birmingham Museum of Art. Samuel H. Kress Collection
Catalogue il p $1.50 ABM   2931
Bosch to Beckmann, 22 paintings from 5 centuries (1450-
1950) 43 p 13 il 1950 p $.25 NBuA   2932
Denver Art Museum. European art, the Denver Art Mu-
seum's collection, a comprehensive catalogue of paintings
and decorative arts 108 p 116 il $1. CoDA   2933
----. Samuel H. Kress collection of paintings and sculpture.
Masterpieces of Renaissance art 80 p 37 il (5 c) $1.
CoDA   2934
The development of the medieval collection (City Art Museum, St. Louis) 32 p 26 il p $.75; $.10 post MoSCA
                                                              2935
de Young (M. H.) Memorial Museum. Samuel H. Kress Col-
lection 41 il (9 c) p $2. CSfDeY   2936
Eighteenth century English and Italian landscape painting,
representing Bellotto, Canaletto, Guardi, Magnasco, Tie-
polo, Girtin, Bonington, Scott and Wilson; introduction by
W.G. Constable 43 il 1940 p $.50 CtY-A   2937
European artists teaching in America, 1941 64 p 49 il p $2.
MAnP-A   2938
European masterpieces p $.25 MdHagM   2939
Expressionism, 1900-1955 p $1. MnMW   2940
High Museum of Art. Paintings in the Kress Collection p
$2. GAHM   2941
Homage to Mozart: A loan exhibition of European painting,
1750-1800, honoring the 200th anniversary of Mozart's
birth; introduction by Evan H. Turner 23 p 29 il p $1.
CtHWA   2942
Houston Museum of Fine Arts. Edith A. and Percy S. Straus
Collection Early painting, bronzes p $.50 TxHM   2943

----. The Kress Collection--High Renaissance, Italian and
Spanish p $1.50 TxHM   2944
Hubbard, R.H.   European paintings in Canadian collections
p $7.50 CaOONG; CaOTAG   2945
Los Angeles County Museum.   Catalogue of paintings I.
Italian, French, and Spanish paintings, XIV-XVIII century
il 1954; Catalogue of paintings II.   Flemish, German,
Dutch and English paintings, XV to XVII century il 1954
p $2.60 ea CLCM   2946
----. Kress Collection p $.48 CLCM   2947
Masterpieces of art: European paintings from the New York
and San Francisco World's Fairs, 1939: A catalogue of
the exhibition 23 p 21 pl 1940 p $.25 NjNM   2948
Metropolitan Museum of Art.   Allen, Josephine L., and
Elizabeth E. Gardner.   A concise catalogue of the Euro-
pean paintings in the Metropolitan Museum of Art 104 p
1 il c 1954 p $1. NNMM   2949
----. A catalogue of paintings in the Bache Collection 82
p 63 il 4th ed 1944 p $.50 NNMM   2950
----. Wehle, Harry B., and Margaretta Salinger.   Catalogues of early Flemish, Dutch, and German paintings
243 p 169 il 1947 p $3.50 NNMM   2951
Milwaukee Art Center.   Inaugural exhibition catalogue: El
Greco, Rembrandt, Goya, Cezanne, Van Gogh and Picasso
p $2.   WMA   2952
Modern European masters 131 il (4 c) 1957 p $2. MBMu
                                                        2953
Museum of Fine Arts, Boston.   Summary catalogue of European paintings in oil, tempera and pastel in the Museum
of Fine Arts, Boston; paintings acquired to January 1955,
listed by artist, giving school and dates, and for each
painting: medium, size, whether signed and dates,
source from which acquired 72 p 1955 p $.75 MBMu 2954
National Gallery of Art.   Christensen, Erwin O.   Objects of
medieval art from the Widener Collection (NGA Hdbk 3)
32 p 15 il 1952 p $.35 DSI-GA   2955
----. Masterpieces of Impressionist and Post=Impression-
ist painting 64 p 50 il 1959 p $2.   DSI-GA   2956
----. Painting and sculpture from Samuel H. Kress Collection, with foreword by John Walker 468 p il (6 c) 1959
$4.75 DSI-GA   2957
One hundred paintings from the Sao Paulo Museum of Art il
1957 p $1.   OTM   2958
Paintings from the Collection of Walter P. Chrysler, Jr.,
an exhibition of paintings selected from the Chrysler Collection comprising European examples from the 16th century through the 20th century p $1.75 CSfPL   2959

Philadelphia Museum of Art. Handbook of the display collection of the art of the middle ages; a discussion of
Early Christian, Romanesque, and Gothic related to the
Museum's collection 46 p il p $.25 PPPM   2960
----. John G. Johnson Collection. 1953: Italian, Dutch,
Flemish, German, Spanish, French, English, and 19th
century paintings; foreword by Henri Marceau 272 p 228
pl (3 c) p $3.75; Selected paintings, a picture book 65 pl
1948 p $1: Catalogue of paintings, arranged by schools,
giving artists, dates, dimensions of paintings, signatures
and inscriptions; foreword by Henri Marceau 73 p 1 pl c
1941 p $.50 PPPM						2961
----. George Gray Barnard Collection, Art of the Middle
Ages--including capitals from early Christian to Gothic
sculpture in wood and stone, paintings, architectural elements, stained glass, decorative arts, the Antwerp Altar-
piece; introduction by George Robinson 109 p 62 pl 1941
$2.50 PPPM						2962
Philbrook Art Center. Samuel H. Kress Collection p $1.
OkTP							2963
Pictures of everyday life: Genre painting in Europe, 1500-
1900, catalogue 1954 p $1.25 PPiCIA			2964
Ponti, Giovanni, and Gyorgy Kepes. Ponti-Kepes p $.25
MBI							2965
Portland Art Museum. Kress Collection paintings of the
Renaissance $2.50 OrPA					2966
Poussin, Nicolas, and Peter Paul Rubens. Poussin-Rubens
1948 p $.25 OCA						2967
Religious art of the middle ages and Renaissance, in the col-
lection of the Wadsworth Atheneum; introduction by Esther
I. Seaver 29 p 23 il 1950 p $.75 CtHWA			2968
Rorimer, James J. The Cloisters: The building and the
collection of Medieval art in Fort Tryon Park 158 p 87 il
1955 p $1. NNMM						2969
Seattle Art Museum. European paintings and sculpture,
Samuel H. Kress Collection; introduction by Richard E.
Fuller 80 p il (4 c) p $1.50 WaSA			2970
Tonny, Kristians, Paul Tchelitchew, Christian Berard,
Leonid Berman. Tonny, Tchelitchew, Berard, Berman--
notes on each artist 10 p 5 il 1931 p $.25 CtHWA	2971
Toronto Art Gallery. Some European paintings from the Art
Gallery's Collection p $.25 CaOTAG			2972
Younger European painters; foreword by James Johnson
Sweeney 33 il p $1.25 NNGu				2973

--Art, European--Sculpture

Los Angeles County Museum. Gothic and Renaissance sculp-
    tures in the collection of the Los Angeles County Museum,
    catalogue and guide 185 p il 1951 p $3. CLCM   2974
National Gallery of Art. Renaissance bronzes: Statuettes,
    reliefs, and plaquettes, medals and coins from the Kress
    Collection (former Dreyfus Collection), with foreword by
    David E. Finley, and introduction and notes by Perry B.
    Cott   178 p il 1950 p $3. DSI-GA   2975

--Art, European--Decorative Arts and Design

Remington, Preston. European decorative art. A picture
    book 72 p 99 il 1954 p $1.   NNMM   2976
Ricketson, Edith B. Barbarian jewelry of the Merovingian
    period (repr, Bul, Jan 1947) 8 p map 15 il 1947 p $.10
    NNMM   2977
Cummings, Virginia L. Laces of old Europe (F 12) p $.20
    NBuM   2978
The gift of Leo Wallerstein. Some French and English tole
    in the museum (MC v 2, no 3) il p $.15 NNCoo   2979
Books of the Middle Ages; an introduction to Medieval manu-
    scripts with reference to the Museum collection 11 p il
    (facsim c pl) p $.35 CaOTRM   2980
Decorated book papers, 17th-20th century (C 6) 6 il p $.15
    NNCoo   2981
Illuminated books of the Middle Ages and Renaissance 85 p
    fron c 80 pl 1949 $4; p $3. MdBWA   2982
Incunabula typographica, a descriptive catalogue of the books
    printed in the fifteenth century in the library of Henry
    Walters 519 p 109 il 1906 $10. MdBWA   2983
Medieval and Renaissance illuminated manuscripts p $1.92
    CLCM   2984
Miner, Dorothy E. The development of Medieval illumina-
    tion, as related to the evolution of book design 20 p il c
    1958 p $1. MdBWA   2985
Pierpont Morgan Library. Treasures from the Pierpont
    Morgan Library, an exhibition of Medieval and Renaissance
    illuminated manuscripts, incunabula, fine binding and liter-
    ary manuscripts and master drawings p $2.50 CSfPL
                                                          2986
Gothic room p $.50 CLCM   2987
Thorne, Narcissa. European rooms in miniature 64 p 34 pl
    1948 p $1.   ICA   2988
Thorne period rooms, European (Art Bul) 24 p 14 il p $.75
    MoSCA   2989

--Art Dutch and Flemish

Corcoran Gallery. Dutch and Flemish paintings in the W.A.
Clark Collection in the Corcoran Gallery 52 p 29 il (1 c)
1955 p $1. DCGA (op)   2990
Dutch painting: The Golden Age, an exhibition of Dutch pic-
tures of the seventeenth century; preface by Blake-More
Godwin, introduction by Theodore Rousseau, Jr. 94 p 102
il (9 c) 1955 p $1.50 NNMM; OTM; $1. CaOTAG   2991
Dutch paintings of the 17th century il 1937 p InIJ   2992
Dutch paintings, 17th century, a picture book 24 p 16 il 1931
p $.15 PPPM   2993
Early Dutch painting, 1460-1540 (C 4) 28 p 8 il 1944 p $.25
MiDA   2994
Fansler, Roberta M., and Margaret R. Scherer. Painting
in Flanders 36 p 36 il, 1 folded 1945 p $1. NNMM 2995
Flemish paintings, a picture book 24 p 16 il 1931 p $.15
PPPM   2996
Hals, Frans, and Rembrandt van Rijn. Hals--Rembrandt
$1.92; p $1.20 CLCM   2997
Life in seventeenth century Holland: Views, vistas, pas-
times, pantomimes, portraits, peep shows; introduction
by Charles C. Cunningham 26 p 28 il 1951 p $1. CtHWA
                                                         2998
The little masters--paintings by artists of the Netherlands
and Belgium lent from the Collection of Walter P. Chrys-
ler, Jr. 16 il p $.35 ViRMu   2999
National Gallery of Art. Broadley, Hugh T. Flemish paint-
ing in the National Gallery of Art (NGA Book 5) 1959 p
$.25 DSI-GA   3000
----. Dutch painting in the National Gallery of Art 1960 p
$.25 DSI-GA   3001
Seventeenth century Dutch paintings 12 p il p $.15 NAlAI
                                                         3002
Toledo Museum of Art. Dutch art in the Toledo Museum of
Art (Museum News, Fall 1957) 20 p p $.50 OTM   3003

--Art, Dutch and Flemish--Individual Artists

Ensor, James. Tannenbaum, Libby. James Ensor, loan
exhibition in Museum 1951 110 il (8 c) $4. OClMA   3004
Gogh, Vincent van. Rich, Daniel Catton, and Theodore Rousseau, Jr. Van Gogh: Paintings and drawings 96 p 4 pl
c 62 il 1949 p $2.50 NNMM   3005
----. Van Gogh exhibition catalog il p $1. CSfDeY   3006
----. Van Gogh--loan exhibition of paintings, drawings, and
prints; introduction by John Rewald 37 il p $.50 CLMA
                                                         3007
----. Van Gogh: Paintings and drawings 96 p il 1949 p

$.50 ICA   3008

----. Vincent van Gogh exhibition; foreword by Fiske Kimball 80 p 29 pl (13 c) 1953 p $.50 PPPM   3009

----. Works of Vincent van Gogh, selected examples from
an exhibition in the Museum, 1948 51 il (1 c) p $.50
OClMA   3010

Mondrian, Piet. Piet Mondrian: The earlier years, checklist of an exhibition focusing on the years, 1904-1920 5 il
p $.25 NNGu   3011

Rembrandt van Rijn. The young Rembrandt p il 1958 $1.
InIJ   3012

----. Valentiner, W.R. Rembrandt and his pupils 123 p
85 il p $1. NcRMA   3013

Rubens, Peter Paul. An exhibition of 60 paintings and some
drawings by Peter Paul Rubens (C 1) 72 p 23 il 1936 p
$.35 MiDA   3014

--Art, Dutch and Flemish--Graphic Arts and Drawing

Cleveland Museum of Art. Dutch drawings, selected examples from an exhibition in Museum 1959 53 il p $1.75
OClMA   3015

Dutch drawings, masterpieces of five centuries; introduction
by Prof. Dr. J.Q. van Regteran Altena 104 p 54 il 1958
p $1.75 DSI-GA; MBMu   3016

Rembrandt van Rijn. Rembrandt drawings from American
collections, an illustrated exhibition catalogue, with an introduction by Jakob Rosenberg 128 p 69 pl 1960 $6;   p
$3.50 NNPM   3017

----. Rosenberg, Jacob. Rembrandt the draughtsman 1956
p $.75 MH-FA   3018

Rubens, Peter Paul. Rubens drawings and oil sketches
from American collections 1956 p $1.50 MH-FA   3019

--Art, Dutch and Flemish--Decorative Arts and Design

Four late Gothic Flemish tapestries of virtues and vices from
the collection of William Randolph Hearst (PB 9) 12 p 6 il
1956 p $.10 MiDA   3020

Rorimer, James J., and Margaret B. Freeman. The Nine
Heroes tapestries at the Cloisters, a picture book   24 p
31 il 1953 p $.50 NNMM   3021

Glass vessels in Dutch paintings of the 17th century, a narrative guide to exhibition organized by the Museum 31 p
10 il 1952 p $.50 NCorniC-M   3022

--Art, English

Allen, Robert J.   Life in eighteenth century England, port-
   folio of 42 plates (12x16.5) with explanatory captions, 40
   p text p $5.   MBMu   3024
British art p $.35 MBI   3025
British contemporary painters 97 p 72 il, incl port 1946 p
   $1.   NBuA   3026
British painting in the eighteenth century 150 p 82 il (8 c)
   1958 p $1.50 CaOONG; CaOTAG; OTM   3027
Contemporary British art, catalogue of paintings 65 p 37 il
   1942 p $.50 OTM   3028
English conversation pieces of the eighteenth century (C 12)
   40 p 20 il (front c) 1948 p $.50 MiDA   3029
English paintings by Hogarth, Reynolds, Gainsborough, Rom-
   ney and Lawrence 24 p 5 il c 1945 p $1. NBuA   3030
Exhibition of contemporary British art, catalogue of oil paint-
   ings, water colours, drawings, prints from the British
   Pavilion, New York World's Fair, 1939 58 p 22 il 1940 p
   $.10 MBMu   3031
National Gallery of Art.   British painting in the National
   Gallery of Art 1960 p $.25 DSI-GA   3032
The Pre-Raphaelites 1946 p $1.50 MH-FA   3033
Prospects: An exhibition of English landscape water colors
   from English and American private collections, from
   about 1750-1850; introduction by Ray Livingston Murphy
   il 1950 p $.75 CtY-A   3034
S. and M.R. Bancroft Pre-Raphaelite Collection il p $.25
   DeWS   3035
Scottish painters, organized by the British Council in asso-
   ciation with the Toledo Museum of Art and the National
   Gallery of Canada, Ottawa 45 p 12 il (5 c) p $.25 DCGA
                                                                3036
Sutherland, Graham Vivian, and Henry Moore.   Graham
   Sutherland and Henry Moore p $.25 MBI   3037
Williams, Franklin B.   Elizabethan England, portfolio of 41
   pl (12x16.5) with explanatory captions, 36 p text 1939 p
   $5.   MBMu (op)   3038

--Art, England--Individual Artists

Blake, William.   The art of William Blake, with introduction
   by Elizabeth Mongan 48 p 21 il (1 c) 1957 p $1.75 DSI-
   GA   3039
----.   William Blake: Water color drawings (PB) 34 il
   1957 p $1.25 MBMu   3040
Gainsborough, Thomas.   Paintings and drawings by Gainsborough, including many of the Museum's collection 1931 p
   $.75 OCA   3041

Turner, J.M.W.   Turner in America il p 1955 $1. InIJ
                                                        3042
Some British drawings on loan to the American Federation of
    Arts from the collection of Sir Robert Witt 32 p 4 il 1951
    p $.25 CtHWA   3043
The Prince Regent's Style: Decorative arts in England,
    1800-1830 (C 12) il p $.50 NNCoo   3044
LaMar, Virginia A.   English dress in the age of Shake-
    speare il p $.75 DFo   3045
A picture book of English domestic embroidery (PB 5) 40 p
    34 il 1948 p $.50 MiDA   3046
Remington, Preston. English domestic needlework of the
    sixteenth, seventeenth and eighteenth centuries 80 p 70 il
    1945 p $1.50 NNMM   3047
Bateman, Hester.   English silver, eighteenth century 1948 p
    $.25 MH-FA   3048
English silver cream jugs of the eighteenth century, Munro
    Collection 46 p il 1952 p $2.86 CLCM   3049
English silver, XVII-XVIII century--collection of Archibald
    Alexander Hutchinson 1950 p $.25 MH-FA   3050
English silver--seven centuries of English domestic silver p
    $2. CaOTRM   3051
Buhler, Kathryn C.   English porcelains, 1750-1775: 40 il-
    lustrations of outstanding pieces from the Museum's col-
    lection (PB 3) c p $.50 MBMu   3052
Gordon, G.B.   Floor tiles from Westminster Abbey Chapter
    House (MJ v 14, no 4) 24 p 27 il diag 1923 p $1. PU-
    Mu   3053
Grigaut, Paul L.   English pottery and porcelain, 1300-1850
    (C 28) 111 p 139 il 1954 p $3.50 MiDA   3054
Merritt, Arthur H.   The romance of Old Blue china (repr,
    Q. Bul, Oct 1944) 11 p 5 il p $.50 NHi   3055
Old Wedgwood 1944 p $.50 MH-FA   3056
British tradition. Illustrated catalogue of an exhibition of
    historical documents, autograph and illuminated manu-
    scripts, drawings and printed books, eleventh to nineteenth
    century. Introduction by Samuel C. Chew 46 p 1 pl 1941
    p $.50 NNPM   3057
Picture book of English doorways 10 p il 1946 p $.15 ICA
                                                        3058
The Shakespearean gardens p $.50 DFo   3059

--Art, French

Art from France; introduction by Jean Cassou 24 p 14 pl
    1956 p $1. CLCM; CSfMA   3060
Barnes, Albert C., and Violette de Mazia.   The French

primitives and their forms $5.   PMeB   3061

Boyd, Catherine E.   The French renaissance, portfolio of
42 plates (12x16.5) with explanatory captions, 52 p text
1940 p $5.   MBMu   3062

Byrnes, James E.   French painting of the last half of the
19th century il 1956 p $.60 McRMA   3063

Cunningham, Charles C., and Henry P. Rossiter.   Independent painters of the nineteenth century, Paris--includes
works of Carrier, Cheret, Daumier, Degas, Forain,
Guys, Manet, Monet, Pissarro, Rafailli, Renoir, and
Toulouse-Lautrec 86 p 30 il 1935 p $1.   MBMu   3064

Denver Art Museum.   French painting collection, catalogue
--nineteenth century French paintings in the collection
(Denver Art Museum Quarterly) 19 p 6 il $.25 CoDA
                                                                  3065

Forty French pictures in the Smith College Museum of Art,
by Henry-Russell Hitchcock, with a foreword by George
Heard Hamilton 72 p 40 pl 1953 p $.50 MNS-MA   3066

French painting, 1100-1900, catalogue 1951 $5; p $2.
PPiCIA   3067

French painting of the latter half of the nineteenth century--
masterpieces of Cezanne, Degas, Corot, Manet, Monet,
Pissarro, Redon, Renoir, Seurat, Sisley, Toulouse-Lautrec, and van Gogh il 1950 p $.50 CtY-A   3068

French painting of the twentieth century 1945 p $.25 OCA
                                                                  3069

From Ingres to Gauguin--French nineteenth century paintings
owned in Maryland; foreword by Adelyn D. Breeskin,
notes on the exhibition by Gertrude Rosenthal, essay
"French paintings in history," by George H. Hamilton 48
p 45 il 1951 p $1.   MdBMA   3070

Great French paintings: An exhibition of paintings in memory of Chauncey McCormick 60 p il 1955 p $1. ICA (op)
                                                                  3071

Grigaut, Paul L.   French taste in the eighteenth century (C
30) 112 p 183 il 1956 p $2. MiDA   3072

----.   From David to Courbet (C 17) 60 p 33 il 1950 p $1.
MiDA   3073

----.   The two sides of the medal--French painting from
Gerome to Gauguin (C 29) 72 p 72 il 1954 p $2.25 MiDA
                                                                  3074

Metropolitan Museum of Art.   Sterling, Charles.   Catalogue
of French paintings: XV-XVIII centuries 211 p 126 il
map 1955 $7.50; p $5. NNMM   3075

Musee de Nationale de Paris p $.75 MnMW   3076

Museum of Fine Arts, Boston.   Edgell, George Harold.
French painters in the Museum of Fine Arts: Corot to

Utrillo, second half of the nineteenth century and early
twentieth century 100 p 108 il (10 c) 1949 p $2.50 MBMu
                                                                3077
National Gallery of Art. Cooke, Hereward Lester. French
painting of the 16th-18th centuries in the National Gallery
of Art (NGA Book 4) 1959 p $.25 DSI-GA   3078
----. Einstein, Lewis, Looking at French 18th century
pictures of the National Gallery, Washington 38 p 38 il
(1 c) 1958 p $.50 DSI-GA   3079
----. Evans, Grose. French paintings of the 19th century
in the National Gallery of Art (NGA Book 2) 1959 p $.25
DSI-GA   3080
----. French paintings from the Chester Dale Collection,
with introduction by John Walker 98 p 78 il (1 c) 1941
p $.75 DSI-GA   3081
Nineteenth century French painting 6 il p $.50 ViRMu 3082
The Romantic circle: French romantic painting--Delacroix
and his contemporaries; introduction by Charles C. Cun-
ningham 18 p 20 il 1952 p $.50 CtHWA   3083
Rouart, Denis. Berthe Morisot and her circle: The Rouart
Collection 37 p 30 il 1952 p $.50 CaOTAG; NNMM 3084
School of Paris 1959 p $1.50 MnMW   3085
Surrealism and its affinities. The Mary Reynolds Collection,
a bibliography 131 p il 1956 p $4. ICA (op)   3086
Three brothers: Jacques Villon, Raymond Duchamp-Villon,
Marcel Duchamp; foreword by James Johnson Sweeney,
essays on each artist by Rene-Jean, Walter Pach, and
Andre Breton 44 il (6 c) $3.75 NNGu   3087
Twentieth century French paintings from the Chester Dale
Collection, foreword by John Walker, and introduction by
Maud Dale 74 p 60 il (4 c) 1952 p $.75 DSI-GA 3088
Visionaries and dreamers, an exhibition illustrating the influ-
ence of the French symbolist artists on succeeding gener-
ations 32 p 22 il 1956 p $1. DCGA   3089

--Art, French--Individual Artists

Berard, Christian. Christian Berard p $1. MBI   3090
Bonnard, Pierre. Rewald, John. Pierre Bonnard, loan exhibition sponsored by Museum of Modern Art, New York,
and Cleveland Museum of Art 1948 109 il (5 c) $5; p
$1.75 OClMA   3091
Bosse, Abraham. Hogan, Marie-Germaine, et al. (With the
American Federation of Arts.) Abraham Bosse 32 p 15 fig
1956 p $.50 MNS-MA   3092
Braques, Georges. Georges Braques, introduction by Thomas W. Leavitt 10 il (2 c) 1960 p $1. CPA   3093

Buffet, Bernard. Bernard Buffet p $.15 CLCM   3094
Cezanne, Paul. Barnes, Albert C., and Violette de Mazia.
The art of Cezanne PMeB   3095
----. Paul Cezanne 1947 p $.25 OCA   3096
----. Paul Cezanne sketchbook, Curt Valentin, ed 1951 2 v
boxed $8. ICA   3097
Corot, Jean B.C. Venturi, Lionelli. Corot exhibition;
translated by Henry Furst; foreword by Henry Marceau
112 p 97 il (2 c) 1946 p $1. PPPM   3098
Daumier, Honore. Daumier, an anniversary exhibition 74 il
1958 p $1.50 MBMu   3099
----. Honore Daumier, loan exhibition of prints, drawings,
water colors, paintings and sculpture 72 p il 1958 p
$2.50 CLCM   3100
Degas, Edgar. Works of Edgar Degas, selected examples
from an exhibition in Museum, 1947 78 il (1 c) p $.50
OClMA   3101
----. Edgar Degas, loan exhibition of paintings, drawings,
prints and sculpture 100 p 85 il (6 c) 1958 p $2. CLCM
                                                    3102
Duchamp, Marcel. Marcel Duchamp: From the Green Box,
trans and preface by George Heard Hamilton p $3. CtY-A
                                                    3103
Dufy, Raoul. Cassou, Jean. Raoul Dufy 44 p 48 pl (6 c)
1954 CLCM $1.50; $1. CSfMA   3104
Forain, Jean-Louis. Jean-Louis Forain exhibition catalogue
1956 p $.25 MSMFA   3105
Gauguin, Paul. Gauguin--paintings, drawings, sculpture,
prints p $1.50 ICA (op)   3106
Leger, Fernand. Fernand Leger $5.75 MBI   3107
Maillol, Aristide. Aristide Maillol exhibition; introduction by
John Rewald 39 p 40 pl 1958 p $1.50 PPPM   3108
----. Maillol p $.96 CLCM   3109
Matisse, Henri. Barnes, Albert C., and Violette de Mazia.
The art of Henri Matisse PMeB   3110
----. Matisse--a loan exhibition of paintings by Henry Ma-
tisse in cooperation with the Museum of Modern Art; in-
troduction by Alfred H. Barr, Jr. 20 il p $.50 CLMA
                                                    3111
----. Matisse: Catalogue of an exhibition of sculptures,
paintings, and drawings; foreword by Perry T. Rathbone,
introduction by Jean Cassou 9 il 1955 p $.50 MBMu 3112
Nain, Louis Le, and Mathiew LeNain. The brothers LeNain
52 p il 1947 p $.25 OTM   3113
Poussin, Nicolas. Poussin, an exhibition of seventeen paintings by Poussin from collections in the United States and
Canada; introductions by Sir Anthony Blunt, and Walter

Friedlaender 28 p il 1959 p $1. OTM   3114
Renoir, Pierre A.   Barnes, Albert C., and Violette de
Mazia. The art of Renoir PMeB   3115
----. Renoir, articles by Grace L. McCann Morley, Jean
Renoir, and Richard F. Brown 76 p 68 pl (6 c) 1955 p
$1.50 CSfMA   3116
----. Renoir in the Art Institute 9 c pl portfolio 1954
$1.95 ICA   3117
Richier, Germaine. Germaine Richier p $.35 MnMW   3118
Roualt, Georges. Roualt, retrospective exhibition, loan
sponsored by Museum of Modern Art and Cleveland Mu-
seum of Art 30 il p $.50 OClMA   3119
Seurat, Georges. Seurat: Paintings and drawings 92 p il
1958 p $1. ICA   3120
Sicard, Pierre. Pierre Sicard p $.75 CLCM   3121
Signac, Paul. Signac p $.75 CLCM   3122
Toulouse-Lautrec, Henri.   The Art Institute presente Tou-
louse-Lautrec 28 p il 1949 p $.75 ICA   3123
----. A bestiary by Toulouse-Lautrec 47 p il 1954 p $.50
ICA; (PB 3) 1954 p $.50 MH-FA   3124
----. Toulouse-Lautrec exhibition catalogue p $.25 CaOTAG
3125
----. Toulouse-Lautrec--loan exhibition of drawings, prints,
posters, and paintings; introduction by John Rewald 41 il
(1 c) p $.50 CLMA   3126
Venard, Claude. Claude Venard 1957 p apply TxSaMc 3127

--Art, French--Graphic Arts and Drawing

French drawings: Masterpieces from five centuries.   An exhibition organized by L'Association Francaise d'Action
Artistique and circulated by the Smithsonian Institution;
foreword by Annemarie H. Pope, introduction by Jacque-
line Boachot-Soupique 62 p 49 il 1952 p $2. NNMM 3128
Clson, Ruth, and Abraham Chanin. French drawings from
American collections--Clouet to Matisse 362 p 224 pl p
$3.50 NNMMA   3129
Bresdin, Rodolphe. Rodolphe Bresdin, etchings, lithographs
and drawings 20 p 1931 p $.50 ICA   3130
Callot, Jacques. Jacques Callot--prints and drawings 42 p
il 1957 p $.50 CLCM   3131
Daubigny, Charles Francois. Wickenden, Robert J. Charles
Francois Daubigny (repr, Print Collector's Q) 1914 p
$.25 MBMu   3132
Gauguin, Paul. Gauguin prints--from the Art Institute col-
lection p $.50 ICA   3133
Gavarni (pseud of Sulpice Guillaume Chevalier, 1804-1866).

Gavarni p $.24 CLCM   3134
Jacque, Charles. Wickenden, Robert J. Charles Jacque
    (repr, Print Collector's Q) 1914 p $.25 MBMu   3135
LaLanne, Maxime. Bradley, William A. Maxime LaLanne
    (repr, Print Collector's Q) 1914 p $.25 MBMu   3136
Redon, Odilon. Redon: Etchings and lithographs 47 p il
    1929 p $.50 ICA   3137
Saint Memin, C.B.J. Febret de. Engraved portraits by C.
    B.J. Febret de Saint Memin (1797-1852), in the Corcoran
    Gallery 18 p p $.25 DCGA   3138
----. Saint-Memin: An exhibition of his work 68 p 20 il
    1941 p $1. ViRVM   3139
Toulouse-Lautrec, Henri. Toulouse-Lautrec, posters and
    other lithographs from the collection of Mr. and Mrs. Nel-
    son Gutman; foreword by Adelyn D. Breeskin, introductory
    essay by Lincoln F. Johnson 35 p 13 il 1951 p $1.
    MdBMA   3140

--Art, French--sculpture

Bourdelle, Antoine. Bourdelle p $.35 MnMW   3141
Lipschitz, Jacques. Jacques Lipschitz, selected examples of
    sculpture exhibition in Museum, 1954 96 il p $1. CClMA
                                                               3142
Maillol, Aristide. Selected examples of sculpture exhibition
    in Museum, 1958 40 il p $1.25 OClMA   3143
Rodin, Auguste. Watkins, Fridolyn G. Rodin Museum, the
    building and its contents, gift of Jules E. Mastbaum 24 p
    16 pl 1931 p $.25 PPPM   3144

--Art, French--Decorative Arts and Design

Frick Collection Limoges enamels, check list p $.05 NNFC
                                                               3145
Contemporary French tapestries, assembled by Galerie
    Chalette, New York 1956 p $.25 OCA   3146
Lefebure, Ernest. Les points de France, translated by
    Margaret Taylor Johnston 103 p front il 1912 p $1.
    NNMM   3147
Two centuries of French fashions; introduction by Michelle
    Murphy 66 p 49 il (Manikin dolls showing fashion 1715-
    1906) 1949 p $.50 NBB   3148
The Unicorn tapestries at the Cloisters. A picture book; in-
    troduction by James J. Rorimer 24 p 20 il 3rd ed 1947
    p $.35 NNMM   3149
Freedburg, Anne Blake, ed. The Raven: Poe's famous po-
    em with Manet's lithographic illustration reproduced from

the original French edition (PB 10) c p $.50 MBMu 3150

--Art, German and Austrian

German Expressionists p $.72 CLCM   3151
National Gallery of Art. German painting in the National
    Gallery of Art 1960 p $.25 DSI-GA   3152

--Art, German and Austrian--Individual Artists

Beckmann, Max. Max Beckmann, catalogue of the Museum's
    retrospective exhibition 116 p 61 il p $1.60; $.10 post
    MoSCA   3153
Grosz, George. Baur, John I.H. George Grosz retrospec-
    tive exhbition 40 il (2 c) 1954 p $1. NNW   3154
Hoetger, Bernhard. Bernhard Hoetger p $.48 CLCM   3155
Holbein, Hans. Holbein and his contemporaries il 1950 p
    $1. InlJ   3156
Kirchner, Ernst Ludwig. Valentiner, W.R.E. L. Kirchner,
    German Expressionist 132 p 82 il 1958 p $1.50 NcRMA
                                                     3157
Kollwitz, Kathe. Fink, June-Marie. Kollwitz, with an es-
    say by Leonard Baskin 24 p 2 pl 1958 p $.25 MNS-MA
                                                     3158
Marcks, Gerhard. Gerhard Marcks p $.50 MnMW   3159
Wotruba, Fritz. Caneti, Elias. Fritz Wotruba 63 p il 1955
    p $2. (Verlag Bruder Rosenbaum, Wien) MBI   3160

--Art, German and Austrian--Graphic Arts and Drawing

Austrian drawings p $.48 CLCM   3161
German drawings 28 il 1955 p $1.25 MBMu   3162
German drawings, masterpieces from five centuries; fore-
    word by Peter Halm 90 p 29 il 1955 p $1. DSI-GA 3163
German drawings, selected examples from an exhibition in
    Museum, 1955 26 il p $1.25 OClMA   3164
Durer, Albrecht. Durer, drawings and prints. Description
    and checklist of an exhibition 16 p 1955 p $.25 NNPM
                                                     3165

--Art, German and Austrian--Decorative Arts and Design

Gardner, Paul Vickers. Meissen and other German porce-
    lain in the Alfred Duane Pell Collection (Pubn 4356) 66 p
    31 pl 11 fig 1956 p $2. DSI-FA   3166

--Art, Mediterranean Area--Prehistoric and Classical

Classic tradition in contemporary art p $.75 MnMW   3167
Denver Art Museum.   Ancient Mediterranean art, the Denver
   Art Museum's collection of Egyptian, Greek and Roman
   objects 32 p 31 il $.50 CoDA   3168
Museum of Fine Arts, Boston.   Chase, George H.   Greek
   and Roman antiquities; a guide to the classical collection
   169 p 230 il 1950 p $2.75 MBMu   3169
University Museum.   The Greco-Roman section (MJ v 4, no
   4) 2 p 1913 p $.50 PU-Mu   3170
Museum of Fine Arts, Boston.   Caskey, L.D.   Catalogue of
   Greek and Roman sculpture in the Museum--134 sculptures in Museum illustrated, described, and discussed 228
   p 210 il 1925 p $5.   MBMu (op)   3171
Walters Art Gallery.   Hill, Dorothy Kent.   Catalogue of classical bronze sculpture in the Walters Art Gallery 170 p
   56 pl 1949 p $6.25 MdBWA   3172
Jewelry of the ancient world--Greek, Roman, and Near East-
   ern jewelry from about 3000 B.C. to 600 A.D. (B, Divi-
   sion of Art and Archaeol no 20) 36 p il 1953 p $.75
   CaOTRM   3173
Richter, Gisela M.A.   Catalogue of engraved gems: Greek,
   Roman, Etruscan (Published for the Museum by "L'erma'
   di Bretschneider," Rome) 143 p 658 il 1956 p $15.
   NNMM   3174
Carnegie Museum.   Scribner, Henry S.   A catalogue of the
   Spang Collection of Greek and Italian vases and Etruscan
   urns in the Carnegie Museum (M v 11, no 6, p 315-52)
   6 pl p $1.50 PPiCM   3175
Greek and Roman vases (Rhode Island School of Design, B
   v 27, no 2-3, Dec 1939) p $.50 RPD-M   3176
Museum of Fine Arts, Boston.   Fairbanks, Arthur.   Cata-
   logue of Greek and Etruscan vases. v. 1.   Early vases
   preceding Athenian black-figured ware (vases earlier than
   VI cent B.C.)   235 p 100 pl 1928 p $10. MBMu   3177
The Stoddard Collection of Greek and Italian vases p $.25
   CtY-A   3178

--Art, Mediterranean Area--Prehistoric and Classical--
Greece

Fairbanks, Arthur.   Greek gods and heroes, as represented
   in the Classical collection of the Museum 4th ed 1948,
   rev by George H. Chase 84 p 85 il p $1. MBMu (op)
                                                         3179
The Greek tradition; symposium papers read at Baltimore
   Museum of Art, edited by George Boas 206 p front 1939
   $2.25 MdBMA   3180

Greek vases, jewelry, terracottas and other objects in the
Eugene Schaefer Collection (The Museum, ns, v 3, no 2,
Spring 1951) p $.50 NjNM   3181
Hall, E.H. Decorative art of Crete in the Bronze Age (T
v 2, no 1) 41 p 38 il table 1906 p $1. PU-Mu   3182
----. Examples of Mycenaean and Minoan art (MJ v 5, no
3) 23 p 18 il 1914 p $1. PU-Mu   3183
----. Fresco representing a hunt from the Later Palace at
Tiryns (MJ v 5, no 4) 4 p 4 il 1914 p $1. PU-Mu 3184
Museum of Fine Arts, Boston. Beazley, J.D. Attic vase
paintings in the Museum, Pt. II 103 p 50 pl 1954 p $20.
MBMu   3185
Richter, Gisela M. Greek painting, the development of pic-
torial representation from Archaic to Graeco-Roman Times
24 p 36 il 2nd ed 1952 p $.50 NNMM   3186
Stow, Hester Harrington. Greek athletics and festivals in the
fifth century, portfolio of 40 plates (12x16.5) with explanatory captions, 32 p text 1939 p $5. MBMu   3187

--Art, Mediterranean Area--Prehistoric and Classical--
Greece--Sculpture

Attic grave stele (MJ v 7, no 1) 4 p 1 il 1917 p $1. PU-
Mu   3188
Dohan, E.H. An archaic head from Cyprus (MJ v 12, no 3)
2 p 2 il 1921 p $1. PU-Mu   3189
----. Three Greek grave monuments (MJ v 19, no 3) 11 p
10 il 1928 p $1. PU-Mu   3190
Emerson, A. Torso of Hermes (T v 1, no 3) 6 p 2 il 1905
p $1. PU-Mu   3191
Head of Ariadne, 2 pl with explantory notes (MJ v 15, no 4)
1924 $1. PU-Mu   3192
Head of youthful Herakles (B v 3, no 2) 2 p 1 il 1931 p
$.35 PU-Mu   3193
Luce, S.B. Greek torso (MJ v 7, no 2) 3 p 1 il 1916 p $1.
PU- Mu   3194
----. Tanagra figurine (MJ v 10, no 1-2) 4 p 1 il 1919 p
$2. PU-Mu   3195
Rambo, E.F. A group of funerary stelae (MJ v 10, no 3)
6 p 3 il 1919 p $1. PU-Mu   3196
Young, J.H., and S.H. Young. Terracotta figurines from
Kourion in Cyprus (MM) 260 p 74 pl 3 plan 16 fig 1955
$5.50 PU-Mu   3197

--Art, Mediterranean Area--Prehistoric and Classical--
Greece--Decorative Arts and Design

The Albert Gallatin Collection of Greek vases (B v 5, no 5)
1 p 1 il 1935 p $.35 PU-Mu   3198
Amphora by the "Berlin Painter" (B v 3, no 2) 2 p 1 il 1931
p $.35 PU-Mu   3199
Attic vases from Memorial Hall (B v 5, no 6) 3 p 4 il 1935
p $.35 PU-Mu   3200
Black-figure and red-figure Greek pottery PB 5 p 11 pl p
$.50 CaOTRM   3201
Caskey, L. D.   Geometry of Greek vases (Communications to
the Trustees v 5), discussion of Greek design as inter-
preted by Jay Hambridge's theory of Dynamic Symmetry
235 p 267 il 1922 p $3.   MBMu   3202
Corinthian amphora (B v 4, no 2) 3 p 2 il 1933 p $.35
PU-Mu   3203
A Greek cup by "Foundry Painter" (B v 3, no 1) 2 p 1 il
1931 p $.35 PU-Mu   3204
Hall, E.H.   Attic vases from Orvieto (MJ v 4, no 4) 15 p
15 il 1913 p $.50 PU-Mu   3205
----.   Four covered bowls from Orvieto (MJ v 6, no 4) 5 p
5 il 1915 p $1. PU-Mu   3206
----.   Red-figured amphora signed by the potter Meno (MJ
v 5, no 1) 6 p 4 il 1914 p $1. PU-Mu   3207
----.   Red-figured kylix (MJ v 4, no 4) 1 p 2 il 1913 p
$.50 PU-Mu   3208
----.   Red-figured stamnos of the Periklean Period (MJ v 5,
no 1) 4 p 3 il 1914 p $1.   PU-Mu   3209
----.   Some Greek and Italian vases in the Museum (MJ v 5,
no 4) 12 p 9 il 1914 p $1.   PU-Mu   3210
----.   Two black-figured amphorae from Orvieto (MJ v 6,
no 2) 5 p 5 il 1915 p $1.   PU-Mu   3211
----.   Two black-figured amphorae with scenes portraying
the Birth of Athena (MJ v 3, no 4) 7 p 6 il 1912 p $.50
PU-Mu   3212
Luce, S.B.   Attic black-figured panel amphora in the University Museum (MJ v 6, no 4) 3 p 3 il 1915 p $1. PU-Mu
3213
----.   Attic vases from Orvieto (MJ v 11, no 1) 11 p 9 il
1920 p $1.   PU-Mu   3214
----.   Exploits of Herakles on Greek vases on the Univer-
sity Museum (MJ v 8, no 2) 10 p 11 il 1917 p $1. PU-
Mu   3215
----.   A group of Greek vases (MJ v 8, no 1) 13 p 6 il
1917 p $1.   PU-Mu   3216
----.   A loan of three Greek vases (MJ v 8, no 3) 13 p 5 il
1917 p $1.   PU-Mu   3217
----.   Red-figured pyxis (MJ v 7, no 4) 6 p 2 il 1916 p $1.
PU-Mu   3218

Rambo, E. F.   Attic black-figured skyphos (MJ v 10, no 1-2)
5 p 2 il 1919 p $2.   PU-Mu   3219
----. On the design of Greek vases (MJv 10, no 1-2) 6 p
5 il 1919 p $2.   PU-Mu   3220
----. Stories on Greek vases (MJ v 13, no 1) 7 p 3 il 1933
p $1.   PU-Mu   3221
Brett, Agnes Baldwin.   Catalogue of Greek coins--Coins
from Warren Collection, and nearly 1,000 others never before published; all coins illustrated, some greatly en-
larged 340 p 115 pl $25.   MBMu   3222
Hall, E.H.   A pair of bits from Corneta   (MJ v 5, no 4) 4
p 6 il 1914 p $1.   PU-Mu   3223
Luce, S.B.   Ancient helmets from Italy (MJ v 11, no 1) 8 p
7 il 1920 p $1.   PU-Mu   3224
Pair of earrings from Cyprus (B v 5, no 2) 1 p 1 il 1934 p
$.35 PU-Mu   3225

--Art, Mediterranean--Prehistoric and Classical--Italy

The Age of Diocletian: A symposium, including Casper J.
Kraemer "The Historical pattern;" Eberhard F. Bruck
"Law in a changing world;" William L. Westermann
"Price controls and wages;" Erwin R. Goodenough "The
religious aspirations;" Gilbert Highet "Books and the cri-
sis;" Rhys Carpenter "Art in transition" 78 p 18 il 1953 p
$1.50 NNMM   3226
De Cour, H.F.   Antiquities from Boscoreale in Field Mu-
seum of Natural History (FA 7:4) 68 p 66 il 1 map 1912
$2.50 ICF   3227
An Egyptian landscape at Minturnae (B v 5, no 1) 4 p 1 il
1934 p $.35 PU-Mu   3228
The Etruscans and their art (B v 28, no 1, July 1940) p
$.75 RPD-M   3229
The Gallery of Italic and Etruscan art (B v 4, no 6) 26 p
24 il 1933 p $.35 PU-Mu   3230
Lehmann, Phyllis Williams. Roman wall paintings from
Boscoreale in the Metropolitan Museum of Art, appendix
by Herbert Bloch (The Archaeological Institute of America)
173 p 81 il 42 pl 1953 $12.   NNMM   3231
Luce, S.B.   Five Roman mosaics in the Museum collection
(MJ v 7, no 1) 9 p 3 il 1916 p $1. PU-Mu   3232
Richter, Gisela M.A.   Roman portraits 72 p 173 il 1948 p
$2.   NNMM   3233
Tarbell, F.B.   Three Etruscan painted sarcophagi (FA 6:4)
9 p 9 il 1917 $.25 ICF   3234

--Art, Mediterranean--Prehistoric and Classical--Italy--
Sculpture

Hall, E.H.   A colored marble statuette (MJ v 5, no 2) 1 p
   1 il 1914 p $1.   PU-Mu   3235
----.   Neo-Attic relief and Roman portrait head (MJ v 5, no
   1) 4 p 2 il 1914 p $1.   PU-Mu   3236
----.   Roman portrait head (Menander) (MJ v 5, no 2) 2 p
   1 il 1914 p $1.   PU-Mu   3237
----.   Roman relief from Pozzuoli (MJ v 4, no 4) 4 p 2 il
   1913 p $.50 PU-Mu   3238
----.   A seated Dyonysos (MJ v 4, no 4) 4 p 1 il 1913 p
   $.50 PU-Mu   3239
----.   Two marbles from Lake Nemi (MJ v 5, no 2) 3 p 2
   il 1914 p $1.   PU-Mu   3240
Italic heads (B v 5, no 3) 1 p 1 il 1934 p $.35 PU-Mu 3241
Legrain, L.   Tomb sculptures from Palmyra (MJ v 18, no
   4) 26 p 15 il 1927 p $1.   PU-Mu   3242
Locrian terra cotta plaques (B v 8, no 2-3) 6 p 5 il 1940 p
   $.50 PU-Mu   3243
A statue of Athena (B v 5, no 6) 1 p 1 il 1935 p $.35 PU-
   Mu   3244
Two sculptures from Minturnae (B v 4, no 1) 3 p 2 il 1932
   p $.35 PU-Mu   3245
Two Syrian sculptured portraits (B v 6, no 4) 2 p 1 il 1939
   p $.35 PU-Mu   3246
Vates, W.N.   Sculptures from Lake Nemi (MJ v 1, no 2) 2
   p 2 il 1910 p $.50 PU-Mu   3247

--Art, Mediterranean--Prehistoric and Classical--Italy--
Decorative Arts and Design

Chase, George H.   Catalogue of Arretine pottery 112 p 30 pl
   1916 p $2.50 MBMu   3248
Luce, S.B.   Early vases from Apulia (MJ v 10, no 4) 9 p
   8 il 1919 p $1.   PU-Mu   3249
Pottery from Minturnae (B v 5, no 6) 1 p 1935 p $.35 PU-
   Mu   3250
Sigillate pottery of the Roman Empire, catalogue of excava-
   tions made chiefly by Archer Milton Huntington, 1898 61
   p 124 il (front c) 1937 $1.   NNH   3251
Hall, E.H.   A collection of antique glass (MJ v 4, no 4) 22
   p 34 il 1913 p $.50 PU-Mu   3252
Rambo, E.F.   The John Thompson Morris Collection of an-
   cient glass (MJ v 10, no 3) 9 p 11 il 1919 p $1.   PU-Mu
                                                              3253
Wace, Alan J.B.   Preliminary historical study: A late

Roman tapestry from Egypt (Workshop notes no 9) p
$1.25 DTM   3254
Hall, E.H.   Bronze blade from the Dictaean Cave (MJ v 5,
no 3) 3 p 1 il 1914 p $1.   PU-Mu   3255
A model of a Roman town house (B v 4, no 6) 1 p 1 il
1933 p $.35 PU-Mu   3256

--Art, Mediterranean--Renaissance to Contemporary--Italy
The age of Canova, an exhibition of the Neo-Classic il 1957 p
$.35 RPD-M   3257
The art of the Italian Renaissance from the Samuel H.
Kress Foundation p $1.50 ScCoM   3258
Canaday, John.   Sienese paintings (Metropolitan Museum of
Art Miniatures, Album XK)   25 p 24 il c 1957 p $1.25
PPPM   3259
Contemporary Italian art--printing, drawing, sculpture 44 p
50 il 1955 p $1; $.10 post MoSCA   3260
Contemporary Italian paintings   p $.35 MBI   3261
Italian paintings, from the Jarves and Griggs Collections
(PB no 1) 33 il p $.50 ICA   3262
Einstein, Lewis.   Looking at Italian pictures in the National
Gallery of Art 132 p 68 il 1951 p $1.75 DSI-GA   3263
Shapley, Fern Rusk.   Early Italian painting in the National
Gallery of Art (NGA Book 3) 1959 p $.25 DSI-GA   3264
----.   Later Italian painting in the National Gallery of Art
(NGA Book 6) 1959 p $.25 DSI-GA   3265
Pontormo to Greco   il p 1954 $1.   InIJ   3266
Richards, Edgar P.   The adoration with two angels by An-
drea Verrocchio and Leonardo da Vinci (PB 10) 32 p 39
il (3 c) 1957 p $.75 MiDA   3267
Three Baroque masters; exhibition catalogue of the works of
Bernardo Strozzi, Giuseppe Maria Crespi, Giovanni Bat-
tista Piazzetta; foreword by Adelyn D. Breeskin, introductory essay by Hans Tietza, bibliography 63 p 42 il
1944 p $1.   MdBMA   3268
Twentieth century Italian art: Catalogue of an exhibition 16
p 4 il 1956 p $.25 NjNM   3269
Valentiner, W.R.   Italian Gothic painting; treatise on Gothic
period of Italian art, XIV-XVIII century (G 4) 35 p 22 il
1944 p $.50 MiDA   3270
Venetian painting of the 18th century (Art Bul) 36 p 25 il p
$.75; $.10 post MoSCA   3271
Venetian tradition, selected examples from an exhibition in
Museum, 1956 56 il p $.50 OClMA   3272
Leonardo da Vinci 144 p 77 pl 1949 p $2. CLCM   3273
Marino Marini, sculpture and drawings 1953 p $.25 OClMA 3274
Modigliani, Amedeo.   Amedeo Modigliani 1957 c $.25

TxSaMc   3275
Contemporary Italian prints p $.48 CLCM   3276
Drawings from Lombardy p $1. CLCM   3277
Estrin, Rochelle, et al. Drawings of the Italian Renais-
    sance from the Scholz Collection 60 p 50 fig 1958 p $1.
    MNS-MA   3278
Boccioni, Umberto. Boccioni: Drawings and prints from
    the Mr. and Mrs. Harry Lewis Winston Collection 16 p il
    1958 p $.75 ICA   3279
Modigliani, Amedeo. Modigliani: An exhibition of drawings
    in the J.W. Alsdorf Collection 58 p il 1955 p $.25 ICA
                                                            3280
Piranesi, by Robert O. Parks, with essays by Philip Hofer,
    Karl Lehmann and Rudolf Wittkower 160 p 57 pl 1960
    $3.50 MNS-MA   3281
Paintings, drawings, and prints by the two Tiepolos (Gio-
    vanni Battista Tiepolo; Giovanni Domenico Tiepolo) 78 p
    il p $.50 ICA   3282
Pompeo, Leoni. Pompeo Leoni: Work in marble and ala-
    baster in relation to Spanish sculpture--sepulchral monu-
    ments of Italian working in Spain, 1556-1608 80 p 29 il
    1956 p $1.50 NNH   3283
Grigaut, Paul L. Decorative arts of the Italian Renaissance,
    1400-1600 (C 34) 180 p 173 il (cov and 5 c) 1958 p $4.
    MiDA   3284
Italy at work: Her renaissance in design today 124 p il
    1950 p $1. ICA   3285
Italian drawings for jewelry, 1700-1875 (C 7) il p $.15
    NNCoo   3286
Breckenridge, James D. Italian maiolica in the W.A. Clark
    Collection (B v 7, no 3) 1955 p $.50 DCGA   3287
Capodimonte and Buen Retiro porcelains, period of Charles
    III 100 p 55 il 1955 $2.25 NNH   3288
Erdberg, Joan Prentice von, and Marvin C. Ross. Cata-
    logue of the Italian majolica in the Walters Art Gallery
    58 p 64 pl 1952 $5. MdBWA   3289
A pieta in Doccia porcelain (repr, The Conoisseur, Nov 1957,
    p 197-202) front c 1957 p $.50 NNH   3290
Three great centuries of Venetian glass, special summer ex-
    hibition 116 p 128 il (7 c) 1958 p $2; post $.15
    NCorniC-M   3291

--Art, Russian and Eastern European

Bronze bird figures from Russia (Perm Region) (B v 5, no
    2) 3 p 2 il 1934 p $.35 PU-Mu   3293
Russian art; Icons and decorative arts from the origin to the

20th century 88 p 60 il 1959 p $3. MdBWA   3294
Shamanist bird figures of the Yenesei Ostyak (Siberia) (MJ
   v 10, no 4) 3 p 2 il (1 c) 1919 p $1. PU-Mu   3295
d'Ebneth, Lajos. d'Ebneth sculptures, drawings 3 il 1948 p
   $.10 DCGA   3296
Ross, Marvin C. Faberge, Carl. Faberge PB 12 p il p
   $.30 MdBWA   3297
Kandinsky, Wassily. Bill, Max. Wassily Kandinsky (Text
   in French) $5.50 OClMA   3298
----. Wassily Kandinsky $6.50 MBI   3299
Marcoussis, Louis. Louis Marcoussis: An American pre-
   miere 1959 p apply TxSaMc   3300
Miestchaninoff, Oscar. Miestchaninoff p $.72 CLCM   3301
Moholy-Nagy, Laszlo. Moholy-Nagy 16 p il 1947 p $.50
   ICA (op)   3302

--Art, Scandanavian

Danish silver p $1.50 MnMW   3303
Milles, Carl. Carl Milles p $1. MBI   3304
----. Milles fountain leaflet p $.10 TxHM   3305

--Art, Spanish

Fourteenth-century painting in the Kingdom of Aragon Beyond
   the Sea 30 p 10 il 1929 p $.25 NNH   3306
Guidol, Jose. Spanish paintings 146 p 89 il 1941 p $5.
   OTM   3307
Hispanic Society of America. Trapier, Elizabeth du Gue.
   Catalogue of paintings (14th and 15th centuries) in the col-
   lection 256 p 95 il 1930 $1; -- . Catalogue of paintings
   (19th and 20th centuries) in the collection 2 v 342 il 1932
   set/$2. NNH   3308
----, ----. Pinturas por artistas del siglo XVI in la colec-
   cion de la Hispanis Society (repr, Boletin de la Sociedad
   Espanola de Excusiones) 1953 p $.25 NNH   3309
A painting from the apse of the church of Santa Maria de
   Mur, Catalonia, Spain, XII century, and two paintings
   from the Hermitage Church of San Baudelio de Berlanga,
   Castile, Spain, XII century 8 p 8 il p $.15 MBMu (op)
                                                             3310
The School of Madrid and Van Dyck (repr, Burlington Maga-
   zine, Aug 1957, p 265-73) 1957 p $.35 NNH   3311
The Spanish masters of 20th century painting: Picasso,
   Gris, Miro; articles by Donald Gallup, Herbert Read,
   Sidney Janis, et al 103 p 72 il 1948 p $1.50 CSfMA
                                                             3312

Spanish painting in the National Gallery of Art 1960 p $.25
   DSI-GA   3313

--Art, Spanish--Individual Artists

El Greco.   El Greco: Early years at Toledo, 1576-1586
   $2.25 NNH   3314
----.   El Greco in the Farnese Palace, Rome (repr, Ga-
   zette des Beaux-Arts, February 1958, p 73-90) 1958 p
   $.35 NNH   3315
Goya, Francisco.   Goya p $.72 CLCM   3316
----.   Goya, a study of his portraits, 1797-1799 72 p 35 il
   1955 $2. NNH   3317
Lopez Mezquita, Jose Maria.   Lopez Mezquita in the collection 28 p 13 il 1930 p $.25 NNH   3318
Lucas Y Padilla, Eugenio.   Eugenio Lucas Y Padilla 90 p 50
   pl 1940 p $1.   NNH   3319
Miro, Joan.   Soby, James Thrall.   Joan Miro 164 p 148 pl
   (35 c) $8.50 NNMMA   3320
Morales, Luis de.   Luis de Morales and Leonardesque influences in Spain--an account of the influence of Leonardo
   and his followers on Spanish artists, especially in Valencia on Ferrando de Llanos, Ferrando Yanez, and Juan de
   Juanes in the early 16th century, and on the Etremenian
   Morales (d 1586), represented in the collection by 3 paint-
   ings 36 p 21 il p 1956 $.75 NNH   3321
Picasso, Pablo.   Picasso exhibition: Paintings, drawings,
   sculpture, ceramics, prints, and books; preface by Henry
   Clifford, essay by Carl Zigrosser "Picasso as a graphic
   artist" 144 p 290 pl (3 c) 1958 p $2.50 PPPM   3322
----.   Picasso, inaugural exhibition 1954 p $.25 TxSaMc
                                                            3323
Quiros, Cesareo Bernaldo do.   Trapier, Elizabeth du Gue.
   Exhibition of paintings by Cesareo Bernaldo de Quiros,
   Gaucho life in Argentina (province of Entre Rios) 1850-
   1870, at the Hispanic Society of America 57 p 25 il (front
   c) 1932 p $.50 NNH   3324
----.   Brinton, Christian.   Cesario Bernaldo de Quiros; an
   exhibition of paintings of Gaucho life in the province of
   Entre Rios, Argentina, 1850-1870, at the Hispanic Society
   of America 23 p 22 il 1932 p $.50 NNH   3325
Ribera, Jose de.   Ribera 306 p 177 il 1952 $9. NNH 3326
----.   Ribera in the collection 15 p 8 il 1952 p $.25 NNH
                                                            3327
Rico Y Ortega, Martin.   Martin Rico Y Ortega in the collec-
   tion 44 p 958 il 1937 $2.50 NNH   3328
Sorolla Y Bastida, Joaquin.   Sorolla Room--Provinces of

Valdes Leal, Juan de   233

Spain by Joaquin Sorolla Y Bastida in the collection 8 p
   15 il p $.05 NNH   3329
Valdes Leal, Juan de. Valdes Leal: Baroque concept of
   death and suffering in his paintings--a technical and icono-
   graphical study of the paintings of this 17th-century Sevil-
   lian, called the "Painter of the Dead" 60 p 27 il 1956 p
   $1.50 NNH   3330
Velazquez, Diego Rodriguez. Velazquez--a chronological
   record of his life, with a study of his paintings emphasizing development of his technique 434 p 252 il 1948
   $7.50 NNH   3331
----. Velzaquez--portraits in the collection 27 p 11 il 1952
   p $.25 NNH   3332
Vierge, Daniel Urrabieta. Daniel Urrabieta Vierge in the
   collection 186 p 25 il 1936 $1; -- plates, 265 collotype
   il 1936 $2.50 NNH   3333
----. Urrabieta Vierge and illustrators of Don Quixote
   (19th and 20th centuries): An exhibition from books in
   the library 36 p front 1934 p $.25 NNH   3334
Viladrich, Migue. Viladrich in the collection 74 p 39 il
   1930 p $.25 NNH   3335

--Art, Spanish--Graphic Arts and Drawing

Woodcuts from 15th-century books in the library, with com-
   parative material folder 20-24 p, chiefly il; (1) Gorricio
   de Novaria, Gaspar. Contemplaciones sobre el rosario,
   Sevilla, 1495; (2) Oliveros de Castilla. Burgos, 1499
   $.05 ea NNH   3336
Goya, Francisco. Font, Eleanor Sherman. Goya's source
   for the Maragato Series, $.75 NNH   3337
----. Goya, drawings and prints il p $.75 CSfDeY (op)
                                                        3338
Galicia, Jose Luis. Prints by Jose Luis Galicia p $.75
   WMA   3339
Picasso, Pablo. Picasso drawings 40 p 34 il 1949 $1.
   NjP-A   3340
----. Picasso--graphic art 30 p il 1957 p $.50 ICA; (PB
   7) 1957 p $.50 MH-FA   3341
----. Picasso--lithographs since 1945 p $1.50 OCA   3342

--Art, Spanish--Sculpture

Proske, Beatrice Giman. Castilian sculpture (Gothic to
   Renaissance) 525 p 328 il 1951 $15. NNH   3343

--Art, Spanish--Decorative Arts and Design

Frothingham, Alice Wilson. Alcora statuettes after bronzes
by Giovanni Bologna (repr, The Connoisseur, March 1957,
p 59-63) p $.35 NNH   3344
----. Lustreware in Spain--history of development in Spain
from 10th to 18th centuries, emphasizing designs, shapes
and techniques 310 p 221 il (front c) 1951 $8.50 NNH
                                                             3345
Goggin, John M. The Spanish majolica in the New World
(P 22; FIT 2) (in prep) LNT-MA   3346
Hispanic Society of America. Catalogue of Hispano-Moresque pottery in the collection 291 p 99 il 1936 $1. NNH
                                                             3347
----. Twentieth-century ceramics in the collection, with
comparative material folders 6-12 p, chiefly il: (1)
Aragon and Cataluna; (2) Basque provinces; (3) Castilla
and Andalucia; (4) Fajalauza Ware; (5) Fraga, Lerida,
and Verdu; (6) Manises; (7) Muel; (8) Sevilla; (9) Span-
ich Galicia; (10) Talavera; (11) Valencia $.05 ea NNH
                                                             3348
Picasso, Pablo. Picasso--ceramics (C 11) il p $.50
NNCoo   3349
Prehistoric pottery in the collection from El Acebuchal, site
near Carmona, province of Sevilla 25 p 35 il p $.60
NNH   3350
Talavera pottery 191 p 157 il 1944 p $3. NNH   3351
Van de Put, Albert. The Valencian styles of Hispano-
Moresque pottery, 1404-1454; a companion to the Apuntes
sobre Ceramica Morisca of the late G.J. de Osma 99 p
7 il 1938 $.75 NNH   3352
Frothingham, Alice Wilson. Barcelona glass in Venetian
style; detailed account of Barcelona glass in its historical
background from the 14th through the 17th century, de-
veloped from a study of glasses with enamel decoration in
the museum 80 p 39 il (front c) 1956 p $2. NNH   3353
Hispanic glass 204 p 125 il 1941 p $1.50 NNH   3354
Modern glass from Valencia and Cataluna in the collection,
with comparative material folder, 12 p 17 il $.05 NNH
                                                             3355
Anderson, Ruth Matilda. Costumes painted by Sorolla in his
Provinces of Spain 208 p 109 il (front c) 2 map 1957 $4.
NNH   3356
Gallegan Provinces of Spain: Pontevedra and La Coruna
496 p 682 il (front c) 1939 $2. NNH   3357
Hispanic lace and lace making; technique and designs from
the Middle Ages to the twentieth century 417 p 432 il
1939 $2. NNH   3358
Kuhnel, Ernst, and Louisa Bellinger. Catalogue of Spanish

rugs, **XII-XIX** century 1953 $15.   DTM   3359
May, Florence Lewis.   Silk textiles of Spain (8th to 15th
   century)--history of silk fabrics produced in Spain from
   the Umalyad conquest through the reign of the Catholic
   Kings, with descriptions of weaves and patterns...296 p
   167 il (6 c) 1957 $14. NNH   3360
Spanish costumes: Extramadura 334 p 393 il map 1951 $11.
   NNH   3361
Johnson, Ada Marshall.   Hispanic silverwork, 14th through
   19th century 308 p 265 il 1944 p $4. NNH   3362
Cannon by Jose Solano in the collection   23 p 6 il 1935 p
   $.25 NNH   3363
Miles, George Carpenter.   The coinage of the Umayyads of
   Spain 591 p 15 pl 1950 2 pts p $10. NNH   3364
----.   The coinage of the Visigoths of Spain, Leovigilt to
   Achila **II**   520 p 44 pl 1952 p $10. NNH   3365
----.   Coins of the Spanish Muluk Al-Tawa'if 168 p 15 pl
   1954 p $4.50 NNH   3366
Penney, Clara Louisa.   The book called Celestina in the li-
   brary (reduced facsimile)--bibliographical description of
   36 editions before 1635, followed by a listing of those to
   which reference has been found, with identifying facsimiles
   157 p 161 il 1954 $3. NNH   3367
Spalding, Frances.   Mudejar ornament in manuscripts--in
   Spain from 12th to beginning 16th century, based on Spanish choir books in the collection 58 p 38 il 1953 $2. NNH
                                                       3368
Thomas, Sir Henry.   Anti-English propaganda in the time of
   Queen Elizabeth, being the story of the first English printing in the Peninsula 20 p 2 facsim 1946 p $1. NNH 3369

--Art, Swiss

Carl Bodmer paints the Indian frontier p $.50 MnSSci 3370
Fuseli, Henry.   Fuseli drawings; illustrated catalogue of a
   loan exhibition organized by the Pro Helvetia Foundation
   and circulated by the Smithsonian Institution 32 p 12 pl
   1954 p $.50 NNPM   3371

--Art, Oriental

Cincinnati Art Museum.   Near and Far Eastern galleries (B
   v 2, no 1) p $.25 OCA   3372
Denver Art Museum.   Oriental catalogue 101 il $.50 CoDA
                                                       3373
----.   Kwan Yin (Denver Art Museum Q) $.25 CoDA   3374
Museum of Fine Arts, Boston.   The Charles B. Hoyt Collec-

tion, memorial exhibition, including fine examples of Chinese, Korean, Japanese, Siamese, Persian, Graeco-Roman ceramics as well as Chinese bronzes, paintings from China, Korea, and Japan, objects of jade, lacquer, and ivory, and several remarkable examples of Chinese sculpture 204 p 802 il (front c) 1952 p $2. MBMu   3375

Paine, Robert T.   Animals in Eastern art: A selection from the works of Eastern art of all periods (PB 9) c p $.50 MBMu   3376

Rowland, Benjamin, Jr. The Harvard outline and reading lists for Oriental Art 1958 p $1.50 MH-FA   3377

Dimand, M.S. The Ballard Collection of oriental rugs, City Art Museum 216 p 69 il (13 c) $5. MoSCA   3378

Oriental rugs--Kalman Collection p $.25 CaOTRM   3379

Robinson, John. Oriental numismatics 102 p il 1913 $6.50 MSaE   3380

Oriental dolls and their accessories (The Museum, ns, v 3, no 4, Fall 1951) p $.50 NjNM   3381

--Art, Oriental--Far East

Toda, Kenji. The Ryerson collection of Japanese and Chinese illustrated books 465 p 1931 p $7.50 ICA   3382

Art in Buddhism 7 p 4 il 1958 p $.50 NjNM   3382a

Philadelphia Museum of Art.   Lee, Jean Gordon, and Horace H.F. Jayne. Handbook of the Far Eastern Wing; foreword by Henry Marceau 42 p il p $.50 PPPM   3383

A picture book of the art of India, China and Japan (PB 4) 2nd ed 1959 p $.50 MiDA   3384

University Museum. Sayce, A.H. Oriental art in the University Museum (MJ v 7, no 3) 3 p 1916 p $1. PU-Mu
3385

Religious wood-block prints of the Far East 1946 p $.25 MH-FA   3386

Sculpture of the Far East (B v 1, no 5-6) p $.25 ea OCA
3387

Laufer, Berthold. The decorative art of the Amur tribes (M v 7; JNP v 4) 86 p 33 pl 24 fig 1902 p $3. NNM
3387a

Far Eastern ceramics, Charles M. Pratt Collection 1940 p $.50 NPV-A   3388

Exhibition of East Asiatic glass--glass from east of the Himalaya Mountains, representing 2500 years of interest in glass making 22 p il 1948 p $4. OTM   3389

--Art, Oriental--Far East--China

Additions to the Chinese collection (B v 3, no 1) 2 p 1 il
    1932 p $.35 PU-Mu   3390
Annotated outlines of the history of Chinese arts, multig, il
    1953 p $1.75 DSI-F   3391
Arts of the Chou Dynasty p $2. CStM   3392
Bishop, C.W. The Chinese expeditions (MJ v 8, no 3) 4 p
    1917 p $1. PU-Mu   3393
Camman, S. Chinese Mandarin squares. Brief catalogue of
    the Letcher Collection (B v 17, no 3) 73 p 35 il p $.50
    PU-Mu   3394
Chinese antiquities from Ch'ang-Sha, lent by John Hadley Cox
    il 1939 p $.15 CtY-A   3395
Chinese dragons (for the younger reader) (B v 5, no 1) 2
    p 1 il 1934 p $.35 PU-Mu   3396
Chinese painting from the Witter Bynner Collection p $.25
    NmRMA   3397
Chinese paintings p $1.92 CLCM   3398
Chinese rubbings (B v 5, no 5) 1 p 1 il 1935 p $.35 PU-
    Mu   3399
Ch'ing Ming Shang Ho: Spring festival on the river; intro-
    duction and notes by Alan Priest 14 p 30 pl 1948 $20.
    NNMM   3400
----: ----; rendered by Albert Carman, portfolio 1945 p
    $5. NNMM   3401
An exhibition of Oriental art (MJ v 7, no 1) 17 p 11 il 1916
    p $1. PU-Mu   3402
Fernald, H.E. Another fresco from the Moon Hill Monas-
    tery (MJ v 19, no 2) 20 p 6 il 1928 p $1. PU-Mu   3403
----. Ladies of the Court, an early Chinese scroll painting
    (MJ v 19, no 4) 16 p 10 il 1928 p $1. PU-Mu   3404
----. Two sections of a Chinese fresco newly acquired
    (MJ v 20, no 2) 10 p 5 il 1929 p $1. PU-Mu   3405
Fong, Wen. The Lohans and a bridge to heaven (FOP v 3,
    no 1; Smithsonian I, pubn 4305) 64 p 18 pl 1958 p $1.
    DSI-F   3406
4000 years of Chinese are, an exhibition organized and lent
    by C.T. Loo; preface by Evan H. Turner, introduction by
    Kojiro Tomita 30 p 11 il 1958 p $1. CtHWA   3407
Gettens, Rutherford J., and Bertha M. Usilton, comps.
    Abstracts of technical studies in art and archaeology,
    1943-1952 (FOP v 2, no 2; Smithsonian I, pubn 4176) 408
    p 1399 items p $3. DSI-F   3408
Grigaut, Paul L. The arts of the Ming Dynasty (C 24) 48 p
    119 il 1952 p $2. MiDA   3409
Lee, Jean Gordon. Chinese art from the neolithic age
    through the Sung Dynasty 24 p 1 il 1942 p $.25 NjTM
                                                          3410

Magnificent Manchus p $.50 CStM   3411
Masterpieces of Chinese bird and flower painting 1951 p $.75
    MH-FA   3412
Modern Chinese painting--David Kwok   24 p il 1955 p $1.
    ICA   3413
Palace Ladies, Chinese scroll painting attributed to Chow Wen
    Wu (B v 6, no 3) 2 p 2 il 1936 p $.35 PU-Mu   3414
Po Shan Lu, Hill Censer (B v 6, no 5) 3 p 1 il 1936 p $.35
    PU-Mu   3415
Salmony, Alfred. Art of the northern Chinese frontier (F 5)
    p $.20 NBuM   3416
Tupper, Emily Hartwell. Birthplace: China--A book of ani-
    mals 32 p p $1.50 WaSA   3417
University Museum. Jayne, H.H.F. The Chinese collections
    of the University Museum (B v 9, no 2-3) 63 p 60 il 1941
    p $1. PU-Mu   3418
Vassar College Art Gallery. Catalogue of the Chinese paint-
    ing for the 75th anniversary 1940 p $.50 NPV-A   3419
Wenley, A.G. The Grand Empress Dowager Wen Ming and
    the northern Wei necropolis at Fang Shan (FOP v 1, no 1;
    Smithsonian I, pubn 3861) 28 p 3 drg 1947 p $.40 DSI-F
                                                                     3420
Yale University Art Gallery. Hackney, Louis Wallace, and
    Yau Chang-Foo. A study of Chinese paintings in the Col-
    lection of Ada Small Moore; index to Chinese names,
    words, terms seals 1940 $25. CtY-A   3421
Zao Wou-Ki. The prints of Zao Wou-Ki 1955 p $.25 OCA
                                                                     3422
Bishop, C.W. Notes on Chinese statuary (MJ v 7, no 3)
    25 p 13 il 1916 p $1. PU-Mu   3423
----. Recent accessions of Chinese sculpture (MJ v 9, no
    2) 24 p 15 il (2 c) 1918 p $1. PU-Mu   3424
----. Two early Chinese Buddhist sculptures (MJ v 7, no 4)
    17 p 8 il 1916 p $1. PU-Mu   3425
----. Two sculptured Chinese heads (MJ v 5, no 3) 4 p 2
    il 1914 p $1. PU-Mu   3426
Chinese sculpture 16 pl, with explanatory notes (MJ v 15, no
    4) 1924 $1. PU-Mu   3427
Chinese shadow puppets (B v 4, no 3) 2 p 1 il 1933 p $.35
    PU-Mu   3428
An early Chinese sculpture (B v 5, no 2) 2 p 4 il 1935 p
    $.35 PU-Mu   3429
An example of T'ang sculpture (B v 1, no 3) 2 p 1 il 1930 p
    $.35 PU-Mu   3430
Fernald, H.E. A Chinese Buddhist statue in dry lacquer
    (MJ v 18, no 3) 10 p 3 il 1927 p $1. PU-Mu   3431
----. Mortuary figures of the T'ang Dynasty (MJ v 16, no

3) 27 p 14 il (2 c) 1925 p $1. PU-Mu   3432

----. Some Chinese grave figures (MJ v 17, no 1) 15 p 7 il 1926 p $1. PU-Mu   3433

Inscription of the St. Louis Stele of 505 (Chinese) (repr, Art Bul, v 22, 1941) 2 il facsim p $.15; $.10 post MoSCA   3434

Maitreya and guardians (B v 9, no 1) 6 p 4 il 1941 p $.50 PU-Mu   3435

Salmony, Alfred. Monumental Chinese sculpture (F 11) p $.20 NBuM   3436

Cammann, S. The story of Hornbill ivory (B v 15, no 4) 29 p 12 il 1950 p $.50 PU-Mu   3437

Chinese jewelry. A picture book; introduction by Alan Priest 24 p 22 il 2nd ed 1947 p $1.50 NNMM   3438

Getz, J. Imperial Chinese sculpture (MJ v 5, no 1) 1 pl, with explanatory notes 1914 p $1. PU-Mu   3439

Jayne, H.H.F. Archaic Chinese jades, special exhibition 58 p 17 pl 1940 p $1. PU-Mu   3440

Salmony, Alfred. Archaic Chinese jades from the collection of Edward and Louise B. Sonnenschein 279 p 107 pl 1952 $25. ICA   3441

----. Collecting ancient Chinese jades (F 2) p $.20 NBuM   3442

A bonnet and pair of mitts from Ch'ang-Sha (MC v 2, no 10) il p $.50 NNCoo   3443

Fernald, Helen E. Chinese court costumes 51 p 37 pl (4 c) p $1.10 CaOTRM   3444

Priest, Alan. Costumes from the Forbidden City 72 p 56 il 1945 p $1.50 NNMM   3445

Simmons, Pauline. Chinese patterned silks 40 p 48 il 1946 p $1.50 NNMM   3446

Laufer, Berthold. Chinese baskets (DS 3) 38 il 1925 p $1.25 ICF   3447

--Art, Oriental--Far East--China--Ceramics

Bishop, C.W. Horses of T'ang T'ai Tsung (MJ v 9, no 3-4) 28 p 19 il 1918 p $2. PU-Mu   3448

----. A pottery statue of a Lohan (MJ v 5, no 3) 6 p 1 il 1914 p $1. PU-Mu   3449

Buffalo Museum of Science. Hochstadter, Walter. Early Chinese ceramics in the Buffalo Museum of Science (F 9) p $.30 NBuM   3450

Chinese ceramics, catalogue of an exhibition lent by Mr. and Mrs. Eugene Bernat 50 p 25 il 1947 p $.50 MBMu 3451

Chinese ceramics of the Sung Dynasty p $.50 InIJ   3452

Chinese export porcelain exhibition catalog p $1. DeWS 3453

Chinese porcelain, Neolithic to Ming p $.10 MNS-MA   3454
Chinese pottery figurines PB 16 p il p $.50 CaOTRM   3455
Christensen, Erwin O. Chinese porcelains of the Widener
    Collection (NGA Hdbk 2) 40 p 19 il 1946 p $.35 DSI-GA
                                                          3456
Fernald, H.E. Three Ming pottery figures (MJ v 17, no 1)
    11 p 4 il 1926 p $1. PU-Mu   3457
Freer Gallery of Art. Ming pottery in the Freer Gallery of
    Art, a picture book with introductory text 38 p pl and
    table 1953 p $.50 DSI-F   3458
Gordon, G.B. Chinese ceramics (MJ v 5, no 1) 8 p 7 il
    1914 p $1. PU-Mu   3459
Hobby, Theodore Y. Chinese porcelains in the Altman Col-
    lection 32 p 1 il c 28 pl (15 c) 1953 p $.95 NNMM   3460
In defense of the horses of T'ang T'ai Tsung (B v 9, no 4)
    9 p 2 il 1941 p $.50 PU-Mu   3461
Lee, Jean Gordon. Chinese porcelain, the Alfred and Mary
    Caspary Memorial gift 38 p 30 pl 1957 p $1.50 PPPM
                                                          3462
----. Ming Blue and White, blue decorated porcelain 72 p
    154 pl 1949 p $1.50 PPPM   3463
Orientalia, catalogue of the Whitridge Collection of Chinese
    pottery and porcelain; historical introduction by Ralph M.
    Chait. Glossary, bibliography 132 p 42 il 1932 $1.
    MdBMA   3464
Pope, John A. Chinese porcelains from the Ardebil Shrine
    (Smithsonian I, pubn 4231) 194 p 142 pl 1956 p $10.
    DSI-F   3465
----. Fourteenth-century blue-and-white, a group of Chinese
    porcelains in the Topkapu Sarayi Musesi, Istanbul (FOP v
    2, no 1; Smithsonian I, pubn 4089) 85 p 44 pl 1952 p $2.
    DSI-F   3466
Salmony, Alfred. Chinese prehistoric painted pottery (F 6)
    p $.20 NBuM   3467
----. Early Chinese ceramics as funerary offerings (F 7) p
    $.20 NBuM   3468
----. Wei and T'ang Chinese ceramics as funerary offerings
    (F 8) p $.20 NBuM   3469
Two pottery tiles from a Han Dynasty tomb (B v 4, no 4) 4
    p 2 il 1933 p $.35 PU-Mu   3470

--Art, Oriental--Far East-China--Metal Work

Archaic Chinese bronzes (B v 8, no 2-3) 8 p 2 il 1940 p
    $.50 PU-Mu   3471
Bishop, C.W. Two Chinese bronze vessels (MJ v 9, no 2)
    20 p 3 il 1918 p $1. PU-Mu   3472

Kelly, Charles Fabens, and Ch'en Meng-Cha. Chinese
    bronzes from the Buckingham Collection 164 p il 1946
    $7. 50 ICA   3473
St. Louis City Art Museum. Kidder, J. Edward. Early
    Chinese bronzes in the City Art Museum Collection 112 p
    37 pl $10; $. 25 post MoSCA   3474
Salmony, Alfred. Chinese metal mirrors (F 4) p $. 20
    NBuM   3475
----. Early Chinese bronzes (F 3) p $. 20 NBuM   3476

--Art, Oriental--Far East--China---Architecture

Amithaba Altar (B v 7, no 3) 7 p 9 il 1939 p $. 50 PU-Mu
                                                          3477
The doors of the waiting dogs, sixth century tomb doors (B v
    8, no 4) 4 p 2 il 1940 p $. 50 PU-Mu   3478

--Art, Oriental--Far East--Japan

Annotated outlines of the history of Japanese arts, multig il
    1955 p $1. DSI-F   3479
The collection of John Taylor Spaulding, 1870-1958, with
    Japanese prints and sword-mounts from the William S. and
    John T. Spaulding Collection 58 p 36 il (1 c) 1948 p $. 50
    MBMu   3480
Fuller, Richard E. Sketch of the historical background of
    Japanese art p WaSA   3481
Japanese art il p $1. 50 CSfDeY   3482
Otsu-E (Japanese peasant painting from the village of Otsu)
    1950 p $. 20 MH-FA   3483
Seattle Art Museum. Japanese painting of the Kamakura
    period in the Seattle Art Museum (repr, Art Quarterly,
    Autumn 1949) 10 il p $. 50 WaSA   3484
Tomioka Tessai, loan exhibition from Japan 29 il (5 c) p $2.
    MBMu   3485
Treasures from Japan, foreword by R. P. Griffing, Jr.,
    preface by Natatakeasano (published jointly by Honolulu
    Academy of Arts and Tokyo National Museum) 92 p il
    1957 p $1. 50 HHo   3486
Contemporary Japanese prints (The Museum, ns, v 8, no 4,
    Fall 1956) p $. 50 NjNM   3487
Gunsaulus, Helen C. The Clarence Buckingham Collection of
    Japanese prints--Primitives 277 p 530 il, 8 c pl; ltd ed
    of 500 numbered copies, v 1 of a planned 8 v 1955 $50.
    ICA   3488
Japanese prints (The Museum, ns, v 5, no 1, Winter 1955)
    p $. 50 NjNM   3489

Japanese prints: A selection from the Charles J. Morse
    and Jared K. Morse Collection; foreword by Charles C.
    Cunningham, introduction by Kojiro Tomita 490 p 32 il
    1951 p $1.   CtHWA   3490
Priest, Alan.   Japanese prints from the Henry L. Phillips
    Collection 22 p front c 52 il 1947 p $2.25 NNMM   3491
Masterpieces of Japanese prints 50 p il 1955 p $1. ICA3492
Hokusai.   Day and night sketches in the four seasons PB 48
    il 1957 p $1. MBMu   3493
Kiyonaga.   Hirano, Chie.   Kiyonaga, a study of his life and
    works 545 p, portfolio: 138 pl (8 c) 1939 $50. MBMu
                                                               3494
Sengai.   India-ink drawings by the famous Zen priest Sengai
    p $.50 COA   3495
Fernald, H.E.   The T. Broom Belfield Collection of Japa-
    nese netsuke (MJ v 19, no 3) 21 p 9 il 1928 p $1. PU-
    Mu   3496
A panorama in miniature: Japanese netsuke (The Museum,
    ns, v 9, no 4, Winter 1957) p $.75 NjNM   3497
Warner, Langdon.   Japanese sculpture of the Suiko Period
    $40.   OClMA   3498
Japanese potter--old and new (C 25) 28 p 24 il 2nd ed 1952
    p $.75 MiDA   3499
Morse, Edward S.   Catalogue of the Morse Collection of
    Japanese pottery 364 p 68 pl, 1545 potters' marks in text
    1901 $75. MBMu   3500
Gunsaulus, Helen C.   Japanese costume (A-PS 12) 26 p 8 il
    1923 p $.20 ICF   3501
Lucy T. Aldrich Collection of Japanese No Drama costumes
    and priests' robes il 1937 p $.25 RPD-M   3502
Some Japanese textile-printing blocks: An album of Chin-
    nery drawings (MC v 2, no 1) il p $.10 NNCoo   3503
Bishop, C.W.   A Mausumane blade (MJ v 5, no 4) 6 pl
    1914 p $1.   PU-Mu   3504
Gunsaulus, Helen C.   The Japanese sword and its decoration
    (A-PS 20) 21 p 4 il 1924 p $.15 ICF   3505
Japanese sword mountings in the bequest of George Cameron
    Stone (MC v 1, no 7) il p $.15 NNCoo   3506
A prehistoric bell and cast metal mirror from Japan (BFM
    v 2, no 4) 2 p 2 il 1900 p $.50 PU-Mu   3507

--Art, Orient--Far East--Korea

Korean treasures p $3.84 CLCM   3508
Masterpieces of Korean art 187 il (4 c) 1958 p $4. MBMu
                                                               3509
Rogers, Millard B.   Korean ceramics in the Seattle Art Mu-

seum 25 p 19 il p $1.50 WaSA   3510

--Art, Oriental--Far East--Tibet

Bishop, C.W.   Tibetan sacred art (MJ v 5, no 4) 16 p 10 il
    1914 p $1. PU-Mu   3511
Cammann, S.   Glimpses of the Lama religion in Tibet and
    Mongolia (B v 14, no 2) 36 p 13 il 1949 p $.50 PU-Mu
                                                     3512
Gordon, G.B.   Some art objects from Tibet (MJ v 5, no 1)
    4 p 3 il 1914 p $1. PU-Mu   3513
Notes by the Lama Dousand Up of Darjeeling on the Alexander
    Scott Collection (MJ v 5, no 2) 45 p 38 il 1914 p $1.
    PU-Mu   3514
Thirteen Tibetan tankas, Buddhist birth stories told by ban-
    ner paintings of the City Art Museum 15 il front c 14 fig
    $9.95; $.25 post   MoSCA   3515
Tibetan collection and other Lamaist articles in the Newark
    Museum: A catalogue. v 1. Introduction and definition
    of terms; symbols in Tibetan Buddhist art 60 p il 1950
    p $1.50; v 2. Prayer and objects associated with prayer;
    Music and musical instruments; Ritualistic objects 82 p
    il 1950 p $1.50 NjNM   3516

--Art, Oriental--Near and Middle East

Dumbarton Oaks Research Library and Collection, handbook
    of the collection 1955 p $2. DDO   3517
Early Christian and Byzantine art 172 p 121 pl 1947 $5.75;
    p $3.75 MdBWA   3518
Ettinghausen, Richard.   Studies in Muslim iconography, I.
    The unicorn (FOP v 1, no 3; Smithsonian I, pubn 3993)
    209 p 48 pl 5 il 1950 p $1.50 DSI-F   3519
Gordon, G.B.   Arabic art (MJ v 13, no 1) 54 p 30 il (15 c)
    1922 p $1. PU-Mu   3520
----.   Baalbek (Syria) (MJ v 12, no 3) 21 p 7 il (1 c)
    1921 p $1. PU-Mu   3521
----.   The walls of Constantinople (MJ v 12, no 4) 30 p 15
    il 1921 p $1. PU-Mu   3522
Islamic art, selected examples from an exhibition in Mu-
    seum, 1945-1946 50 il (1 c) p $1.25 OClMA   3523
Laufer, Berthold.   Ostrich egg-shell cups of Mesopotamia
    and the ostrich in ancient and modern times (A-PS 23) 50
    p 19 il 1926 p $.30 ICF   3524
Legrain, L.   The Sabean Collection (South Arabia) (B v 4,
    no 1) 1 p 2 il 1932 p $.35 PU-Mu   3525
Rainey, A.   Afghanistan (B v 17, no 4) 17 p 10 il 1953

p $.50 PU-Mu   3526
Caskel, Werner. Arabic inscriptions in the collections;
    translated from German by Beatrice Gilman Proske--
    Catalogue of gravestones, chiefly Almeria, and other Mu-
    hammadan works of art, with translations of the inscrip-
    tions 44 p 60 il 1936 p $1. NNH   3527
Dunham, Dows. Naga-ed-Der-Stelae of the First Intermedi-
    ate Period 124 p 34 pl 6 drg 1937 p $10. MBMu   3528
Brehier, Louis. Byzantine silver p $.50 OClMA   3529
Small bronzes of the ancient world (C 10) 48 p 36 il 1947 p
    $.50 MiDA   3530
Rice, D.S. Wade cup, Islamic metal work p $4. IClMA
                                                                 3531
Bellinger, Louisa. Textile Analysis: Pile techniques in
    Egypt and the Near East (WN 12) p $1.25; Developing
    techniques in Egypt and the Near East, pt 5, 6 (WN 15,
    16) p $1.25 ea DTM   3532-3
----. Patterned stockings: Possibly Indian, found in Egypt
    (WN 10) p $1.25 DTM   3534
----. Textile Analysis: Early techniques in Egypt and the
    Near East, pt 1-3 (WN 2, 3, 6) p $1.25 ea DTM   3535
The Bible as a source book for the study of textiles (WN
    18) p $1.25 DTM   3536
Greene, Francina S. Preservation of dated Tiraz fabrics
    (WN 8) p $1.25 DTM   3537
Cooper Union Museum for the Arts of Decoration. Hispano-
    Islamic textiles in the Cooper Union Collection (MC v 1,
    no 10) il p $.15 NNCoo   3538
Museum of Fine Arts, Boston. Britoon, Nancy Pence. A
    study of some early Islamic textiles in the Museum of
    Fine Arts 90 p 100 il, 1 map 1938 p $3.50 MBMu   3539
Kuhnel, Ernst, and Louisa Bellinger. Catalog of dated Tiraz
    fabrics, Umayyad, Abbasid, Fatimid (imperfect copy)
    1952 $6.25 DTM   3540

--Art, Oriental--Near and Middle East--Egypt

The background of Egyptian art (B v 27, no 1, July 1939)
    p $.75 RPD-M   3541
Brooklyn Museum. Cooney, John D. Egyptian art in the
    Brooklyn Museum collection, selected to show major peri-
    ods through the New Kingdom PB 48 p 51 il 1952 p $1.
    NBB   3542
----, ----. Late Egyptian and Coptic art, an introduction
    to the collections of the Brooklyn Museum 24 p 54 il 1943
    $1.50; p $1. NBB   3543
Cleveland Museum of Art. Egyptian collection of the Museum

designed for school notebook by members of the Museum's
Educational Department Staff   p $.50 OClMA   3544
Coptic Egypt, papers read at a symposium in connection with
an exhibition: "Paganism and Christianity in Egypt" 58 p
1944 p $.75 NBB   3545
Five years of collecting Egyptian art, 1951-1956 63 p 96 il
1956 p $3.50 NBB   3546
Hayes, William C.   The burial chamber of the treasurer
Sobk-Mose from Er Rizeikat (P 9) 40 p front 6 pl 1939
p $1. NNMM   3547
The Meydum Room (B v 3, no 2) 2 p 1 il 1931 p $.35 PU-
Mu   3548
Museum of Fine Arts, Boston. Dunham, Dows. Egyptian
Department and its excavations 129 il (1 c) p $2.50
MBMu   3549
Phillips, Dorothy. Ancient Egyptian animals, a picture book
24 p 41 il 1948 p $.35 NNMM   3550
Randall-MacIver, D., and Leonard Woolley.   Areika, with a
chapter on Meroitic inscriptions by F.L. Griffith (Coxe
Exp v 1) 56 p 43 pl (5 c) 1909 $3.50 PU-Mu   3551
Riefstahl, Elizabeth.   Toilet articles from ancient Egypt 32
p 40 il 1943 p $.40 NBB   3552
Scott, Nora A.   The home life of the ancient Egyptians, a
picture book 32 p 35 il 1950 p $.50 NNMM   3553
Smith, William Stevenson.   Ancient Egypt as represented in
the Museum of Fine Arts, Boston 215 p 132 il (4 c) map
4th ed 1960 $2. MBMu   3553a
----.   Country life in ancient Egypt: 47 illustrations of
sculpture in the round, reliefs, painted scenes from sarcophagi, and other important objects from the Egyptian
collections of the Museum (PB 2) c p $.50 MBMu   3554
----.   A history of Egyptian sculpture and painting in the
Old Kingdom 422 p 239 fig 208 il on 63 pl (3 c) 1950 p
$25. MBMu   3555
University Museum.   Ranke, H.   The Egyptian Collections of
the University Museum (B v 15, no 2-3) 112 p 56 il 1950
p $.50 PU-Mu   3556
An Egyptian tombstone of the New Kingdom (Abydos) (B v 9,
no 1) 4 p 3 il 1941 p $.50 PU-Mu   3557
A granite relief of Ptolemy II (B v 7, no 1) 3 p 1 il 1937 p
$.50 PU-Mu   3558
Hall, E.H.   A granite sphinx from Memphis (MJ v 4, no 2)
6 p 2 il 1914 p $1. PU-Mu   3559
A head from an Egyptian royal statue (B v 5, no 3) 2 p 2 il
1934 p $.35 PU-Mu   3560
A late Saitic statue from the Temple of Neith, at Sais (B v
9, no 4) 4 p 2 il 1942 p $.50 PU-Mu   3561

A portrait head of Aknaten (B v 1, no 1) 1 p 1 il 1930 p
   $.35 PU-Mu   3562
Ranke, H.   An Egyptian tombstone (B v 13, no 3) 6 p 1 il
   1948 p $.50 PU-Mu   3563
A sculpture from Meydum (B v 3, no 6) 1 p 1 il 1932 p
   $.35 PU-Mu   3564
A statuette of the Goddess Hathor (Dendereh) (B v 8, no 4)
   3 p 1 il 1940 p $.50 PU-Mu   3565
Steindorff, George.   A royal head from ancient Egypt (FOP
   v 1, no 5; Smithsonian I, pubn 4022) 30 p 29 pl 1951 p
   $.35 DSI-F   3566
An unfinished statue of the Twelfth Dynasty (B v 8, no 2-3)
   2 p 2 il 1940 p $.50 PU-Mu   3567
Walters Art Gallery.   Steindorff, George.   Catalogue of
   Egyptian sculpture in the Walters Art Gallery 187 p 119
   pl 1946 $17.50 MdBWA   3568
Hall, H.B.   Early painted pottery from Gournia (T v 1, no
   3) 14 p 11 il 1905 p $1. PU-Mu   3569
Hayes, William C.   Glazed tiles from the palace of Rameses
   II at Kantir (P 3) 46 p 11 il 13 pl 1937 p $1. NNMM
                                                                 3570
Luce, S.B.   An early potter's wheel (MJ v 11, no 4) 5 p
   2 il 1920 p $1.   PU-Mu   3571
Riefstahl, Elizabeth.   Glass and glazes from ancient Egypt
   24 p 34 il 1948 p $.40 NBB   3572
Egyptian Rug fragment with dated Tiraz (WN 22) 1960 $1.25
   DTM   3573
Kuhnel, Ernst, and Louisa Bellinger.   Cairene rugs and
   others technically related 1957 $15. DTM   3574
Dam, C.H.   An Egyptian kursi (MJ v 19, no 3) 5 p 2 il
   1928 p $1.   PU-Mu   3575
Davies, Norman de Garis.   The temple of Hibis in El
   Khargeh oasis.   Pt. 3.   The decoration.   Ludlow Bull and
   Linsley F. Hall, eds; foreword by H.E. Winlock (Publi-
   cations of the Metropolitan Museum of Art Egyptian Expe-
   dition v 17) 48 p 6 il 80 pl (2 c) 1953 $35. NNMM 3576
Early Egyptian door-socket (Hierakonpolis) (B v 5, no 1) 2
   p 2 il 1934 p $.35 PU-Mu   3577
Fisher, C.S.   The throne room of Merenptah (Memphis) (MJ
   v 12, no 1) 6 p 1 il c 1921 p $1. PU-Mu   3578
Mileham, G.S.   Churches in Lower Nubia (Coxe Exp v 2)
   57 p 39 pl (1 c) 1910 $3.50 PU-Mu   3579

--Art, Oriental--Near and Middle East--India

Art of greater India 128 p 138 pl 1950 p $2. CLCM   3580
Arts of India from 1500 B.C. to the late 19th century; in-

troduction by W. Norman Brown 16 p 1944 p $.25 NjTM
3581
Coomaraswamy, A.K.   A statuette of Vishnu from Kashmir
(MJ v 17, no 1) 2 p 1 il 1926 p $1. PU-Mu   3582
Gandhara sculpture 6 pl, with explanatory notes (MJ v 15,
no 4) 1924 $1.   3583
Relief from inscription from Kashmir (B v 2, no 6) 2 p 1 il
1931 p $.35 PU-Mu   3584
Bronzes of India and Greater India il 1955 p $.35 RPD-M
3585

Lewis, Albert Buell.   Block prints from India for textiles
(DS 1) 26 il (2 c) 1924 p $.50 ICF   3586
Brown, W. Norman.   A pillared hall from a temple at Ma-
dura, India (U of Pennsylvania Press) 126 p 16 il 1940
$1. PPPM   3587

--Art, Oriental--Near and Middle East--Jewish

Art in Judaism, past and present: Catalogue of an exhibition
6 p 1957 p apply NjNM   3588
Beauty in holiness, the treasures of Judaism's rich art herit-
age... (repr, The Bulletin of the Hebrew Union College--
Jewish Institute of Religion, October 1956) il p $.25
OCH-Mu   3589
Brooklyn Museum Aramaic papyri, new documents of the
fifth century B.C. General historical introduction by Emil
G. Kraeling 319 p 23 il 1949 $10. NBB   3590
Exhibition of Jewish ceremonial art (C 26) 45 p 25 il 1951 p
$.50 MiDA   3591
Fitzgerald, G.M.   The earliest pottery of Beth-Shan (MJ v
24, no 1) 18 p 10 pl 1935 p $1. PU-Mu   3592
----.   The four Canaanite temples of Beth-Shan (The pottery)
(Beth Shan Excav v 2, pt 2) 43 p 51 pl 1930 p $7.50
PU-Mu   3593
Jewish art, from the Hebrew Union College and other col-
lections, a special exhibition in honor of the three hun-
dredth anniversary of Jewish settlement of America,
sponsored by the Greater Hartford Jewish Tercentenary
Committee and Wadsworth Atheneum   23 p 3 il 1955 p
CtHWA   3594
Jewish ceremonial art $2; post additional NNJ-Mu   3595
Rowe, A.   The four Canaanite temples of Beth-Shan--
Temples and cult objects (Beth Shan Excav v 2, pt 1) 101
p 71 pl 1940 p $12. PU-Mu   3596
----.   The two royal stelae of Beth-Shan (MJ v 20, no 1)
10 p 2 il 1929 p $1. PU-Mu   3597
Royal Ontario Museum.   Needler, Winifred.   Palestine, an-

cient and modern, a handbook and guide to the Palestine
collection 116 p 35 pl maps p $.50 CaOTRM   3598
Seven painters of Israel p $.40 MBI   3599
Two incense burners from Beth-Shan (Bv 4, no 3) 3 p 2 il
1933 p $.35 PU-Mu   3600

--Art, Oriental--Near and Middle East--Mesopotamian (including Sumerian and Babylonian)

Clay, A.T.   An ancient antiquary (MJ v 3, no 2) 3 p 2 il
1912 p $.50 PU-Mu   3601
Langdon, S.   A tablet of the mysteries of Babylonian symbolism (MJ v 9, no 2) 6 p 1 il 1918 p $1. PU-Mu 3602
Legrain, L.   The boudoir of Queen Shubad (MJ v 20, no 3-
4) 35 p 19 il 1929 p $2.   PU-Mu   3603
----. The culture of the Babylonians from their seals in
the collection of the Museum. Pt. 1. Text 367 p; Pt. 2.
64 pl (PBS v 14) 1925-1927 p $10. PU-Mu   3604
----. Note on the inlay standard (MJ v 20, no 1) 2 p 1929
p $1.   PU-Mu   3605
----. Old Sumerian art (MJ v 19, no 3) 27 p 8 il (1 c)
1928 p $1.   PU-Mu   3606
----. Sumerian art shop (MJ v 19, no 4) 25 p 53 il 1928 p
$1.   PU-Mu   3607
Montgomery, J.A.   A magical skull (MJ v 2, no 3) 3 p 1911
p $.50 PU-Mu   3608
Hare, Susanna, and Edith Porada. The Great King, King of
Assyria. Assyrian reliefs in the Metropolitan Museum of
Art, photographs by Charles Sheeler 52 p front 2 il 25
pl 1945 $1.98 NNMM   3609
Legrain, L.   Small sculptures from Babylonian tombs (MJ
v 19, no 2) 18 p 22 il 1928 p $1. PU-Mu   3610
----. Sumerian sculptures (MJ v 18, no 3) 31 p 16 il 1927
p $1.   PU-Mu   3611
----. Tomb sculptures from Palmyra (MJ v 18, no 4) 26 p
15 il 1927 p $1.   PU-Mu   3612
----. Terra cottas from Nippur. Pt. 1. Text 52 p; Pt.
2. 77 pl, portf (PBS v 16) 1930 p $12.50 PU-Mu   3613
A note on the Assyrian sculptures (B v 1, no 3) 1 p 1 il
1930 p $.35 PU-Mu   3614
Clay, A.T.   A vase of Xerxes (MJ v 1, no 1) 2 p 1 il
1910 p $.50 PU-Mu   3615
Speiser, E.A.   The pottery of Tell Billa (MJ v 23, no 3)
60 p 25 pl 1932 p $1. PU-Mu   3616
Legrain, L.   Archaic seal impressions (Publications of the
Joint Exp, Ur excavations: Archaeol v 3) 120 p 54 pl
1936 p $10.   PU-Mu   3617

----. Five royal seal cylinders (MJ v 8, no 1) 19 p 5 il
   1922 p $1. PU-Mu   3618
----. Gem cutters in ancient Ur (MJ v 20, no 3-4) 49 p
   23 il 1929 p $2. PU-Mu   3619
----. Nippur's gold treasure (MJ v 11, no 3) 7 p 1 il 1920
   p $1. PU-Mu   3620
----. Seal cylinders (Publications of the Joint Exp, Ur ex-
   cav: Archaeol v 10) 56 p 43 pl 1951 p $6.50 PU-Mu
   (Order from British Museum, London, W.C. 1, England)
                                                                           3621
Fisher, C.S. The archaic arch at Nippur (T v 1, no 3) 9
   p 7 il 1905 p $1. PU-Mu   3622
The builder's art at Ur (MJ v 16, no 4) 90 p 45 il 1925 p
   $1. PU-Mu   3623
Woolley, Charles Leonard. A great temple of Babylonia
   (MJ v 16, no 1) 3 p 1925 p $1. PU-Mu   3624
----. The Ziggurat and its surroundings (Publications of the
   Joint Exp, Ur excav: Archaeol v 5) 150 p 88 pl 1939
   p $18. PU-Mu   3625

--Art, Oriental--Middle and Near East--Persia

The arts of Old Persia il 1952 p $.50 InIJ   3626
Bahrami, Mehdi. Works of Iranian art 11 p 10 il p $.50
   MBMu   3627
Fragment of a mosque carpet and a Persian metallic lustre
   plate (MJ v 16, no 1) 2 pl 1925 p $1. PU-Mu   3628
A fragment of a limestone relief (B v 9, no 1) 1 p 1 il 1941
   p $.50 PU-Mu   3629
Guest, Grace Dunham. Shiraz painting in the sixteenth cen-
   tury (Smithsonian I, pubn 3978) 70 p 50 pl 1949 $2.50
   DSI-F   3630
Persian miniatures: A picture book; introduction by M.S.
   Dimand 24 p 20 il 2nd ed 1944 p $.35 NNMM   3631
Special exhibition of oriental miniatures (Persia and Mughal)
   (B v 1, no 2) 1 p 1 il 1930 p $.35 PU-Mu   3632
Special exhibition of Oriental miniatures (Persian and Mughal)
   (B v 1, no 3) 1 p 1 il 1930 p $.35 PU-Mu   3633
Ackerman, Phyllis. Luristan bronzes (F 10) p $.20 NBuM
                                                                           3634
A collection of bronzes from Luristan (B v 2, no 6) 4 p 2 il
   1931 p $.35 PU-Mu   3635
University Museum. Legrain, L. Luristan bronzes in the
   University Museum (Catalogue, suppl no 1, MJ) 20 p 25
   pl 1934 p $2. PU-Mu   3636
Carpets for the Great Shah (B v 2, no 1) 1948 p $1. DCGA
   (op)   3637

250   Woven treasures

Woven treasures of Persian art 70 p il 1959 $2.40 CLCM
                                                    3638

--Art, Primitive See also Art, Americas--Indians of North
America, --Indians of Mexico, Central and South America

Masterpieces of primitive art 35 il 1958 p $1.25 MBMu3639
Museum of Primitive Art. Selected works from the collec-
   tion--Color in sculpture and ceramics, introduction by
   Douglas Newton 1957 15 p 26 il p $1.50 NNMPA   3640
----. Selected works from the collection--Stone sculpture
   from Mexico, introduction by Gordon Ekholm 1959 32 p
   32 il p $1.50 NNMPA   3641
----. Selected works from the collection--Upper gallery:
   Sculpture in wood; Lower gallery: Works in various
   media 1957 p $1.50 NNMPA   3642
Pre-Columbian gold sculpture, introduction by Junius B. Bird
   and Gordon Ekholm Bronzes from Benin 1958 30 p 53 il
   p $1.50 NNMPA   3643
The Wurtzburger Collection of primitive art (Catalogues of
   African sculpture, Oceanic art, and Pre-Columbian art)
   1958 $4. MdBMA   3644

--Art, Primitive--African

African art, catalogue of an exhibition of African art from
   American sources; foreword by Adelyn D. Breeskin, es-
   say by Dr. Alain Locke 43 p 44 il, map 1946 p $1.25
   MdBMA   3645
African art from the collection of Mr. and Mrs. Raymond
   Wielgus 12 p il 1957 p $.50 ICA (op)   3646
Bascom, William R, and Paul Gebauer. West African art,
   assembled and edited by Robert E. Ritzenthaler (PSH 5)
   83 p 64 pl 1954 p $.75 WMMMu   3647
Dunham, Dows. Royal cemeteries of Kush. v 1. El Kurru
   144 p 73 pl 1 map 1950 p $25; v 2. Nuri 300 p 141 pl 1
   map 1955 p $32.50; ----, and Suzanne E. Chapman, v 3
   Decorated chapels of Meroitic pyramids at Meroe and Bar-
   kal, volume of large folio plates (12.75x18.5) 6 p 34 pl
   (96 drg, 31 photog, 4 map and plan, 1 chart) 1952 p
   $20. MBMu (Reports excavation of Royal Cemeteries in
   Sudan by Harvard University, Boston Museum of Fine Arts
   Egyptian Expedition, 1919-1923. Published for Museum by
   Harvard University Press)   3648
----. Two royal lades of Meroe--report on two tombs in
   the Sudan: Ethiopian period, ca 600 B.C.; Meroitic period,
   ca 25 B.C. (Communications to the Trustees, v 7) 16 p

14 il 1924 p $1. MBMu   3649
Hall, H.U.   Dwarfs and divinities in West Africa (MJ v 18,
   no 3) 5 p 3 il 1927 p $1.   PU-Mu   3650
----.   Examples of African art (MJ v 10, no 3) 24 p 17 il
   (1 c) 1919 p $1. PU-Mu   3651
Nelson, N.C.   South African rock pictures (SG 93; repr,
   Natural History) 12 p 13 il p $.35; $.10 post NNM 3652
Philadelphia Commercial Museum.   A handbook of the Afri-
   can collections of the Commercial Museum p $1.
   PPComm   3653
Plass, Margaret.   African image--a new selection of tribal
   art 34 p 184 il 1959 p $1.50 OTM   3654
Roth, H. Ling.   Personal ornaments from Benin (BFM v 2,
   no 1) 4 p 9 il 1899 p $.50 PU-Mu   3655
University Museum.   African collections (B v 3, no 6) 16 p
   12 il 1 map 1932 p $.35 PU-Mu   3656
----.   The African Galleries (B v 4, no 1) 2 p 1 il 1932 p
   $.35 PU-Mu   3657
----.   Torday, E.   The New Congo collection (MJ v 4, no
   1) 19 p 32 il 1913 p $.50 PU-Mu   3658
----.   Two new collections of African art (B v 1, no 1) 2 p
   3 il 1930 p $.35 PU-Mu   3659
----.   Wieschhoff, H.A.   The African collections of the Uni-
   versity Museum (B v 11, no 1-2) 74 p 26 il 1945 p $1.
   PU-Mu   3660
Wingert, Paul S.   African art (The Museum, ns, v 6, no 4,
   Fall 1954) p $.50 NjNM   3661
African sculpture, lent by New York collectors 1958 p $1.50
   NNPMA   3662
An African wood carving (Lower Congo) (B v 4, no 3) 1 pl
   il 1933 p $.35 PU-Mu   3663
Antelopes and queens--Sculpture from the Bambara tribe of
   the western Sudan 1960 $3.50 NNPMA   3664
The art of the Great Benin (MJ v 3, no 4) 5 p 6 il $.50
   PU-Mu   3665
Coon, Carleton S.   African Negro sculpture: Introduction (B
   v 21, no 4) 75 p 50 il 1 map 1957 p $.50 PU-Mu   3666
Fischer, H.G.   Further remarks on the prostrate kings (B
   v 21, no 2) 6 p 4 il 1957 p $.50 PU-Mu   3667
----.   Prostrate figures (B v 20, no 1) 17 p 15 il 1956 p
   $.50 PU-Mu   3668
Hall, H.U.   Fetish figures of Equatorial Africa (MJ v 11, no
   1) 28 p 23 il 1920 p $1. PU-Mu   3669
----.   An ivory standing cup from Benin (MJ v 17, no 4) 17
   p 2 il (1 c) 1926 p $1. PU-Mu   3670
Plass, Margaret.   African tribal sculpture 57 p 62 il 1 map
   1956 $1.   PU-Mu   3671

Sculpture from three African tribes: Senufo, Baga, Dogan,
  introduction by Robert Goldwater 1959 32 p 22 il p $1.50
  NNMPA   3672
The sculpture of Negro Africa--Exhibition organized by the
  Art Center in La Jolla (California); foreword by Paul S.
  Wingert il 1960 $1. CLMA   3673
Tenenbaum, Frieda, and Edward Bryant.   African sculpture,
  handbook il 1958 p $.25 NBB   3674
The Wurtzburger Collection of African sculpture; foreword
  by Adelyn D. Breeskin, essay on African Negro sculpture
  by Paul S. Wingert 30 p 34 il map rev ed 1958 p $1.50
  MdBMA   3675
Hall, H.U.   Two masks from French Equatorial Africa (MJ
  v 18, no 4) 26 p 3 il 1927 $1. PU-Mu   3676

--Art, Primitive--Pacific Area

Kooijman, S.   The art of Lake Sentani (Dutch New Guinea)
  1959 64 p 117 il $3.50 NNMPA   3677
Art of the South Pacific il p $1.85 CSfDeY   3678
Buck, Peter H.   Arts and crafts of Hawaii (SP 45) 606 p
  350 fig 1957 p $12. HB   3679
Estrin, Rochelle, and Arline Meyer.   Indonesian art 21 p 14
  il 1959 p $.25 NBB   3680
Hall, H.U.   Art of the Marquesas Islands (MJ v 12, no 4)
  39 p 35 il 1921 p $1. PU-Mu   3681
Lewis, Albert Buell.   Carved and painted designs from New
  Guinea (DS 5) 61 il 1931 p $1.25 ICF   3682
----.   Decorative art of New Guinea, incised designs (DS 4)
  56 il 1925 p $.75 ICF   3683
Mead, Margaret.   The Maoris and their arts (SG 71) 38 p
  23 il p $.40; $.10 post NNM   3684
Powell, Jane, and Martin Friedman.   Primitive art of the
  Pacific Islands 20 p 16 il 1957 p $.25 NBB   3685
Souvenirs from the Pacific 9 il p $.25 ViRMu   3686
The Wurtzburger Collection of Oceanic art; catalogue of
  sculpture, paintings, and other arts of Oceania; foreword
  by Adelyn D. Breeskin, essay on Oceanic art by Paul S.
  Wingert, and Douglas F. Fraser 40 p 48 il 1956 p $1.50
  MdBMA   3687
Brigham, William T.   Additional notes on Hawaiian feather
  work (M v 1, no 5) 19 p 4 pl 20 fig 1903 p $1.25; --
  second suppl (M v 7, no 1) 69 p 4 pl 54 fig 1918 p
  $1.25 HB   3688
Lewis, Albert Buell.   Javanese Batik designs from metal
  stamps (DS 2) 26 il (2 c) 1924 p $.50 ICF   3689
Brigham, William T.   Old Hawaiian carvings (M v 2, no 2)

20 p 1 pl 21 fig 1906 p $1.25 HB   3690
Hall, H.U.   Maori wood carving and Moko (MJ v 11, no 4)
   30 p 26 il 1920 p $1.   PU-Mu   3691
----.   Wood carvings of the Austral Islands (MJ v 12, no 3)
   21 p 14 il 1921 p $1. PU-Mu   3692
----.   The orator's staff (Maori) (MJ v 15, no 4) 15 p 5 il
   1924 p $1. PU-Mu   3693
----.   A wood carving from Easter Island (MJ v 16, no 2)
   6 p 1 il 1925 p $1. PU-Mu   3694
Maori war canoe ornaments (B v 5, no 5) 3 p 4 il 1935 p
   $.35 PU-Mu   3695
Shadow puppets from Java (B v 1, no 3) 2 p 1 il 1930 p
   $.35 PU-Mu   3696
Hall, H.U.   New Ireland masks (MJ v 10, no 4) 4 p 2 il c
   1919 p $1. PU-Mu   3697
Lewis, Albert B.   New Guinea masks (A-PS 4) 9 p 6 il
   1922 p $.15 ICF   3698

--Art, Primitive--Pre-Columbian

Art of ancient Peru, selected works from the collection, in-
   troduction by René d'Harnoncourt 1958 30 p 26 il p $1.50
   NNMPA   3699
Cummings Collection of ancient Peruvian art 48 p il 1954 p
   $1.50 ICA   3700
Farabee, W.C.   Decorative arts of the Amazon (MJ v 9, no
   1) 13 p 11 pl 1918 p $1.   PU-Mu   3701
Gordon, G.B.   Native American art (MJ v 9, no 1) 22 p 9
   pl (1 c) 1918 p $1. PU-Mu   3702
----.   The serpent motive in the ancient art of Central
   America and Mexico (T v 1, no 3) 33 p 16 pl 1905 p $1.
   PU-Mu   3703
Kidder, Alfred II, and Carlos Samoyoa Chinchilla.   The art
   of the ancient Maya (C 35) 124 p 106 il (4 c) 1959 p $3.
   MiDA   3704
Latin American antiquities (The Museum, ns, v 6, no 1,
   Winter 1954) p $.50 NjNM   3705
A Peruvian painting set (B v 3, no 1) 2 p 1 pl 1931 p $.35
   PU-Mu   3706
Pre-Columbian art and culture in the Andean area (B v 28,
   no 3, Dec 1940) p $.50 RPD-M   3707
Powell, Jane P.   Ancient art of the Americas 68 p 38 il
   1959 p $1.25 NBB   3708
Valliant, George Clapp.   Artists and craftsmen of ancient
   Central America (SG 88) 102 p 152 il p $1.45; $.10 post
   NNM   3709
The Wurtzburger Collection of Pre-Columbian art; foreword

by Adelyn D. Breeskin, introduction by George Kubler,
notes on the Collection of Pre-Columbian art by George
Kubler 46 p 56 il map 1958 p $1.50 MdBMA   3710
Animal sculpture in Pre-Columbian art 48 p il 1957 p $1.
ICA   3711
Gann, Thomas. Painted stucco heads from Louisville, Brit-
ish Honduras (P 15; MARR v 1, no 4) 4 p 1943 p $.25
LNT-MA   3712
Gordon, G.B. The Ulua marble vase (MJ v 12, no 1) 22 p
22 il 1921 p $1. PU-Mu   3713
Lutz, Frank E. String-figures from the Patomanca Indians
of British Guiana (AP 12:1, p 1-14) 12 fig 1912 p $.25
NNM   3713a
Mason, J. Alden. Costa Rican stone work. The Minor C.
Keith Collection (AP 39:3, p 189-318) 44 fig 1945 p
$2.75 NNM   3713b
-----. Ivory and resin figurines from Cocle (Panama) (B v
8, no 4) 9 p 7 il 1940 p $.50 PU-Mu   3714
-----. A Maya carved stone lintel from Guatemala (B v 3,
no 1) 3 p 3 pl 1931 p $.35 PU-Mu   3715
-----. A remarkable throne from Guatemala (B v 4, no 4) 2
p 1 pl 1933 p $.35 PU-Mu   3716
-----. A stela from Piedras Negras (B v 5, no 2) 3 p 1 pl
1934 p $.35 PU-Mu   3717
-----. Stela 12 from Piedras Negras (B v 4, no 4) 2 p 1 pl
1933 p $.35 PU-Mu   3718
-----. A stucco head from Guatemala (B v 5, no 1) 3 p 1
pl 1934 p $.35 PU-Mu   3719
-----. Three Inca wooden cups (B v 5, no 5) 2 p 1 pl 1935
p $.35 PU-Mu   3720
-----. Zapotec funerary urns from Mexico (MJ v 20, no 2)
3 p 11 pl, with explanatory notes 1929 p $1. PU-Mu 3721
Pre-Columbian sculpture (Art Center, La Jolla and Arts
Club of Chicago) 1956 $2. TxSaMc   3722
Satterthwaite, L., Jr. Another Piedras Negras stela (B v 8,
no 2-3) 4 p 1 pl 1940 p $.50 PU-Mu   3723
-----. Sculptured monuments from Caracol, British Honduras;
with, Wilcox, H. Removal and restoration of monuments
of Caracol (B v 18, no 1-2) 45 p 42 il 3 table, and 27 p
25 il 1954 p $1. PU-Mu   3724
-----. Thrones at Piedras Negras (B v 7, no 1) 5 p 6 il
1937 p $.50 PU-Mu   3725
Saville, M.H. An onyx jar from Mexico, in process of
manufacture (B v 13, no 11, p 105-7) 1 pl 1900 p $.25
NNM   3726
-----. A shell gorget from Huasteca, Mexico (B v 13, no
10, p 99-103) 3 fig 1900 p $.20 NNM   3727

----. The woodcarver's art in ancient Mexico (C v 9) 120
p 15 pl 1925 p $5. NNMAI   3728
Skinner, Alanson. An image and an amulet of nephrite from
Costa Rica (INM v 6, no 4) 3 p il 1920 p $.15 NNMAI
3729
Stone sculpture from Mexico 1959 p $1.50 NNMPA   3730
Wardle, H.N. Guetar (Costa Rica) work in stone (B v 7,
no 3) 3 p 3 pl p $.50 PU-Mu   3731
Wardle, H.N. Taino (West Indies) figures (B v 6, no 3) 2
p 1 il 1936 p $.35 PU-Mu   3732
A new Mexican mask (B v 1, no 1) 2 p 1930 p $.35 PU-Mu
3733
An ancient Paracas manta (B v 7, no 4) 4 p 2 pl 1939 p
$.50 PU-Mu   3734
Benners, E.E. Ancient Peruvian textiles (MJ v 11, no 3)
4 p 13 pl (9 c) 1920 p $1. PU-Mu   3735
Bird, Junius Bouton, and Louisa Bellinger. Paracas fabrics
and Nazca needlework 1954 $18. DTM   3736
Cordry, Donald Bush, and Dorothy M. Cordry. Costumes
and textiles of the Aztec Indians of the Cuetzalan Region,
Puebla, Mexico (Pap 14) 60 p 9 pl 22 fig 1940 $2.50
CLSM   3737
----, ----. Costumes and weaving of the Zoque Indians of
Chiapas, Mexico (Pap 15) 130 p 23 pl 40 fig 1941 p $2.50
CLSM   3738
King, Mary Elizabeth. A preliminary study of a shaped tex-
tile from Peru (WN 13) p $1.25 DTM   3739
Long, Boaz, and Cristobal de Gangotena. The Long Collec-
tion of Ecuadorian rugs (P, ns, 42) 11 p il 1946 p $.25
NmSM-S   3740
Longyear, John M., III. Notes on some spindle whorls
from Quelepa, El Salvador (P 15; MARR v 1, no 3) 3 p
1942 p $.25 LNT-MA   3741
Lothrop, S.K. Polychrome guanaco cloaks of Patagonia (C
v 7, no 6) 30 p il 1929 p $.90 NNMAI   3742
Means, Philip Ainsworth. A study of Peruvian textiles in
the Museum of Fine Arts 83 p 83 il 8 drg 1 map 1932 p
$2.50 MBMu   3743
A new type of Peruvian Ikat (WN 17) p $1.25 DTM   3744
Paracas necropolis headdress and face ornaments, a comparison of gold and feather ornaments with those depicted
in necropolis embroideries (WN 21) p $1.25 DTM   3745
Wardle, H.N. Guatemala textiles (B v 5, no 1) 3 p 1 pl
1934 p $.35 PU-Mu   3746
Beyer, Hermann. Shell ornament sets from Huasteca,
Mexico (P 5; Studies in Mid Am 4) 1934 p $1. LNT-MA
3747

Farabee, W.C.   Ancient American gold (MJ v 11, no 3) 37
   p 22 il 1920 p $1. PU-Mu   3748
----.   A golden hoard from Ecuador (MJ v 12, no 1) 10 p
   8 il 1921 p $1. PU-Mu   3749
Gold: A catalogue of an exhibition of Pre-Columbian gold
   11 p 4 il $.25 CoDA   3750
Mason, J.A.   Jade ornaments from Piedras Negras (B v 4,
   no 2) 3 p 1 pl 1933 p $.35 PU-Mu   3751
----.   Gold and copper ornaments from Peru (B v 4, no 4)
   2 p 1 pl 1933 p $.35 PU-Mu   3752
----.   Turquoise mosaics from northern Mexico (MJ v 20,
   no 2) 19 p 2 il 1929 p $1. PU-Mu   3753
Mead, Charles W.   Prehistoric bronzes in South America
   (AP v 12, no 2, p 15-52) 4 fig 1915 p $.25 NNM   3754
Nuttall, Zelia.   Standard or head-dress?   An historical es-
   say on a relic of ancient Mexico (P v 1, no 1) 52 p 3 pl
   c 1888 sigs $1. MH-P   3755
Report on cenote jade (M v 10, no 1) in prep MH-P   3756
Saville, Marshall H.   A golden breastplate from Cuzco,
   Peru (M 21) 8 p il 1921 p $.40 NNMAI   3757
Borhegyi, Stephan F. de.   Notes and comments on the "duck
   pots" from Guatemala (P 18; MARR v 2, no 1) 16 p il
   1952 p $.75 LNT-MA   3758
Butler, Mary.   A Maya pottery vase (B v 5, no 6) 2 p 1 pl
   c 1935 p $.35 PU-Mu   3759
Examples of Maya pottery in the Museum, and other collec-
   tions.   Pt. 1. Gordon, G.B., ed.   25 pl (23 c) 1925
   $25;   Pt. 2. Mason, J.A., ed.   25 pl (21 c) 1928 $25;
   Pt. 3. Mason, J.A., ed.   16 pl (13 c) 1943 $20; set,
   in 15x20 portf $60. PU-Mu   3760
Farabee, W.C.   Conebo pottery (MJ v 6, no 2) 7 p 4 il
   1915 p $1. PU-Mu   3761
Lothrop, Samuel K.   Pottery types and their sequence in El
   Salvador (INM v 1, no 4) 43 p il 1927 p $.60 NNMAI
                                                               3762
Mason, Gregory.   Pottery and other artifacts from caves in
   British Honduras and Guatemala (M 47) 45 p il 1928 p
   $.40 NNMAI   3763
Mason, J.A.   Peruvian pottery whistles (B v 4, no 1) 2 p 1
   pl 1932 p $.35 PU-Mu   3764
----.   A pottery vessel from Mexico (B v 5, no 3) 3 p 1 pl
   1934 p $.35 PU-Mu   3765
Mercer, Henry C.   The Kabal, or potter's wheel of Yucatan
   (BFM v 1, no 2) 4 p 2 pl 1897 p $.50 PU-Mu   3766
Merwin, B.W.   Dutch Guiana pottery (MJ v 8, no 3) 6 p 6
   il 1917 p $1. PU-Mu   3767
Satterthwaite, L., Jr.   Two Maya bowls; a problem in re-

construction (B v 9, no 4) 1 p 2 pl 1942 p $.50 PU-Mu
3768

Smith, Robert E.   Ceramic sequences at Uaxactun, Guatemala (P 20) 2 v 388 p 86 pl 1955 p $10. LNT-MA   3769

Wardle, H.N.   Fictile art of the Mochicas (B v 8, no 1) 10
p 17 il 1940 p $.50 PU-Mu   3770

Wauchope, Robert. A tentative sequence of pre-classical
ceramics in Middle America (P 15; MARR v 1, no 14)
40 p 1950 p $1.25 LNT-MA   3771

Zimmern, Nathalie H.   Introduction to Peruvian costume 52
p 35 il 1949 p $.75 NBB   3772

Brinton, Daniel G.   The Pillars of Ben (BFM v 1, no 1) 8
p 3 fig 1897 p $.50 PU-Mu   3773

Satterthwaite, L., Jr.   Evolution of a Maya temple. Pt. 1.
(B v 7, no 4) 14 p 12 il 1939 p $.50; Pt. 2. (B v 8, no
2-3) 3 p 2 il 1940 p $.50 PU-Mu   3774

----.   Piedras Negras Archaeology: Architecture. Pt. 1.
Introduction 35 p 2 fig 1 map 1943 p $1.50; Pt. 2.
Temples. no 1. Structure R-9 (Temple and associated
construction) 27 p 21 fig 1944 p $.75; Pt. 4. Ball courts.
no. 1. Ball court terminology; no 2. Structure R-11
(South Group ball court); no 3. Structure K-6 (West Group
ball court) 44 p 25 fig 1944 p $1; Pt. 5. Sweathouses.
no 1. Recognition of sweathouses at Piedras Negras:
Diagnostic traits and terminology; no 2.   Structure N-1;
no 3. Six partially excavated sweathouses (Structures S-19,
J-17, O-4, S-2, and R-13); no 4.   Structure P-7 93 p
69 fig 1952 p $2. (Parts sold only on subscription basis,
estimated total cost: $15.)   PU-Mu   3775

HISTORY, SOCIAL SCIENCES AND TECHNOLOGY

Fisher, Mrs. Samuel H.   The Devil's picture books (playing
cards) p $.15 CtL   3776

You will like geometry p $.15 ICS   3777

Laufer, Berthold.   The prehistory of aviation (FA 18:1) 96
p 13 il 1928 $1. ICF   3778

Cahn, H.A.   Psychical research p $.25 NmRMA   3779

--World Maps

Continental areas based on tilted Mollweide equal area pro-
jections.   Old World areas centered on latitude 20°N,
longitude 80°E; New World on latitude 20°N, longitude
90°W; Bering Strait insert, on latitude 20°N, longitude
160°E.   Large size, ca 19.5x13.5, colored 1928 $1; small

size, ca 10x16, black and white 1930 $.10; small size,
ca 10x16, black and white with Ben Day 1928 $.20 NNM
            3780

World, centered on latitude 20^ON, longitude 0°, tilted Mollweide equal area projection. Large size, ca 19.5x39,
colored 1928 $1; medium size, ca 10x20, black and white,
1930 $.10; small size, 6.5x13, black and white with Ben
Day 1928 $.20 NNM   3781

World, centered on latitude 20^ON, longitude 160^OE, tilted
Mollweide equal area projection. Large size, ca 19.5x
30, colored 1928 $1; medium size, ca 10x20, black and
white 1930 $.10; small size, 6.5x13, black and white with
Ben Day 1928 $.20 NNM   3782

World, hemispherical map, on Lambert's equal area projection, centered on latitude 50^ON, longitude 20^OW (Northern
Hemisphere) 1928 colored, heavy or light paper $.35;
black and white, light paper $.35; Centered on latitude
50OS, longitude 160^OE (Southern Hemisphere) 1930 colored,
heavy or light paper $.35 NNM   3783

World, homolographic base map, median meridians 90^OE,
90^OW; each hemisphere with marginal 15° strips. Adap-
ted from Van der Grinten projection. Bathymetric lines:
200 meters dotted; 4000 meters, dot and dash. Equatorial scale: 15° = 1038 miles; 1 inch = 944 miles, by H.
F. Osborn, et al July 10, 1931 (18x32) colored $.75;
black and white $.50; -- Equatorial scale 15°= 1038 miles;
1 inch = 1878 miles May 1932 (9x16) black and white $.15;
--, with Pacific ocean incised. Continental shelf to depth
of 200 meters, stippled. Equatorial scale: 15°= 1083
miles; 1 inch = 1870 miles May 1932 (9x13.5) black and
white $.15   NNM   3784

World map, 100 fathom, Plio-Pleistocene equal area, Amer-
ican Museum-Osborn-Reeds-Sterling, 1930-32. Drawn by
D. F. Levett Bradley ca 17x25 1933 black and white with
Ben Day $.20 NNM   3785

--Americas

Casey, Clifford E. Inter-American cooperation 1939 $1.50
    TxAl   3786
Taylor, Philip, Jr. Hemispheric security reconsidered
    (Pubns 18; MARR v 2, no 5) 1957 p $1. LNT-MA   3787

--Americas--Maps

Arctic regions. Allowance for distortion by insertion of
    gores. Projected and drawn by A. Briesemeister (Amer

Mus of Nat Hist, and Am Geographical Soc) colored, and
black and white 1912 $.25 NNM   3788
Gulf of Mexico, Caribbean Sea and adjacent ocean basins, to-
gether with certain elevations and drainage lines of the in-
cluded land areas. Data from official sources to June,
1916. Soundings in hundreds of fathoms, elevations in
feet. By Chester A. Reeds, drawn by A. Briesemeister
May 15, 1933 black and white $.30 NNM   3789

--Americas--Canada

Bailey, A.G. The John Clarence Webster Collection (SP 1)
1936 $.25 CaNBSM   3790
Baxter, John B.M. Simon Baster, the first United Empire
Loyalist to settle in New Brunswick (SP 4) 1943 $2.
CaNBSM   3791
Clarke, George Frederick. Too small a world, the study of
Acadia (G 46) 1958 $5. CaNBSM   3792
Davidson, W.H. An account of the life of William Davidson
(Hist 7) 1947 $1.75 CaNBSM   3793
Fisher, Peter. History of New Brunswick (G 35) repr 1921
$2. CaNBSM   3794
Ganong, W.F. History of Caraquet and Pokemouche, edited
by S.B. Ganong (Hist 6) 1948 $2.75 CaNBSM   3795
----. History of Miscou and Sheppegan, edited by S.B.
Ganong (Hist 5) 1946 $2.75 CaNBSM   3796
----. Ste. Croix (Dochet) Island, edited by S.B. Ganong
(M 3) 1945 $2.75 CaNBSM   3797
Hannay, James. History of New Brunswick (Genl 38) 2 v
1909 unbd $1. ea CaNBSM   3798
Harper, J. Russell. Portland Point, crossroads of New
Brunswick history (Hist 9) 1956 $1. CaNBSM   3799
Loyalist Centennial souvenir, 1883 (Genl 43) $4. CaNBSM
3800
Loyalist Souvenir, 1933, 150th anniversary of the landing of
the Loyalists in New Brunswick (Genl 40) $.50 CaNBSM
3801
MacBeath, George, ed. Champlain and the St. John, 1604-
1954 (Genl 41) 1954 $.50 CaNBSM   3802
----. Johnny Woodboat, the story of the St. John River
Woodboats (Genl 2) 1957 $.50 CaNBSM   3803
----. The story of the Restigouche (Hist 8) 1954 $1.25
CaNBSM   3804
Milner, W.C. The Basin of Minas and its early settlers
(Genl 21) $2. CaNBSM   3805
----. Early history of Dorchester and other parts of New
Brunswick (Genl 21) $2. CaNBSM   3806

----. History of Sackville, New Brunswick (Genl 23) 1934
$1.50 CaNBSM   3807
Montpetit, Edouard.   French Canadian Co-operation, J.
Clarence Webster Lectures for 1928-1929 (Genl 18) $1.
CaNBSM   3808
"Over the Rockies," the discovery and mapping of the Can-
adian West, 1700-1886, an exhibition held at the Royal
Ontario Museum, March and April 1956 17 p map c p
$.50 CaOTRM   3809
Pierce, Lorne.   New history for old, the J. Clarence Web-
ster Lectures for 1929-1930 (Genl 16) $1. CaNBSM 3810
Raymond, W.O.   The London lawyer--Elias Hardy (Genl 27)
1894 $.50 CaNBSM   3811
Second report of the Bureau of Archives for the Province of
Ontario, 1905, United Empire Loyalists, enquiry into the
losses and services in consequence of their loyalty; evi-
dence in the Canadian claims (Genl 39) 2 v $1. ea
CaNBSM   3812
Sellar, Robert.   The tragedy of Quebec: The expulsion of
its Protestant farmers (Genl 44) 1907 $2.50 CaNBSM
                                                        3813
Squires, W.A.   The Reversing Falls portage (NB Ethnol 1)
1941 $.50 CaNBSM   3814
"Sweet Water," the discovery and mapping of the Great Lakes,
1522-1703 11 p map c 1954 p $.50 CaOTRM   3815
Synopsis of Canadian law of copyright p $.25 CaOTAG 3816
Thomas, L.O.   New Brunswick, Canada (Genl 42) 1930 $2.
CaNBSM   3817
Wallace, Elizabeth.   Godwin Smith, Victorian liberal $5.
CaOTAG   3818
Webster, J.C., ed.   Acadia at the end of the seventeenth
century: letters, journals, and memoirs of Villebon (M
1) $4. CaNBSM   3819
----. The building of Fort Lawrence in Chignecto, 1750,
from a journal in the Gates Collection, New York Histori-
cal Society (Hist 3) $1.25 CaNBSM   3820
----. Catalogue of the John Clarence Webster Canadian Col-
lection (Cat 1-3).   Catalogue 1 1939 $4; Catalogue 2
1946 $3; Catalogue 3 1949 $2.50 CaNBSM   3821
----. Charles des Champs de Boisherbert (G 3) 1931 $1.
CaNBSM   3822
----. Cornelius Steenwyck, Dutch governor of Acadia (G 5)
1929 $.75 CaNBSM   3823
----. The forts of Chignecto, a study of the eighteenth
century conflict between France and Great Britain in
Acadia (G 15) 1930 $15. CaNBSM   3824
----. History in a government house, a study of admini-

strators of Acadia and Nova Scotia to 1874 (G 12) 1926
$.25 CaNBSM   3825
----. A history of Shediac, New Brunswick (SP 3) repr
1953 $.50 CaNBSM   3826
----. Joseph Frederick Wallet des Barres and the Atlantic
Neptune (G 11) (repr, Transactions of the Royal Society
of Canada) 1927 $1.25 CaNBSM   3827
----. Life of John Motresor (G 6) (repr, Transactions of
the Royal Society of Canada) 1928 $1. CaNBSM   3828
----. Memorial on behalf of the Sieur de Boishebert, from
a statement by the attorney defending Boishebert (Hist 4)
1942 $1.50 CaNBSM   3829
----. Ourselves and others, or Does history pay, the project of establishing a National Historical Park amid the
ruins of the Fortress of Louisburg (G 13) 1924 $.25
CaNBSM   3830
----. The proposed Vauquelin Monuments (G 9) 1928 $.10
CaNBSM   3831
----, ed. Re-capture of St. John's Newfoundland, 1762 (G
7) 1928 $.75 CaNBSM   3832
----. Robert Laird Borden (G 10) (repr, Transactions of
the Royal Society of Canada) 1928 $.10 CaNBSM   3833
----, ed. The siege of Beausejour in 1755; a journal of the
attack...by de Fiedmont (H 1) $1.50 CaNBSM   3834
----. William Francis Ganong (G 8) (repr, Transactions of
the Royal Society of Canada) 1942 $.10 CaNBSM   3835
----. William Francis Ganong memorial (SP 2) 1942 $.50
CaNBSM   3836
Willard, Abijah. Journal, 1755, edited by J.C. Webster (G
4) (repr, New Brunswick Historical Society Bul 13) $1.50
CaNBSM   3837
Winslow, Joshua. Journal, recording his participation in the
events...1750, edited by J.C. Webster (G 2) 1936 $1.50
CaNBSM   3838
Wood, William. Behind the scenes of Canadian war history,
the J. Clarence Webster Lectures for 1925-1926 (G 17)
$1. CaNBSM   3839
Wright, Esther Clark, The Loyalists of New Brunswick (G
45) 1955 $4. CaNBSM   3840

--Americas-- United States

American Antiquarian Society. Manuscript records of the
French and Indian War (TC v 11) 1909 $4. MWA   3841
----. Royal proclamations relating to America, 1604-1783
(TC v 12) 1912 $4. MWA   3842
The Amish in American culture (Leaflet 12) 4 p p $.05

HParH   3843
Baldwin, Christopher Columbus.   Diary, 1829-1833 (TC v 8)
    1901 $25.   MWA   3844
Beauregard, Nettie H., comp.   Lindbergh's decorations and
    trophies, received following his trans-Atlantic flight of
    May 20-21, 1927 64 p of il p $.50 MoHi   3845
Bullock, Helen.   The Williamsburg art of cookery 306 p il
    $2.95; leather $5.   ViWC   3846
Carpenter and blacksmith--The pioneer builders of America
    (The Museum, ns, v 9, no 1.   Winter 1957) p $.75
    NjNM   3847
Chapin, Howard M.   The artistic motives of the United
    States flag (Providence, Pavillon Club) 1930 p $2. RHi
                                                          3848
----.   Civic heraldry, a roll of arms of cities and towns in
    the United States (Providence, Pavillon Club) 54 p 100 il
    1935 p $5. RHi   3849
Clay for President, a political footnote, 1832-1956.   Two
    letters from William Woods about the first major political
    convention (Attic Press, Richmond) 10 p 1956 $1. ViRVM
                                                          3850
Cummings, Carlos E.   East is East and West is West;
    some observations on the World's Fairs of 1939 (B v 20)
    $3.70 NBuM   3851
Day, Caroline Bone.   Study of some Negro-White families
    in the United States (repr, HA v 10) 126 p 57 pl 1932 p
    $3.25 MH-P   3852
Emblems of unity and freedom.   45 drawings from the Index
    of American Design, compiled by W.P.A., foreword by
    Holger Cahill 32 p 45 il 1942 p $.25 NNMM   3853
Fithian, Philip Vickers.   Journal and letters, edited by
    Hunter Dickinson Farish 304 p il by Fritz Kredel $6.95
    ViWC   3854
Gee, Joshua.   Narrative of Joshua Gee of Boston, Massa-
    chusetts, while he was captive in Algeria of the Barbary
    Pirates, 1680-1687; foreword by Charles A. Goodwin, in-
    troduction by Albert Carlos Bates (Marine Rm Pbn 1) 30
    p 1943 p $1. CtHWA   3855
General Washington's sword and campaign equipment; an il-
    lustrated catalog of military memorabilia in the Mount
    Vernon collection 60 p $.50 ViMt   3856
Goodman.   Profile of a genius, 7 pamphlets on Franklin p
    $.10 PPF   3857
Herreshoff, L. Francis.   Nathanael Greene Herreshoff, 1848-
    1938, a life and appreciation of his work by his son;
    foreword by Charles A. Goodwin (Marine Rm Pubn 2)
    1944 p $1. CtHWA   3858

Hewett, Edgar L.   The limits of idealism (P ns 33) 6 p 1943
   p $.25 NmSM-S   3859
----.   Lummis the inimitable (P ns 35) 14 p port 1944 p
   $.25 NmSM-S   3860
Holland, W.J.   An autograph letter of Lieutenant General
   U.S. Grant to the Hon. Edwin M. Stanton, Secretary of
   War (A v 8, no 1, p 188-9) 2 pl p $.15 PPiCM   3860a
----.   In memoriam: J.B. Hatcher (A v 2, no 4, p 597-
   604) p $.15 PPiCM   3861
Lincoln combination: Alexander Gardner photog; copy of
   Gettysburg Address in Lincoln's handwriting ea 8.5x11.5
   $.15 ICHi   3862
Mack, Gene.   Hall of Fame cartoons p $.50 NCooN   3863
Mechanical models: A collection of the Newark Museum
   (The Museum, ns, v 6, no 3, Summer 1954) p $.50
   NjNM   3864
Meet Dr. Franklin $1. PPF   3865
Mercer, Henry C.   Ancient carpenters' tools, eighteenth cen-
   tury 339 p 250 il 3rd ed 1960 $7.50 PDoBHi   3866
Miers, Earl Schenck.   Blood of freedom, the story of the
   British colonists in America 192 p $3.50 ViWC   3867
Pantorba, Bernardino de.   Una gran hispanista norteameri-
   cana Elizabeth du Gue Trapier (offset repr, Arte Espanol,
   v 20, 1955) 1957 p $1. NNH   3868
Springer, Frank.   Theodore Roosevelt memorial service (P
   43) 34 p 2 port 1919 p $.25 NmSM-S   3869
Sweeney, John A.H.   Lafayette--the nation's guest, memen-
   tos including furniture, fabrics, ceramics and glass 24 p
   42 il 1957 p $.60 DeWint   3870
Tales of the immortals (Trotting Horses) p $.50 NGo 3871
Wildung, Frank H.   Woodworking tools at Shelburne Museum
   $2.50 VtHi   3872

--Americas--United States--Eastern States

American Antiquarian Society.   Diaries of John Hull, Massa-
   chusetts Bay Company records, etc. (TC v 3) 1857 $5.
   MWA   3873
Atwood.   The Pilgrim story p $.50 MP   3874
Bailey, Alfred G.   The conflict of European and Eastern Al-
   gonkian cultures (M 2) 1937 $5. CaNBSM   3875
Baylies.   Plymouth Colony inventories p $.50 MP   3876
Briggs, A guide to Plymouth p $.50 MP   3877
----.   Plymouth rock p $.50 MP   3878
Buel.   Old time industries in Litchfield Town $.35 CtL3879
----.   Tale of the spinning wheel il $1.25 CtL   3880
Cadillac's village, Detroit under the French regime 31 p il

p $.10 MiDHi   3881
Chapin, Howard M.   Illustrations of the seals, arms and
    flags of Rhode Island   77 p 1930 $3.50 RHi   3882
----.   The New England flag, 1636-1686 (Providence, Pavil-
    lon Club) 15 p 1930 p $1.   RHi   3883
Contrasts--Certain views of New York City as seen by our
    ancestors and by us 44 p 41 il 1948 p $.45 NHi   3884
Cooper, James Fenimore.   Reminiscences of Mid-Victorian
    Cooperstown and sketch of William Cooper (Ostego Co Hist
    Soc)   57 p 1936 $.75 NCooHi   3885
Cumrine, Boyd.   The boundary controversy between Pennsyl-
    vania and Virginia, 1784-1785 (A v 1, no 4, p 505-24)
    p $.30; with, ----, ed.   Minute Book of the Virginia
    Court held at Fort Dunmore (Pittsburgh) for the District
    of West Augusta, 1775-1776 (p 525-68) p $.90 PPiCM
                                                         3885a
History of the state flag of Michigan p apply MiLHi   3886
How to display the (Michigan) state flag p apply MiLHi 3887
Krappe, Alexander Haggerty.   Raymond Foul-Che-Delbosc
    15 p 2 il 1930 p $.25 NNH   3888
List of Historical Societies of Michigan p apply MiLHi 3889
Middlebrook, Louis F.   Seals of maritime New England 50 p
    il 1926 $2.50 MSaE   3890
Perley, Sidney.   Salem witches, where they were hanged
    18 p il 1921 p $1. MSaE   3891
Pew, William A.   The first generation of Puritans in New
    England 75 p 1930 $1.75 MSaE   3892
----.   The spirit of Puritanism 10 p 1930 p $.50 MSaE
                                                         3893
Ritchie, William A.   Dutch Hollow, an early historic period
    Seneca site in Livingston County, New York (RR 10)
    $2.25 NRM   3894
Rood, John.   Minnesota story in wood 12 p il by sculptures
    1951 p $.15 MnHi   3895
Stewart, Douglas.   Catalog of Sesqui-Centennial (Pittsburgh)
    relics (A v 5, no 2-3, p 422-51) 7 pl p $.45 PPiCM
                                                         3896
Upham, Charles W.   Salem witchcraft in outline 161 p 1867
    p $6.50 MSaE   3897
Vanderpool.   More chronicles of a pioneer school il $2.
    CtL   3898
Wendell, Barrett.   Salem witches, were they guiltless 19 p
    1892 p $.50 MSaE   3899

--Americas--United States--Eastern States--Maps

Beers, F.W.   Atlas of Chittenden County, Vermont facsim

$7. VtHi   3900
----. Atlas of Windsor County, Vermont facsim $7. VtHi
                                                      3901
Berks County, Pennsylvania, Historical map $.35; $.10 post
  PRB   3902
Bowditch, Nathaniel.   Chart of Harbours of Salem, Marble-
  head, Berly, and Manchester, from surveys 1804-6 21x26
  c $7.50 MSaP   3903
Captain John Smith's map "As discovered and described by
  Capt. John Smith" from an engraving in the Library of
  Congress 16.5x19 bw $1. VWa   3904
Evans, Lewis.   Indian walking purchase map, 1738 drg $1.
  PHi   3905
First map of Pennsylvania under William Penn, 1681 $.50
  PHi   3906
Gorman, Fred.   Map of Penn's manors $.25 PHi   3907
Historic Michigan--map $1.50 MiLHi   3908
Historical map of York Road $2.   PJO   3909
Huden, John C.   Lake Champlain maps, 1542-1792 p $1.
  VtHi   3910
Kalm, P. and Lewis Evans.   Map of Middle Atlantic region,
  1750 $.50 PHi   3911
LeRoy, E.D.   Delaware and Hudson Canal 14x21 $.50 PHoW
                                                      3912
----.   Gravity railroads connecting with Delaware and Hud-
  son Canal, Pennsylvania $.50 PHoW   3913
Map of area in dispute between Pennsylvania and Maryland,
  1753 $.50 PHi   3914
Map of Mays Landing, 1875 $.50 NjSom   3915
Map of New Jersey, marking sites of historical interest $.10
  NjSom   3916
Map of Salem, Massachusetts 1926 $.25 MSaE   3917
Morse, C. Roy.   Map of covered bridges in Vermont, pen
  sketches $1. VtHi   3918
Pollock, William W.   Philadelphia as William Penn knew it,
  1684 $.25 PHi   3919
Riegel, Jacob, Jr.   Pictorial map of Delaware (Delaware
  Tercentenary Commission) 1938 19x25 c $1. De-Ar 3920
Romance map of the Northern Gateway, a colored pictorial
  map, including eastern New York, Lake Champlain, and
  western Vermont showing historical data $2. VtHi   3921
Vermont covered bridge stamps, 24 photographic miniatures
  set/$.50 VtHi   3922
Yorktown campaign map, showing the positions of the French
  and British fleets just before the Battle off the Virginia
  Capes, October 19, 1781, from an engraving in the Library of Congress 16.25x19 sepia and green $5. VWa 3923

--Americas--United States--Southern States

Baltimore's war: A short account of the celebrated defense
    of Baltimore, 1814 2 pl c, map p $.10 MdBPM   3924
Bath, Gerald Horton.   America's Williamsburg 48 p il p
    ViWC   3925
Bridenbaugh, Carl.   Seat of empire: The political role of
    eighteenth century Williamsburg 96 p il $2.75 ViWC 3926
Corbitt, D. L., and L. Polk Denmark.   Chart showing the
    origin of North Carolina Counties 1940 $.10 NcRNC 3927
Cumrine, Boyd, ed.   Minute or Order Book of the Virginia
    Court held for Ohio County, Virginia, at Black's Cabin
    (now Est Library, West Virginia) from January, 1777,
    etc. (A v 3, no 1, p 5-78) p $1.50 PPiCM   3928
----.   Minute Book of the Virginia Court held for Yohogania
    County, first at Augusta Town (now Washington, Pa.) and
    afterwards on the Andrew Heath farm, near West Eliza-
    beth, 1776-1780 (A v 2, no 1, p 71-140) p $2.25; (A v
    2, no 2, p 205-429) p $3.50 PPiCM   3929
The Edward Pleasants Valentine papers, abstracts of records
    in the local and general archives of Virginia relating to a
    number of Virginia families 4 v 1928 $25. ViRVM 3930
Fifty years in Richmond, 1898-1948, a photographic review
    134 photog 1948 p $3.50 ViRVM   3931
Fisher, Louise B.   An eighteenth-century garland, flower
    and fruit arrangements of Colonial Williamsburg 110 p il
    $3.75 ViWC   3932
Goodwin, Rutherford.   Williamsburg, in Virginia   428 p lea-
    ther $9; p $6.95 ViWC   3933
Harbor, 1854-1955:   A century of photographs of the Port of
    Baltimore 36 il, chart p $.50 MdBPM   3934
The history of the Great Seal of the state of North Carolina
    40 p il 6th ptg 1957 p $.15 NcRNC   3935
Klapper, William.   The printer in eighteenth-century Wil-
    liamsburg, an account of his life and times, his office and
    his craft   32 p p $.50 ViWC   3936
Matteo, William de.   The silversmith in eighteenth-century
    Williamsburg, an account of his life and times, and of his
    craft   40 p p $.50 ViWC   3937
Morgan, Edmund.   Virginians at home, family life in the
    eighteenth century 112 p il $2.75 ViWC   3938
Murray, Chalmers S.   This is our land; the story of the
    Agricultural Society of South Carolina, illustrated with
    block prints by Anna Heyward Taylor 290 p 1949 $2.50
    ScCG   3939
The North Carolina state flag 14 p il 4th ptg 1960 p $.10
    NcRNC   3940

Payne, Lloyd.   The miller in eighteenth-century Williams-
   burg, an account of mills and the craft of milling, as
   well as a description of the windmill near the palace in
   Williamsburg 32 p p $.50 ViWC   3941
Rouse, Parker, Jr.   The city that turned time back 52 p il
   $1. ViWC   3942
Samford, Clement.   The bookbinder in eighteenth-century
   Williamsburg, an account of his life and times, and of
   his craft p in prep $.50 ViWC   3943
Smith, D.E. Huger.   A Charlestonian's recollections, 1846-
   1913 162 p 1950 $3.50 ScCG   3944
Valentine, Elizabeth Gray.   Dawn to twilight, work of Ed-
   ward V. Valentine 201 p il 1929 p $2. ViRVM   3945
Williamsburg in color 48 p 71 il c $2.75; p $1.50 ViWC
                                                           3946

--Americas--United States--Southern States--Maps

Hall's map of Georgia, showing original and present counties
   $1.06 G-Ar   3946
Map of North Carolina, 1861-1865, indicating by stars the
   locations of the principal engagements in the State during
   the Civil War, by Betsy Johnson 9.5x22 1957 $.10
   NcRNC   3947
Newport News Shipbuilding and Drydock Company, 1922 aerial
   view, photogravure bw 29x18.5 $.25 VWa   3948
Outline map of North Carolina giving names of the counties
   9x18 1957 $.05 NcRNC   3949
Virginia map, 1602-22 25x18 sepia and blue $1.50 VWa 3950

--Americas--United States--Mid-West States

Angle, Paul M.   Chicago: Highlights of its history 32 p il
   $.25 ICHi   3951
Brainerd, Henry Allen.   History of the Nebraska Press Association 2 v 47 p , 48 p $.50 ea NbHi   3952
Earliest picture of St. Louis, history of ten buildings shown
   on a ten dollar bank note issued by Bank of St. Louis in
   1817 (C v 8, no 7-9) 1941 p $.50 MoHi   3953
Famous guide to Chicago, a street and picture guide of the
   city p $.50 ICHi   3954
Government and history of the State of Illinois, with the
   state constitution 128 p il p $.50 ICHi   3955
KeMoHa.   Oklahoma, illustrated with Woolaroc Museum ma-
   terials p $.25 OkB   3956
Key to Chicago government 63 p p $.50 ICHi   3957
Korth.   The Chicago book 66 p photog $1. ICHi   3958

Lincoln in Chicago 32 p p $.25 ICHi   3959
Panorama, a souvenir booklet (Chicago) p $.50 ICS (op)
                                                      3960
State flag of North Dakota repr p $.25 NdHi   3961
This is Cook County 76 p il p $.40 ICHi   3962

--Americas--United States--Western States

Baldwin, Percy M., tr and ed. Discovery of the seven
   cities of Cibola, by Fray Marcos de Niza, Spanish and
   English (P v 1) 59 p 1926 p $1. NmSM-H   3963
Bloom, Lansing B. Early bridges in New Mexico (P ns 7)
   22 p il 1925 p $.25 NmSM-S   3964
Building the West 48 il p $.50 CoDA   3965
Days of gold in '49 p $.05 CLCM   3966
Desert in pictures (Palm Springs, California) p $.50 CPs
                                                      3967
Early days of the Northwest--Stenzel Collection 38 p 24 pl
   1959 $1. OrPA   3968
The fiesta book (P ns 13) 100 p il 1925-26 p $.25 NmSM-S
                                                      3969
First gold discovery (California) p $.05 CLCM   3970
Fisher, Reginald, and Ralph Douglas. The way of the cross
   35 p 1958 $15. NmSM-S   3971
Hewett, Edgar L. Kit Carseon, "He led the way" (P ns 41)
   8 p port 1946 p $.25 NmSM-S   3972
----, and Wayne L. Mauzy. Landmarks of New Mexico,
   3rd ed rev by Wayne L. Mauzy (Published with U of New
   Mexico) 194 p il 1953 $4.50 NmSM-S   3973
Hooper, Samuel L. The discovery of Wrangel Island (OP
   24) 27 p 1 chart 3 fig 1956 p $1. CSfA   3974
Houston, Victor S.K. The Hawaiian flag 1955 p $.15 HB
                                                      3975
Johnson, William Templeton. The Santa Fe of the future (P
   31) 23 p il map 1916 p $.25 NmSM-S   3976
Los Angeles catalogue, 1781-1850 p $.72 CLCM   3977
Meyer, Theodosius, O.F.M. St. Francis and the Francis-
   cans in New Mexico 40 p 1926 p $1.50 NmSM-H   3978
Northwestern Indian expedition repr p $1. NdHi   3979
Ortega, Joaquin. The intangible resources of New Mexico
   (P ns 37) 15 p 1945 p $.25 NmSM-S   3980
Palm Springs long ago p $.25 CPs   3981
Regional culture of the Southwest: A symposium 1953 $1.50
   TxAl   3982
Richards, Adrian F., and Bayard H. Brattstrom. Bibliog-
   raphy, cartography, discovery and exploration of the Islas
   Revillagigedo (P v 29, no 9, p 315-60) 4 fig 1959 p

$1.50 CSfA   3983
Romance of the brands (California) p $.05 CLCM   3984
Schulz. Road guide to Lassen Volcanic National Park p
    $.30 CMi   3985
Stage coach days in California p $.05 CLCM   3986
Texas through 250 million years p $.20 TxAuM   3987
Twice-told tales of Texas p $.20 TxAuM   3988
Western heritage, historic backgrounds of Colorado including
    Indian heritage, Spanish-American contributions and Yankee
    commerce 23 p 17 il $.25 CoDA   3989
When cow hides were dollars p $.05 CLCM   3990

--Americas--United States--Western States--Maps

Driving, riding, and hiking guide to Palm Springs (California)
    p $1. CPs   3991
Haynes, Jack E. Haynes guide to Yellowstone, a general
    guide with road logs, maps, geyser tables 190 p il p
    $1.70 WyY   3992
Historical map of early Colorado $.50 CoHi   3993
Jackson, William Henry. Map: Pony Express route $.75
    NbG   3994
----. Map: Trails of the Old West $.75 NbG   3995
Military forts and sites, Oregon Country, 1859 facsim U.S.
    War Dept map 22x33 $1. OrHi   3996
North Dakota pioneer historical map 17x23 $.50 NdHi   3997
Oregon County 1848, pictorial map 18x22 c $.50 OrHi   3998
The Oregon Country, pictorial highlights 22x33 c OrHi   3999
Oregon's historic trails and "story spots" 2nd ed pictorial
    map 18 x 22 c $.50 OrHi   4000
Rockwood, Paul C., and Dorothy B. Barrere. Map of Hono-
    lulu, 1810 1957 p $.50 HB   4001
Seattle map, 1889 $1. WaSMu   4002
Unidentified German Artist. The Pacific Northwest in 1875,
    steel engraving 14x17 bw $.50 IdHi   4003

--Americas--Mexico, Central and South America

An Amazon rubber camp (B 8) $.05 PRM   4004
Lowe, S.K., and Maurice Ries. Experiments with rubber in
    Mexico, 1785-1798 (P 11; PD v 1, no 3) 85 p 1944 p $2.
    LNT-MA   4005

--Europe

Curtis, W.E. The authentic letters of Columbus (GMP-HV 2)
    106 p 19 il 1895 p $2. ICF   4006

Parthian stations of Isidore of Charax p $1. PPComm   4007
Periplus of Hanno p $1. PPComm   4008
Periplus of the Erythraen sea p $2. PPComm   4009
Periplus of the Outer Sea p $1. PPComm   4010
Thompson, Craig R.   Schools in Tudor England il p $.75
    DFo   4011
----.   Universities in Tudor England il p $.75 DFo   4012

HEALTH

Calorie card, wallet size $.10 OClH   4013
Cummings, Carlos E.   Fall in love intelligently--popular
    article on genetics (BSNS) p $.15 NBuM   4014
----. Germ cells and fertilization, based on exhibits in the
    Hall of Heredity and Environment (BSNS) p $.15 NBuM
                                                      4015
Farnsworth, Dana L.   Emotions in education p $.25 OClH
                                                      4016
How to make health visible, catalog of Cleveland Health Mu-
    seum exhibits p $1. OClH (op)   4017
Martin, Dean.   Juno--a symbol of all women p $.25 OClH
                                                      4018
Medical beliefs and superstitions, key to Museum exhibit p
    $.06 NBuM   4019
Weiss, Mildred H.   What we should know about alcohol p
    $1.50 OClH   4020

RELIGION See also Anthropology and Archaeology

Burland, C.A.   Four directions of time, comparison of Mex-
    ican and Navajo conceptions of religion 16 p il c 1950 $5.
    NmSMN   4021
Carrasco, Pedro.   Tarascan folk religion (P 17; SSM 1) 64
    p 1953 p $2. LNT-MA   4022
Correa, Gustavo.   El espiritu del mal en Guatemala: En-
    sayo de semantica cultural (P 19; FIT 2) 68 p 1955 p $2.
    LNT-MA   4023
Emory, Kenneth P.   Tuamotan religious structures and
    ceremonies; including marae chants, prayers and legends
    (B 191) 102 p 2 pl 21 fig 1947 p $2. HB (op)   4024
Hall, H.U.   Some gods of the Yoruba (MJ v 8, no 1) 5 p
    4 il (2 c) 1917 p $1. PU-Mu   4025
Hambly, Wilfrid D.   Serpent worship in Africa (FA 21:1) 86
    p 8 photog 1 map 1931 $1.25 ICF   4026
Lucifer and the crucifer: The enigma of the Penitentes

44 p $.75 CoCF   4027

Madsen, William.   Christo-pagainsm: A study of Mexican
   religious syncretism (P 19; FIT 3) p $1.50 LNT-MA
                                                                        4028

Nuttall, Zelia.   A penitential rite of the ancient Mexicans
   (P v 1, no 7) 26 p 5 pl 8 il 1904 p $.50 MH-P   4029
Penitentes of New Mexico and Colorado, including translation
   of part of hymn and constitution il p $.05 CoCF   4030
Thompson, Craig R.   The English Church in the 16th century il p $.75 DFo   4031
Thompson, Donald E.   Maya paganism and Christianity: A
   history of the fusion of two religions (P 19; FIT 1) 36 p
   1954 p $1.   LNT-MA   4032

PART I ADDENDA

PUBLICATIONS IN ANTHROPOLOGY, ARCHAEOLOGY & ART ISSUED 1960-1961, AND OTHER ADDITIONAL PUBLICATIONS

MUSEUMS AND MUSEUM WORK

American Association of Museums. Museum directory of the United States and Canada 1961 $7.50 DAMu   4033

American paintings, Catalog of the Fleischmann Collection $3.50 WMA   4034

Arizona State Museum pictorial p $.50 AzTuMu   4035

Atlanta Art Association, Handbook il 1961 $1. GAHM   4036

Baker, Richard Brown, Collection--Selections p 1961 (in press) MnMW   4037

Brewington, M.V. Catalogue of the nautical instruments in the Peabody Museum 1962 MSaP   4038

Brundage Collection, Selections from the Avery p $1. CSfDeY   4039

Complete list of American and European drawings, paintings and watercolors in the collection of the Lyman Allyn Museum, Edgar de N. Mayhew 63 p 8 il 1960 p $.50 CtNlL   4040

Dowty, John. Illustrated guide to Kern County Museum's Pioneer Village p 1960 $.15 CBakHi   4041

Essex Institute Historical Collections (Centennial Issue) 1959 p $2. MSaE   4042

Ford, Henry, Museum, guidebook p $.25 MiDbFM   4043

Gardner, Isabella Stuart, Museum. Selective guide to the collection 1960 MBIMu   4044

Greenfield Village, guidebook p $.25 MiDbFM   4045

Griffing, R.P., Jr. The Samuel H. Kress Collection in the Honolulu Academy of Arts 63 p 27 il p $1. HHo   4046

Guggenheim, Solomon R., Museum. Inaugural selection; checklist of the work of 74 artists; introduction by James J. Sweeney 6 pl $.25 NNGu   4047

Halpert, Edith Gregor, Collection 16 p 13 il 1960 $1. DCGA   4048

Handbook for the Gallery of Oriental Arts 1960 CSC   4049

Honolulu Academy of Arts, guide, with introduction by Robert

P. Griffing, Jr. 48 p il p $1. HHo   4050
La Jolla Art Center. First annual painting and sculpture ex-
    hibit 7 il 1960 p $.25 CLajA   4051
Mount Vernon handbook 82 p 48 il (c) p $.50 ViMt   4052
Munson-Williams-Proctor Institute. Inaugural booklet 28 p
    il p $.50 NUtM   4053
Newark Arts Festival: Events and catalogue of exhibition,
    1959 20 p 7 il apply NjNM   4054
Newark Museum. Accessions to the painting and sculpture
    collection since 1956 (M v 13, no 1 & 2, Winter-Spring
    1961) 1961 p $1. NjNM   4055
Paintings from the Musee National d'Art Moderne; selections
    from the best works in one of the world's most compre-
    hensive and modern museums; 40 works documented and
    illustrated; biographies of the 35 artists 40 pl 1958 p $1.
    MBI   4056
Phoenix Art Museum. Guidebook $.25 p AzPhA   4057
Reiss, John J., Collection catalog $.50 p WMA   4058
Roby, Sara, collection 1959 p $1. InIJ   4059
Roby, Sara, Foundation collection; a catalogue 30 il (4 c) p
    $1.25 NNW   4060
Royal Ontario Museum (repr, Archaeology) $.15 CaOTRM
                                                       4061
San Diego Fine Arts Gallery. Catalogue of the collections
    il 1960 $5; p $4. CSdF   4062
Smith, William E. William Holmes McGuffey 5 p folder
    port apply OOxM-Mc   4063
----. The McGuffey Museum of Miami University 5 p folder
    il apply OOxM-Mc   4064
Soby, James Thrall. The James Thrall Soby Collection 70
    p 73 il (4 c) p $1.50 NNMMA   4065
Society of Western Artists, 20th annual exhibition 1960 $.75
    p CSfDeY   4066
Springfield Museum of Fine Arts. Handbook of the collec-
    tions--25th anniversary edition 96 p 116 pl (16 c) 1958
    MSMFA   4067
Toronto Art Gallery. Handbook il p $1.50 CaOTAG   4068
Treasures from Woburn Abbey--From the Collection of the
    Duke of Bedford. Catalog of an exhibition of paintings,
    silver, tapestries, including "The History and Treasures
    of Woburn Abbey; Guide Book" $1.50 OrPA   4069
Wisconsin prints and drawings. Annual exhibition catalog
    $.25 p WMA   4070

                ANTHROPOLOGY AND ARCHAEOLOGY

Bandelier, Adolphe F. The romantic school in American

archaeology.   An address 14 p 1885 $.20 NHi   4071
Burns, Jack F.   Media of exchange used in state and federal
    penitentiaries (A v 35, no 16, p 341-78) 1960 $1.50
    PPiCM   4072
Powell, Louis H., and Elden Johnson.   Rise of civilizations
    (chart) 1957 $.20 MnSSci   4073

--Indians of the Americas

Canoes of the American Indians 1961 (in press) VWa   4074
Excavating Indian sites p $.15 CaOTRM   4075
Woodbury, Natalie, and Watson Smith, eds.   The Hendricks-
    Hodge Expedition; based upon the field notes and observa-
    tions of Frederick Webb Hodge (C--in press) il 1961
    NNMAI   4076

--Indians of North America

Adams, William Y., et al.   Survey and excavations in Lower
    Glen Canyon, 1952-1958 (B 36) (in press 1961) AzFM
                                                       4077
Bell, Robert E.   The Scott Site, Le Flore County, Okla-
    homa (A 26) 1953 $.35 OkU-S   4078
Breternits, David A.   Excavations at Nantack Villate, Point
    of Pines, Arizona (AP 1) 1959 p $1.75 AzTuMu   4079
Brighton, H.D.   Archaeological sites in Custer County, Okla-
    homa (A 22) 1951 $.30 OkU-S   4080
Butler, B. Robert.   The old Cordilleran Culture of the Pa-
    cific Northwest (OP 4) 1960 IdPIMu   4081
Cadzow, Donald A.   Archaeological studies of the Susque-
    hanock Indians 217 p 1936 $1.50 PHarH   4082
The complete story of Osceola; nine articles about his life,
    capture, disappearance of his head, various portraits,
    etc. (repr, Florida Historical Quarterly, Jan-Apr 1955)
    $1. FStA   4083
Cooper, Leland.   Indian Mounds Park Archaeological site,
    Rice Lake, Wisconsin 1959 p $1.15 MnSSci   4084
Dittert, Alfred E., Jr., et al.   An archaeological survey of
    the Navajo Reservoir District 1961 $5. NmSm-S   4085
The Flint River site, Mao, 48, an analysis of an Archaic
    and Woodland occupied mound on the Tennessee River in
    Alabama $1. KyU-Mu   4086
Gaines, Xerpha M.   An annotated catalogue of Glen Canyon
    plants (T 4) 18 p 1960 p $1. AzFM   4087
Gallaher, Art.   Goodman Site, Custer County, Oklahoma
    (A 23) 1951 $.30 OkU-S   4088
Gatschet, Albert S.   Full ethnographic sketch of the Klamath

and Modoc People, Southwestern Oregon (RP 5) 1961 (in
   press) OrK   4088a
Hayden, Julian D.   Excavations, 1940, at the University
   Indian Ruin p $4. AzTuMu   4089
Haury, E.W.   Ventana Cave $15. AzTuMu   4090
Hollon, W. Eugene.   A Spanish arrastra in the Wichita
   Mountains (repr, Chronicles of Oklahoma) 1956 OkU-S
                                                                 4091
Honey Lake Paiute ethnology.   (AP 4) 1961 (in press)
   NvCM   4092
Huron ossuary p $.45 CaOTRM   4093
Laidlaw, Sally Hean.   Federal Indian land policy and the
   Forest Hall Indians (OP 3) 1960 IdPIMu   4094
Liljeblad, Sven.   Indians of Idaho; a condensed history IdHi
                                                                 4095
Little Bear Creek Site, Ct^{O}8; a deep shell midden on the
   Tennessee River in Alabama, inhabited by Archaic, Wood-
   land, and Mississippian Indians $1. KyU-Mu   4096
McCarthy, Richard L., and Harrison Newman.   The Iro-
   quois; social, industrial, and religious life il p $.50
   NBuHi   4097
McMahon, Margaret M.   Lenni Lenape Indians (EP 16)
   NjPatM   4098
Martin, Paul S., and John B. Rinaldo.   Excavations in the
   Upper Little Colorado Drainage.   Eastern Arizona (FA 51:
   1) 127 p 61 il 1 map table 1960 p $4. ICF   4099
Orr, Phil C.   Radiocarbon dates from Santa Rosa Island,
   Pt. 2 (DAB 3) 10 p 4 pl 2 table 1960 CStbMu   4100
Painter, Muriel Thayer.   Easter at Pasqua Village p $1.
   AzTuMu   4101
The People of the Longhouse.   A brochure on the Indian
   Groups p $.10 NAlMu   4102
Peterson, Harold L.   American Indian tomahawks; a study of
   all forms known, with descriptive materials relating to the
   typology, use and techniques of manufacture (C--in press)
   250 il 1961 NNMAI   4103
Pre-historic people of Western New York p (in prep) 1961
   $.50 NBuHi   4104
Shaeffer, James B.   The McCarter Site, a Late Archaic oc-
   cupation at Muskogee, Oklahoma (repr, Texas Archeologi-
   cal Society Bulletin) 1957 OkU-S   4105
Shead, Ralph B.   Bear Zuni fetish (C 5) $.15 OkU-S   4106
Shutler, Richard, Jr.   Pueblo occupation of Southern Nevada
   (AP 5) 1961 (in prep) NvCM   4107
----.   Stuart Rock Shelter (AP 3) 1961 (in press) NvCM
                                                                 4108
----.   Surface archaeology in the Humbolt Sink, Nevada

(AP 6) 1961 (in prep) NvCM   4109
Speck, Frank G. The Tutelo spirit adoption ceremony 125 p
    1942 $2. PHarH   4110
Spiro Mound Village (Model Village on display) (M 161) $.05
    OkU-S   4111
Starr, S. F. The archaeology of Hamilton County, Ohio 130
    p 58 il chart 1960 p $1.25 OCMN   4112
Swartz, B. K. , Jr. A bibliography of Klamath Basin anthro-
    pology, with excerpts and annotations 117 p 1960 p $1.75
    OrK   4113
Ritchie, W. A. , and D. W. Dragoo. Eastern dispersal of
    Adena (B 379) 80 p 16 pl 2 fig 5 table 1960 p $1.25
    NAlMu   4114
Turner, Christy G. , II. The location of human skeletons
    excavated from sites in southwestern United States and
    northern Mexico (T 3) 25 p 1960 p $1. AzFM   4115
Two cities of Latin America, a comparative description of
    social classes (B 9) 1960 $3.50 WBB-Lo   4116
Underhill, Ruth. Workaday life of the pueblos p $1.
    AzTuMu   4117
Vivian, Gordon, and Paul Reiter. The Great Kivas of Chaco
    Canyon and their relationships (M 1) 1960 $2.50 NmSM-S
                                                             4118
Weslager, C. A. The Nanticoke Indians. A refugee tribal
    group of Pennsylvania 159 p 1948 p $1.50 PHarH   4119
White, Marian E. Iroquois culture history in the Niagara
    Frontier Area of New York State (AP 16) 1961 (in press)
    $2. (?) MiU-A   4120
Wimberly, Steve. Archaeological investigations in Mobile
    County and Clarke County, Southern Alabama (MP 36)
    1961 (in press) AU-Mu   4121

--Indians of Mexico, Central and South America

Borhegyi, Stephen. Pre-Columbian cultural connections...
    MesoAmerica and Ecuador. Addenda (P 18, Preprint 7)
    1960 p $.30 LNT-MA   4122
Coe, William R. Piedras Negras archaeology: Artifacts,
    caches, and burials (MM) 245 p 69 fig 1959 $5. PU-Mu
                                                             4123
Edmonson, Munro S. The Mexican truck driver (P 25, Pre-
    print 2) 1959 p $.85 LNT-MA   4124
----. Nativism, syncretism, and anthropological science (P
    19, Preprint 4) 1960 p $1. LNT-MA   4125
Godfrey, William S. , Jr. The archaeology of La Magdalena;
    excavations in the eastern Bajio, Mexico (B 10) 1961 (in
    prep) WBB-Lo   4126

Hinton, Thomas B.   A survey of Indian assimilation in
   Eastern Sonora (AP 4) 1959 p $.75 AzTuMu   4127
Mayer-Oakes, William J.   A developmental concept of
   Pre-Spanish urbanization in the Valley of Mexico (P 18,
   Preprint 8) 1960 p $.75 LNT-MA   4128
Owen, Ruth C.   Marobavi: A study of an assimilated group
   in Northern Sonora (AP 3) 1959 p $1.25 AzTuMu   4129
Reina, Ruben E.   Chinautla, A Guatemalan Indian community
   (P 24, Preprint 2) 1960 p $2.50 LNT-MA   4130
Thieme, Frederick P.   The Puerto Rico population. A
   study in human biology (AP 13) 156 p 4 fig 2 map $2.50
   MiU-A   4131

--Europe

Okladnikov, A.P.   Ancient population of Siberia and its cultures (RT1:1) 96 p 24 pl 3 map 1950 p $3.50 MH-P 4132

--Orient

Chinese mortuary pillows p $.50 CaOTRM   4133
Egyptian mummies p $.25 CaOTRM   4134
Fariservis, Walter A., Jr.   Archeological surveys in the
   Zhob and Loralai Districts, West Pakistan (AP v 47, pt 2,
   p 273-448) 23 pl 84 fig 500 designs 7 table 1959 NNM
                                                     4135
Gordon, Edmund I.   Sumerian proverbs: Glimpses of every-
   day life in ancient Mesopotamia (MM) 556 p 79 pl 1961
   $7.50 PU-Mu   4136
Miner, Horace M., and George DeVos.   Oasis and casbah:
   Algerian culture and personality in change (AP 15) 235 p
   10 fig 15 table $2.50 MiU-A   4137
North Arabian Desert Archaeological Survey, 1925-50 (P v
   45, no 2) 224 p il 1960 $8.25 (MH-P)   4138
Sweet, Louise E.   Tell Toquaan: A Syrian village (AP 14)
   280 p 54 fig $2.50 MiU-A   4139

--Pacific Area

Force, Roland W.   Leadership and cultural change in Palau
   (FZ 50:1) 211 p 28 il 4 map 1960 p $5. ICF   4140
Stoller, Marianne C.   Cultures of the South Pacific 1961 (in
   press) CoCF   4141

--Physical Anthropology

Bunak, V.V., et al.   Contributions to the physical anthro-

pology of the Soviet Union (RT 1:2) 192 p 5 map 1960 p
$4.50 MH-P

--Folk Literature and Folk Lore

Curtin, Jeremiah.   Modoc myths (RP 4)1961 (in press) CrK
                                                            4143
Eagle and Bead myths (B 3) rev ed 1961 $.50 NmSMN 4144
Giddings, Ruth Watern.   Yaqui myths and legends (AP 2)
    1959 p $1.25 AzTuMu   4145
Navajo creation myth (B 6) rev ed 1960 $.50 NmSMN 4146
Painter, Muriel Thayer.   The Yaqui Easter ceremony p
    $.25 AzTuMu   4147
-----.   Yaqui Easter Sermon p $.80 AzTuMu   4148
Texts of the Navajo Creation Chants, translated by Harry
    Hoijer.   Foreword by Mary C. Wheelwright and commen-
    tary ("The form of Navajo ceremonial music") by David P.
    McAllester (Peabody Museum, Harvard University) 1950,
    repr 1961 36 p $1.25 NmSMN   4149

--Language and Linguistics

Hartesveldt.   Place names of Yosemite Valley (Special issue,
    Yosemite Nature Notes) p $.30 CYo   4150
Huden, John.   Indian place names of New England; a listing,
    with translations, of place names derived from various
    Indian languages (C--in press) 1961 NNMAI   4151

--Music

Brown, Donald M.   Drums, rattles and flutes: Musical in-
    struments of the Pueblos, Apache and Navaho (1961 (in
    press) CoCF   4152
Good Morning dance book: Music, calls and directions for
    old-time dancing as revived by Mr. and Mrs. Henry Ford
    p $1.25 MiDbFM   4153

                        VISUAL ARTS

Abstract art: 1910 to Today; catalogue of exhibition, 1956
    12 p 1 il apply NjNM   4154
Application of science in examination of works of art, 1958
    (Proceedings of the Seminar, September, conducted by the
    Research Laboratory, Museum of Fine Arts) $7.50; post,
    $.25 MBMu   4155
"At Work;" catalog $.15 WMA   4156

Bacchiacca and his friends 1961 $1.25 MdBMA   4157
Discovery of the West $.50 AzPhA   4158
Dragons and other animals; a coloring book for children 24 p
    1960 p $.50 MdBWA   4159
Enduring memory; an illustrated handbook of famous memori-
    als $2.50 NNNSS   4160
Exotic art from ancient and primitive civilizations from the
    collections of Jay C. Leff, 1959-60; exhibition catalogue
    p $2. PPiCIA   4161
Figures at a table (B v 1, no 1) FSR   4162
Fruit and flowers 1961 $.75 MdBMA   4163
Jones, Frances Follin, and Reuben Goldberg. Ancient art in
    the Art Museum, Princeton University 1960 71 p 33 il $3.
    NjP-A   4164
Kaltenbach, G.E. Dictionary of pronunciation of artists'
    names 75 p (1953) repr p $.75 ICA   4165
Lindstrom, Miriam. Children's art (University of California
    Press) $1.50 CSfDeY   4166
The logic and magic of color; catalogue p $.50 NNCoo 4167
Messer, Thomas M. Image lost and found; exhibition cata-
    log of thematic exhibition tracing the disappearance and
    re-emergence of recognizable subject matter during the
    last 100 years of Western painting; reading suggestions
    28 pl (3 c) 1960 p $1. MBI   4168
Taylor, Harold. Art and intellect; two lectures to the Na-
    tional Committee on Art Education 62 p p $.75 NNMMA
                                                     4169
Whitehill, Walter Muir. George Crowninshield's yacht Cleo-
    patra's Barge, and a catalogue of the Francis B. Crown-
    inshield Gallery 68 p 34 pl 1959 $2. MSaP   4170

--Americas

The Allied Artists of America--29th Annual Exhibition 16 il
    1942 $.25 NHi   4171
American painters of the South 44 p 20 il (3 c) 1960 $1.
    DCGA   4172
Art across America 168 p il p $2. NUtM   4173
Baur, John I.H. MacIver--Pereira; catalogue 38 il (2 c)
    p $1. NNW   4174
----. Philip Evergood; catalogue 94 il (16 c) p $2. NNW
                                                     4175
----. William Zorach; catalogue 34 il (4 c) 1959 p $1.50
    NNW   4176
Belknap, Waldron Phoenix. American colonial painting; Ma-
    terials for a history, including an exposition on English
    mezzotint, colonial portraits and articles on the identity of

Robert Feke, and New York painters   328 p 289 il 1959
$12.50 DeWint   4177
Bemelmans, Ludwig.   Bemelmans $1. AzPhA   4178
Bingham, George Caleb.   George Caleb Bingham; catalogue
(B v 3, no 2) MoKNG   4179
Bolton, Theodore, and Irwin F. Cortelyou.   Ezra Ames of
Albany: Portrait painter, craftsman, Royal Arch Mason,
banker, 1768-1838, with a catalogue of his works   398 p
120 il 1955 $4.95; Cortelyou, Erwin F.   A supplement to
the catalogue of pictures by Ezra Ames of Albany (repr,
Quarterly, April 1957) 20 p 8 il $.60 NHi   4180
Breeskin, Adelyn.   Milton Avery; catalogue (Published by
the American Federation of Arts) 35 il (1 c) 1960 p $.50
NNW   4181
Business buys American art; catalogue 50 il (3 c) 1960 p
$1.50 NNW   4182
Caeser--Evergood.   Doris Caeser--Philip Evergood.   An ex-
hibition circulated by the Whitney Museum of American
Art, 1960; with introductory notes by Charles C. Cunning-
ham and Edward A. Bryant 36 p 16 il $.75 1960 p
CtHWA   4183
Cahill, Holger.   The Museum and American Contemporary
Art (repr, Creative Art Magazine, March 1929) 5 p il
apply NjNM   4184
Clowes, George Alexander, Memorial p $1.   InIJ   4185
Davis, Lew.   Lew Davis $5. AzPhA   4186
Devree, Charlotte.   Jose de Creeft; catalogue (Published by
the American Federation of Arts) 20 il (2 c) 1960 p $.50
NNW   4187
DeWitt, McClellan Lockman, N.A., 1870-1957.   Memorial
exhibition, May 14-May 15, 1958 47 p 32 il 1958 $.25
NHi   4188
Eight from Connecticut: Bernard Chaet, Cleve Gray, John
Gregoropoulos, Joseph P. Gualtieri, Thomas Ingle, Irgin
Katzenstein, Howard Rackcliffe, Anthony Terenzio. Cata-
logue of an exhibition, April 22-May 29, 1960; with intro-
ductory notes by Charles C. Cunningham and Edward A.
Bryant 19 p 8 il 1960 p $.75 CtHWA   4189
Famous likenesses; exhibition catalog--34 portraits (painting
and sculpture) of 20th century personalities by renowned
artists   34 il (3 c) 1961 p $1. MBI   4190
Ford, Alice.   Edward Hicks, 1780-1849; a special exhibition
devoted to his life and work   22 p 7 il 1960 p $1. ViWR
4191
Four Boston masters 1959 $1.25 MWelC-A   4192
Friedman, Martin L.   The Precisionist view in American Art
32 il (4 c) 1960 p $2. MnMW   4193

Goodrich, Lloyd, and John I.H. Baur. American art in our
   century 1961 (in prep) NNW   4194
Hultberg, John (CAA 30) 1959 $.10 DCGA   4195
Intimate American paintings, from the collection of Mr. and
   Mrs. Norman B. Woolworth il 1960 MeRF   4196
Jones, Agnes Halsey, and Louis C. Jones. New-found folk
   art of the young republic; catalog of American primitive
   paintings in the collection of the New York State Historical Association--80 paintings acquired in 1958 1960 p
   $1.25 NCooHi   4197
Kuhn, Walt. Walt Kuhn, a memorial exhibition, 1960; 155
   paintings and drawings, with biographical data 60 il (12 c)
   $5. OCA   4198
Latin America: New departure; exhibition catalogue of contemporary painting by 11 artists from 7 Latin American
   countries representing the latest generation to reach artistic maturity in Central and South America; foreword by
   Thomas M. Messer, introduction by Jose Gomez-Sicre.
   Full biography of each artist; statements by artists 35 pl
   (4 c) 1961 p $1. MBI   4199
Lieberman, William S., ed. Max Ernst 64 p 85 il (front c)
   p $2.50 NNMMA   4200
McDermott, John Francis. The art of Seth Eastman (Smith-
   sonian Traveling Exhibition Service Catalog) 34 p 9 pl fig
   1959 p DSI-FA   4201
MacIver, Loren (CAA 31) 1959 $.10 DCGA   4202
McMahon, Margaret M. Alexander Hamilton (EP 32) 1961
   NjPatM   4203
Montgomery, Charles F. Accessions--1960, catalogue of an
   exhibition 60 p 34 il 1960 DeWint   4204
Murphy, Robert Cushman. John James Audubon (1785-1851):
   An evaluation of the man and his works (repr, Quarterly,
   October 1956) 40 p 19 il $.35 NHi   4205
The Museum and its Friends. 18 living American artists se-
   lected by the Friends of the Whitney Museum of American
   Art 1959 36 il p $1.25 NNW   4206
O'Keefe, Georgia. Georgia O'Keefe; Forty years of her
   art; an exhibition catalogue 54 p 24 il 1960 p $1.25 MWM
                                                          4207
Orfuss, Elsie. Elsie Orfuss-paintings   folder port il apply
   1960 NNJ-Mu   4208
Our Militia, 1765-1865: A selection from the Anne S.K.
   Brown Collection 16 p 11 il 1960 p $1. DCGA   4209
Parsons, Charles. Charles Parsons--a catalog, with bio-
   graphical note il $1. NjMonA   4209a
Portraits of Americans by Americans: Exhibition of the Na-
   tional Association of Portrait Painters, April-May 5, 1945

129 p 80 il 1945 $1; p, $.50 NHi   4210

Quinn, Robert M. Gallego, Fernando. The retablo of
Ciudad Rodrigo 53 p 27 il (1 c) 1960 AzU-A   4211

Ranger, Henry Ward. Henry Ward Ranger centennial exhibition, 1858-1958 30 p 1 pl (Smithsonian I pubn 4349) 1958
DSI-FA   4212

Rathbone, Perry T. Lee Gatch; catalogue (Published by the
American Federation of Arts) 44 il (2 c) 1960 p $.50
NNW   4213

Rhys, Hedley Howell. Maurice Prendergast, 1859-1924; catalogue (Published by Harvard University Press) 113 il
(36 c) 1960 $2.75 NNW   4214

Romantic America 1961 p $.50 InIj   4215

Rothschild, Lincoln. Hugo Robus; catalogue (Published by
the American Federation of Arts) 24 il (2 c) 1960 p
$.50 NNW   4216

Selz, Peter. Mark Rothko 44 p 30 il (6 c) p $2.25
NNMMA   4217

Sixteen young Minnesota artists 1960 p $.75 MnMW   4218

Sixty American painters: 1960 1961 p (in press) MnMW
                                                            4219

Sizer, Theodore, ed. The recollections of John Ferguson
Weir [West Point before the Civil War; Tenth Street
Studios, New York City, 1860's; Yale School of Fine Arts,
1869-1877] (repr, Quarterly, April, July, October 1957)
93 p 10 il index $2. NHi   4220

Sport and the horse; catalogue of an exhibition 1960 ViRMu
                                                            4221

Stamos, Theodore. (CAA 32) 1959 $.10 DCGA   4222

Sugimoto, Tetsuro 1960 p $1. CSfDeY   4223

Tolman, Ruel Pardee. The life and works of Edward Greene
Malbone, 1777-1807; with an introduction by Theodore
Bolton, and a foreword by John Davis Hatch, Jr. (v 13--
Jones Fund) 322 p 226 il index 1958 $12.50 NHi   4224

Treasures in America, catalogue of an exhibition 1961
ViRMu   4225

Turn-of-the century paintings from the William T. Evans
Collection 8 p 1959 DSI-FA   4226

The United States collects Pan American art 50 p il 1959
$1. ICA   4227

Vail, R.W.G. The case of the Stuyvesant portraits, with a
checklist of the forty known family likenesses covering
three centuries and eight generations (repr, Quarterly,
April 1958) 36 p 33 il $.60 NHi   4228

View 1960; New England painting and sculpture in 1960. 45
artists with work illustrated and full biography; introduction by Thomas M. Messer 45 pl 1960 p $1. MBI   4229

Vignettes in the 18th century in America $1. WMA   4230
Watson, Nan. Still life by Nan Watson; catalogue of a loan
    exhibition, 1960; with an introduction by Olin Dows 6 p
    1960 p $.35 CtHWA   4231
Young America, 1960--Thirty American painters under 36
    54 il p $1.25 NNW   4232

--Indians of the Americas

Collier, Donald. Indian art of the Americas (Handbook) 64
    p 65 il 1959 p $1; post, $.09 ICF   4233
Dockstader, Frederick J. Indian art in America; the arts
    and crafts of the American Indian   250 il (70 c) (New
    York Graphic Society) 1961 $25. NNMAI   4234
Enjoy your Museum: 4 pamphlets. Hopi pottery; Indian
    pottery of the Rio Grande; Navajo rugs; Apache blankets
    p $.20 ea AzTuMu   4235
Ancient treasures of Peru; catalogue of a loan exhibition 31
    p 24 il 1960 p $.75 MWM   4236
Powell, Louis H. Pipes and pipestone 1955 $.40 MnSSci
                                                             4237
Shead, Ralph B. Bear claw necklace--Osage (TM 3) 1947
    $.15 OkU-S   4238
----. Engraved shells of the Spiro Mound (A 51) 1952 $.35
    OkU-S   4239
Stewart, T.D. A unique carved bone object from Delaware.
    18 p 1958 p $.25 De-Ar   4240
Wyman, Leland C. Navaho sand painting: The Huckel Col-
    lection 1960 p $1.75 CoCF   4241

--Europe

Baird, Thomas P. Dutch painting in the National Gallery of
    Art (NGA Book 7) 1959 p $.25 DSI-GA   4242
Barnes, Albert C., and Violette de Mazia. Art of Henry
    Matisse 1961 $3.75 PMeB   4243
----, and ----. Art of Renoir 1961 $3.75 PMeB   4244
Baroque painters of Naples (B v 1, no 2) 1961 FSR   4245
Broadley, Hugh T. German painting in the National Gallery
    of Art (NGA Book 9) 1959 p $.25 DSI-GA   4246
Cooke, Hereward Lester. British painting in the National
    Gallery of Art (NGA Book 8) 1959 p $.25 DSI-GA   4247
Courbet, Gustave. Gustave Courbet: Catalogue of the ex-
    hibition, 1959-1960, Museum of Fine Arts, Boston and
    Philadelphia Museum of Art; foreword by Henry Clifford;
    text by Rene Huyghe; notes and material in great part
    prepared by M. Gaston Delestre 79 p 19 il (6 c) $4; p,

$2.50; post, $.25 MBMu: PPPM   4248
Evans, Grose. Spanish painting in the National Gallery of
    Art (NGA Book 10) 1959 p $.25 DSI-GA   4249
Fifteen painters from Paris 24 p 36 il (6 c) 1960 $1.
    DCGA   4250
The Four Continents: From the collection of James Hazen
    Hyde; exhibition catalogue (MC 3:1-2) 1961 (in press)
    NNCoo   4251
Garlick, Kenneth, ed. Sir Thomas Lawrence, Regency
    painter; a loan exhibition of his portraits 63 p 25 il 1960
    p $1.25 MWM   4252
Greek and Roman portraits, 470 B.C.-500 A.D. (Picture
    Book) 77 il 1959 p $1.50; post, $.25 MBMu   4253
Hitchcock, Henry-Russell. Gaudi 48 p 85 il p $1.95
    NNMMA   4254
Impressionism ScCoM   4255
Kennedy, Ruth Wedgwood, and Leona Gabel. Renaissance
    portraits 21 p (mimeo) 1953 MNS-MA   4256
Modigliani; paintings and drawings; with a biocritical essay
    by Frederick S. Wight (University of California) 79 p il
    (bw and c) 1961 $3.50 CLCM   4257
O'Hara, Frank. New Spanish painting and sculpture; 16
    avant-garde artists, including biographies and selected
    bibliography 64 p 58 pl p $2.75 NNMMA   4258
100 years of French painting: 1860-1960 $.50 AzPhA 4259
Pozzatti. 1960 p $.20 MnMW   4260
Rewald, Joh. History of impressionism, rev and enl ed
    625 p 635 pl (86 c) $20. 1961 NNMMA   4261
Richter, Gisela M.A. Catalogue of Greek and Roman an-
    tiques in the Dumbarton Oaks Collection, 1956 $5. DDO
                                                     4262
Roman portraits 1961 MWM   4263
Smit, Philippe. Philippe Smit, a 20th century Dutch Master,
    exhibition catalogue il 1957 MSMFA   4264
The Splendid Century, French Art: 1600-1715; a catalogue
    of the exhibition of paintings, sculpture, drawings, and
    tapestries lent by museums, churches, and institutions
    throughout France and shown in the National Gallery of Art
    in November, 1960. Historical introduction of 21 pages
    by Theodore Rousseau, Jr.; detailed notes for each of the
    166 works of art shown 270 p 155 il 1960 p $3. DSI-GA
                                                     4265
Taylor, Joshua G. Futurism, 1910-1916 154 p 141 il (22 c)
    $6.50 NNMMA   4266
Trapier, Elizabeth DuGue. Valdes Leal, Spanish Baroque
    painter 263 p 161 pl (4 c) 1960 $1. NNH   4267
2500 years of Italian art and civilization 76 p 72 il 1956 p

$.50 WaSA   4268

--Orient

The art of Nepal and Tibet; bulletin (no 265) and catalogue
    17 p 10 il (cover c) and 16 p 1960 p $1. PPPM   4269
The arts of Thailand; a handbook of the architecture, sculp-
    ture and painting of Thailand (Siam), and a catalogue of
    the exhibition in the United States in 1960-61-62, with
    critical and historical statements: "Architecture and
    sculpture of Siam," by A. B. Griswold; "A note on Thai
    painting," by Elizabeth Lyons; and catalogue and notes by
    M. C. Subhadradis Diskul 219 p il (1 c) 1960 $3.50
    CLCM; HHo; MBMu; NNMM   4270
Ecke, Gustav. Chinese painting in Honolulu 1961 (in press)
    HHo   4271
Fuller, Richard E. Japanese art in the Seattle Art Museum;
    an historical sketch of Japanese art illustrated with 244
    examples from the collection 192 p 208 il 1960 p $2.50
    WaSA   4272
Gralapp, Leland. Balinese painting: The Taylor Museum
    Collection 1961 (in press) CoCF   4273
Griffing, Robert P., Jr. Japanese folk art (in, News Bul
    and Calendar, v 15, no 1, 1953) 12 p il p $.50 HHo
                                                      4274
Gutman, Joseph. The second commandment and the image in
    Judaism 1961 p $1. OCH-Mu   4275
Hokusae: Paintings and drawings in the Freer Gallery of
    Art (Smithsonian I pubn 4419) 36 p 36 il 1960 p $1. DSI-
    F   4276
Icons--Eastern Orthodox Christian images Fall, 1961 CStM
                                                      4277
Landsberger, Franz. The origin of the decorated Mezuzah
    1960 p $1. OCH-Mu   4278
Minorsky, V. Calligraphers and painters, a treatise by
    Qadi Ahmad, Son of Mir-Munshi (Smithsonian I pubn 4339)
    223 p 8 pl 1959 $4. DSI-F   4279
Olson, Eleanor. Tibetan art 1960 NmSMI   4280
Parks, Robert O. Neolithic to Ming; Chinese objects--with
    a foreword by Charles MacSherry 11 p 4 fig 1957 MNS-
    MA   4281
Tessai, Tomioka. Japanese paintings, 1836-1924 p $.50
    CSfDeY   4282
Tseng Yu-Ho $.20 1960 p MnMW   4283
Yanagi, Soetsu. The way of tea, with foreword by Robert P.
    Griffing, Jr. 18 p reprint ed 1960 p $1. HHo   4284

PRIMTIVE ART

Aspects of primitive art (Lecture Series no 1--three lectures
  by Robert Goldwater, Melville J. Herskovits, and Gordon
  F. Ekholm)   100 p 12 il 1959 $2.75 NNMPA   4284a
Forge, Anthony, and Raymond Clausen.   Three regions of
  Melanesian art: New Guinea and New Hebrides   24 p 30
  il 1960 $1.50 NNMPA   4284b
Goldwater, Robert.   Bambara sculpture from the Western
  Sudan 64 p 114 il 1960 $3.50 NNMPA   4284c
The latest Ife finds, with a note by William Fagg 12 p 2 il
  1958 p $.25 NNMPA   4284d
The Lipschitz Collection, introduction by Jacques Lipschitz
  34 p 34 il 1960 $1.50 NNMPA   4284e
Newton, Douglas.   Art styles of the Papuan Gulf 100 p 265
  il 1961 $5. NNMPA   4284f
The Wielgus Collection, introduction by Raymond Wielgus 31
  p 31 il 1961 $1.50 NNMPA   4284g

--Drawing and Graphic Arts

American drawings and watercolors, in the Smith College
  Museum of Art--a checklist 1961 MNS-MA   4285
American prints today, assembled by the Print Council of
  America p $1.25 OCA   4286
Baltimore through the Civil War; text and 23 reproductions
  of Civil War lithographs p $1. MdBPM   4287
Bruegel, Pieter, the Elder.   Prints and drawings of Pieter
  Bruegel the Elder; exhibition catalogue, Los Angeles
  County Museum; introduction by Ebria Feinblatt 67 p 105
  il 1961 p $2.25 CLCM   4288
The Civil War, A centennial exhibition of eyewitness draw-
  ings; a catalogue of the exhibition held at the National
  Gallery of Art, January 8 through February 12, 1961.
  With a foreword by John Walker, 92 pages of essay by
  William P. Campbell, 37 pages of notes on each of the
  281 drawings and 105 half-tone illustrations   156 p 1961 p
  $3.25 DSI-GA   4289
Color woodcuts by Josef Domjan 1958 p $.25 OCA   4290
Eastman, Alvin Clark.   Nala-Damayant drawings, study of a
  portfolio of drawings, 18th century, illustrating an early
  Indian romance   49 il (1 c) 1959 $12.50; post, $.35
  MBMu   4291
Eighteenth century Italian drawings 1960 p $1. MWelC-A
                                                        4292
Fink, June-Marie.   British drawings and watercolors in the
  Smith College Museum of Art 17 p (mimeo) 1958

MNS-MA   4293
----. European drawings in the Smith College Museum of
    Art 17 p (mimeo) 1958 MNS-MA   4294
Five centuries of drawing, the Cooper Union Centennial Ex-
    hibition, 1959-61 il p $.60 NNCoo; $.75 MH-A   4295
International Biennial of Prints, 1960 p $1. OCA   4296
International color woodcut exhibition, arranged by the Vic-
    toria and Albert Museum, London 1956 p $.25 OCA 4297
Italian drawings, masterpieces of five centuries; a catalogue
    of the exhibition of drawings from the 14th-18th centuries
    shown at the National Gallery of Art in October, 1960.
    Introduction by Dr. Giulia Sinibaldi, Director of the Gabi-
    netto Disegnie Stampe of the Uffizi Gallery in Florence;
    an extensive bibliography; 63 pages of detailed notes on
    the 154 drawings in the exhibition 118 p 53 il 1960 p
    $1.75 DSI-GA   4298
Kennedy, Ruth Wedgwood. Italian drawing, 1330-1780 88 p
    1 fig 1941 p $.50 MNS-MA   4299
----, and George Swinton. The first hundred years of print-
    making 24 p (mimeo) 1951 p MNS-MA   4300
Modigliani: Drawings from the collection of Stefa and Leon
    Brillouin 1959 p $2.50 MH-A   4301
Nineteenth century master drawings 76 p 65 il 1961 p $1.50
    NjNM   4302
Parks, Robert O. Five drawings by Jacques Louis David
    6 p (mimeo) 1956 MNS-MA   4303
----. Shaker inspirational drawings; with an essay by Ed-
    ward Deming Andrews 1960 p $.25 MNS-MA   4304
Polish graphic art, exhibition arranged under the auspices of
    the Polish Committee for Cultural Relations with Foreign
    Countries 1956 p $1. OCA   4305
Rembrandt drawings from American collections 1960 $5; p,
    $2.85 MH-A   4306
Statler, Oliver. Japan's modern prints--Sosaku Hanga 58 p
    il 1960 p $1. ICA   4307
Thirty-three French drawings from the collection of John S.
    Newberry 1960 p $.50 MH-A   4308
Venetian drawings, 1400-1630 p $1. CSfDeY   4309
Venetian drawings, 1630-1800, from the collection of Janos
    Scholz p $1.20 CSfPL   4310

--Photography

Steichen, Edward. Steichen the photographer, catalogue of
    the retrospective exhibition, with texts by Carl Sandburg
    and Alexander Liberman, and a biographical outline by
    Grace M. Mayer 80 p 54 il p $2.50 NNMMA   4312

--Sculpture

Calder, Alexander. Alexander Calder, by Alexander Milne
     and Alexander Sterling p 1961 $.50 DeWS   4313
Contemporary sculpture, 1961 p $1. InIJ   4314
Cook, Walter W.S. A Saint Martin altar frontal in the
     Walters Art Gallery 13 p il 1948 p $.25 MdBWA   4315
Hard, Frederick. Sculptured scenes from Shakespeare. Il-
     lustrations and descriptions of nine panels on the main
     facade of Folger library, illustrating scenes from Shake-
     speare's plays p $.75 DFo   4316
Lipschitz, Jacques. Jacques Lipschitz: A retrospective ex-
     hibition of sculpture and drawings 16 p 9 il 1960 p $.75
     DCGA   4317
Masks p $2. CaOTRM   4318
Rawinsky, Hans. Hans Rawinsky--metal sculptures folder il
     1960 apply NNJ-Mu   4319
Robinson, Henry S. Cypriote limestone head (TM 1) 1947
     $.15 OkU-S   4320
The sculpture of Negro Africa 22 photog 1960 p $1. CLajA
                                                         4321
Soper, Alexander Coburn. Four columns from a Chinese
     temple (SS v 1) 35 p il 1947 p $1. HHo   4322
Whitney Museum of American Art. Annual exhibition of
     sculpture and drawings, 1960 46 il p $1. NNW   4323

--Decorative Arts

Cahill, Holger. American design: Old and new paths--an
     address, November 6, 1936 p apply NjNM   4324
----. Old and new paths in American design: 1720-1936
     12 p apply NjNM   4325
Constantine, Mildred, and Arthur Drexler. The package, an
     illustrated catalogue 40 p 54 pl p $1.25 NNMMA   4326
Craftsmanship, 2nd Biennial Exhibition of Southern California
     Designer-Craftsmen 1960 36 p il p $1.25 CLCM   4327
Crosses in the collections of the Museum (M v 12, no 2,
     Spring 1960) $.75 p NjNM   4328
Design in Germany today; catalogue il p $.75 NNCoo   4329
An event to remember: The Our Town exhibition, November
     13, 1957-March 16, 1958. A picture book 52 p apply
     NjNM   4330
Gottesman, Rita Susswein, comp. The arts and crafts in
     New York, 1777-1799. Advertisements from New York
     City newspapers 484 p il index 1954 $4. NHi   4331
Lichten, Frances. Pennsylvania Dutch folk art from the
     Geesey Collection, and other 32 p 63 il (cover c) p 1958

$1.25 PPPM   4332
The Lightbulb Angel...a definition of the Folk Museums at
    Cooperstown (repr, Curator, v 3, no 1, 1960) 65 p il
    $.75 NCooHi   4333
Morgan B. Brainard's Tavern signs; a descriptive catalog il
    $5; p, $4. CtHi   4334
Paper dolls p $.35 CaOTRM   4335
Popular antiques at the Henry Ford Museum p $1. MiDbFM
                                                             4336

Peabody, Robert E. American sailing ships; a handbook of
    the ship model collection in the Addison Gallery of Amer-
    ican Art 112 p 77 il 1961 $3.50 MAnP-A   4337
Stackpole, Edouard A. Figureheads at Mystic Seaport p 1961
    (in press) CtMy   4338
----, and James Kleinschmidt. Small craft at Mystic Sea-
    port 1959 p CtMy   4339
Stacy, Harold G. Holland submarine (EP 33) 1961 NjPatM
                                                             4340
Sportscars in review, 1956 $.15; 1960 $.30; 1961 $.50
    MiDbFM   4341

--Ceramics

Association of San Francisco Potters, 1960 p $.20 CSfDeY
                                                             4342
Chinese pottery figurines p $.25 CaOTRM   4343
Colton, Harold S. Pottery types of the Arizona Strip and ad-
    jacent areas in Utah and Nevada (C 1) 98 p 1952 p (loose-
    leaf) $2. AzFM   4344
Duncan, Julia H. How to make pottery and ceramic sculp-
    ture 96 p 134 il p $1.95 NNMMA   4345
Ecke, Gustav. Hui Hsien Ware in Honolulu (SS v 2) 42 p
    1954 p $2. HHo   4346
Eighteenth century English porcelain, a special exhibition
    loaned by members of the Seattle Ceramic Society 64 p
    32 il 1956 $.50 WaSA   4347
Greek Black and Red pottery p $.25 CaOTRM   4348
Griffing, Robert P., Jr. The Barbara Hutton Collection of
    Chinese porcelain 36 p il 1956 p $2. HHo   4349
Hitchcock, Henry-Russell. Wedgwood, Then and Now; an
    exhibition of continuity of design 5 p (mimeo) 1952 MNS-
    MA   4350
Medieval Near Eastern ceramics (Smithsonian I pubn 4420)38
    p 40 il 1961 p $1. DSI-F   4351
Pottery types of the Southwest. a. Colton, Harold S.
    Wares 8A, 9A, 9B (Tusayan Gray, Tsuayan White, Little
    Colorado Gray, Little Colorado White) 98 p 1955 p $2;

b. Abel, Leland J.   Wares 5A, 10A, 10B, 12A (San Juan
Red, Mesa Verde Gray, Mesa Verde White, San Juan
White) 66 p 1955 p $1.75; c. Colton, Harold S.   Wares
5A, 6A, 6B, 7A, 7B, 7C (San Juan Red, Tsegi Orange,
Homolovi Orange, Winslow Orange, Awatovi Yellow, Jed-
dito Yellow, Sichomovi Red) 1956 $2. AzFM   4352-4

--Gems and Jewelry

The Lillian Thomas Pratt Collection: Russian Imperial
   Jewels, catalogue of the collection 1960 ViRMu   4355
Loan and exhibition of classical jewelry and vases $.15
   OkU-S   4356
Martin, Charles J., and Victor D'Amico.   How to make
   modern jewelry 96 p 220 il p $1.95 NNMMA   4357

--Glass

Caley, Earle R.   Analyses of ancient glass, 1790-1957 1961
   (in press) NCorniC-M   4358
Early Canadian glass p $.50 CaOTRM   4359
Stained glass (B v 10, no 1) 1958 p $.50 DCGA   4360

--Textiles

Chinese court costumes p $1.10 CaOTRM   4361
History of color as used in textiles p $.25 NNSM   4362
Fibres p $.50 CaOTRM   4363
Ontario textiles p $1. CaOTRM   4364
Oriental rugs p $.25 CaOTRM   4365
Preliminary study of Spanish Colonial Textiles (WN 23) 1961
   p $1.25 DTM   4366
Printed textiles of Europe and America (M v 12, no 1,
   Winter 1960) $.75 NjNM   4367
Repeated patterns in Near Eastern silks (WN 24) 1961 p
   $1.25 DTM   4368
Wexberg, Ernest.   Textile designs (EP 31) 1961 NjPatM
                                                           4369

--Metal Work

American silver in the Mabel Brady Garvan Collection p $1.
   CtY-A   4370
Blacksmith and wheelwright tools at Shelburne Museum 1961
   (in press) VtSM   4371
Coins in the Frank I. Liveright Collection of the Museum
   (B v 12, no 3, Summer 1960) $.75 NjNM   4372

Guns from Long Island Collectors 1960 NBLiSt   4373
Hammer and Tongs; catalogue p $.10 NNCoo   4374
Masterpieces of American silver; catalogue of an exhibition
   1960 ViRMu   4375
Medieval and Renaissance arms and armour from the Metro-
   politan Museum (published by the Washington County Mu-
   seum of Fine Arts, Maryland) 36 p 38 il 1955 p $1.
   NjNM   4376
Paul Revere Silver (Picture Book) $1. MBMu   4377
Robinson, Henry S. Greek and Roman coins. Pt. 1. Materials and methods of coining--preservation and discovery
   of ancient coins (C 3) $.15; Pt. 2. The earliest Greek
   coins (C 4) 1948 $.15 OkU-S   4378
Silver catalogue; Royal Ontario Museum p $1. CaOTRM4379

--Book Arts

The artist and the book, 1860-1960 232 p 62 il (7 c) 1961
   $10. MBMu   4380
Bible in print p $.25 CaOTRM   4381
Books, Middle Ages p $.25 CaOTRM   4382
Dana, John Cotton. John Cotton Dana (Memorial Book),
   1856-1929 125 p front 1930 (The Merrymount Press) $1.
   NjNM   4383

--Architecture and Interior Design

Albany. Institute of History and Art. Furniture in the Col-
   lection 1961 (in prep) NAlAI   4384
Beirne, Rosamond R., and John H. Scarff. William Buck-
   land, 1733-1774; architect of Virginia and Maryland 1958
   $7.50 MdHi   4385
Building Arts 1960 p $1. InIJ   4386
The chair in China p $1. CaOTRM   4387
Dorman, Charles G. Delaware cabinetmakers and allied
   artisans, 1655-1855 (Published by the Historical Society of
   Delaware) 107 p 31 il 1960 $4. DeWint   4388
Drexler, Arthur. Three structures by Buckminster Fuller
   folder 15 il $.25 NNMMA   4389
A flexagon of structure and design, catalog of the Arthur J.
   Carrara Exhibition $1.25 WMA   4390
Furniture in French Canada p $.50 CaOTRM   4391
Huxtable, Ada L. Four walking tours of modern architecture
   in New York City 72 p il 1961 p $.95 NNMMA   4392
Kimball, Fiske, et al. Samuel McIntire--A bicentennial sym-
   posium--1757-1957; a collection of articles on various as-
   pects of McIntire's achievement; with a selected bibliogra-

phy by Benjamin W. Labaree 65 il $4. MSaE   4393
The Portuguese Chapel in the Samuel Fleisher Memorial,
    Philadelphia; a catalogue 1961 PPPM   4394
Seymour, George Dudley, Furniture Collection; catalog
    $3.50; p, $2.50 CtHi   4395
Sleepy Hollow Restorations, descriptive brochure of three
    historic houses: Sunnyside, Van Cortlandt Manor, and
    Philipsburg Manor folder apply NTaS   4396
Van Cortlandt Manor, Croton-on-Hudson, descriptive bro-
    chure folder apply NTaS   4397

HISTORY, SOCIAL SCIENCES, AND TECHNOLOGY

Carson, Linda. New Jersey history (EP 28) NjPatM   4398
Civil War panorama p $.50 MiDbFM   4399
The Erie Canal 24 p il p $.50 NUtM   4400
Excavating Ontario history p $.15 CaOTRM   4401
Henry Ford: A personal history p $.50 MiDbFM   4402
Henry Ford: Highlights of his life p $.25 MiDbFM   4403
Four firsts in Berks: Berks County in the Civil War 1961
    $1; post, $.10 DPG   4404
Illustrated guide to Richmond, the Confederate capital; a
    facsimile reprint of the City Intelligencer of 1862, with 24
    woodcuts, lithographs and engravings of Richmond in 1861-
    1865 (Published by the Confederate Museum and the Valen-
    tine Museum) 1960 p $1. ViRVM   4405
Jehl, Francis. Menlo Park reminiscences 3 v $.50 ea; p,
    $.25 ea MiDbFM   4406
Johnson, Gerald W. Mount Vernon: The story of a shrine;
    including extracts from diaries and letters of George
    Washington concerning the development of Mount Vernon,
    selected and annotated by Charles C. Wall 122 p $1.75
    ViMt   4407
LaMar, Virginia A. Travel and roads in England (Tudor and
    Stuart) p $.75 DFo   4408
McMahon, Margaret M. Nathan Barnert (EP 11) NjPatM
                                                      4409
Merrill, Walter M. New England treasury of American be-
    ginnings, Essex Institute; A Newcomen lecture describing
    the development of the Essex Institute from the Social Li-
    brary of 1760 to the organization at the present day; with
    8 original illustrations from the Institute collections (New-
    comen Society of America) 1957 p $.75 MSaE   4410
The Mount Vernon Gardens, a history with ground plans and
    plant lists il 24 p 1960 $.25 ViMt   4411
Neale, John E. England's Elizabeth. A lecture delivered
    at the Folger Library on November 17, 1958, the Fourth

Centenary of the accession of Elizabeth I   p $.50 DFo
4412

Read, Conyers.   The government of England under Eliza-
beth   p $.75 DFo   4413
Stone, Lilly C.   English sports and recreations (Tudor and
Stuart) p $.75 DFo   4414
Texas grew from hide to horn (IC 2) mimeo 1960 $.25
TxAuM   4415
Washington, George.   Last will and testament, with schedule
of property and will of Martha Washington, edited and an-
notated by John C. Fitzpatrick 67 p $.50 ViMt   4416

PUBLICATIONS IN ANTHROPOLOGY, ARCHAEOLOGY AND ART--INDEX

Authors and subjects are listed in the index. Subjects are shown in full capitals. The numbers used in the index refer to the publication number as listed in the bibliography.

A

ABBEY, EDWARD AUSTIN 2274-5
'ABD AR-RAHMAN AS-SUFI 1543
Abel, A.H. 394
Abel, L.J. 2807, 4353
ABO MISSION 2716
ABRAHAM (Jewish Patriarch) invention of improved plow 1145
Abraham, C. 3129
ABSTRACT CLASSICISM 2372
ABYDOS
    Stela of Sisopduyenhab 1233
    tombstone 3557
ACADIA 3792, 3819
    administrative history 3825
    Chignecto Forts 3820, 3824
    Governor Steenwyck 3823
ACCULTURATION
    and material culture 192
    Delaware Indians 362
ACHAEANS AT KOURION 1021
ACHESON, ALICE 2404
Ackerman, P. 3634
ACKMEN-LOWRY AREA, COLORADO 499
    Basketmaker sites 500
    culture change 505
ACOLMAN, MEXICO, report in 1580 899
ACOMA INDIANS, weaving 2836

ACROPOLIS, Tepe Gawra 1165
Adams, J.C. 1647
Adams, N.K. 579
Adams, R. 961
Adams, W.Y. 578-9, 4077
Adams-Clement Collection 1762
Addison Gallery of American Art, handbook 2158; shipmodels 4337
ADENA PEOPLE See also Hopewell Culture 279, 4114
    Adena trait list 279
    Kentucky 357
Adlow, D. 2446
Admiralty Islands, kinship 1329
ADOBE PALACE, Santa Fe 2703
ADOBES
    California 2704, 2706, how to build 2707
    Fort Tejon 2705
ADOPTION CEREMONY 4110
ADVERTISEMENTS
    American artists in 1754-1820 2222
    arts and crafts of New York City in 1726-76 2551
    Fifty advertisements of the Year 2631
AESTHETICS 1677-88
AFGHANISTAN 3526
    archaeology 1075

Shamshur Ghar cave site
1070
AFRICA See also names of
areas, as Liberia
anthropology and archaeology 1093-1120
art, 3643, 3645-76
botany, drug plants 1099
colonial policies in 1119
food resources 1100
maman, prehistoric 1398
mineral resources 1114
myths 1404
religion 4025-6
AGADE, DYNASTY OF 1191
AGE
aged models and painters
1937
societies, Plains Indians
553
AGRICULTURE See also
Ethnobotany, Food
culture and 198
folk lore 1405
Hopi 693
World crops from Indians
of North America 275
Zuni harvest time 690
AIRPLANES IN ART 2387
Aitken, R.T. 1265
AKHNATEN 3562
AKKADIANS
inscriptions 1179
personal names 1507
ALABAMA
archaeology 4121--Besse-
mer site 598, Colbert
County 415B, Flint River
415A, 2686, Hale County
400, Lauderdale County
415C, Little Bear Creek
415B, 4096, McQuor-
quodale Mound 420, Mad-
ison County 415A, Mound-
ville 400, Perry site
415C
physical anthropology 1363

ALASKA See also Eskimos
archaeology 800, 803-4--
Central Alaska 810, Hot
Springs, Port Moller 818,
Point Barrow 805
Indians--Eyak 786, native
art 2739
Alaska, University of, Museum,
guide 71
ALBANIA
Ghegs, race and culture
1040
Albany Institute of History and
Art, furniture collection
4384
ALBERS, ANNI 1818
ALBERS, JOSEF 2405-6
ALBERT, CALVIN 2531
Albright Art Gallery 1689-92
ALCOHOL 4020
ALCORA STATUETTES 3344
Aldrich, Edward B., Collec-
tion 1998
Aldrich, Larry, Collection
1815
Aldrich, Lucy T., Collection
3502
ALEUTIAN ISLANDS
art, prehistoric 2750
burial 823
harpoon heads 817
pottery 2809
Alexander 1661
Alexander, H.B. 1408
Alexander, H.G. 580
ALEXANDER, JAMES 2596
ALGERIA, anthropology 4137
man, prehistoric 1112
ALGONKIAN INDIANS
conflict with Europeans 3875
myth 1432
village, Levanna, New York
375
ALIIS 1273
ALITOA
socio-economic life 1330
Allen, F.H. 2302

Allen, G.M. 479, 1588
Allen, H.F. 195
Allen, J.L. 2949
Allen, R.J. 3024
Allen, T.G. 1225
Allied Artists of America, an-
    nual exhibition 1830, 4171
Allison, V.C. 466
ALLSTON, WASHINGTON
    2276-7
Alsdorf, J.W., Collection
    3280
ALTARPIECES AND ALTARS
    See also Santos
    Amithaba 3477
    Antwerp altarpiece 2962
    St. Martin 4315
Altman, Harold 2491
Altman Collection 3460
AMAZON AREA
    decorative arts 3701
    expeditions and explorations
        834--Amazon River
        headwaters 861, mouth
        864, Guiana 861, Mundi-
        rucu 861
    myths 1442
    rubber camp 4004
AMBRYM ISLAND, Craniom-
    etry 1384
American Academy of Fine
    Arts 1758
American Antiquarian Society
    antiquities of Western
        States 2640
    French and Indian war re-
        cords 3841
    Hull diaries 3873
    Massachusetts Bay Company
        records 3873
    paintings catalog 1693
    Royal proclamations re
        America 3842
American Art Union 1758
American Association of Mu-
    seums
    annual meeting 1; annual

report 2; constitution and
    by-laws 6; membership
    folder 8; Museum Direc-
    tory 4033; proceedings 7;
    publications--index 7, 27,
    list 63
American Indian Painting Com-
    petition, annual 2719
American Jewish Tercentary
    2366
American Museum of Natural
    History
    guide 72
    quipu 190
    Roosevelt memorial murals
        2379
American primitive paintings
    2164
American School of Indic and
    Iranian Studies 1255
AMERICAS See also Indians of
    Mexico, Central and
    South America; Indians of
    North America
    archaeology 221
    ethnography, North Pacific
        Coast 215
    ethnology 237, 242
    man, prehistoric 218, 257,
    gold 945, use of metals
    946
    maps 3788
    security and cooperation
        3786, military 3787
AMES, EZRA 4180
AMISH MENNONITES in Amer-
    ican culture 3843
AMITHABA ALTAR 3477
AMOXIUMQUA EXCAVATIONS
    660
AMPHORAE 3212-3
    "Berlin Painter" 3199
    Corinthian 3203
    Meno 3207
    Orvieto 3211
Amsden, C.A. 218, 581-2
AMUR TRIBES, decorative art
    3387A

296

ANAA, ISLAND OF, legends 1466

ANASAZI CULTURE See also Basket-Maker Indians; Pueblo Indians
Paa-ko village 628
pottery 2802

ANDALUCIA CERAMICS 3348

ANDAMAN SKULLS 1402

ANDEAN CULTURE See also Indians of Mexico, Central and South America
and art 3707
history 841

Anderson, A.J.O. 1568

Anderson, C.P. 2703

Anderson, R.M. 3356

Andrews, E. 1512

Andrews, E.D. 4304

Andrews, E.W. 962

Andrews, W.P. 1517

Angle, P.M. 1518, 3951

ANGOLA
anthropometry 1399
Ovimbundu 1106

ANIMALS IN ART See also names of specific animals, as Birds, Horses
Chinese dragons 3396
Egyptian 3550
illuminations, illustrations 1873, 4159
Maya codices 1588
Muslim unicorns 3519
Oriental 3376, Chinese 3417
Pre-Columbian 3711
sculpture 2536, domestic animals 2535

ANMERKAR and the Lord of Arratta 1448

ANNAPOLIS, furniture 2641

Anrus, V.D. 2612

Ant, red, chant 1426

Anthes, R. 1201-4

Anthony, H.E. 49

ANTHROPOID PRIMATES See Man, Prehistoric

ANTHROPOLOGY AND ARCHAEOLOGY See also specific regions, as Africa, North America; specific groups, as Indians of North America, Sherbro; and specific cultural and physical aspects, as Ethnobotany, Craniometry
176-1403, 4071-4142
material culture 188-94
methodology 200-13
physical anthropology 1337-1403
regional anthropology 214-1335
social life and customs 195-9
exhibits--Buffalo Museum of Science 83, University Museum 163

ANTHROPOLOGY, PHYSICAL See Physical Anthropology

ANTHROPOMETRY
Cholti Indians 1372
Fiji 1386
Hawaiians 1383
Labrador 1365
Northwest Territories, U.S. 1348
Sioux Indians 1366
Solomon Islands 1386

ANTIQUES See also names of collections and museums, as American Antiquarian Society; Burnap Collection; Cooperstown; Ford, Henry, Museum; Shelburne Museum; Williamsburg
Suffield, Ct. 2642

ANTLER ARTIFACTS
Iroquois figurine 2777
Ontario spoons 2778

ANTWERP ALTARPIECE 2962

APACHE INDIANS See also Jicarilla Indians; South-
west Indians
basketry 2853, 2871, 4235,
San Carlos Apaches 2870
devil dance 713, music
4152
mythology, San Carlos A-
paches 1414, White
Mountain Apaches 1415
APACHE LANGUAGE AND
LITERATURE 1564-5
APALAI (APALAII) INDIANS
862
APOLLO, baths 1023 sanctuary of, Kourion 1017,
1021
APPLIQUE QUILTS 2587
APPONEGANSETT, Quaker
meeting house 2683, 2693
APULIA vases 3249
AQUARIUMS 50
directories 65
Steinhart 160
ARABIAN DESERT archaeol-
ogy 1082
ARABIC ART See Art, Mo-
hammedan
ARABIC LANGUAGE AND
LITERATURE 1589, 1628
ARABS
archaeology, Beth-Shan
1241; Iraq 1080
ARAGON
ceramics 3348
painting 3306
ARAMAIC LANGUAGE AND
LITERATURE 1608
papyri 3590
ARAPAHO INDIANS
ceremonial organization 545
folk literature and folk lore
542
music 1662
Offerings Lodge ceremony
538
sacred bundles 571

Sun dance 538
ARAPESH, MOUNTAIN 1330
Arapoff, Alexis Paul, Memori-
al exhibition 1828
Arapoff, C.G. 1828
ARATTA, LORD OF 1448
ARBORETUMS See Botanical
Gardens
ARCH OF TRAJAN, Beneven-
tum 1028
ARCHAEOLOGY See also An-
thropology and Archaeol-
ogy; Pipeline Archaeology
American 4071,
human and animal remains
519--Folsom points and
glacial man 694, Guada-
lupe mountains 584, Ne-
braska 530, 532, Nevada
748, New Mexico 700,
Utah 479
human remains and geologi-
cal deposits, Texas 695
Indians of North America--
Kivas, N.M. 692, Ridge
Ruin, Ariz 631, Winona
Village, Ariz 631-2
Mexican-Southwest parallels
600
sketch book 1031
technology 3408
ARCHAIC INDIANS 4086, 4096,
4105
ARCHES, Nippur 3622
ARCHITECTURAL ELEMENTS,
Medieval 2962
ARCHITECTURAL MODELS
See also Thorne Rooms
American 2657A
Roman town house 3256
ARCHITECTURE See also types
of structures, as Acrop-
olis, Basilica, Baths,
Churches, Monuments,
Palaces, Ruins, Stele
(archaeological), Temples,
Ziggurats

298

1864, 2113-4, 4384-97
American 2661-2718--Early
  Empire of West 2663,
  history 2676, in 1615 to
  1812 2184, Spanish Co-
  lonial 2703-17
Baltimore 2665
Batak (Sumatra) sacred edi-
  fices 1054
California 2685, 2704
Canadian 2131
Charleston 2684
Detroit Institute of Arts
  2662
Ipswich 2696
Mission 2709, 2713-4, 2716
New Mexico 2703, New York
  City 4392
Octagonal Buildings, New
  York 2686
paintings of 1928
Panama-California Interna-
  tional Exposition 2710
Pennsylvania 2666
Piedras Negras 3775
Santa Fe 2715, Thai 4270
Ur 3622-3, Virginia and
  Maryland 4385
Williamsburg 2697
ARCHITECTURE, DOMESTIC
  See also Dwellings;
  Shelters; names of struc-
  tures, as Arnold Man-
  sion, Corbit House, De-
  catur House, Derby Man-
  sion, Fenimore House,
  Park Houses, Penn House,
  Philipsburg Mansion,
  Sunnyside
  Boxford, Mass 2681
  Charleston 2684
  Contemporary 2670
  Hawaii 2688
  Maryland, Colonial period
    2671
  Salem 2695
  San Francisco 2667

ARCTIC REGIONS, map 3788
ARCTIC WOODLAND CULTURE,
  Kobuk River 806
ARDEBIL SHRINE 3465
AREIKA 3551
Arensberg, Louise and Walter,
  Collection 1788
ARGENTINA, paintings of
  3324-5
ARGILLITE CULTURE, Tren-
  ton 406
ARIADNE 3192
ARIEGE See Montardit
ARIKARA INDIANS
  societies 555
Ariss, R. 222
ARIZONA For Anthropology
  and Archaeology see
  listings under Indians of
  North America--South-
  west
  Indian pottery--prehistoric
    2812; types 2794, 4344
Arizona, University of, Art
  Gallery
  American collection 2351
  Gallagher Collection 1694
  Kress Collection 2926
Arizona-Sonora Desert Museum
  73-4
Arizona State Museum, pictori-
  al 4035
ARKANSAS
  Caddo Indians 324
ARMENIANS
  Ethnology 1089
ARMS AND ARMOR See also
  names of specific types,
  as Atlatl; Axes; Bows
  and Arrows; Darts;
  Guns; Harpoons; Hel-
  mets; Missiles; Shields;
  Spear throwers; Toma-
  hawks; War Clubs 2077-
  83
  American 2624-6--Pilgrim
    2626

armorers' marks 2077
edged weapons 188
historical 2079
history 2077
medieval 2080, 4376
renaissance 2080, 4376
Spanish 3363
catalogs--Borrowdale Collection of weapons 2078, Hearst Collection 2078, St. Louis Art Museum 2083, Severance Collection 2077
Armstrong, M.K. 2663
Arnason, H.H. 2418, 2463
ARNHEIM LAND
anthropometry 1387
Arnold Arboretum, guidebook 75
ARNOLD MANSION 2679
ARRASTRA 4091
Ars Medica 1972
ART 1404-3775, 4154-4383
censorship 1680, 4275
education 40
education and 1681
history 1833, 1844, 1847, 1910
influence on printing 2108
installation of exhibits 41
insurance 46
international exchange 39
libraries, Harvard guide 1852
musical instruments in 1655
packing 46,
"representational" 4168
safeguarding 45-6
science in examining 4155
storage 45-6
study and teaching--European artists in America 2938
symbols See also Christian art and Symbolism; Signs and Symbols 2760
transportation 46

catalogs--See Private Collections, and names of Museums and Galleries
ART, ABSTRACT 4154
nature in 1923
ART, AFRICAN 3639-76, 4284C-G
ART, AMERICAN 2166, 2178, 2158-2718, 4171-4241
18th century 2258-9
Indians of North America 2719-2909, 4233-4241
Negro 2382
Pacific Coast 2380
Spanish Colonial See Architecture; Santos
survey 2373
catalogs--See also names of museums and galleries, as Addison Gallery of American Art; Walters Art Gallery; Whitney Museum of American Art
Brussel's World's Fair 2159
Freer Gallery of Art 1730
New England 2167-8
San Antonio Collections 2160
20th century 4194
Yale Collection, prints and drawings 1964
ART, ANCIENT See also Art, Near East; and headings under Anthropology and Archaeology 4161, 4164
Egyptian 3541-79
Mediterranean Area 3167-3256
Mesopotamian 3601-25
theatre in 1634
ART, ASIAN See Art, Oriental
ART, ASSYRIAN See Art, Mesopotamian
ART, AUSTRIAN See Art, German; Drawings
ART, BABYLONIAN See Art, Mesopotamian
ART, BAROQUE 3268

ART, BUDDHIST See also Buddha and Buddhism; Lamaism 3382A
Chinese lacquer statue 3431
ART, BYZANTINE
Dumbarton Oaks Collection 3517-8
Silver 3529
ART, CANADIAN 2116-57
ART, CHILEAN, contemporary 2911
ART, CHILDREN'S 4166
ART, CHINESE 3384, 3390-3478, 4281
animals in 3376, 3417, 3396
Chou Dynasty 3392
history 3391, 3410
catalogs--exhibitions 3407; University Museum 3418
ART, CONTEMPORARY 1680, American 4184
classic tradition in 3167, Spain 4258
catalogs--Albright Art Gallery 1689, 1691-2, Arizona, Univ. of, Art Gallery 1694, Yale Collection 1964
ART, COPTIC 3543, 3545
ART, DUTCH AND FLEMISH 2990-3022, 4264
ART, EARLY CHRISTIAN 2960, 3518
ART, EGYPTIAN 3541-79
Denver Art Museum 3168
ART, ENGLISH 3026-59, 4177, 4293
ART, ETRUSCAN 3229-30,3234
ART, EUROPEAN 2925-3371, 4242-68
surveys 2932
catalogs--Denver Art Museum 2933, Freer Gallery of Art 1730
ART, FRENCH 1869, 3060-3150, 4265
ART, GOTHIC 296
Italian painting 3270
tapestries 3020

ART, GREEK 3167-3225, 4253, 4262
ART, HAWAIIAN 3679
carvings 3690
feather work 3688
ART, INCA 3699-3700
wooden cups 3720
ART, INDIAN 3384, 3580-7
ART, INDONESIAN 3680
ART, IRAN See Art, Persian
ART, ITALIAN See also Art, Medieval
Prehistoric and Classical 3167-78, 3226-56, 4268
Renaissance to Contemporary 3257-91
ART, JAPANESE 3375, 3384, 3479-3507, 4272
ART, JAVANESE 3689
ART, JEWISH 3588-3600, 4275, 4278
ART, KOREAN 3375, 3508-10
ART, MAORI 3684
canoe ornaments 3695
staff 3693
wood carvings and Moko 3691
ART, MAYA 3699-3775
ART, MEDIEVAL See also Books and Book Arts; Tapestry
The Cloisters 2969
catalogs--Barnard Collection 2962, Buckingham Collection 2927, City Art Museum 2935, Philadelphia Museum of Art 2960, Wadsworth Atheneum 2968, Widener Collection 2955
ART, MESOPOTAMIAN 1073, 3601-25
ART, MEXICAN See also Art, Pre Columbian
Modern (1920-) 2913
Spanish Colonial 2910
ART, MINOAN 3183
ART, MODERN See also Museum of Modern Art 1685

301

catalogs--Art Institute of Chicago 1695
ART, MOHAMMEDAN See also Art, Persian 3520, 3523, 3627
gravestones 3527
metal work 3531, Saracenic 3575
unicorns in 3519
ART, MYCENAEAN 3183
ART, NEAR AND MIDDLE EAST 3372, 3517-3676
ART, NEPALESE 4269
ART, OCEANIC See Art, Pacific Area
ART, ORIENTAL 3372-3638
Asia and the West 1874, 1877, 1894
ART, PACIFIC AREA 3639-44, 3677-98, 4284B
ART, PERSIAN See also Art, Mohammedan 3375, 3626-38
Iran 1073
ART, PRE-COLUMBIAN 3639-3775, 4236
ART, PRIMITIVE 3699-3775, 4161
ART, RELIGIOUS See also Christian Art and Symbolism, Christmas in Art, Jesus Christ; and names of religions, as Buddha and Buddhism; Lamaism; Art, Buddhist; Art, Mohammaden; and forms and periods of religious art, as Art, Medieval; Santos 1883, 4304
ART, RENAISSANCE See also Kress Collection; Straus Collection
French 3062
Italian 3284
catalogs--Wadsworth Atheneum 2968
ART, ROCOCO 2925

ART, ROMAN 3226-56, 4253, 4262-3
catalogs--Denver Art Museum 3168, Museum of Fine Arts, Boston 3169, University Museum 3170, 3230
ART, ROMANESQUE 2960
ART, RUSSIAN 3294
bronze bird figures 3293, 3295
ART, SIAMESE 3375
ART, SPANISH 3306-68, 4270
ART, SPANISH AMERICAN See also Architecture, American; Santos 2115
ART, SUMERIAN 3606-7
ART, THAI 3375, 4270
ART, TIBETAN 3511-6
ART, TWENTIETH CENTURY See Art, Contemporary
ART and SCIENCE 4155
ART AND SOCIETY 1680
ART CLEANING AND RESTORATION 45
Paintings 44
Art Institute of Chicago
Buckingham Medieval Collection 2927
Eddy Collection 1695
paintings--15th and 16th century 1696, 19th century 1697
Winterbotham Collection 1698
ART MUSEUMS 36-48, 4033-70
Catalogs, guides, history 1689-1827
Exhibitions 1828-94
ARTAXERXES I, Documents from reign of 1180
ARTIFACTS see cultural groups, as Indians of North America--Implements, and other headings; and specific classes of artifacts, as Arms and Armor; Ceramics

302

ARTIFICIAL DEFORMITIES
1341, 1343, 1345
ARTISTS See also exhibitions
under such areas as
California, New Jersey
American 1754-1822 2222;
in American history
2174; in Italy, 1830-75
2270
European teaching in America 2938
Names, pronunciation 4165
Artists of Washington, annual
2356
ARZBERGER SITE, S.D. 510
ASCHER, MARY G. 2407
ASHTAROTH, TEMPLE OF
1247
ASIA See also Orient, and
names of countries, as
China; Japan
anthropology 214
body markings 1057
ethnography 215
tobacco 1059
Askew, R.K. 171
"Aspects of primitive art"
4284A
ASSIMILATION, Sonora 4127,
4129
L'Association Francaise d'Ac-
tion Artistique 3128
ASSYRIA-BABYLONIA
archaeology 1121-1200
art 3601-38
legends 1445, 1447, 1450-5
ASTRONOMICAL OBSERVA-
TORIES AND PLANE-
TARIUMS
Newark Museum 137
Rittenhouse Orrery 167
ASTRONOMY
Caroline Islands 1324
Mayas 1587, codices 999
Navaho star lore 1410
Near East 1593
Star myth 1411

ATAYAL, FORMOSA
folklore 1464
ATHENA 3213, 3244
Athenaeum (Boston) influence
on American literature
1557
Athenaeum Gallery 1699
Atlanta Art Association, hand-
book 4036
ATLASES See Maps, Atlases
and Charts
ATLATL See also Spear
throwers
Chiggerville site, Ky 293
Mexico, ancient 953
Read Shell Midden, Ky 371
Val Verde Co, Texas 688
ATTITUDES See also Culture,
change and transition
foreign colonization in
Guatemala 973
ATONEMENT RITE
Babylonian kings 1188
ATTU ISLAND, art 2762
Atwood, 3874
AUDUBON, JOHN JAMES 4205
AURACANIAN INDIANS
culture change 926
singing 1669
AURIGNACIAN CULTURE 1003
Austin, A.E. 171, 1405
Austin, Mary 1519-20
Auslander, J. 1627
AUSTRAL ISLANDS, carvings
3692
AUSTRALIA
anthropology 1266
anthropometry and race
problem 1387
canoes 1307
hunters, primitive 1325
AUTHORS See names of au-
thors, as Shakespeare
Ireland 1542
Kentucky 1538
Minnesota 1537
North Carolina 1555

303

AUTOMATA, Arabic treatise
on 1589
AUTOMOBILES 4341
AVERY, MILTON 2408, 4181
Avery Memorial, Wadsworth
Atheneum 172
AVIATION 3778
AVINOFF, ANDREW 1895
AVOYELLES, PARISH, LA,
archaeological site 310
AWATOVI, ARIZ, ceramics
4354
Franciscan mission 648
kiva murals 2755
AXES
Babylonian axe head 1164,
1184
Indians of North America--
double axe symbol 2731,
tomahawks and trade
axes 256
Ayer, M.Y. 584
AYMARA INDIANS, magic 997
AYMARA LANGUAGE 1497
AZILIAL skeletal remains
1380
AZQUELTAN, Pinole fiesta
984
AZTALAN, WIS archaeologi-
cal site 283
AZTEC LANGUAGE AND LIT-
ERATURE 1568
Codex Hall 1573
Codex Nuttall 1572
Florentine Codex 1568,
1583
AZTEC RUIN 650-1
great kiva 698
AZTECS
costumes and textiles 3737
Tizoc, Lord of the Aztecs
910

B
BAALBECK 3521
BACCHIACCA, IL 4157

BABYLONIA See Assyria-
Babylonia
BABYLONIAN LANGUAGE
AND LITERATURE 1594-
1619
Bache, C. 1122
Bache Collection 2950
Backus, Leroy M., Collection
1805
Bacon, L. 1623
Baer, Curtis O., collection
1956
Baerreis, D.A. 223, 467
Baffer Memorial Collection
1744
BAFFIN LAND ESKIMO 801
BAGA (African tribe) sculp-
ture 3672
BAGOBO TRIBE 1284
Bahrami, M. 3627
Bailey, A.G. 3790, 3875
Bailey, F.L. 710
Bailey, V.H. 2357
BAILLIE, ROBERT A. 2532
Baird, T.P. 4242
BAJIO, MEXICO, culture in-
tegration 1000, 4126
Baker, Richard Brown, Col-
lection 4037
Baldwin, C.C. 3844
Baldwin, P. 3963
BALISE RIVER, in 1769   850
Balken, E.D. 2161
Ball, W.W.   2684
BALL COURTS
Piedras Negras 3775
Winona Village, Ariz 632
BALL ROOM 2655
Ballard Collection 3378
BALTIMORE
architecture 2665, 2672
furniture 2641, painted 2641
harbor views 3934, in art
4287
Baltimore Museum of Art 1701
Cone Collection 1700
BALTIMORE's WAR 3924

BALUCHI AREA, archaeology 1075
BAMBARA (African tribe) sculpture 3664, 4284C
Bamberger, Louis, Memorial 1776, 1780
Bancroft, S., and M.R., Collection 3035
BANDBOXES AND HATBOXES Shelburne Museum 2548
Bandelier, A.F. 585-6, 963, 4071
BANNER PAINTINGS, Tibetan 3515
BANNOCK INDIANS 732, 745
BARAMA RIVER CARIBS, British Guiana 868
BARBARY PIRATES 3855
Barbeau, M. 2118, 2145
Barbour, E.H. 120-1, 468, 519, 530
BARCELONA GLASS 3353
BARD, JAMES 2278
BARD, JOHN 2278
Bargon, G.A. 1445
BARK See also Birchbark Dakota Indian houses 2898
BARK-CLOTH See Tapa
Barker, V. 2170
Barksdale, A. 1650-2
Barnard, George Gray, Collection 2962
BARNERT, NATHAN 4409
Barnes, A.C. 1681, 3061, 3095, 3110, 3115, 4243-4
Barnes Foundation 1681
BARNETT, HERBERT PHILLIP 2409
BARNEY, ALICE PIKE 2279
BARNHART, RAYMOND 2533
BAROQUE PAINTING 4245, 4267
Barr, A.H. 1757, 3111
Barrere, D.B. 4001
Barrett, R. 2576
Barrett, S.A. 283-4, 444,

730-1, 751-2, 835, 1409
Barringer, B. 1094
Barrodas, J.P. de 1834
BARTH CO, KY, site 357
Bartlett, H.H. 1054
Bartlett, Helen Birch, Memorial 1905
Bartlett, K. 681-2
Barton, G.A. 1167-8, 1594
Bascom, W.R. 3647
BASEBALL HALL OF FAME 3863
BASILICA, Kourion 1017
BASIN OF MINAS, settler 3805
BASKET MAKING AND BASKETS
    Chinese 3447
    Indians of Americas 2852-77--Apache 4235, California Indians 741
    Newark Museum 251
BASKET-MAKER INDIANS See also Anasazi Culture 581-2
    Ackmen-Lowry Area 500
    Arizona 596, 630
    Big Bend 635
    Oklahoma 495
BASKIN, LEONARD 1524, 2528
BASQUE ceramics 3348
BATAK, Sumatra, sacred edifices 1054
Bateman, H. 3048
Bates, A.C. 3855
Bates, N.I. 1115, 1118, 1516
Bates, O. 1118
Bates, W.N. 1028-9
Bath, G.H. 3925
BATHS, American Indian 3775
    Apollo Baths, Kourion 1023
BATIK designs 3689
BATONS See also Staffs and Sceptres
    Tlingit 2753
Batz, G. de 1835
Baucke, W.C. 1301

Baur, J.I.H. 1923, 2252, 2324, 2358, 2374, 2475, 3154, 4174-6, 4194
BAY OF HONDURAS, in 1769 850
BAYOU GOULA, LA, site 367
Bay Printmakers' Society exhibition 2486
Baylies 3876
Baxter, J.B.M. 3791
BAXTER, SIMON 3791
BEAD MYTHS 4144
BEADS AND BEADWORK See Quill and Beadwork
Beaglehole, E. 1267, 1390
Beaglehole, P. 1267, 1390
Beal, M.D. 732
Beale, M. 2664
BEAR CEREMONY, Delaware 459
BEAR CLAW NECKLACE 4238
BEAR FETISH, Zuni 4106
Beatty, J.W. 2137
Beauregard, N.H. 3845
BEAUSEJOUR, SIEGE OF 3834
BEAUTY CHANT 1421
BEAVER INDIAN LANGUAGE AND LITERATURE 1560
BEAVER INDIANS See Tsattine Indians
Beazley, J.D. 3185
BECKMANN, MAX 2932, 3153
Bedford, Duke of 4069
BEDOUINS 1068
Beers, F.W. 3900-1
Beggs, T.M. 1759-60, 2249, 2279, 2325, 2540
Beirne, R.R. 4385
BIESAN, PALESTINE archaeology 1216, 1222, 1237-8, 1243, 1248-9
BELCHER ISLANDS archaeology 816
Belfield, T. Broom, Collection 3496
BELIZE RIVER, in 1769 850

Belknap, J. 285
Belknap, W.P. 4177
BELKNAP, ZEDEKIAH 2223
Bell, R.E. 4078
BELLACOOLA INDIANS, mythology 1412
Bellinger, L. 2028, 3359, 3532-3, 3540, 3574, 3736
BELLOTTO, BERNARDO 2937
BELLOWS, GEORGE 2280, 2282
prints and drawings 2281
BELLS, Japanese 3507
BELTS
Bird quill, Suak or Fox 2880
Treaty, Huron 2848
Wampum 2842-3, Penn Indian 2849
BEMELMANS, LUDWIG 4178
BENEVENTUM, ITALY Arch of Trajan 1028
BENGTZ, TURE 2410
BENIN
art 3665
bronzes 3643
ivory cup 3670
personal ornaments 3655
BENJAMIN, KARL 2372
Benners, E.E. 3735
Bennett, W.C. 836-40
Bennett, Wm. C. 841
BENNINGTON CERAMICS 2576
Benson, E.M. 1785
BENSON, FRANK WESTON 2257
BEN-ZION 2411
BEOTHUK INDIANS 829
BERARD, CHRISTIAN 2971, 3090
Berard-Haile, Father 1410, 1435
Berendt Linguistic Collection 1495
Berger, F.P. 2065
BERING SEA
early man, North Coast 767

306

BERKS COUNTY, PENNSYL-
VANIA
Historic map 3902, in Civil
War 4404
Indians 330
rock shelter 435
Berlin Museums 2929-30
"BERLIN PAINTER" 3199
BERLY, MASS, harbor chart
3903
BERMAN, EUGENE 171, 1638
Bernat, Mr. and Mrs. Eu-
gene 3451
Bessaraboff, N. 1672
BESSEMER, ALA, site 598
BESTIARIES See also Animals
in Art
Toulouse-Lautrec 3124
BETH-SHAN (Scythopolis)
archaeology 1241-2
incense burners 3600
pottery 3592
stelae 3597
BETH-SHEAN, archaeology
1240
BETH-SHEMESH 1244
Betzenez (Geronimo warrior)
587
"BEVERLY," MASS, deriva-
tion 1476
Beyer, H. 941, 964, 1569-70,
3747
BEXAR CO, TEXAS, sites
421
BIBLE See also Christian Art
and Symbolism; Jesus
Christ
Biblical prints 1968
English language, 1525-
1611 1553, printed 4381
printing, influence on 2096
stoves and stove plates
depicting 2618
Sumerian literature, parallels from 1446
textile design source 3536
BIBLIOGRAPHY

anthropology--Africa 1105,
Klamath Basin 4113,
Peru 852
Archaeology--Europe, paleo-
lithic 1007, Ohio 356,
Palenque 908, Xochical-
co 909
Art 47, 1853--Oriental 3377
Aymara language 1497
Egypt, history 1221
England, printing in time of
Queen Elizabeth I 3369
Hispanic Society of America
Museum and Library--
printed books before 1601
in Library 2103, 1601-
1700 2106, publications
104, woodcuts in 15th
century books 3336
incunabula 2983
Indians of North America--
New Jersey 300
Indians of the America--
theses and dissertations
219
Kechua language 1497
linguistics, Behrendt Collection 1495
Maya language 1500
Mayas, Palenque 908
Middle American Research
Institute--manuscripts
112, 1501, Yucatan let-
ters 111
museums and museum work
34--art 47, science 58
New York Historical Soci-
ety--de Peyster books
128, Library 129-32
printing, English in Spain
3369
Rio Grande pueblos, New
Mexico 585
rugs and carpets, history
2049
science, natural, museum
58

Valentiner, W.R., writings 1837
Walters, Henry, Library 2983
Biddle, Hon. and Mrs. Francis, Collection 1913
Biennial Exhibition of Contemporary American Paintings 2359
Biennial of American Artists 2360
BIG BEND, TEXAS
    archaeological material and geological deposits 695
    Basket makers 635
    painted pebbles 684
BIG HAWK VALLEY, ARIZ, excavation 665
Bill, M. 3298
Billington 286
BINGHAM, GEORGE CALEB 4179
Bingham, L.A. 1677
BIOTECHNOLOGY 2005
BIRCHBARK See also Bark
    and the Indian 224
    canoe, Chippewa 434, Penobscot 426
    Eastern Indians, uses 441
    Montagnais art 2757
Bird, J.B. 824, 841-2, 960, 3736
BIRD QUILL WORK 2880
BIRDS
    in art--American birds 2194, Chinese painting 3412, Pueblo Indian rainbird 2743, Russian bronze 3293, 3295
Birmingham Museum of Art, Kress Collection 2931
BIRTH RITES AND CEREMONIES See Natal Customs and Ceremonies
Bishop, Bernice P., Museum, guide 76
Bishop, C.W. 1055, 1062,
    3393, 3423-6, 3448-9, 3472, 3504, 3511
Bishop, E. 2294
BISON OCCIDENTALIS See also Buffaloes
    and associated arrow point 530
    and associated dart points 519
Bissell, C.W. 2642
BITS, Corneta 3223
BLACK-FIGURE POTTERY See Ceramics, Greek
BLACKFOOT INDIANS 469
    crafts 2720
    dance societies 576, Sun dance 577
    medicine-pipe ceremony 561
BLACKSMITHS, pioneer, U.S. 3847, tools 4371
BLAKE, WILLIAM 3039
    water color drawings 3040
BLAKELOCK, RALPH ALBERT 2283
Blake-More, G. 2991
BLANKETS
    Indians of North America--chief 2829, Navaho 2823, 2832, pictorial 2826, Salish 2817, slave 2828
BLATAS, ARBIT 2390
Bloch, H. 3231
Blom, F. 942, 965, 1370
BLOOD GROUPS
    Fiji and Solomon Islands 1386
BLOOM, HYMAN 2412-3
    drawings 2500
Bloom, L.B. 3964
Bloom, M.M. 588
Bloomberg, M. 12
BLUE AND WHITE PORCELAIN 3463, 3466
BLUFF DWELLERS 482
    Cave Hollow site 350
Bluhm, E.A. 589
Blunt, A. 3114

308

Boachot-Soupique, J. 3128
Boas, B. 1999
Boas, F. 765, 783, 794, 801,
    1348, 1412, 1478, 1559,
    2764
Boas, G. 1700, 2925, 3180
BOATS See also Cattail Boats;
    Canoes and Canoeing;
    Dugouts; Ships
  spirit boat, Dwamish 787
BOCCIONI, UMBERTO 3279
BODMER, CARL 2727, 3370
BODY MARKINGS See Tattoo-
    ing
BOETIA, pottery (Lekanai)
    1090
Bogoras, W. 1037-9, 1444
BOISEHEBERT, CHARLES
    DES CHAMPS DE 3822,
    3829
BOLIVIA
  archaeology 839
  quipu, modern 958
BOLOGNA, GIOVANNI 3344
Bolton, C.K. 1924
Bolton, T. 4180, 4224
BONE ARTIFACTS See also
    Scrimshaw Indians of
    North America--Cali-
    fornia, Southern, inlaid
    2765, Delaware 4240,
    Hawikuh 2770, Iroquois,
    antler figurines 2777,
    Ohio, engraved 2768,
    Ontario, antler spoons
    2778
  Mexican rattles 941
  Tairona Culture 889
  Tibet, human, use of 1060
BONE CAVE, NEBR, site 488
BONNARD, PIERRE 3091
BONINGTON, RICHARD
    PARKES 2937
Bonsor, G.E. 1002, 1031
BOOK OF CHILAM BALAM
    1571, 1578, 1586
BOOK PAPERS, European,

2981
BOOKATZ, SAMUEL 2414
BOOKBINDING
  animals in 1873
  history 2100
  Pierpont Morgan Library
    2986
BOOKS AND BOOK ARTS See
    also Calligraphy; Illumi-
    nation of Books and Man-
    uscripts; Illustration of
    Books; Printing; and
    names of book designers,
    as Rogers, B.; and of
    languages, as Aztec Lan-
    guage and Literature;
    Maya Language and Lit-
    erature
  2096-2110, 4380-3
  American 2627-39
  Aramaic papyri 3590
  botanical books 1875
  English 3057
  garden books 2112
  medieval 2980, design 2985
  Oriental 3382
  Roman 3226
  exhibits--Children's books
    2629, Fifty Books of the
    Year 2633, Guild of
    Book Workers 2099
BOONE CO, KY, sites 298,
    374, 389
Booth, Ralph and Mary, Col-
    lection 1768
BOOTS AND SHOES
  mocassins, Plains Indians
    2851
  sandals, Kentucky caves
    2833
Booy, T. de 843
BORAX LAKE, CALIF, site
    736
BORDON, ROBERT LAIRD
    3833
Borhegyi, S.F. de 844, 3758,
    4122

Borrowdale Collection of
Weapons 2082
BORUCA INDIANS 917
BOSCH, HIERONYMUS 2932
BOSCOP SKULL 1398
BOSCOREALE
antiquities 3227
wall paintings 3231
BOSSE, ABRAHAM 3092
BOSTON painters 4192
Prendergast water colors
2321a
Sargent's 2332
Boston Public Library
Abbey's murals 2274
handbook 77
Sargent's decorations 2333-
4
BOTANICAL GARDENS
directories 65, 70, New York
City 68
Arnold Arboretum 75
Rancho Santa Ana 151
BOTANY
in art 1875
nomenclature, Yuki Indians
1479
exhibits--Buffalo Museum of
Science 83
BOUCHE, LOUIS 2349
BOUGAINVILLE See Solomon
Islands
Boulton, M. 2191
BOURDELLE, ANTOINE 3141
Bowditch, C. P. 966
Bowditch, N. 3903
Bowlin, A. 1988
BOWLS
Mayan 3768
Orvieto 3206
"BOW-PULLER" 1011
BOWS AND ARROWS 189
arrow release 2081
arrowpoint with Bison Oc-
cidentalis 530
BOXFORD, MASS, houses 2681
Boyce, G. K. 2097

Boyd, C. E. 3062
Boyd, E. 2250, 2517, 2606
Boyd, H. A. 1009
BRACELETS, Indian, silver
2788
Bradfield, W. 590
Bradley, D. F. L. 3785
Bradley, W. A. 3136
Bradshaw, G. A. 2552
Braidwood, R. J. 176
BRAINARD, MORGAN P. 4334
Brainerd, G. W. 845
Brainerd, H. A. 3952
Brainerd, N. C. 2645
BRAQUE, GEORGES 3093
Brattstrom, B. H. 3983
BRAZIL
Serente Indians 898
BREAD, Zuni 683
BREAST PLATE, Peru 988,
3757
Tahitian featherwork 2879
Breckenridge, J. D. 2925, 3287
Breeskin, A. D. 1655, 1700-1,
1866, 1931, 1937, 1947,
2063, 2212, 2507, 2538,
2925, 3070, 3140, 3268,
3645, 3675, 3687, 3710,
4181
BRESDIN, RODOLPHE 3130
Breternitz, D. A. 591, 4079
Breton, A. 846, 3087
Brett, A. B. 3222
Brett, K. B. 2029, 2119
Brewerton, N. Y., site 382, 384
Brewington, M. V. 4038
Brewster, J. 2223
BREWSTER CO, TEXAS, rock
shelter 520
BRIBRI INDIANS 913
BRIDAL CEREMONY, Tlingit
799
BRIDAL GOWNS 2598
Bridenbaugh, C. 3926
BRIDGES
New Mexico, early 3964
Vermont, covered 3918,
3922

BRIDLES, Indian, silver
2788
Briesemeister, A. 3788-9
Briggs 150, 3877-8
Briggs, L.C. 1095-6
Brigham, W.T. 3688, 3690
Brighton, H.D. 4080
Brillouin, S. and L., Collection 4301
Brinton, C. 3325
Brinton, D.G. 1010-1, 1495, 2841, 3773
Britoon, N.P. 3539
BRITISH ART See Art, English
BRITISH COLUMBIA
archaeology 775, cairns 793
Fraser River 781
Indians--bronze figurine 2764, Lillooet 783, Ntlakyapamuk 785, Shuswap 784, Thompson 785, Tsimshian 777, 788
Lytton 778
Queen Charlotte Islands 782
Thompson River 780
BRITISH GUIANA
Caribs, Barama River 868
Patomanca, string figures 3713a
warclubs 955
BRITISH HONDURAS
archaeology 907
Mayas, ethnology 925
pottery 3763
San Jose Ruins skeleton 1373
stucco heads 3712
British Pavilion, New York World's Fair, art 3031
Broadley, H.T. 3000, 4246
Brock Collection of Indian Baskets 2876
BRONZE AND BRONZES
ancient 3530, restoration 2076
Benin 3643
British Columbia figurine 2764

Bologna, G. 3344
Chinese 3375, 3471-4, 3476
gilt bronze furniture mounts 2114
Greek 3255
Indian 3585
Luristan 3634-6
Pre-Columbian 3754
Remington, F. 2255
Russell, C.M. 2255
Russian, bird figure 3293, 3295
sculpture 1988
catalogs--Field Museum of Natural History 2072, National Gallery of Art, renaissance 2975, Straus Collection 2943, Walters Art Gallery, classical 3172
BRONZE AGE
Crete, decorative art 3182
Kourion, Greece 1021
Russia 1046
Brookgreen Gardens
History 1976
sculpture 1977, 2518
verses in 1978
BROOKLYN BRIDGE 2171
Brooklyn Museum
Aramaic papyri 3590
Egyptian art 3542, and Coptic 3543
National Print annual 2487
painting, American 2185
pewter, American 2615
Brooklyn Society of Artists Biennial 2361
Broom, R. 1398
BROTHERTON INDIANS 285
Brown, A.G. 2278, 2519
Brown, A.P. 422
Brown, A.S.K. 4209
Brown, D.N. 4152
Brown, W.N. 3581, 3587
Bruck, E.F. 3226
BRUEGEL, PIETER, THE

ELDER 4288
Brundage, Avery, Collection 4039
Brussels World's Fair, American art 2159
Bry, D. 2514
Bryan, K. 252
Bryant, E.A. 4183, 4189
Bryant, William L., Foundation 313
Buchanan, D.W. 2150
Buck, J.H. 2607
Buck, P.H. 1268-70, 1306, 1319, 3679
Buckingham Collection 3473
Buckingham, Clarence, Collection 3488
Buckingham, Lucy Maud, Medieval Collection 2927
BUCKLAND, WILLIAM 4385
Buckley, C.E. 1818, 1979
BUCKS CO, PA, names geographical 1472
Bucks County Historical Society Museum, guide 78
BUDDHA AND BUDDHISM See also Art, Buddhist; Kuan Yin 3382a
    Amithaba altar 3477
    birthstones, Tibetan tankas 3515
    Chinese sculptures 3425
    lohans 3406, 3449
    maitreya 3435
Buel 3879-80
Buell, R.L. 1097
BUEN RETIRO PORCELAIN 3288
Buermeyer, L. 1678, 1681
Buffalo Historical Society Museum 79
Buffalo Museum of Science 80-4
    and schools 81
    Chinese ceramics 3450
    guides 83
    history 84

Indian exhibits 82
Buffalo Society of Natural History
    Babylonian tablets 1597
BUFFALOES See also Bison Occidentalis
    Buffalo robes 2830, biography 524
    Indians of North America and 267
BUFFET, BERNARD 3094
BUHEN, archaeology 1220
Buhler, K.C. 2608-9, 3052
BUKIDON of Mindanao 1275
Bull, L. 3576
Bullock, H. 3846
BULTOS See Santos
Bunak, V.V. 4142
BUNDLES, sacred and ceremonial See Charms
BUNDY, HORACE 2223
BUNGI INDIANS
    medicine ceremony 274
BURCHFIELD, CHARLES 2501
BURIAL AND BURIAL MOUNDS
    See also Cemeteries;
    Mortuary Customs;
    Mound Builders; Sepulchral Monuments
    Aleutian 823
    Aztec Ruin 650
    Early Woodland burial cult 453
    Hopewell 451
    Maine 464
    Massachusetts 463
    Persia 1260
    Peru 963, 980
    Piedras Negras 4123
Burkitt, R. 847, 967, 1441
Burland, C.A. 4021
Burnap collection 2643-4
Burnett, E.K. 470, 2765
Burns, J.F. 4072
Burns, W.A. 51
Burroughs, A. 1727, 2233
Burrows, E. 1595

312

Burrows, E.G. 1271-2, 1457, 1676
Buschbeck, E.H. 2928
Bushell, D.I. 287
Buston, F.W. 2318
Butler, B.R. 4081
BUTLER, HOWARD RUSSELL 2284
Butler, M. 288, 3759
Butler Art Institute, catalog 1702-4
BUTLER CO, KY, site 291, 371
Butterfield, L.H. 1521
BUTTONS, Emilio Collection of Military 2089
Byers, D. 978
Bynner, Witter, Collection 3397
Byrnes, J.E. 1837, 2362, 3063
BYZANTINE EMPIRE
    archaeology, Beth-Shan 1241

C

C & O MOUNDS, Paintsville, Ky 289
C 14 See Radiocarbon Dating
CABINETMAKERS See Furniture; Rooms; and names of artists, as McIntire, S; Sanderson, E. and J. Delaware 4388
CADDO INDIANS
    Arkansas 324
    grass houses 2899
CADDOAN INDIANS
    Spiro Mound 470
Cadzow, D.A. 814, 4082
CAESAR, DORIS 2374, 4183
Cahill, H. 2162, 2507, 3853, 4184, 4234-5
Cahn, H.A. 3779
CAHOKIA 287
Cahoon, H. 1533
CAIRENE RUGS 3574
CAIRNS See also Mound Builders

British Columbia and Washington 793
Cairns, H. 1753-4
CAISERMAN, GHITTA (Mrs. Alfred Pinsky) 2154
CALAVERAS CO, CALIF,
    Moaning Cave excavations 742
CALDER, ALEXANDER 2415, 4313
    mobiles 1979
Caldwell, J.R. 445
CALENDAR See also Chronology
    Indians of North America 271
    Winnebago calendar stick 431
Calendar, Engagement, National Gallery of Canada 1770
Caley, E.R. 4358
CALIFORNIA See also Los Angeles, Oakland, etc.
    abstract classicist painting 2372
    adobes 2704-6, how to build 2707
    architecture--contemporary 2685, ranch house 2704
    cattle brands 3984
    gold discoveries 3966, 3970
    Gold Rush Centennial exhibition 1891
    history 3990
    leather jackets 2599
    missions 2714, Santa Clara 2713
    prints and drawings 2488
    prints depicting 2490
    sculpture 2524
    stage coaches 3986
CALIFORNIA AREA INDIANS 730-64
    art, prehistoric, Southern California 2748
    baskets 2859, 2866
    craniology 1358
    inlaid stone and bone artifacts, Southern California 2765

skeletons 1359-60
California Palace of the Legion of Honor, handbook 1705
California Water Color Society, national exhibition 2363
California, Southern, Designer-Craftsmen 4327
Callawy, E.B. 2560
CALLEJON DE HUAYLAS, PERU, excavations 840
Callender, J.M. 290
CALLIGRAPHY See also Manuscripts; Writing
2098-9, 4279
Zapf, H. 2636
CALLOT, JACQUES 3131
Calorie card 4013
CALUMET 272
CAMEOS 2010, 2012
CAMERON CREEK VILLAGE, N M 590
Cammann, S. 3394, 3437, 3512
Camoes, L. de 1623
CAMP KILMER, N.J. 43
Campbell, W. 2164, 4289
CANAANITE TEMPLES, Palestine 3593, 3596
CANADA See also Art, Canadian
archaeology 830--Georgian Bay 826, Hopedale Area 824, Ontario 826-7
arts 2120
design, French Canadian 2632
history 3790-3840
Indians See also culture areas, as Eastern Woodlands Indians; and names of tribes, as Chipewyan Indians 824-33
portraits, 18th century 2125
Canaday, J. 1786, 3259
CANADIAN COLLECTIONS, European painting 2945
CANADIAN DAKOTA INDIANS

See Dakota Indians
CANALETTO (ANTONIO CANALE) 2937
CANALINO INDIANS
social life and customs 762
CANALS, Delaware & Hudson, map 3912
CANANDAIGUA, N.Y., site 380
CANARY ISLANDS ancient inhabitants 1107
CANETE VALLEY, PERU, archaeology 877
Caneti, E. 3160
Canfield, A.A. 2379
Cannon, C. 1646
CANNONBALL RUINS, COLO 649
CANNONS See Guns
CANOES AND CANOEING
American Indians 4074
Chippewa birchbark 434
Maori canoe oranments 3695
Melanesia 1307
New Guinea 1307
Oceania 1307, 1310
Penobscot 427, birchbark 426
Queensland 1307
CANOVA, ANTONIO 3257
CAPE FLATTERY, Makah Indians 771
CAPITALS (architecture), Medieval 2962
CAPITOLS, STATE See names of states, as Ohio, Pennsylvania, Virginia
CAPODIMONTE PORCELAIN 3288
CAPPADOCIA, tablets 1197
CARACOL, monuments 3724
CARAQUET, history 3795
CARBON 14 See Radiocarbon Dating
CARDIFF GIANT 226
CARIB INDIANS
Barama River, British Gui-

ana 868
Central Caribs 863
CARIBBEAN AREA, map 3789
Carlisle, L. B. 158, 2548,
2561, 2587
CARLOS ANNIS MOUND 291
Carman, A. 3401
Carmer, C. 2686
CARMONA NECROPOLIS 1031
Carnegie Institute
International Exhibition of
Contemporary Painting,
Annual 1839, 1896
Painting in the U.S., annual
2364
Carnegie Museum
Classic vases and urns 3175
Mummy labels 195
watches 2084
CAROLINE ISLANDS, astron-
omy 1324
Carpenter, E. 802
Carpenter, R. 3226
CARPENTERS, pioneer, U.S.
3847
CARPETS See Rugs and Car-
pets
CARRARA, ARTHUR J. 4390
Carrasco, P. 4022
CARRIAGES, WAGONS AND
CARTS
carriage mounts 2567
conestoga wagon 2563
covered wagons 2568
ox carts 2568
Shelburne Museum 2561
Suffolk Museum, Stony
Brook, carriages 2562
CARRIERE, EUGENE 3064
CARSON, CHRISTOPHER
(known as Kit) 3972
Carson, L. 4398
Carson, W.G.B. 1639
Carter, M. 1732
CARTS See CARRIAGES, WAG-
ONS AND CARTS
Cartwright, B. 1273

CARVING AND CARVINGS
African, wood 3663
Austral Islands 3692
Easter Island 3694
Hawaiian 3690
Indians of North America
2785--Eskimos 2676,
Ivory, walrus 2784, Ma-
hican, wood cup 2769,
Ohio, bone 2768, wood
2726
Maori, wood 3691
Mayan lintel 3715
Mexico, ancient, wood 3728
New Guinea designs 3682
scrimshaw 2525, 2529a
CASA DE ADOBE 2704
Casey, Clifford B. 3786
Caskel, W. 3527
Caskey, L.D. 3171, 3202
Caspary, Alfred and Mary,
Memorial 3462
CASS CO, NEBR, site 486
CASSATT, MARY 2269
CASSITE RULERS
documents from reign of
1173
letters to 1195
Cassou, J. 3060, 3104, 3112
CASTENADA, FRANCISCO DE
report on Mexican towns in
1580 899
CASTILE, ceramics 3348
sculpture 3343
CASTILLA, OLIVEROS DE
3336
CASTILLOS DE SAN MARCOS,
excavation 322
CASTLE WINDY MIDDEN, FLA
313
CASTS, latex 59
CATALUNA, ceramics 3348,
glass 3355
CATAWBA INDIANS
Hunting, trapping and fishing
458
Cater, H.D. 1522

CATLIN, GEORGE 2285, 2727
CATS IN ART 1886
CATTAIL BOAT 756
CATTAIL HOUSE 756
Catterall, L. F. 2687
CATTLE BRANDS 3984
CAUCASUS, anthropology 1045
CAVE HOLLOW, Ozark Bluff-
    Dweller site 350
CAVES (archeology)
    Bone Cave, Mo 488
    Copan caverns 869
    Gypsum Cave, Nev 737
    Hermit's Cave, N.M. 599
    Hueco area 594
    Iran 1251
    Jemez Cave, N.M. 580
    Lee Mill Cave 407
    Loltun Cave, Yucatan 922
    Mammoth Cave, Ky 360
    Moaning Cave 742
    Reserve Area, N.M. 640
    Shamshir Ghar, Afghanistan
        1070
    Shumla Cave, Texas 634,
        688
    Tangier 1108
    Upper Gila Area 594
    Val Verde Co, Texas 702
    Williams Cave 584
    Woodchuck Cave, Ariz 630
    Yucatan 872a
CAYAPO (CAYAPA) INDIANS
    835
CAYUGO CO, N.Y., 378
    Algonkian site 375
CELESTINA 3367
CELT, native copper, Ontario
    833
CEMETERIES See also Burial
    and Burial Mounds; Sep-
    ulchral Monuments;
    Tombs and Coffins
    Fang Shan, China 3420
    Giza 1228
    Hittite, Gourdion 1194
    Karanog 1235

Kish, Mesopotamia 1086-7
Kush, Sudan 3648
Old Birch Island cemetery,
    Ontario 826
Pachyammos, Crete 1024
Roman necropolis 1031
Ur 1200
CENOTE OF SACRIFICE, Yuca-
    tan 927
    jade 3756
    metals 952
Censorship of Art 1680, 4275
Ceramic International, exhibi-
    tion 2013
CERAMIC TECHNOLOGY,
    Tairona Culture 889
CERAMICS See also Pottery;
    and names of articles, as
    Amphorae; Bowls; Cups;
    Tiles; Urns; Vases
    American 2015, 2576-83,
        early 2552
    Babylonian 3615-6
    Bennington 2576
    Buen Retiro 3288
    Capodimonte 3288
    Chinese 1835, 3448-70, 4343,
        4349
    descriptive standards 207
    Doccia 3290
    Egyptian 3569-71
    English 3052, 3054, 4347,
        4350
    Etruscan 3175, 3177, 3248
    European 2015
    Fajalanza ware 3348
    German 3166
    Greek 3175-8, 3181, 3198-
        3221, 4348--black figure
        3201, 3211-3, 3219, red
        figure 3201, 3207-9, 3218
    instructions for making 4345
    Hispano-Moresque 3347
    Indians of North America
        2791-2816, 4344, 4352-4
    Japanese 3499-3500
    Korean 3510

316

Lustreware 3345
Majolica--Italian 3287,
   3289, Mexican 2716,
   Spanish-American 3346
Mayan 3759-60
Meissen 3166
Mexican--contemporary
   2917-9, Oaxaca black
   pottery 2916, Near East
   4351
New Jersey 2578-9
Old Blue china 3055
Oriental 3375, 3384
Palestine 3592-3
Pennsylvania 2577
Persian 3628
Pre-Columbian 3758-72
primitive 3640
Roman 3175-8, 3210, 3249-
   51
Spanish 3344-52
Talavera pottery 3348, 3351
terminology 2016
Tucker china 2583
Wedgwood 3056, 4350
Worcester porcelain 2582
catalogs--Aldrich, E.B.,
   Collection 1998, Arre-
   tine pottery 3248, Cleve-
   land Museum of Art 1709-
   10, sigillate pottery,
   Roman 3251
exhibitions--2017, Interna-
   tional 2016
CEREMONIAL BUNDLES See
   Charms
CEREMONIES See Rites and
   Ceremonies
Cervantes, M. de 1624
CEZANNE, PAUL 2592, 3068,
   3095-6
   sketchbook 3097
CHACO CANYON, N.M., site
   610; ruin 686--kivas
   4118
Chaet, B. 4159
CHAIRS, Chinese 4387, Con-

necticut 2645
Chait, R.M. 3464
CHAMA VALLEY, N.M., ar-
   cheology 678
CHAMPE, NEBR, site 487
CHAMPLAIN, SAMUEL DE
   3802
CHAMPLAIN, LAKE, map
   3910
CHANCAY-TYPE GRAVE,
   Peru 980
CHANCE HORIZON 377
CH'ANG-SHA, CHINA
   antiquities 3395
   costume 3443
CHANHU-DARO, archaeology
   1255
Channing, W. 1337
CHANTS See also Rites and
   Ceremonies; Songs
   Indians of North America
   1421, 1423, 1426, 1436,
   1438, 4149
   Navaho Indian night chant
   719
   Polynesian 1463
   Tuamotuan 4024
CHAPELS, Portuguese 4394,
   Sudan 3648
Chapin, H.M. 292, 3484-9,
   3882-3
Chapin, J. P. 52
Chapman, K.M. 2792
Chapman, S.E. 3648
Chappell, H.G. 1382
CHARLESTON
   architecture 2684, 2690
   memoir 3944
Charlot, J. 1274
CHARMS See also Incantations;
   Magic; Medicine-man;
   Rites and Ceremonies
   Costa Rica amulet 3729
   Indians of North America--
   Arapaho 571, Crow 574,
   Fox 428, hunting 260,
   Menominee 456, mystery

317

packs 269, Pawnee purification of sacred bundles 547, Zuni bear fetish 4106
CHARTS See Maps, Atlases and Charts
Chase, A.E. 1925
Chase, G.H. 3169, 3179, 3248
CHASE, WILLIAM MERRITT 2286
CHASE CO, NEBR, DISMAL RIVER ASPECT 484
CHASTA COSTA LANGUAGE 1491
CHAVIN DE HUANTAR, PERU, excavations 840
CHAVINA, PERU, Nazca burial 981
CH'EN MENG-CHA 3473
CHEMUNG VALLEY, N.Y., artifacts 424
CHERET, JULES 3064
CHEROKEE INDIANS, Tennessee 325
CHESTS--Hadley chest 2650
CHETHROKETL, N.M. 610
CHEVALIER, SULPICE GUILLAUME See Gavarni
Chew, S.C. 3057
CHEYENNE INDIANS
ceremonial organization 539
music 1662
Sun dance 539
CHIAPAS, MEXICO
archaeology 853, 876
Cholti Indians 1372
Indian uprising 985, 1867-70
monuments 948
Palenque 908
Zoque Indians 3738
CHICAGO
guidebook 3954
history 3951
Indians 333
Lincoln in 3959
politics and government 3957
theatre, Swedish 1642
views 3958, 3960

Chicago Academy of Sciences 85
Chicago Historical Society
guide 87
history 86
Chicago Natural History Museum
bronzes 2072
colorama 88
guide 89
history 91
Japanese Collections 90
CHICHE, GUATEMALA, collection 939
CHICHEN ITZA 871
Cenote of Sacrifice 927, 952, 3756
Cheira, E. 1169-70, 1507-9
CHIGGERVILLE, Ky, site 293
CHIGNECTO, CANADA 3820
CHILAM BALAM OF CHUMAYEL, BOOK OF 1571, 1578, 1586
CHILE
archaeology 842
art, contemporary 2911
CHILDREN art of 4166
Hawaii, growth 1397
in art 1836, 1876
Children's Book Show 2629
CHILKAT INDIANS
dwellings 790, whale house 789
kinship 790
screens 790
social life and customs 798
totem poles 790
Chillada, Eduardo 1986
CHILTON, KY, site 294
CHINA See also Art, Chinese
anthropology and archaeology 1055, 1058, 1062-5
man, early 1400, 1403
musical instruments, ancient 1675
religion, Shantung 1062
sculpture 3427
Chinautla 4130

318

Chinchilla, C.S. 3703
CH'ING MING SHANG HO
3400-1
CHINOOK JARGON, hymns
1665
CHIPEWYAN INDIANS
Eskimo relations with 812
language and literature 1561
tales 1418
CHIPPENDALE FURNITURE
2641
CHIPPEWA INDIANS 295
canoe, birchbark 434
dance, dream 444
health and hygiene 454
Northern Saulteaux 828
Plains-Cree--cults, politi-
cal organization, rites
and ceremonies 567
CHITIMACHA INDIANS
basketry 2868
CHITTENDON CO, VT, map
3900
CHOCOLA, GUATEMALA, ex-
cavations 847
CHOIR BOOKS, Spanish 3368
CHOLTI (CHOL) INDIANS
anthropometry 1372
CHORETEGANS See Mangue
Indians
CHORIS, LOUIS 1274
CHOU DYNASTY arts 3392
CHOW WEN WU 3414
CHRIST See Jesus Christ
Christensen, E.O. 2955, 3456
CHRISTIAN ART AND SYM-
BOLISM See also Art,
Medieval; Art, Renais-
sance, Bible; Jesus
Christ
designs for 1996, Eastern
Orthodox 4277
Egypt 3543, 3545
illuminated manuscripts
2107
in industry 1997
prints 1968

Spanish Colonial art 2115
catalog--Wadsworth Athen-
eum 2968
CHRISTIANITY AND PAGAN-
ISM See also Santos
Mayas 4032
Penitentes 4027, 4029-30
CHRISTMAS IN ART 1887
CHRONOLOGY See also Calen-
dars; Dating (Archaeolog-
ical)
Babylonian 1596--Dynasty of
Agade 1191, kings reign-
ing 3500-3000 B.C. 1192
Florida 359
Mayas 966, 991, 1577, 1582
--correlation with Chris-
tian calendar 964, 983,
986, 989, 996, hiero-
glyphic stairway, Copan
962, reduction of dates
995, Tikal stelae 993
Northwest Indians, string
records 797
Peru--calendar interpreta-
tion 988, cultural chron-
ology 943
Zuni Indian ruins 705
Chrysler, Walter P., collec-
tion 2959, 2999
Chrysler Corporation 2391
CHUCUITO, PERU, Aymara
Indians 997
CHUKCHI (CHUCKCHEE)
religion 1037
social life and customs 1038
CHULTUNES OF LABNA 921
CHURCHES See also Altar-
pieces and Altars; Chap-
els; Shrines
American church silver
2605, 2607
Charleston 2296, 2684
England, 16th century 4031
Nubia 3579
Quaker meeting house 2683,
2693-4

Spanish chapels 2717
Churchward, S. 1513
CIBOLA, SEVEN CITIES OF
3963
Hawikuh, N.M., one of so-
called cities 619
Cid 1625
Cincinnati and Vicinity Artists,
annual 2354
Cincinnati Art Museum
guide 1706
Lehman Collection 1707
Near and Far Eastern
Galleries 3372
CINTLAPA, MEXICO, arche-
ology 876
CIRCULATION
New York City, native and
foreign-born 1345
CITIES AND TOWNS, planning
2701
Ciudad Rodrigo Retablo 4211
CIVIL WAR See United States
--History--Civil War
CIVILIZATION, Rise of (chart)
4073
Claflin, W.H. 296
CLANS AND CLAN SYSTEM
See Kinship
Clark, E.W., Collection 1300,
1309
CLARK, HORACE 2416
Clark, Stephen C., Collection
2163
Clark, W.A., Collection 2990,
3287
Clarke, G.F. 3792
Clarke, S.A. 746
CLARKE COUNTY, sites 4121
CLASS DISTINCTION, Latin
America 4116
CLASSICAL ANTIQUITIES See
also Art, Mediteranean
Area
catalogs--Museum of Fine
Arts, Boston 3169, Uni-
versity Museum 3170,

Walters Art Gallery 3172
CLASSICISM
Greek tradition 3180
in contemporary art 3167
CLASSICISM, ABSTRACT 2372
Clausen, R. 4284b
Clawson, H.P. 80
Clay, A.T. 1160, 1171-6,
1180, 3601, 3615
CLAY, HENRY 3850
CLAY CO, FLA, mounds 351
CLAY TABLETS See Tablets
and Cylinders
CLEANING
rugs and carpets 2048
textiles--cotton 2053, old
and fragile 2051, Tiraz
3537
Cleghorn, J.C. 758
CLEMENS, SAMUEL L. 1523
Clements, F.E. 470
Cleopatra's Barge (ship) 4170
"CLEOPATRA'S NEEDLE"
2699
CLEVELAND
nature trails 53
Cleveland Health Museum 4017
Cleveland Museum of Art
contemporary art 1712
Degas works 3101
Dutch drawings 3015
Education Department 42
Egyptian Collection 3544
handbook 1711
paintings 1708
Prentiss Bequest 1709
Severance Bequest 1710
Severance Collection of
Arms and Armor 2077
CLIFF CITIES NATIONAL
PARK, proposed 618
Clifford, H. 1788, 2924, 3322,
4248
CLIMATE, INFLUENCE OF
See Man, Climate Influ-
ence
CLOAKS, Patagonia 3742

320

CLOCKS AND WATCHES
2084-7
catalogs--Heinz Collection
2084, Strause Collection
2085
THE CLOISTERS 2969
Nine Heroes tapestry 3021
Unicorn tapestry 3149
CLOTHING See Costume and
Adornment
CLOUDS
Indian rain cloud myth 1408
CLOUET, JEAN 3129
CLOVIS, N.M., archeology
700
CLOWES, G.A., MEMORIAL
4185
COHOMO CO, MISS, mounds
364
COAL
prehistoric Arizona mine
689
Coburn, F.W. 2257, 2310
COCLE, PANAMA
archeology 882
figurines 3714
COCHISE, N.M., sites 641
COCKBURN, JAMES PATTI-
SON 2138
CODE
of Lipit-Ishtar 1618
oldest written 1617
CODEXES See also Books and
Book Arts
Dresden Codex 1575, 1582
Florentine Codex 1568, 1583
Hall 1573
Mayan--animal figures in
1588, astronomy 999
Nuttall 1572
Perez 1576
Coe, W.R. 848, 4123
Coffin, E.F. 520
COINS AND MEDALS See also
Money 4372
American coins, curiosities
of 2091

ancient coins 2088
French medals 2186
Greek coins 3222, 4378
Newark medals 2610
Oriental coins 3380
Renaissance 2975, Roman
4378
Spanish 3364-6
catalogs--Emilio Collection
of Military Buttons 2089,
Knox Collection of Money
2090
COLBERT CO, ALA, Little
Bear Creek site 415b
COLCHESTER REEF LIGHT-
HOUSE 2553
Cole, F.C. 1112, 1275-6,
1308, 1320-1
COLE, THOMAS 2287
Coleman, L.V. 13-15, 64
Colgate, W. 2144
COLLAGE
Barnhart, R. 2533
COLLEGE AND UNIVERSITY
MUSEUMS 14
Collie, G.L. 1003
Collier, D. 849, 943, 4233
Collocott, E.E.V. 1458
COLONIAL WILLIAMSBURG
See Williamsburg
COLONIALISM
Africa, policies in 1119
COLOR 4167
Indians of North America,
art 2721
influence of 1679, 1993
use in textiles 4362
COLOR PRINTS, JAPANESE
3489, 3492-4
contemporary 3487, 4307
primitives 3488
Spaulding Collection 3480
catalogs and exhibits--
Buckingham Collection
3488, Morse Collection
3490, Phillips Collection
3491, Yale Collection
1964

COLORADO
archaeology--Ackmen-Lowry area 499, Basket Maker sites 500, culture change 505, Uncapahagre Plateau 518
history 3989
Indians 490--Cannonball Ruins 649, Denver 493, Lo Daiska site 493
map, historic 3993
Spanish language in 1504
COLORADO INDIANS (Ecuador) 935
Colorado State Museum, guidebook 93
Colt Memorial, Wadsworth Atheneum 172
Colton, H.S. 200-1, 592-3, 2793-5, 2807, 4344, 4352, 4354
COLUMBIA
archaeology--Santa Marta 889, Tairona culture 889
Indians--San Agustin 936, Tierradentro Reservation 936
COLUMBIA CO, GA, Stalling's Island mound 296
COLUMBUS, CHRISTOPHER, letters 4006
COLUMNS See also Capitals
temple, China 4322, India 3587
Comer, G. 801
Comfort, C. 2127
Commager, H.S. 2174-5
COMMEDIA DE LL' ARTE
influence on arts 1878
COMMERCE AND TRADE
Arapesh 1330
Babylonian documents 1166-75, 1177
design and printing for 263
New Guinea 1335
Tinguianes 1320

Committee on Art Education 40
COMPOSERS, biography 1650
CONDYLO-DIAPHYSIAL ANGLES
Alabama Indians 1363
Cone Collection 1700
CONEBO POTTERY 3761
CONESTOGA WAGON 2653
Confederate Museum 4405
CONFORMITY 1680
CONNECTICUT
names, geographical 1492
painting 2402
Connecticut Historical Society 2645
Conrad, J. 2630
CONSERVATION OF RE-SOURCES, teaching 61
CONSTABLE, G.W. 1889
Constantine, M. 4326
CONSTANTINOPLE, walls of 3522
CONSTRUCTIONS IN SPACE 1979
Contemporary Annual painting, Corcoran Biennial 2368
CONTRACTS
Babylonian 1170
CONVERSATION
hieroglyphic record 1620
CONVERSATION PIECES
English, 18th century 3029
Cook, Lt. James 850
Cook, W.W.S. 4315
Cook Collection 1856
COOK COUNTY, ILL
history 3962
Indians 333
COOK INLET
Eskimo carvings 2767
COOK ISLANDS
physical anthropology 1396
Cooke, E. 53
Cooke, H.L. 3078, 4247
COOKERY See also Food
Williamsburg 3846

Coomaraswamy, A.K. 1589, 3582

Coon, C.S. 1040, 1056, 1098, 1116, 1251, 3666

Cooney, J.D. 3542-3

Cooper, C. 486-7

COOPER, JAMES FENIMORE 1521

Cooperstown 133, 3885

Cooper, L. 297a, 4084

Cooper, L.R. 297

Cooper, P. 471

Cooper, W. 3885

Cooper Union Museum 1713-4, drawings 4295

engravings and etchings 1952-5

textiles 2032-3, Hispano Islamic 2538

COOPERSTOWN 153, 2646-7, 3885, 4333

Co-ordinator of Inter-American Affairs 875, 905, 930, 1376

COPAN, HONDURAS
caverns of 869
hieroglyphic stairway 1579, dates 962
ruins 954

COPLEY, JOHN SINGLETON 2189
paintings, pastels, miniatures, drawings 2228
portraits, American 2229

COPPER AND COPPERSMITHING
Indians of Mexico, Central and South America-- Guatemala 854, Peru 3752
Indians of North America 225--Eskimos 809, 814, Ontario celt 833, prehistoric implements 264

COPPER AGE
Russia 1046

COPPER ESKIMOS See Eskimos

COPTIC EGYPT 3545

COPYRIGHT LAW, Canadian 3816

CORA INDIANS
Nayarit, directed culture change in 971

CORBIT HOUSE 2692

Corbitt, D.L. 2253, 3927

Corcoran Gallery of Art 1715
American paintings 2176
American prints 2489
Artists of Washington, annual 2356
Biennial of American oil painting 2368
Clark Collection of Dutch and Flemish paintings 2990

CORDILLERAN CULTURE 4081

Cordry, D.M. 3737-8

CORINTH, amphora 3203

CORINTH, LOUIS 2288, 2502

CORMORANT, domestication in China and Japan 1058

CORNER, THOMAS C. 2212

CORNETA, bits from 3223

Corning Glass Center 94

Corning Museum of Glass 94, 1716

COROT, JEAN BAPTISTS CAMILLE 3068, 3077, 3098

Correa, G. 968, 1646, 4023

Cortelyou, I.F. 4180

Cortissoz, R. 2275

Cosgrove, C.B. 594-5

COSTA RICA
archaeology, Diquis Delta 951
Indians--Boruca 917, Bribri 913, image and charm 3729, stone work 3713b, 3731, Talamanca 918

COSTUME AND ADORNMENT
See also Face Painting; Tattooing and Body Marking; and names of cos-

tume articles, as Belts;
Boots and Shoes; Gar-
ters; Hats; Jewelry
American 2598-2604, Co-
lonial 2601
Aztecs 3737
Benin 3655
bridal gowns 2598
California jackets 2599
Chinese 3443-5, 4361
Egyptian 1221
French 3148
history 2064, 2600
Indians of North America
2840-51
Japanese 3501-2
Papua skull decoration 1322
Paracas 3745
Peruvian 3772
Spanish 3356-7, 3361
Zoque Indians 3738
catalogs--McCormick Col-
lection 2066, Wadsworth
Atheneum 2065
COSTUME DESIGN, theater
1634
Cott, P. 2975
COTTON
American, historic scenes
2591
Pueblo Indian 2821
textile cleaning 2821
Coulson, T. 102
COUNCIL OF THE INDIES,
official reports to 899
COUNTERPANES See Quilts
and coverlets
"Country Style" 2177
COURBET, GUSTAVE 3073,
4248
COVERED BRIDGES, Vermont
3918, 3922
COVERED WAGONS See Car-
riages, Wagons and
Carts
Cowdrey, B. 1758, 2292
Cox, D.H. 1012

Cox, E.M. 2352
Cox, J. 2289
Cox, J.H. 3395
Coxe, E.B., Expeditions
1206, 1209, 1212, 1219-
20
COYOTE myth and chant 1411,
1436
CRABLE, ILL, site 399
CRADLES, Indians of North
America 254, 258, 2729
CRAFTS See Decorative Arts;
Handicrafts
Cranbrook Institute of Science
guide 95
history 96
CRANBROOK LAKE, vegeta-
tion 286
Crane, H. 1524
CRANIOLOGY See also Man,
Prehistoric
Ambryn Island 1384
American 1367
Andamese 1401
artificial deformities 1341,
1343
Boscop skull 1398
California, San Miguel Is-
land 1358
Ecuador 1377
Europe, central 1381
Gazelle Peninsula 1389
Hawaii 1382
Indians of North America
1369
Michigan perforated crania
1353
Negrite 1401
New Guinea 1385
New Jersey, Trenton, and
antiquity of man 1352
Nippur 1402
North Pacific Coast 1357
Papuan decoration of skull
1322
Punin calvarium 1377
Tibetan use of skull 1060

CRANIOMETRY 1346
Crawford, M. 2034, 2602
CRAWFORD, RALSTON 2369, 2417
CRAWFORD, THOMAS 2193
CREATION MYTH
Babylonian 1455
Navaho 1435, 1437, 4146, 4149
Creative Projects 36
CREE INDIANS 365
Eastern Cree 828
Plains-Cree 498--cults 567
CREEK INDIANS
songs 1668
CREMATION See also Burial and Burial Mounds; Mortuary Customs
Indians of North America, ceremonies 760
CRESPI, GIUSEPPE MARIA 3268
Cresson, H.T. 423
CRETE
archaeology 1013
Bronze age 3182
Pachyammos cemetery 1024
Sphoungoras 1019
Vrokastro 1020
CRICKETS, China, champions 1063
CRIGLER MOUNDS, KY 298
Critics' Choice of American Painting 2370
CRITTENDEN CO, KY, Tolu site 410
Crocker, E.B., Art Gallery 1717,
Oriental arts 4099
Crosby, Bob, Collection 1799
Cross, D. 299-300
CROSSES 4328
CROSSES, Racial
Maya-Spanish, Yucatan 998
CROW INDIANS 529
art 2741
beadwork 2892

dance, Sun 558
folk literature and folk lore 566, 1419
material culture 528
medicine bundle 574
religion 554
rites and ceremonies 551
social life and customs 552
societies 556--tobacco 560
Crowninshield, Frances B., Gallery 4170
Crowninshield, George 4170
Crystal Palace, exhibition catalog 1840
CUAHTITLAN pottery 2918
CUAUHTEMOC, Aztec ruler of Mexico
official announcements of 1498
CUBA
Indians 851--Pre-Columbian 872
CUCURBIT MATERIALS, Peru 960
CULTS, Indians of North America 567
Culin, S. 202, 268, 472, 851, 1995
Cullimore, C. 2705
CULTURE AND CULTURES
See also Acculturation; and specific areas and tribes, as New World; America; Incas
and agriculture 198
Andean, history of 841
Delaware Indians 362
Ghegs 1049, Iroquois 4120
Kapingamarangi 1306
Koryaks 1048
method of study 203
Mexico 897--Bajio, integration 895
Middle America 895
Mohave 703
Navaho 646
Pacific Area 1299, 4141

Pre-Columbian 844, 4122
San Carlos, security 972,
    Siberia 4132
U.S., Indian culture areas
    231, map of North
    America 250
Yukaghir 1051
CULTURE CHANGE AND
    TRANSITION
    Ackmen-Lowry Area 505,
        Algeria 4137
    Auracanian Indians 926
    Cora Indians, directed
        change 971
    Guatemala 961
    Mexico 987, Palau 4140
    Viru Valley, Peru, 943
Cummings, C.E. 3851, 4014-
    5
Cummings, V.L. 2978
Cummings Collection 3700
Cummins, H. 1370-1
Cumrine, B. 3885a, 3928-9
CUNEIFORM WRITING See
    listings under Assyria-
    Babylonia
Cunningham, C.C. 1884, 1928,
    1930, 1941-2, 2063,
    2389, 2396, 2402, 2445,
    2998, 3064, 3084, 3490,
    4183, 4189
Cunningham, W.M. 301
CUPS
    "Foundry Painter" 3204
    Inca, wooden 3720
    ivory 3670
    ostrich egg-shell 3524
    Islamic 3531
Curtin, J. 4143
Curtin, L.S.M. 1479
Curtis, F.S. 2082
Curtis, W.E. 4006
Cushing, F.H. 683
CUSTER COUNTY, sites 4080,
    4088
CUTLER, CHARLES 2369
Cutler, F.S. 1349

Cutting, E.E. 1405
Cutting, Mrs. C. Suydam,
    Collection 1903
CUZCO, PERU
    archaeology 905
    golden breastplate 3757
CYLINDER SEALS See Seals
CYLINDERS See Tablets and
    Cylinders
CYPRUS
    archaeology 1014
    earrings 3225
    head, archaic 3189--lime-
        stone 4320
    Kourion figurines 3197
CYPRESS CREEK VILLAGES,
    KY 302
Czechoslovakian Expedition
    1041, 1044

D

DAHOMEYANS, songs 1674
Daifuku, H. 596
Dailey, G. 2667
DAKOTA INDIANS 507
    bark houses 2898
    Canadian Dakota 831
    dance societies 549
    medicine ceremony 274
    shield 533
Dale, Chester, Collection 3081
Dam, C.H. 3575
DAMASCENING 3575
DAMGHAN, archaeology 1262
D'Amico, V. 4357
Dana, J.C. 16-7, 37, 2178
    about 24, 4383
DANCES AND DANCING See
    also Rites and Cere-
    monies; and names of
    specific dances, as Devil
    Dance, Dream Dance,
    Sun Dance
    Eskimos 820; Indians of
        North America 272--
    societies 276, 544, 549-50,
        576

326

Daniel, J.F. 1015
Daniels, M.H. 2111
Danson, E.B. 597
DARIUS II, business docu-
    ments from reign of
    1171-2
DARTS
  Stefansson Collection 265
  with Bison Occidentalis 519
DATING (ARCHAEOLOGICAL)
  Radiocarbon--Middle and
    South America 938,
    Santa Rosa Island, Calif
    743, 4100
  Tree rings 209--Jemez
    Pueblo, N.M. 660, pre-
    history, N.M. 610
DATSOLALEE INDIANS,
    basket 2877
DAUBIGNY, CHARLES
    FRANCOIS 3132
DAUMIER, HONORE 3064,
    3099, 3100
Davenport, J.W. 684
DAVID, JACQUES LOUIS 3073,
    drawings 4303
Davidson, B. 2500
Davidson, D.S. 303, 795,
    2722
Davidson, Marshall B. 2339,
    2584
Davidson, W. 3793
Davidson, W.H. 3793
Davies, N. de G. 3576
Davis, C.G. 2569
Davis, E.H. 711, 759-60
DAVIS, LEW 4186
DAVIS, STUART 2418
Dawson, G.E. 1525
Dawson, H. 1379
Day, C.B. 3852
Dearstyne, H. 2698
DEATH See also Mortuary
    Customs
  African pageant 1094
  Dieguenos ceremony of
    death images 759

D'EBNETH, LAJOS 3296
de Booy, T. 944
DECAPOLIS, City of, excava-
    tions 1092
DECATUR HOUSE 2664
DECORATIVE ARTS See also
    Ceramics; Costume and
    Adornment; Gems; Glass;
    Ivory; Leather; Metal
    Work; Tapestry; Tex-
    tiles; Toys, Dolls,
    Ships; etc.
  Amazon area 3701
  American 1992, 2546-60
  Amur tribes 3387a
  contemporary 2001
  Crete, Bronze Age 3182
  English, 1800-1830 3044
  European 1992, 2976--
    Thorne Rooms 2988-9
  Gothic 2987
  Indians of North America
    2723, 2734
  Italian--contemporary 3285,
    renaissance 3284
  medieval 2962
  New Guinea 3682-3
  New Jersey 2557
  origin of 1995
  Shaker 2554
  catalogs--Aldrich Collection
    1998, Denver Art Mu-
    seum European decora-
    tive arts 2933, Lehman
    Collection 1707
De Cou, H.F. 3227
De Coursey, F. 1023
DECOYS, Shelburne Museum
    2549
de Fiedmont, 3834
DEFORMITIES AND PATHOL-
    OGY
  digital 1339
  dwarf skeletons, Moundville
    1364
  skulls--artificial deformity
    1341, 1343, perforated
    1353

teeth 1350
DEGAS, EDGAR 3064, 3068,
3101-2
DeJarnette, D. L. 415a-c, 598
DELACROIX, EUGENE 3083
de Laguna, F. 786, 803-4,
815, 1718, 2766-7
DELAWARE
archaeology--Pile-struc-
tures, Claymont 423
map, pictorial 3920
portraits 1718, in Dela-
ware 1938
DELAWARE INDIANS 4098
bear ceremony 459, carved
bone 4240
culture and acculturation
362
folk lore 460
Lenape masks 2781
medicine practice 460
social life and customs 449
Delestre, G. 4248
Delaware State Portrait Com-
mission 1718
DELAWARE VALLEY, archae-
ology 414
DEMOCRACY AND ART 1680
DEMOGRAPHY See also
Population
Easter Island 1277
DENDEREH, archaeology 1212
DENDROCHRONOLOGY
archaeological dating 209,
610, 660
Denmark, L. P. 3927
Densmore, F. 304, 521, 1662-4
DENTITION See Teeth
DENVER, COLO, Lo Daiska
site 493
Denver Art Museum
American Indian art 2723
costume, history 2600
Egyptian, Greek and Roman
art 3168
European art 2933
French painting, 19th cen-
tury 3065

Kress Collection 2934
Kwan Yin 3374
Oriental catalog 3373
de Peyster, J.W. 128
DERBY, ELIAS HASKET,
MANSION 2673
DERMATOGLYPHICS
Indians of Mexico and Cen-
tral America 1371, 1374-5
DESERTS See names, as
Arabian Desert; Palm
Springs; Sahara Desert
DESIGN 1687, 2003, American
4324-5
Batik 3689,
California, Southern 4327
Canadian 2632
commercial 2631, 2634
Germany 4329
Greek vases 3203, 3220
human body and 2005
Indian art areas 2724
language of 2007
modern 2004, 2006
New Guinea 3682-3
U.S., 20th century 2555-6
Design for Christmas,
annual 1996
Design in industry 1997
DES BARRES, JOSEPH FRED-
ERICK WALLET 3827
Deserontyon, J. 446
DETROIT
French settlement 3881
museums 67
Detroit Collections 1855
Detroit Historical Museum,
guidebook 97
Detroit Institute of Arts
architecture of 2662
arms and armor, Hearst
Collection 2078
guide 1721
painting 1720, 20th century
1723
Whitcomb Bequest 1722
Deuel, T. 203, 473-5, 537,
753

328

Devereux, G. 761
DEVIL DANCE 968, Apache 713
DEVIL'S PICTURES (playing cards) 3776
DeVos, G. 4137
Devree, C. 4187
De Vries, R.W.P. 2335
Dewdney, S. 2725
DEWEY, GEORGE 2244
Dewey, J. 1681
DEWITT, M.L. 4188
de Young, M.H., Memorial Museum
  handbook 1719
  Kress Collection 2936
THE DIAL 1841
Dial Collection 1841
Dibble, C.E. 1568, 1573
DICKINSON, ANSON 2290
Dickson, H.E. 2306, 2666
DICTAEAN CAVE, bronze blade 3255
DIEGUENO INDIANS
  cremation ceremonies 760
  death images 759
DIGITAL MALFORMATION, inheritance of 1339
Dikaios, P. 1015-6
Dimand, M.S. 3378, 3631
Dimick, M.T. 1207
DIOCLETIAN, Age of 3226
DIONYSIA, sarcophogi 1084
DIONYSUS 3239
DIORAMAS See also Exhibits
  cigar-box 57
DIQUIS DELTA, COSTA RICA, archaeology 951
DIRECTORIES
  aquariums 65
  arboretums 70
  botanical gardens 65, 70, New York City 68
  historic houses, New York City 68
  historical societies, Michigan 3889

museums--American Association of museums
  members 63, Detroit 67, Michigan 66, New York 69, New York City 68, South America 64, U.S. and Canada 4033
  zoological parks 65, New York City 68
DIRT-EATING 196
Disbrow, Dr. William S., Collection 1845
DISCOVERIES (in geography) See Explorations and Discoveries
Diskul, M.C.S. 4270
DISMAL RIVER ASPECT, NEBR 484
Dittert, A.E. 4085
Dixon, K.A. 685
Dixon, R.B. 214, 733, 1413
DOCCIA PORCELAIN 3290
Dockstader, F.J. 219, 4234
DOCUMENTS See Assyria-Babylonia; Council of the Indies; Tablets and Cylinders
Dodge, E.S. 427
DOGON (African tribe), sculpture 3664
DOGS
  Chinese tomb doors 3478
  Hidatsa culture 575
Dohan, E.H. 3189-90
DOLL HOUSE, Colleen Moore's 2092
DOLLS See also Katcinas
  American 2093
  European 2093
  French fashion 3148
  Greek jointed 1022
  Indians of North America 2893-5
  Oriental 3381
  paper 2094, 4335
d'Olwer, L.N. 1574
DOMESTIC ANIMALS See

names of animals, as
Cormorants; Crickets;
Dogs; Horses; Pigs
Dominican Astrophysical Ob-
servatory 98
Dominick, Bayard, Expedition
1296
DON QUIXOTE, illustrations
3334
DOORS
Chinese tomb 3478
English 3058
DOOR-SOCKET, Egyptian 3577
DORCHESTER, NEW BRUNS-
WICK 3806
DORFLINGER, CHRISTIAN,
GLASS WORKS 2586
Dorman, C.G. 4388
Dorsey, G.A. 522, 538-43,
712, 787, 852, 1322
Dotremont, Philippe, Collec-
tion, Brussels 1921
Douglass, J.M. 305
Douglas, R. 3971
DOUGLAS, STEPHEN ARNOLD
Lincoln-Douglas debates
1518
DOUGLAS CO, NEBR, Champe
site 487
DOVE, ARTHUR G. 2419
Dows, O. 4231
Dowty, J. 4041
DRAGON, TRIAL OF THE
GOLDEN 1417
DRAGONS, 4159, Chinese
3396
Dragoo, D.W. 306, 4114
DRAKE MOUND, KY 358
Drapkin, I. 1277
DRAWING See also names of
individual artists, as
Blake, W.; Daumier, H.;
Durer, A.; Gainsborough,
T.; Marino, M.; Modi-
gliani, A.; Rubens, P.;
Seurat, G.; Toulouse-
Lautrec

1958, 1967, 1986, 4285-
4310
American 2350, 2485-2511,
4285, 18th century 2259,
history 2494, 2496-7
Austrian 3161
botanical 1875
California 2488
contemporary 1951
Dutch 3015-6, 4306
English 3031, 3043, 3057,
4293
European 1835, 4294
French 3128-9, 4265, 4301,
4303, 4308, 4317
German 3162-4, Indian 4291
Italian 3260, 3278, 4292,
4298-9, 4309-10 for jew-
elry 3286
Lombardy 3277
Mississippi and Missouri
Rivers 1885
New England 2186,
19th century 4302
Pierpont Morgan Library
2986
Wisconsin 2491
catalogs--Allyn Museum
4040, Baer Collection
1956, Cooper Union Mu-
seum 1955, Cutting Col-
lection 1903, Freer Gal-
lery of Art 1730, Gard-
ner Museum 1734, Hall
Collection 1960, Jones
Collection 1817, Lehman
Collection 1707, Museum
of Fine Arts, Boston,
water color 1752, Price
Collection 1970, Pulitzer
Collection, modern 1728,
Rewald Collection 1898,
Wellesley College, Euro-
pean and American 1825,
Whitney Annual 4323,
Yale Collection, 20th century and American 1964

DREAMS, Babylonian tablet interpreting 1186
Dreier, K.S. 1827
Dreier, Katherine S., Collection 1849
DRESDEN CODEX 1575, 1582
Drexler, A. 4326, 4389
Dreyfus Collection 2975
Drucker, P. 766, 853
DRUGSTORE, Nippur 1162
DRUGS See also names of drugs, as Peyote; Tobacco
African plants 1099
DRUM, Pueblo, Apache, Navaho 4152, Voodoo 1671
DRYOPITHECUS 1378
DUCHAMP, GASTON See Villon, Jacques
DUCHAMP, MARCEL 1827, 3087, 3103
DUCHAMP-VILLON, RAYMOND 3087
"DUCK POTS" 3758
Dudley, D.H. 18, 2610
DUFY, RAOUL 3104
DUGOUTS, Eskimo 815
Dumbarton Oaks Research Library and Collection, handbook 3517, Greek and Roman antiquities 4262
DUMUZI (Sumerian God) 1615
Dunham, D. 3258, 3549, 3648-9
Dunlap, W. 2291
Dunn, J.T. 226, 1383
Dunton, W.R. 2543
DUPAGE CO, ILL, Indians 333
Dupertuis, C.W. 1379
du Pont, Henry Francis, Winterthur Museum, accessions in 1960 4204
garden guide 1724
silver, American 2614
Dupree, L.B. 1070
DURA-EUROPOS, excavations 1091

Durant, J. and A. 2646
DURER, ALBRECHT 3165
DURRIE, GEORGE HENRY 2292
Dustin, 425
DUTCH GUIANA, pottery 3767
DUTCH HOLLOW, N.Y. 3894
DUTCH NEW GUINEA See New Guinea
Dutton, B.P. 615, 686, 854, 2226, 2797
DUVAL CO, FLA, mounds 351
DUVENECK, FRANK 2293
DWAMISH INDIANS, spirit boat 787
DWARVES
African art 3650
Indians of North America, skeletons 1364
DWELLINGS See also Architecture, Domestic; Shelters; Indians of North America
Roman 3256
Tuamotus 1313
DYES AND DYEING Fabric 4362, Indians of North America, art 2721, vegetable dyes 2820
Navaho Indians 2831
New York early fabrics 2594
Dymond, J.R. 152
DYNAMIC SYMMETRY 3202
DYNATION 2371
Dyson, R.H. 1071-2

E
EAGLE MYTHS 4144
EAGLE TRAPPINGS, Hidatsa Indian 534
EARL, RALPH 2230
EARLY CHRISTIAN ART 2960, 3518
EARLY CHRISTIAN CAPITALS 2962

331

EARRINGS, Cyprus 3225
EARTH LODGES, Hidatsa Indian 535
EARTHWORKS See also Fortifications; Mound Builders
Indian, Michigan 425
Mount Horeh, Kentucky 358
East India Marine Society Museum 142-3
EASTER, celebration 4101, 4147-8
EASTER ISLAND
carving 3694
demography 1277
EASTERN DAKOTA INDIANS See Dakota Indians
EASTERN ORTH ODOX CHURCH, icons 4277
EASTERN WOODLANDS CULTURE AREA 279-465
burial cult 453
iconology 2756
quillwork 2884
wampum 2841, belt 2842-3
Eastman, A.C. 4291
EASTMAN, SETH 4201
Ecke, G. 4271, 4346
ECLIPSES, Maya calendar 964
ECOLOGY
Pueblo 672
ECUADOR
archaeology--La Plata Island 867, Manabi 956, Southern area 849
craniology 1377
gold 3748
Indians--Cayapo 835, Colorado 935, Meso America and 844, Pre-Columbian culture connections 4122
rugs 3740
EDEN VALLEY, WYO, sites 501
Finley site 531

Eddy, Arthur Jerome, Collection 1695
Eddy, O.T. 2262, 2294
EDGED WEAPONS See also AXES, etc. 188
Edgell, G.H. 2252, 3077
Edmonson, M.S. 855, 4124-5
EDUCATION See also Museum Instruction
art 40, 43, art and 1681
Buffalo Society of Natural History 81
Cleveland Museum of Art 42
conservation 61
cooperation, Guatemala and U.S. 974
emotions in 4016
science museum 62, children 56
Sumerian scribe, of 1599
University Museum 166
Edward, G.R. 1032
EEL, electric, myth 1442
Eells, M. 1665
EFFIGY MOUND CULTURE, Wisconsin 390
EFFIGY PIPES See Pipes
EGYPT See also Art, Egyptian
archaeology 1201-35, 4134
history--Napoleon's time 1224, reading lists 1221
life in ancient 3553-4
EGYPTIAN LANGUAGE AND LITERATURE
conversation and calls on tomb walls 1620
hieroglyphics 1221
Middle Kingdom papyrus 1620
Ehrich, R.W. 307
Eifert, V.S. 476
THE EIGHT 2254
EIGHTEENTH CENTURY, English--ceramics 4347, --life 3024, Indian drawings

4291 intellectual cur-
rents 2925, Italian draw-
ings 4292, landscape
painting, English and
Italian 2937
painting, British 3027,
conversation pieces 3029
Einstein, L. 3079, 3263
Ekholm, G.F. 856-7, 4284a
EL ACEBUCHAL, ceramics
3350
EL GRECO (Domenico Theo-
tocopuli) 2952, 3266,
3314-5
El Paso Natural Gas Com-
pany Projects
pipeline archaeology 679
EL RITO DE LOS FRIJOLES,
N M, excavations 611
EL SALVADOR See Salvador
Elam, C.H. 145, 2672
ELDER, JOHN ADAMS 2295
ELEGANCE, AGE OF 2925
ELEPHANTS, mounting ex-
hibit of 54
Eliot, H.W. 1073
Eliot, T.G. 1073
ELIZABETH I, QUEEN OF
ENGLAND 4412
England in time of 3038,
anti-English propaganda
in Spain 3369
Ellis, B.T. 669
Ellsworth, C. 189
Ellis, D.M. 1521
ELMIRA, N.Y., Mark Twain
in 1523
Elmore, F.H. 687
Elmslie, George Grant 2682
EMBROIDERY
English 3046
Paracas 3745
Pueblo Indian 2827
samplers 2557
techniques 2050
catalogs--Hispanic Society
of America 2039

EMBRY, MORRIS 2420
Emerick, D. 2784
Emerson, A. 3191
Emerson, F.G. 1353
Emery, I. 2036-7
Emilio Collection 2089
Emmons, G.T. 788-9
Emory, K.P. 1279-81, 1310-
3, 1323, 4024
ENAMELS, Limoges 3145
ENGLAND See also Art, English
church, 16th century 4031
colonists--in Acadia 3824,
in America 3867
costume and adornment,
age of Shakespeare 3045
decorative arts 3044
18th century life 3024,
Elizabethan government
4413, --life 3038
music, Elizabethan 1673
propaganda against in Spain
3369,
travel 4408
Tudor--schools 4011, uni-
versities 4012
ENGLISH LANGUAGE, Bible in
1553
ENGRAVINGS See also Carv-
ings; and names of
graphic arts techniques,
as Etchings; Wood Cuts
and Wood Engravings
American--early 2496, 18th
century 2259
catalogs--Cooper Collection
1952, Hearn Collection
1953
"Enjoy your museum" 4235
ENSOR, JAMES 3004
EPICS, Sumerian 1448, 1450-
1, 1453
EN KHEGAL, tablet of 1168
ER RIZEIKAT 3547
Erdberg, J.P. von 3289
Erickson, C.O.A. 2503

ERIE CANAL 4400
Ernst, A.H. 1640
ERNST, MAX 1909, 4200
ERYTHREAN SEA 4009
ESKIMOS
    anthropometry 1365
    art 2762, pictorial 2742
    Baffin Land 801
    boats (dugouts) 815
    carvings 2767
    Copper Eskimo 809, cop-
        per objects 814
    dances 820
    Forest Eskimos in 1880's
        807
    Hudson Bay 801
    hunting 819
    mask, Tun-Ghat 2783
    Point Barrow, prehistory
        805
    Polar 813
    prehistory 811
    relation with Chipewyan
        Indians 812
    Siberia 1039
    spearthrower 255
    Western Eskimo 808
ESKIMO CULTURE AREA
    800-23
ESMERALDAS figurines 2785
Espinosa, A.M. 1504
Essex Institute
    Hawthorne memorabilia 99
    historical collections 4042
    history of 100, 4410
    New England early history
        2654
    Oak Knoll collection 1551
    portraits in 1725-6
Estrin, R. 3680
ETCHINGS
    catalogs--Avery Collection
        1954, Cooper Collection
        1952, Hearn Collection
        1953
ETHNOBOTANY See also Ag-
    riculture; Food

Africa drug plants 1099
Gilbert Islands 1291
Glen Canyon 4088
Hopi Indians 708
Navaho Indians 687, Ramah
    Navaho 707
Peru, ancient 975
University of Michigan Eth-
    nobotanical Laboratory
    110
Yuki Indians 1479
"Ethnographical Album,"
    North Pacific Coasts of
    America and Asia 215
ETHNOGRAPHY See Ethnol-
    ogy
ETHNOLOGY See also Anthro-
    pology and Archaeology
Africa--living races of Sa-
    hara Desert 1095, North-
    west, Stone Age races
    1096
Americas 237, north Pa-
    cific coast 215
Arabs, Iraq 1080
Armenians 1089
Asia 1056, north Pacific
    coast 215
Eskimos 807
Fiji 1304
Futuna 1271
Ghegs, Albania 1040
Havasupai Indians 667
Iowa Indians 508
Kentucky, prehistoric 399a
Klamath 4088a
Mahikan Indians 397
Mangareva 1268
Manihiki 1269
Mayas, British Honduras
    925
Melanesia 1288
Mexico, southern 942
Micronesia 1290
Modoc 4088a
Near East 1088
New Guinea 1283

334

Pacific Area 1299
Paiute 4092
Polynesia 1290
Powhatan Indians 401
Puka Puka 1267, 1295
Rakahangra 1269
Saipan 1303
Sauk Indians 509
Shoshonean Indians 497
Siberia 1042
Southwest, prehistoric 662
Syrians 1089
Tokelau Islands 1294
Tonga 1305
Tubai 1265
Uvea 1272
Zunis, Hawikuh 662
ETHNOPSYCHOLOGY See Anthropology; Personality
Etienne-Martin 1986
ETIQUETTE, Mohave Indian 761
ETRUSCAN LANGUAGE, inscriptions 1029
ETRUSCANS 3229-30, 3243
Ettinghausen, R. 3519
EUPHRATES-TIGRIS REGION, anthropology 1078
EUROPE See also Art, European
anthropology and archaeology 1001-53, 4132
man, prehistoric 1378, 1381
musical instruments, ancient 1672
population movements, map 1006
tobacco, introduction of 1005
Evans, G. 3080, 4249
Evans, L. 3911
Evans, Lewis, 3905
EVANS, LUCILLE 2378
Evans, William T., Collection 4226
Everard, L.C. 65
EVERGOOD, PHILIP 4175,

4183
Evers, E. 504
EVOLUTION, human pelvis 1342
Ewers, J.C. 2338, 2727, 2892
Ewing, J.F. 1338
Ewing, L. 1435-6, 1438
Ewing, L.H. 1573
EXCAVATION, ARCHAEOLOGICAL, method 205, 4075
EXCHANGE MEDIA, U.S. Penitentiaries 4072
EXEKIAS, GREECE, classical site 1018
EXHIBITS
art installation 41, 45, 46
dioramas, cigar-box 97
museumobile 29
natural history, elephant group 54
preparation and installation 5
window 28
EXPLORATIONS AND DISCOVERIES
Canadian West 3809
Champlain, Samuel de 3802
Cibola, Seven Cities of 3963, Hawikuh 619
Great Lakes 3815
Islas Revillagigedo 3983
Smith, Capt. John, map of 3904
Wrangel Island 3974
EXPLORERS, Pacific Area 1270
Exposition of Indian Tribal Arts 2728
EXPRESSIONISM 2940
American 2182, 2374
German 3151
EXTINCT ANIMALS AND HUMAN REMAINS See Archaeology--Human and Animal Remains
EXTRAMADURA, SPAIN, cos-

tume 3361
EYAK INDIANS, ceremonial
    paddle 786

F
FABERGE, CARL 3297
FACE PAINTING See also
    Tattooing and Body
    Marking
    British Columbia Indians
    794
    Mohave Indians 763
"Faces of Asia" 1056
FACTORY WORKERS, India
    1236
FAGES, ISABEL LOPEZ DE
    2706
Fagg, W. 4284d
Fairbanks, A. 3177, 3179
FAIRMONT PARK, Park
    Houses 2678
FAIRS See names of specific
    fairs, as Brussels
    World's Fair; Golden
    Gate International Expo-
    sition; New York World's
    Fair
Fairservis, W.A. 1074-5,
    4135
FAIRY TALES See also Folk
    Literature and Folk
    Lore
    Polynesian 1462
FAJALAUZA WARE 3348
Fales, M.G. 2614
FALL OF MAN, legend of,
    Sumer 1453
"Family of Man" 2513
FANNING ISLAND, archaeol-
    ogy 1279
Fansler, R.M. 2995
FAR EAST See Art, Oriental;
    Orient; and names of
    countries, as China
FARA, archaeology 1128, 1153
Farabee, W.C. 447, 523, 861-

5, 945-6, 969, 1339,
    1442, 2729, 2842-3,
    3701, 3748-9, 3761
FARANESE PALACE, El Gre-
    co's works in 3313
Farish, H.D. 3854
Farmer's Museum 134, 2647
    flax, story of 2593
Farnsworth, D.L. 4016
FARR, FRED WHITE 2528
Farrand, L. 824a, 2858
Farwell, B. 1988
Farwell, O.A. 183
FASHION See also Costume
    and Adornment
    French 3148
FASHIONS IN ART 2179
    American, 1900's 2265
FATES, determiners of, leg-
    end 1456
Faville, F.H. 448
Faxon, W. 144
FAYETTE CO, KY, sites 358,
    374
    Fisher site 309
FEATHER MYTH 1439
FEATHERWORK See also
    Quill and Beadwork
    Hawaiian 3688
    Paracas 3745
    Tahitian breastplate 2879
FEEBLE-MINDED, hard pal-
    ate 1337
Feher, J. 1459
Feinblatt, E. 4288
FEININGER, LYONEL 1899,
    2421
FEITELSON, LORSER 2372
FEKE, ROBERT 2231-2, 4177
FENIMORE HOUSE 2647, 2668
FENWAY COURT 1732
Fenyes, E.S. 2706
Ferdon, E.N. 599-600, 866,
    2785
Ferguson, H.L. 308
Fernald, H.E. 1675, 3403-5,
    3431-3, 3444, 3457, 3496

FERRELL, BARBARA 2378
FERRY, ILL, site 478
FETISHES See Charms; Fig-
    urines
FIBERS AND SPINNING See
    also Textiles; Weaving;
    and types of textiles, as
    Cotton; Silk; Wool 4363
  American aboriginal,
    Eastern 2839
  history 2034, 2047
  Navaho Indian 2831
  Salvador 3741
  warp yarns 2028
FICTILE ART See Ceramics;
    Pottery
Field, H. 1045, 1057, 1076-82
Field Columbian Museum See
    Chicago Natural History
    Museum
FIELD WORK, ARCHAEO-
    LOGICAL See names of
    areas, as Egypt; South-
    west; and Dating (Ar-
    chaeological); Pipeline
    Archaeology
  methodology 200, 206, 213
    --excavation 205
  potsherds in historic re-
    construction 201
  pottery description stand-
    ards 207
  survey system 210
Fierro, M. 1627
"Fifty Books of the Year" 2633
"Fifty Packages of the Year"
    2634
"Fifty Record Album Covers
    of the Year" 2634
Figulla, H.H. 1177-8
FIGUREHEADS OF SHIPS
    2529, 4338
"Figures at a table" 4162
FIGURINES See also names of
    media, as Ceramics;
    Sculpture; and form of
    figurines, as Pipes

African fetishes 3669
Alcora statuettes 3344
British Columbia, bronze
    2764
Chinese pottery 3455,
    3457, 4343
Cocle, Panama 3714
Esmeraldas 2785
Iroquois, antler 2777
Italian 3235
Kashmir 3582
Kentucky, modern 2775
Kourion 2197
Patomanca Indians, string
    figure 3713a
Southwest, clay 2805
Tanagra 3195
West Indies 3732
FIJI
  anthropometry of blood
    types 1386
  archaeology 1314
  ethnology, Lau 1304
  population 1278
  social life and customs
    1326
"Film Index" 1975
Fink, A.Jay, Collection 1931
Fink, J.-M. 4293-4

Finley, D.E. 1761, 1766-7,
    2164, 2975
FINLEY, WYO, site 531
FIRE ENGINES
  Smith Museum Collection
    2564
  "Vigilant," fire engine 2566
FIRST HOLLAND, submarine
    2565
Fischer, H.G. 3667-8
FISHBONES, archaeological,
    Fiji 1314
Fisher, A.K. 1350
Fisher, C.S. 1212-3, 1228,
    1240, 3622, 3578
Fisher, G. 971
Fisher, L.B. 3932

Fisher, P. 3794
Fisher, R.G. 227, 602, 2709, 3971
Fisher, Mrs. Samuel H. 3776
FISHER SITE, KY 309
FISHERMEN AND FISHING
Catawba 458
cormorant, domestic, China and Japan 1058
Rappahannock Indian 442
FISHERS ISLAND, N.Y., site 308
FISHHOOKS, California coast, Hawaiian 1311
Pacific Area 1315
shell 757
FISHING IN ART 1889
Fishler, S.A. 2760
FISHTRAPS, Marshall Islands 1318

Fithian, P.V. 3854
Fitzgerald, G.M. 1241-2, 3592-3
Fitzgerald Memorial Exhibition 2129
FLAGS See also Heraldry; Signs and Symbols; Totems and Totemism
Hawaiian 3975
Michigan 3886-7
New England 3883
North Carolina 3940
North Dakota 3961
Rhode Island 3882
United States 3848
FLAGSTAFF, ARIZ
Pueblo milling stone 682
Sinagua Culture 593
Winona Village 631-2
FLANNAGAN, JOHN 2534
FLASKS, American 2024
FLATHEAD INDIANS See Salish Indians
FLAX See also Linen
history of 2593
Fleischman, Lawrence and

Barbara, Collection of American Art 2173, 4034
Fleisher, Samuel, Memorial 4394
Fleming, H.C. 603
Fletcher, 1661
FLETCHER, AARON DEAN 2223
FLINT QUARRIES, Indians of North America 252
FLINT RIVER, ALA, site 415a, 4086
FLINTLOCKS, Iroquois Indian 430
FLOOD LEGEND
Babylonian 1447
Sumerian 1453--Epic of Gilgamesh 1450-1
FLORENTINE CODEX 1568, 1583
FLOWERS IN ART See also Still Life Painting
1926, 1930, 1947, 2112
Chinese painting 3412
FLORIDA
archaeology--Catillos de San Marcos 322, Castle Windy Midden 313, chronology 359, Clay Co mounds 351, Duval Co mounds 351, St. Augustine 322
Indian pottery 2813
FLUTES, Pueblos, Apache, and Navaho 4152
Fogg Art Museum
Harvard portraits 1727
Pulitzer Collection of modern art 1728
FOGEL, SEYMOUR 2422
Folger Shakespeare Library, description 101
facade panels 4316
FOLINSBEE, JOHN 2423
FOLK ART See also Pennsylvania Dutch Art; Santos;

338

and Art, Primitive
American 2177--paintings
2161, 2164-5, 4197,
4333, sculpture 2515
folk wandering art 2000,
2187
Indians of North America
2735,
Japanese 4274
Mexican 2914
New Mexico, colonial 2250
catalogs--New York St.
Historical Assn. 4197,
Rockefeller Collection
1797, 2203-4
FOLK LITERATURE AND
FOLK LORE 1404-66
African myths 1404
Babylonian 1445, 1447-8,
1450-2
Greek myths 3179, 3221
Indians of North America
1408-40
Arapaho 542
Crow 566
Delaware 460
Hopi 714, 729
Meearmeear 461
Osage 541
Quinault 796
Shawnee 462
Indians of South America
1441-3
Indians of Americas 1404
raincloud myth 1408
Koryaks myth 1440
Marquesan 1460
Nebraska 1407
New York State 1405-6
Pacific Area 1404, 1458-66
Papuan 1283
Philippine Islands 1464
Siberian 1444
Sumerian 1446, 1448-9,
1453
Tinguaians 1321
Tuamotuan 4024

FOLSOM POINTS, and Gla-
cial Man 694
Fong, W. 3406
Font, E.S. 3337
FOOD See also Ethnobotany;
and culture groups, as
Indians of North Ameri-
ca
Africa, resources 1100
dirt-eating 196
Huaca Prieta, Peru 960
Iroquois Indians 429
New Guinea 1289
Pueblo Indian 701
Zuni breadstuffs 683
FOOTE CANYON PUEBLO,
ARIZ 661
FORAIN, JEAN LOUIS 3064,
3105
FORAMEN MAGNUM, crani-
ology 1358
Forbes, E.W. 171
FORBIDDEN CITY, costumes
3445
Force, J. 2373
Force, R.W. 4140
Ford, A. 4191
FORD, HENRY 4402-3--Mr.
and Mrs. 4153
Ford, Henry, Museum, an-
tiques 2649, 4336, guide-
book 4043
Ford, J.A. 310-2, 805, 919,
2730
FOREST ESKIMOS See Eski-
mos
Forge, A. 4284b
FORGERY OF ANTIQUITIES
Cardiff Giant 226
FORGES AND FORGING
Philippines 1308
FORMOSA, folklore 1464
Forsey, G.A. 867
Forstemann, E. 1575
FORT ANCIENT ASPECT,
Ohio 319, 354
FORT APACHE INDIANS 659

FORT HALL INDIANS 4094
FORT HILL, OHIO, site 355
FORT LAWRENCE, building 3820
FORT PITT, archaeology 409
FORT SNELLING, OLD, archaeology 290
FORT TEJON, adobes 2705
FORTIFICATIONS See also Earthworks; Mound Builders
Canandaigua, N.Y., prehistoric village 380
FORTRESS OF LOUISBERG 3830
FORTS, Indians of New England 2903
FORUM, Minturnae 1034
FOSSIL MAN See also Man, Prehistoric
Tangier 1116
Foster, G.M. 2917
Foster, J.W. 1850
Foster, S. 1659
FOUL-CHE-DELBOSC, R. 3888
"FOUNDRY PAINTER" 3204
"The Four Continents" 4251
Fowke, G. 220, 477, 793
Fowler, H.W. 1314
Fowler, M.L. 478, 754
Fox, T. 2333
FOX INDIANS
beaded garters 2881
quill belt 2880
sacred bundles 428
FRAGA CERAMICS 3348
FRANCE
in Acadia 3824
in America 2616
in Detroit 3881
man, prehistoric 1380
proverbs 1558
FRANCISCANS
Awatovi Mission, Ariz 648
New Mexico 3978
Frank, G. 1558

Frank, L. P. 2267
FRANKENTHALER, HELEN 2424
Frankenstein, A. 2321
FRANKLIN, BENJAMIN 3857, 3865
Franklin Institute 102
Frary, I.T. 19, 2603, 2669
FRASCONI, ANTONIO 2504
woodcuts 2505
Fraser, C. 2296
Fraser, D.F. 3687
FRASER RIVER, B.C., INDIANS 781, 784
FRAUDS, ARCHAEOLOGICAL
Cardiff Giant 226
FRAUDS AND FORGERIES, gold 2071
Frazer, J.T. 2434
Freedburg, A.B. 3150
FREEDOM IN ART 1848
Freeman, M.B. 3021
Freer Gallery of Art
American and European arts, Whistleriana 1730
Chinese art, history outline 3341
handbook 1729
Hokusai collection 4276
Japanese arts, history outline 3479
Ming pottery 3458
FREMONT CULTURE 517, Utah 652
FREMONT I, prehistoric Nebraska village 487
French, H. 2313
French, Herbert Greer, Collection 1957
FRENCH AND INDIAN WAR, 1755-1763 3741
FRENCH CANADA
arts 2116
furniture 2136, 4391
painting 2118
FRENCH CANADIANS 3808
FRESCOES See Murals

Frick Collection
  Limoges enamels 3145
  paintings 1731
FRIEDLAENDER, JOHNNY
  2506
Friedlaender, W. 3114
Friedman, M.L. 3685, 4193
FRIENDS OF THE WHITNEY
  2397-8
FRIJOLES, N.M., excavations
  612
FRINGES 2033
Frits, M.A. 153
Frothingham, A.W. 3344-5,
  3353
Fullen, R.P. 313
Fuller, Alvine T., Memorial
  Exhibition 1829
Fuller, B. 4389
Fuller, R.E. 2474, 2970,
  3481, 4272
FULLER, SUE 2425
Fulton, W.S. 604
FULTON CO, ILL, Crable
  site 399
Furness, W.H. 1066
FURNITURE See also articles
  of furniture, as Cradles;
  Chairs; Chests; Tables
  4395
  American 2640-60, early
  2552, 18th century 2259
  Baltimore 2641
  Canadian, French 2136,
  4391
  Chinese chairs 4387
  mounts, gilt bronze 2114
  New Jersey, early 2557,
  2648
  catalogs--Albany Institute of
  History and Art 4384,
  Aldrich Collection 1998,
  Cleveland Museum of Art
  1709-10, Suffield, Ct.
  2642, "Sunnyside" 2657
Furst, H. 3098
FURTON, MICH, site 316

FUSELI, HENRY 3371
FUTUNA
  ethnology 1271
  songs 1457
FUTURISM 4266

G

Gabel, 4256
Gabinetto Disegnie Stampe
  4298
GABO, NAUM, kinetic con-
  structions 1979
Gaertner, Carl, Memorial Ex-
  hibition 1838
GAGNON, CLARENCE A. 2139
GAINSBOROUGH, THOMAS
  3030, 3041
GAINES, X.M. 4087
Galerie Chalette 3146
GALICIA, ceramics 3348
GALICIA, JOSE LUIS 3339
GALISTEO BASIN, N.M.,
  ruins 699
Gallagher, Edward Joseph III,
  Memorial Collection 1694
Gallaher, A. 4088
Gallatin, A.E. 228, 1786
Gallatin, A.E., Collection
  1786a, 3198
GALLEGAN, costume 3357
Gallego, F. 4211
GALLOONS 2033
Gallup, D. 3312
GAMES AND SPORTS See al-
  so Recreation
  ball courts--Piedras Negras
  3775, Winona Village,
  Ariz 632
  England 4414
  Greek, 5th century 3187
  in art 1890, 1941, 2206
  Indians of the Americas 268
  Japanese 1067
  Mesopotamia, horseback
  riding 1190
  Oglala Indians 562

341

Uxmal 965
Gammel, R.H.I. 2318
GANDHARA SCULPTURE 3583
GANGOTENA, CRISTOBAL DE
  3740
Gann, T. 3712
Ganong, S.B. 3295-7
Ganong, W.F. 3795-7, 3835
  memorial 3836
Garbisch, Edgar William and
  Bernice Chrysler, Col-
  lection 2164
GARDENS 2111-2
  miniature 50
  Mount Vernon 4411
  Newark Museum 136
  San Francisco 2718
  Shakespearean 3059
  Williamsburg 2698
Gardner, A. 3862
Gardner, A.T.E. 1946, 2339
Gardner, E.E. 2949
Gardner, F. 688, 1514
GARDNER, ISABELLA STEW-
  ART 1732
Gardner, Isabella Stewart,
  Museum
  exhibited paintings and
    drawings catalog 1734
  Gardner Collection 1733
  general catalog 1735
  guide 1736, 4044
Gardner, P.V. 3166
Garlick, K. 4252
GARTERS, Sauk and Fox In-
  dians 2881
Garvan, Mabel Brady, Collec-
  tion 4370
GATCH, LEE 4213
GATES, MARGARET 2426
GATES, ROBERT 2427
Gates, W.E. 1576
Gates Collection 3820
GATH, ETHEL ROBERTSON
  2428
Gatschet, A.S. 314, 4088a
GAUCHOS 1627, 1629

life of 3324-5
GAUDI Y. CORNET, ANTONIO
  4254
GAUGUIN, PAUL 3070, 3074,
  3106
  prints 3133
GAVARNI (pseudonym of Sul-
  pice Guillaume Cheva-
  lier) 3134
GAWRA See Tepe Gawra
GAZELLE PENINSULA, skulls
  1389
Gebauer, P. 3647
Gebhard, D. 2670
Geesey Collection 4332
Gelb, I.J. 1179
Gellatly Collection 1759
GEM CUTTERS, Ur 3619
GEMS AND PRECIOUS STONES
  See also Jewelry; and
    names of stones, as Jade
  2008, 4355-7
  cameos 2010, 1021
  engraved 2012
  intaglios 2012
  North Carolina 2574
  opals 2011
  catalog--Greek, Roman,
    Etruscan engraved gems
    3174
GENEALOGY See also Herald-
  ry; Kinship
  Hawaii 1273
  Laguna Indians 722
  Stowell Family 1548
GENETICS, popular 4014-5
GENRE PAINTING 1945
  American, 19th century
    2264
  European 2964
  Virginia, 19th century 2263
GEOMETRY 3777
GEOPHAGISM 196
GEORGIA
  archaeology--Columbia Co
    296, Stalling's Island
    mound 296

342

counties, map 3946
GEORGIAN BAY, ONT, trade
  route 826
GERASA, excavations 1092
GEROME, LEON 3073
GERONIMO 587
Getten, R.J. 3408
GETTYSBURG ADDRESS 3862
Getz, J. 3439
GHEGS, Albania, race and
  culture 1040
GHOSTS See Supernaturalism
GIBEON
  archaeology 1245-6
  Hebrew inscriptions and
    stamps 1591
GIBSON, CHARLES DANA 2297
Giddings, J.L. 767, 806-7
Giddings, R.W. 4145
Gifford, E.S. 752
Gifford, E.W. 731, 1314
GIGANTISM
  early man 1403
  Gigantopithecus 1400
GIGANTOPITHECUS blacki von
    Koenigswald,
  fossil hominoid 1400
GIL, ALVAR CARILLO 2429
GILBERT ISLANDS, ethno-
    botany 1291
GILGAMESH, Epic of (Legend
  of the Flood) 1450-1
GILL, IRVING 2700
Gillin, J. 479, 868, 972
Gilman, B.G. 1753
GILMORE, MELVIN R. 110
Gilt Bronze See Bronze
Gimbutas, M. 1046
GIMPS 2033
GIRAFFE, in history and art
  1879
Girard, A. 2434
GIRTIN, THOMAS 2937
Githens, T.A. 1099-1100
GIUSEWA, excavations 660
GIZA, cemetery 1228
GIZEH, archaeology 1209,
  1213

GLACIAL KAME CULTURE
  301
GLACKENS, WILLIAM JAMES
  2298
GLASCO, JOSEPH 2528
GLASS 2018-26, 4358-60
  American 2020, 2024,
    2584-6, early 2552
  ancient 2108, 2022, analy-
    sis 4358, Italy 3252-3
  Canadian, early 2128, 4359
  contemporary 2021
  Dorflinger glass 2586
  drinking vessels 2025
  Dutch painting, depicted in
    3022
  Egyptian 3572
  European 2020
  flasks 2024
  glass making 2023, modern
    2026
  history 2023
  Libbey Glass Co 2019
  New Jersey 2558
  oriental 3389
  pressed, American 3585
  Spanish 3353-5
  stained 4360
  Venetian 3291, 3353
Glazier, William S., Collec-
  tion 2105
GLEN CANYON, ARIZ, archae-
  ology 578, 4077, 4087
GLOBE PLAYHOUSE 1647
Goddard, P.E. 480, 544, 825,
  1414-5, 1560-5
Godfrey, 734
Godfrey, W.S. 4126
GODS See also Folk Litera-
  ture and Folk Lore;
  Magic; Religion, and
  names of Gods, as Bud-
  dha and Buddhism; Jesus
  Christ
  African 4025, West Africa
    3650
  Greek 3179, 3221
  Tuamotuan 1466

343

Godwin, M.O. 1811, 2911
Goggin, J.M. 3346
GOGH, VINCENT VAN 2952,
3006, 3008-10
drawings 3005, 3007
paintings 3005, 3007
prints 3007
GOLD AND GOLDSMITHING
America, prehistoric 945,
947
Ecuador 3749
frauds and forgeries 2071
goldsmithing 2075
Nippur 3620
Paracas 3745
Peru 882, 988, 3752, 3757
Pre-Columbian 3643, 3748,
3750
Gold Museum 1834
Goldberg, R. 4164
Golden State International Ex-
position, San Francisco
1938
art 1857, 3851
European painting 2948
GOLDTHWAITE, ANNE 2507
Goldwater, R. 4284a, 4284c
Golschmann, Vladimir, Col-
lection 1869
Gomez-Sicre, J. 4199
Good Morning, dance book
4153
Goodale, J.C. 163
Goodenough, E.R. 3226
Goodenough, W. 1094
Goodenough, W.H. 1283, 1324
Goodman, 3857
Goodman, J.T. 1577
GOODMAN SITE 4088
Goodrich, L. 1680, 2175,
2219, 2231, 2273-4,
2283, 4194
GOODSPEED, CHARLES E.
142
Goodwin, C.A. 3855, 3858
Goodwin, R. 3933
Gordon, E.I. 4136

Gordon, G.B. 426, 808, 869-
71, 1214, 1416-7, 1443,
1571, 1578-9, 2731,
2768, 2859, 3053, 3459,
3513, 3520-2, 3702-3,
3713, 3760
Gordon, J. 2185
GORKY, ARSHILE 2430
Gorman, F. 3907
GORRICIO DE NOVARIA,
GASPAR 3336
GOTHIC ART 296, 3020, 3270
GOTHIC ROOM 2987
Gottesman, R.S. 2551, 4331
Gould, H.N. 1372
GOURDION, GREECE, pre-
historic site 1012, 1026-
7
Hittite cemetery 1194
GOURNIA, GREECE, excava-
tions 1009
pottery 3569
GOVERNMENT See also names
of countries, as Guate-
mala--Politics and Gov-
ernment
and art 1680
Babylonia, documents 1167,
1169
England 4413
Public Works Art Project
2381
Gowans, A. 2131
GOYA, FRANCISCO D. 2952,
3316
drawings and prints 3338
portraits by 3317
source for Maragato Series
prints 3337
Grace, G.W. 1515
Graham, A.K. 1131
Graham, J.M. 2615
GRAIL
Abbey, F.A., mural 2274
Gralapp, L. 4273
GRAMMAR See Linguistics and
Grammar

GRANADA, petroglyphs 977
GRAND CANYON, ARIZ, archaeology 672
GRAND RIVER MOUND, OKLA 494
Granscay, S.V. 2079
GRANT, ULYSSESS, letter 3860a
GRANT CO, N.M., site 590
GRAPHIC ARTS See also techniques, as
Color prints, Japanese; Etchings; Lithographs; Serigraphs; Woodcuts and Wood Engravings; and names of artists, as Daumier; Durer; Rembrandt; Toulouse-Lautrec
1963, 4285-4310
American 2350, 2485-2511, 4286
Biblical prints 1968
botanical prints 1875
California 2488
Canadian 2126
contemporary 1969, 1971
English 3031
flower prints 2112
gardens in 2111
horological devices 2087
Italian, contemporary 3276
medical prints 1972
Mississippi and Missouri Rivers 1885
New England 2168
painter-printmakers 1902, Polish 4305
religious prints 1968
Rossiter 2259
catalogs--1906, Avery Collection 1954, Cleveland Museum of Art 1709-10, Corcoran Gallery 2489, Cooper Collection 1952, Cutting Collection 1903, First International Ex-

hibition of Prints 1966, Freer Gallery of Art 1730, Hall Collection 1960, Hearn Collection 1953, International Biennial 4296, Rewald Collection 898, Sloniker Collection 1968, Steefel Collection 1969, Walker Art Center 1922, Yale Collection 1964
"Graphics in Packaging" 2635
GRASS HOUSES, Caddo and Wichita Indians 2899
Gray, C. 4189
GREAT BEND ASPECT, KANS 514
GREAT LAKES 3815, Indian tribes 412
GREAT MOUND, TEPE GAWRA 1132
GREECE
archaeology 1009-27, 1090, 1194
art 3167-3225
athletics and festivals 3187
coins 3222
GREEN CORN CEREMONY, Eastern Woodlands 465
GREEN RIVER CULTURE, KY 293, 371
GREENE, BELLA DA COSTA 1684
Greene, Edward B., Collection 1943
Greene, F.S. 2038, 3537
GREENFIELD VILLAGE, guidebook 4045
Greengo, R.E. 940
GREENHOUSE, site 310
Greenman, E.F. 315-7, 826
GREENWOOD, JOHN 2223
Gregoropoulos, J. 4189
Gregory, W.K. 1340, 1351, 1378
Grehier, L. 3529
Greiner, R. 2908

345

Griffin, J.B. 206, 318-9
Griffing, R.P. 4046, 4050, 4274, 4284, 4349
Griffith, F.L. 1229, 3551
Griffith, R. 1641
Griffith, W.J. 320, 973-4
Grigaut, P.L. 1888, 2616, 3054, 3072-4, 3284, 3409
Griggs Collection 3262
GRIMES, JANE 42
GRIS, JUAN 3312
Griswold, A.B. 4270
Griswold, A.W. 1682
Gropp, A.E. 1580-1
Grosjean, S.S. 1370
GROSS, CHAIM 2374
GROSZ, GEORGE 3154
GROUP OF SEVEN 2130, 2132
Grundy, C.R. 20
GUADALQUIVIR RIVER, archaeology 1002
GUADELUPE MOUNTAINS, site 584
GUAJIRO EXPEDITION 900
Gualtieri, J.P. 4189
GUALUPITA, excavations 933
GUAM, dental morphology and pathology, prehistoric 1388
GUANACO CLOAKS 2742
GUARANI INDIANS
    Spanish relations with in colonial Paraguay 911
GUARDI, FRANCESCO DE' 2937
GUARDIAN FIGURES 3435
GUATEMALA See also Art, Pre-Columbian
    anthropology--educational cooperation with U.S. 974, foreign colonization attitudes 973, political changes in Indian communities 961, 4130
    archaeology--873, Chiche 939, Chocola 847, Hol-

mul 894, Nakum 957, Peten 885-6, Tajumulco 854, Tikal 886, 904, 912, Usumatsintla Valley 887-8, Western Highlands 847, Zacualpa 937
government in 1944 994
history 1585, Livingston Codes and crisis of 1837-8 990
Mayas, carving 3715, stucco head 3719, throne 3716
myths 1443
pottery 3763, 3769, "duck pots" 3758
religion 4023
San Carlos Indians 972
textiles 3746
theatre 1646
GUATEMOTZIN See Cuauhtemoc
GUDEA, archaeology 1147
Gudger, E.W. 1315
Guernsey, S.J. 605
Guest, G.D. 3630
GUETAR, stone work 3731
Guggenheim, H.F. 1738
Guggenheim International Award 1846
Guggenheim, Solomon R., Museum 1737-8, 4087
Guidol, J. 3307
Guild of Book Workers, exhibition 2099
GUIANA See also British Guiana
    Amazon expedition 861
GUINEA, twins in 1103
GULF OF GEORGIA, archaeology 779
GUNS See also Arms and Armor 4373
    air 1941
    cannon, Spanish 3363
    flintlock, Iroquois 430
    Northwest gun 2624

Pennsylvania rifle 2625
Gunsaulus, H.C. 90, 1067,
3488, 3501, 3505
GUNTERSVILLE BASIN, pot-
tery 2798
GUSSAVE, MEX, excavations
856
Guthe, A.K. 321
Guthe, C.E. 21-2, 1582
Gutman, Mr. and Mrs. Nel-
son, Collection 3140
Gutmann, J. 4275
GUYS, CONSTANTIN 3064
GWATHMEY, ROBERT 2431
GYPSUM CAVE, NEV, site
737

H
Haas, M. 850
Hack, J.T. 606, 689
Hackney, L.W. 3421
Haddon, A.C. 1307, 1847
HADLEY CHEST 2650
Hadlock, W.S. 427
HAIDA INDIANS, ethnology
782
HAIDA LANGUAGE AND LIT-
ERATURE 1567
HAITI, voodoo drum 1671
Hajdu, Etienne 1986
Hale, B.H. 2385
Hale, R.B. 2350, 2516
Hall, E.H. 1019-20, 3182,
3205-12, 3223, 3235-40,
3252, 3559
Hall, E.R. 107
Hall, E.T. 607
Hall, H.B. 3569
Hall, H.U. 524-5, 1047, 1101-
4, 1284-6, 2879, 3255,
3650-1, 3669-70, 3676,
3691, 3697, 4025
Hall, L.F. 3576
Hall, Laura P., Memorial
Collection 1960
HALL OF FAME 103

HALL OF FAME (BASEBALL)
3863
HALL OF FAME OF THE
TROTTER 3871
Hallmark Art Award 2375
Hall's map of Georgia 3946
Halm, P. 3163
Halpert, Edith Gregor, Col-
lection 4048
HALS, FRANS 2997
Halmby, W.D. 1105-6, 1325,
1346, 1373, 1384-5,
1399, 4026
HAMBRIDGE, JAY 3203
HAMILTON, ALEXANDER
4203
Hamilton, G.H. 1827, 2725,
3070, 3103
HAMILTON CO, OHIO
archaeology 4112
Turner Earthworks 419
HAMMERSLEY, FREDERICK
2372
HAMMURABI
Babylonian letters, from
period of 1198
tablets from dynasty 1511
HAN DYNASTY, tiles 3470
HANDEDNESS, Mexican Indians
1374-5
HANDICRAFTS See also
Decorative Arts; and
media, as Pottery;
Weaving
contemporary 1999
Hawaii 3679
Pre-Columbian 3709
Shaker 2554
Handy, C. 1394
Handy, E.S.C. 1392, 1460
Handy, W.C. 1392, 1394
Hanna, L.C. 1851
Hannay, J. 3798
HANNO (Carthiginian naviga-
tor) 4008
Hansen, H. 1527
Hanson, C. 2624

Hard, F. 4316
HARDIN CO, ILL, Ferry site 478
HARDING, JOHN L. 2223
HARDY, ELIAS 3811
Hare, S. 3609
Hargrave, L.L. 592, 630
HARLEQUIN IN ART 1878
Harper, J.R. 3799
HARPOONS
    Stefansson Collection 265
    toggle heads, Aleutian Islands 817
Harrington, J.E. 322
Harrington, J.P. 1480-4, 1489
Harrington, M. 269, 323-5, 428, 449, 481-3, 526-7, 713, 735-8, 768, 797, 872, 2707, 2880-1
Harris, C.X. 2242
HARRIS, LAWREN 2140
Harshberger, J.W. 975
Hart, C.H. 2493
HART, GEORGE OVERBURY ('POP") 2299
Hartesveldt 4150
HARTFORD, 20th century painting 2396
Hartford Collections 1915
Hartford Festival 1843
Hartford Hospital 1884
Hartford International Exhibition of Photography, annual 1973
HARTLEY, MARSDEN 2432
HARTMAN MOUND, KY 298
Hartzenbusch, J.E. 1626
"Harvard List of Books on Art" 1853
"Harvard Outline and Reading Lists, Oriental Art" 3377
HARVARD UNIVERSITY See also Freer Gallery of Art
    portraits 1727
    library guide, fine arts 1852

HASANLU, Iran 1072
HASELTINE, HERBERT 2535
HASINAI INDIANS
    European reports of, 1687-1772 320
HATBOXES
    Shelburne Museum 2548
Hatch, J.F. 4224
Hatcher, J.B. 3861
HATHAWAY, ANNE, COTTAGE 1543
HATHOR, Egyptian goddess, statue 3565
HATS See also Costume and Adornment; and names of headgear, as Helmets 2070
    Indian warbonnets 2850
    Paracas headdress 3745
    Tlingit Indian clan hats 792
HATSHEPSUT, QUEEN OF EGYPT, contemporary of 1205
Hatt, R.T. 450, 872a
Haury, E.W. 608, 4090
HAVASUPAI INDIANS 609, 2784
    ethnography 667
HAWAII See also Art, Hawaiian; Pacific Area
    anthropology 1333, 1395
    archaeology 1298
    architecture, domestic 2688
    arts and crafts 3679
    children, growth of 1397
    ethnology 1273
    fishhooks 1311
    flag 3975
    history 1282
    physical anthropology 1382-3
    tattooing 1323
    voyages and travels 1287
HAWIKUH, N.M.
    history 619
    kiva 692
HAWIKUH (HAWIKUH ZUNI) INDIANS See Zuni Indians
Hawkes, E.W. 326, 820

Hawley, F.M. 610
HAWTHORNE, NATHANIEL
142
Centennial 1529
memorial 1528
Pot-8-o club 1550
Essex Institute exhibits 99
Hayden, J.D. 4089
Hayes, A.M. 409
Hayes, B.H. 1683, 1685, 2494
Hayes, W.C. 1621, 3547,
3570
Haynes, J.E. 3992
HAYWOOD CO MOUNDS, N.C.
327
HEAD, mummified 969,
sculptured 4320
HEAD HUNTERS, shrunken
heads 199
Heade, M.J. 2300
HEADDRESS, Paracas 3745
HEALTH 4013-20
Chippewa Indians 454
Zuni Indians 603
HEALY, GEORGE PETER
ALEXANDER 2301
Hearst, William Randolph,
Collection 2078, 3020
HEBREW LANGUAGE AND
LITERATURE 1591
Hebrew Union College 3589,
3594
Heckett Collection of Portrait
Miniatures 1932
Heffernan, W. 2308
Heilbron, B.C. 2508
Heimlich, M.D. 2798
Heliker, J. 2393
Hellion, J. 1786a
HELL, Ishtar's journey to
1452
Hellman, M. 1340, 1377-8
HELMETS
Italy, ancient 3224
Kaguantan Indians, shark
helmet 791
Tlingit Indians war helmet
792

Hemenway Collection 1356
Hemenway South Western Ex-
pedition 586
Hendricks-Hodge Expedition
4076
Hendy, P. 1734, 1933
HENRY CO, KY, Chilton site
294
HEPPELWHITE FURNITURE
2641
HERAKLES See Hercules
HERALDRY See also Flags;
Kinship; Signs and Sym-
bols; Totems and Tot-
emism
Chilkat Indians 790
Rhode Island 3849
United States, civic herald-
ry 3882
HERANT'S CAVE, N.M., site
599
HERCULES
head 3193
vases 3215
HERMES 3191
HERMITAGE CHURCH, Cas-
tile, paintings 3310
Hernandez, J. 1627
HEROES, Greek 3179, 3221
Herreshoff, L.F. 3858
Herron, John, Art Institute
1739-40, 2376
Herskovits, M.J. 4284a
HESPEROPITHECUS HAROLD-
COOKI OSBORN 1340,
1351, 1361,
Hewett, E.L. 177-82, 221,
230, 611-8, 873, 1583,
2708-10, 2732, 3859-60,
3972-3
Hewins, A. 2302
Hewitt, J.N.B. 446
Heye, G.G. 260, 327, 755,
2769, 2817,
biography of 185
Heye, George H., Expedition
956
Heye Collection 115

HIBIS, TEMPLE OF 3576
HICKS, EDWARD 4191
HIDATSA INDIANS
    culture, dog and horse in
      575
    dance, Sun 559
    eagle trappings 534
    earth lodge 535
    shrine 564
    social life and customs 552
    societies 556
HIDDEN HOUSE RUIN, ARIZ
    685
HIEROGLYPHICS See also
    Writing; and names of
    languages, as Maya
    Language and literature
    Aztec 1568, 1572-3
    Egypt, ancient 1221
    Maya 1570, Copan stair-
      way 1579
HIGGINS FLAT PUEBLO, N.
    M. 636
High Museum of Art 2941
Highet, G. 3226
HIGHWAY SALVAGE ARCHAE-
    OLOGY See also Pipeline
    Archaeology
    212
Hill, A.T. 484-5
Hill, D.K. 3172
Hill, R.N. 158
"The Hills and the Corn" (Leg-
    end) 967, 1441
Hilpert, J. 103
Hilprecht, H.V. 1133-4, 1180,
    1447, 1596
Hilprecht, Sally Crozer, Col-
    lection 1152
HINDUISM, Vishnu statuette
    3582
Hinkle, W.J. 1161
Hinsdale, W.B. 328-9, 1353
Hinton, T.B. 4127
Hipkiss, E.J. 2258-9, 2651
Hirano, C. 3494
Hispanic Society of America,

Museum and Library
bibliographies--printed
    books, before 1601 in
    Library 2103, 1601-1700
    in Library 2106; publi-
    cations 104
ceramics, Spanish 20th cen-
    tury, catalog 3348
handbook 1741-2
Hispano-Moresque pottery
    catalog 3347
history of Library and Mu-
    seum 1143
lace, modern bobbin, cata-
    log 2040
laces and embroideries cat-
    alog 2039
paintings catalog 3308-9,
    3324
sculpture catalog 1982-3
woodcuts from 15th century
    books 3336
HISPANO-ISLAMIC TEXTILES
    3538
HISPANO-MORESQUE POT-
    TERY 3347-3352
"Historia de los amores de
    Bayad y Riyad" 1628
HISTORIC HOUSES, New York
    City 68
HISTORICAL SOCIETIES,
    Michigan 3889
HISTORY See name of coun-
    try, as United States
HISTORY IN ART
    French paintings in 3070
    occupations in 1882
HISTORY, SOCIAL SCIENCES,
    AND TECHNOLOGY 1469,
    3776-4012, 4398-4416
Hitchcock, H.R. 171, 4254,
    4350
HITCHCOCK CO, NEBR, site
    496
HITTITES, cemetery, Gourdi-
    on 1194
Hobbs, H.R. 854

Hobby, T.Y. 3460
Hocard, A.M. 1326
Hochstadter, W. 3450
Hodge, F.W. 619, 691-2,
    2770, 2786, 4076
Hoebel, E.A. 488
Hoerler, A. 2799
HOETGER, BERNARD 3155
HOFMANN, HANS 2433
HOGARTH, WILLIAM 3030
Hoijer, H. 4149
HOKUSAI 3493
HOLBEIN, HANS, THE
    YOUNGER 3156
HOLLAND See Art, Dutch
    and Flemish; Nether-
    lands
Holland submarine, 2565, 4340
Hollen, W.E. 4091
Holland, W.J. 1181, 2566,
    3860a, 3861
Holloway, H.M. 2591
Holman, L.R. 1287
Holmberg, A.R. 976
Holmes, W.H. 948, 1322,
    1761a
HOLMUL, GUATAMALA,
    ruins 894
Holtz, F.C. 2086
HOLY CITIES AND LANDS
    Babylonia--Nippur 1144
    China--Shantung 1062
HOMER, WINSLOW 2303
    oils and watercolors 2204
HOMINY HOLES 437
HOMO CAPENSIS 1398
HOMOLOVI WARE 4354
HONDURAS See also British
    Honduras
    archaeology 915-6
    Copan 869-954
    Maya chronology 1370
    Xicaque Indians 934
Honey Lake, Paiutes 4092
Honeyman, Robert B., Col-
    lection 1783, 2488
HONOLULU, Chinese painting
    in 4271,
    Hui Hsien ware 4346
    map 4001
Honolulu Academy of Arts,
    guide 4050
    Kress Collection 4046
Hook, S. 1680
HOOKER CO, NEBR, site 496
Hooper, S.L. 3974
Hooton, E.A. 331, 419, 1107,
    1115, 1118, 1379, 1516
Hoover, D. 2137
HOPEDALE AREA, archaeol-
    ogy 824
HOPEWELL CULTURE
    279, 376
    Alabama 420
    burial mounds 451
    chronological position 318
    Illinois 475
    Kentucky 357
    Ohio 352
    Wisconsin 297, 341
HOPI INDIANS
    agriculture 693
    arts and crafts 2733
    baskets 2860
    ceramics 4235
    ethnobotany 708
    folk literature and folk lore
        714, 729
    Franciscan Mission,
        Awatovi 648
    history 620
    katcinas 2896
    kinship 717-8
    names, proper 1493
    Oraibi--Marau ceremony
        725, Natal 726, Oaquol
        ceremony 727, Soyal cere-
        mony 712, summer snake
        ceremony 728
    social life and customs 714
    stories of Shungopovi 1422
    toys 2897
    weaving 2818
HOPKINS CO, KY, Parrish
    Village site 363

HOPPER, EDWARD 2349
HORNBILL IVORY 3437
Hornell, J. 1307
HOROLOGICAL DEVICES 2087
HORSES
  Hidatsa Indian culture 575
  in art 4221
  T'ang Dynasty 3448, 3461
  trotting 3871
HORSEBACK RIDING, Meso-
  potamia 1190
Horton, D. 889
HOT SPRINGS, ARK, Port
  Moller site 818
HOUSE POSTS, Chilkat Indian
  790
HOUSES See Dwellings; Indi-
  and of North America
Houston, V.S.K. 3975
Houston Museum of Fine Arts
  Baffer Collection 1744
  Kress Collection 2944
  New York-Paris exhibition
    1858
  Straus Collection 2943
Howard, E.D. 622-3, 694,
  1354
Howard, R.F. 23
Howe, B. 1108
Howe, W.E. 1747
Howell, C.J. 2042
Howells, J.M. 2689
Howells, W.W. 595, 1386-7
Hoyt, Charles B., Collection
  3375
Hrdlicka, A. 1352
HUACA PRIETA, PERU, foot
  960
HUASTECA, MEXICO, excava-
  tions 857
  shell ornaments 3747, gor-
    get 3727
HUBARD, WILLIAM JAMES
  2305
Hubbard, R.H. 1771, 2945
Huckel Collection 4241
Huckerby, T. 977

Huden, J.C. 1485-6, 3910,
  4151
HUDSON BAY
  Belcher Island archaeology
    816
  Eskimo 801
HUDSON RIVER SCHOOL 2220,
  2260
HUDSON VALLEY, prehistory
  379
HUECO AREA, cave sites 594
HUGHES CO, S.D., Arzberger
  site 510
HUHN, RUDOLF VON 2434
HUI HSIEN WARE 4346
HUICHOL INDIANS, symbolism
  982
HULBERG, JOHN 4195
HULL, J. 3873
HUMAN ENGINEERING 2005
HUMAN FIGURE IN ART 2005
  Jewish art 4275
Humbolt Sink, archaeology
  4109
Hunt, W.B. 2895
Hunt, Mrs. Roy Arthur, Col-
  lection 1875
Hunter, N.E. 2044
Hunter, W.A. 1584
Hunter, W.H. 145, 2672
Hunter Collection 2086
HUNTERS AND HUNTING
  277-8
  Australia 1325
  buffalo 267
  Catawba 458
  Eskimo 819
  family hunting territories--
    Arctic 821, Northwest
    North America 795
  Ohio Valley, archaic 306
  Peru, lizard 976
  Rappahannock taking devices
    442
  Tigara whale hunters 822
HUNTING IN ART 1889
  Tiryns fresco 3184

HUNTINGTON, ANNA HYATT
2536-8
Huntington, A.M. 1530, 1625,
3251
Huntsinger, L.M. 1727
HUPA INDIANS, warfare 761
HURD, PETER 2435
HURON INDIANS
ossuary 452, 4093
treaty belts 2848
Hussey, M.I. 1597
Hutchinson, Archibald Alex-
ander, Collection 3050
Hutton, Barbara, Collection
4349
HUTZLER, ELSA W. 2539
Huxley, H.M. 1088
Huxtable, A.L. 4392
Huyghe, R. 4248
Hyde, James Hazen, Collec-
tion 4251
HYMNS See also Chants
Babylonian 1612
Chinook 1665
Sumerian 1615-6
HYPERBRACHYCEPHALY 1338

I

IBERVILLE PARISH, LA,
Bayou Goula site 367
IBI-SIN, KING 1606
ICONOGRAPHY See Christian
Art and Symbolism;
Heraldry; Marks; Signs
and Symbols
ICONS 4277
IDAHO, archaeology 511
Indians 4095
"IDAHO," derivation and mean-
ing 1474
Idaho State College Museum,
archaeological survey
system 210
Ide, J.J. 1934
Ife, art 4284d

I'i, J.P. 1282
IKAT, Peruvian 3744
ILLINOIS
archaeology and Indians 474,
489--Crable site 399,
Chicago 333, early 537
Ferry site 478, Hardin
Co site 478, Hopewell
Culture 475, 1000 A.D.
records 473, So. Illinois
Woodland Cultures 345
government 3955
history 3955, Indian and
pioneer 476
ILLINOIS INDIANS, quilled
necklace 2890
Illinois State Museum
guide 105
history 106
ILLUMINATION OF BOOKS
AND MANUSCRIPTS
See also Manuscripts
2101
animals in 1873
English 3057
middle ages 2982, 2984,
2986, related to book de-
sign 2985
Mudejar ornament 3368
religious symbolism in 2107
Renaissance 2982, 2984,
2986
ILLUSIONISM PAINTING 1935
ILLUSTRATION OF BOOKS
See also Books and Book
Arts
animals in 1873
Chinese 3382
Don Quixote 3334
international 2102
Japanese 3382
IMPLEMENTS See Tools
IMPRESSIONISM (IN ART)
4255, 4261
French painting 1745
National Gallery of Art
2956

353

INCA LANGUAGE 1496
INCANTATIONS, Aramaic
1608-9, 1611
INCAS See also Andean Area;
Peru
art 3699-3700
musical instruments 1670
quipu 190
wooden cups 3720
INCENSE AND INCENSE
BURNERS
Beth Shan 3600
Piedras Negras 992
INCUNABULA See also Books
and Book Arts
2101
Hispanic Society of Amer-
ica 2103
Pierpont Morgan Library
2986
Walters Library 2983
woodcuts 3336
INDEPENDENT PAINTERS,
Paris, 19th century 3064
INDEPENDENTS OF 1910 2256
INDIA, factory workers 1236
INDIA PRINTS 3586
INDIAN KNOLL, KY, site 332
INDIAN MOUNDS PARK, WIS,
site 297a, 4084
INDIAN RESERVATIONS,
Tierradentro, Columbia
936
INDIAN THEATER, proposed,
Santa Fe 617
INDIANA
art 2376
Glacial Kame Indian Cul-
ture 301
INDIANAPOLIS, artist of 2289
INDIANS OF MEXICO, CEN-
TRAL AND SOUTH
AMERICA See also
names of tribes, linguis-
tic families, and cultures,
as Apalai; Araucanian;
Aymara; Aztecs; Boru-
ca; Bribri; Carib; Caya-

po; Cholti (Chol); Col-
orado; Cora; Guarani;
Huichol; Incas; Itza; Ja-
calteca; Kechua; Kicka-
poo; Lacandon; Mayas;
Mochia; Monagrillo;
Nazca; Paramona; Pa-
tomana; Proto-Lima;
Sana Eulalia; Serente;
Seri; Tairona; Talaman-
ca; Tarahumare; Taras-
co; Toltecs; Tzeltal;
Xicaque, Yaqui
834-1000, 4122-30, 4233-4,
art 3699-3775, 4233-41,
dermatoglyphics 1371, 1374-
5
folk literature and folk lore
1441--Amazonian myth
1442, Guatemala myths
1443--Yaqui 4145
lateral dominance 1374-5
linguistics and grammar
1495-1503
literature 1568-88
mixed blood 980
tribes--Mexico, southern
942, Peru 865
exhibits--University Museum 165
INDIANS OF NORTH AMERI-
CA See also names of
tribes, linguistic fami-
lies, and cultures, as
California Area Indians;
Eastern Woodlands Cul-
ture Area; Northwest
Coast Culture Area;
Plains and Plateau Cul-
ture Area; Southwest
Culture Area; and Aco-
ma; Adena People; A-
leuts; Algonquian; Ana-
sazi; Apache; Arapaho;
Arikara; Bannock; Bas-
ket-Maker; Beaver;
Bellacoola; Beothuk;
Bluff-Dwellers; Bungi;

Caddo; Caddoan; Canadian Dakota; Canalino; Catawba; Cherokee; Cheyenne; Chilicotin; Chilkat; Chipewyan; Chippewa; Chitimacha; Coast People; Cree; Creek; Crow; Dakota; Datsolalee; Delaware; Diegueno; Dismal River Aspect; Dwamish; Early Woodlands; Eastern Cree; Eastern Dakota; Effigy Mound; Eskimos; Eyak; Flathead; Forest Eskimos; Fort Ancient Aspect; Fox; Fremont; Glacial Kame; Great Bend Aspect; Green River; Haida; Hasinai; Havasupai; Hawikuh; Hidatsa; Hopi; Hupa Huron; Illinois; Iroquois; Jemez; Jicarilla; Kaguanton; Kalispel; Kansa; Karankawa; Keresean; Kichai; Kiowa; Klamath; Kwakiutl; Laguna; Lenape; Lillooet; Luiseno; Mahican; Maidu; Makah; Mandan; Massachuset; Meearmeear; Menominee; Micmac; Mimbreno; Mimbres; Mission; Mistassin; Miwok; Modoc; Mogollon; Mohave; Mohawk; Montagnais; Montauk; Mound Builders; Narraganset; Nascapee; Nauset; Navaho; Ntlakyapamuk; Oglala; Ojibwa; Old Copper; Oneida; Oregon Territory; Osage; Oto; Owasco Sequence; Ozark Bluff-Dwellers; Paiute; Pajaritan; Palm Springs; Papago; Patawatomi; Paviotso; Pawnee; Pend d' Oreille; Penobscot; The People; People of the Long House; Pima; Plains; Pomo; Ponca; Potawatomi; Powhatan; Pre-Lenape; Pueblo; Puget Sound; Quinaielt; Quinalt; Rappahannock; Reserve Phase; Salish; Salteaux; San Carlos Apache; Sanilac; Sarsi; Sauk; Seneca; Shawnee; Shell Heap; Shinnecock; Shoshonean; Shoshoni; Shuswap; Sinagua; "Southern Cult;" Stockbridge; Tawakoni; Tetes de Boule; Teton; Tewa; Thompson; Tlingit; Trenton Argillite; Tsattine; Tsimshian; Upper Republican Complex; Ute; Waco; Wahpeton; Wampanoag; Washo; Wichita; Winnebago; Yuchi; Yukian; Zuni. See also aspects of culture as Canoes; Rites and Ceremonies
218-833, 4074-4121
architecture 2898-2909
art 2719-2897, 4233-41
bibliography--New Jersey 300; theses and dissertations 219
costume and adornment--2840-50, Hidatsa 534, Kaguanton 791, Mohave 763, New Jersey 300 Plains 523, Tlingit 792
dwellings 2898-2909--cattail 756, Chilkat 790, whale house 789, Hidatsa earth lodge 535, Kentucky 436-7, Modoc 753-

4, New Jersey 300,
Pennsylvania 435, Pile-
dwelling 423, Pueblo
Modern 647, rock-shel-
ter, Texas 520
folk literature and folk lore
1408-40
linguistics and grammar
1478-94
literature 1559-67
music 1661-8, 4152
physical anthropology--
craniology 1369--teeth
1369
social life and custom 266-
78, 444-65, 537-77, 710-
29, 758-64, 794-9, 819-
23, 4097
INDIANS OF NORTH AMER-
ICA IN ART
Bodmer 2727
Catlin 2285, 2727
portraits 2738
Sohon 2238
INDIANS OF THE AMERICAS
See also Indians of Mex-
ico, Central and South
America; and Indians
of North America
218-221, 4074-6, art 4233-
41
INDIANS, EAST, in Fiji 1278
INDIANS, TREATMENT OF
Pueblo Indians 613, 616
U.S. land policy 4094
INDIC LANGUAGES 1514
INDIVIDUAL AND SOCIETY
1680
INDONESIA, art 3680
INDUS VALLEY, archaeology
1255
INDUSTRIAL DESIGN 1997
INDUSTRIES See also Forg-
ing; Mines and Mining;
Occupations
Iroquois 4097
INFANT CARE, Hawaii 1333

Ingholt, H. 1083
Ingle, T. 4189
INGRES, J.A.D. 3070
INHERITANCE, digital mal-
formation 1339
INLAY WORK See also Da-
mascening; Mosaics
Pueblo Indian beads 2888
INSCRIPTIONS See also Stele
(Archaeological); Tab-
lets and Cylinders
Akkadians 1179
Arabic 3527
Babylonian 1193
Chinese 3434
Etruscan 1029
Hebrew 1591
Indian 3584
Mayan 1569, 1577, 1587
Meroitic 1229, 3551
Minturnae 1033
Nippur 1193
Sumerian 1184
INSECTS, musicians 1063
Institute of Andean Research
875, 905, 930, 1376
INTAGLIOS 2012
INTERIOR DECORATION
2113-4, 4384-97,
U.S. 2640-60
International Biennial of Con-
temporary Color Lithog-
raphy 1959
International Biennial of
Prints 4296
International Color Woodcut
Exhibition 4297
INTERNATIONAL EXCHANGE
IN ARTS 39
International Exhibition, Cer-
amics 2013
International Exhibition of Con-
temporary Glass and
Rugs 2002
International Exhibition of
Photography, Hartford
1973

International Salon of Photographic Art 1974
International Watercolor Exhibition, biennial 1904
INVENTORS AND INVENTIONS
Abraham, improved plow 1145
IOWA (IOWAY) INDIANS
ethnology 508
medicine ceremony 274
tomahawk 526
societies 568
IPIUTAK, and Arctic whale hunting culture 821
IPSWICH, houses 2696
IRAN See also Persia 1071
anthropology and archaeology 1073, 1081--cave exploration 1251, Hasanlu 1072
tribes, map 1069
IRAQ
anthropology 1978-9, 1081, 1139
Arabs 1080
Jazira 1079
Jemdet Nasr 1085
Kurdistan 1079
tribes, map 1069
IRON AGE, Hasanlu, Iran 1072
IRON AND IRONWORK
New Jersey 2619
Pennsylvania Dutch stoves 2618
IRELAND, physical anthropology 1379
IROQUOIS INDIANS 377, 396, 402, 4097, 4120
antler figurine 2777
crafts 2737
flintlocks 430
food 429
legends and myths 1425
Longhouse 2901
masks 2779

New York State Museum 135
tobacco pouch 2754
Irvine, A. 771
IRVING, WASHINGTON 1527
and Sunnyside 1522
diary in Spain 1531
Irwin, C.C. 493
Irwin, H.J. 493
ISHTAR, journey to Hell 1452
ISIDORE OF CHARAX 4007
ISIN, DYNASTY OF 1169
ISLAMIC ART See Art, Mohammedan
ISLAS REVILLAGIGEDO 3983
ISRAEL See also Art, Jewish; Judaism; Palestine
painting 3599
ITALY See also Art, Italian
American artists in 2270; 2302
archaeology 1032--Carmona 1031, Minturnae 1030, 1033-6
ITZA INDIANS See Mayas; also cities of the Itza, as Chichen Itza; Peten
Ives, C.E. 1532
IVORY AND IVORY CARVING
Benin cups 3670
Cocle figurines 3714
Hornbill ivory 3437
Oriental 3375
walrus 2784

J

JACALTECA INDIANS 978
JACKSON, A.Y. 2141-3
Jackson, R.L. 1726
Jackson, W.H. 3994-5
JACOB'S CAVERN, MO, archaeology 466
JACQUE, CHARLES 3135
JACQUERED WEAVING 2045
JADE

357

American 422
Oriental 3375, Chinese 3440-2
Pre-Columbian 3751, 3756
Jaeger, E. 271; 2902
Jaehne, Herman A.E., and Paul C., Collection 1779
JAKETOWN, site 312
JAMAICA, kitchen-middens 933
JAMES, ALEXANDER 2436
Janis, S. 3312
JAPAN
American painters of Japanese origin 2367
archaeology 1055
cormorant, domestication 1058
Luchu Islands anthropology 1066
exhibits--Chicago Natural History Museum 90
JAPANESE PRINTS See COLOR PRINTS, JAPANESE
JAR, Mexican onyx 3726
Jarves Collection 3262
JARVIS, JOHN WESLEY 2306
JAVA
batic designs 3869
giant early man 1403
physical anthropology 1391
Pithecanthropus 1340
puppets 3696
Solo man 1396
JAWS See Craniology
JAY, JOHN, portraits of 1934
Jayne, H.H.F. 1215, 2583, 2738, 3383, 3418, 3440
JAZIRA, IRAQ, anthropology 1079
JEDDITO 264, Basket-Maker III site 596
ware 4354
JEDDITO VALLEY, ARIZ, coal mine, prehistoric 689

Jefferys, C.W. 2144
Jehl, F. 4406
JEMDET NASR, IRAQ, excavations 1085
JEMEE CAVE, N.M. 580
JEMEZ INDIANS, weaving 2836
JEMEZ PUEBLO 660
Jenkins, L.W. 143, 2221
Jenness, D. 816
Jeske, J.A. 494
JESUS CHRIST See also Bible; Christian Art and Symbolism; Christmas in Art
life in art 1880-1, 1946
JEWELRY See also Gems and Precious Stones; and types of jewelry, as Bracelets; Earrings; Necklaces
Chinese 3438
classical 4356
Greek 3173, 3181
Indians of North America 2787, 4238
industry, Newark 2575
instructions for making 4357
Italian 3286
Merovingian 2977
Near East 3173
Roman 3173
Russian Imperial 4355
Jewett, Patty Stewart, Collection 741
JEWISH ART
American Jewish Tercentary 2366
JICAQUE INDIANS See Xicaque Indians
"JICARA," derivation and meaning 1505
JICARILLA INDIANS See also Apache Indians
childhood and youth 721
JICARILLA APACHE LAN-

GUAGE AND LITERA-
TURE 1562
JIVARO INDIANS
mummified heads 969
Jochelson, W. 1048-51
Johnson, A.M. 3362
Johnson, E. 451, 4073
Johnson, G.W. 4407
Johnson, J. 1033-4
Johnson, John G., Collection
2961
Johnson, L.F. 3140
JOHNSON, SAMUEL 1533
Johnson, U.E. 2495-7, 2509
Johnson, W.T. 2710, 3976
JOHNSON CO, KY, site 289
Johnston, E.L. 2552
JOHNSTON, HARRIET LANE
1760
Johnston, M.T. 3147
Jonas, L. 54
JONATHAN CREEK VILLAGE,
KY, site 335
Jones, A.H. 2261, 4197
Jones, F.F. 4164
Jones, F.W. 1347
Jones, L.C. 4197
Jones, M. 1310
JONES, ROBERT EDMOND
1644
Jones, T. Catesby, Collection
1817
JONES, VOLNEY H.   2716
Josenberg, J. 3017-8
JUANES, JUAN DE 3321
JUDAISM, art 3588-9, 3591,
3594-5, 4275
JUGS, English silver cream
3049
Julien, C. 2684
JULIEN, HENRI 2145

K
KABAL 3766
KACHINAS See Katcinas
KAGUANTAN INDIANS, shark

helmet 791
Kahnweiler, W.S. 796
KAHOOLAWE, archaeology
1293
KAIBITO PLATEAU, ARIZ,
archeology 653
KAINEN, JACOB 2437
KALISPEL INDIANS
Sohon's portraits of Pend
d'Oreille Indians 2338
Kalm, P. 3911
Kalman Collection 3379
Kaltenbach, G.E. 4165
KAMAKURA PERIOD, painting
3484
KAMEHAMEHA 1274
KANDINSKY, WASSILY 3298-9
KANSAS
archaeology--McPherson Co
514, Minneapolis I Vil-
lage 514, Ottawa Co 514,
Salina I Village 514
Kansas. University. Museum
of Natural History 107
KAPINGAMARONGI, material
culture 1306
KARANKAWA INDIANS 314
KARANOG
archaeology 1234
Meroitic inscriptions 1229
Romano-Nubian cemetery
1235
KAROLIK, MAXIM 2252, 2259
Karolik, M. and M., Collec-
tion 2188, 2246, 2252,
2258-9, 2266
Heade paintings 2300
KARP, LEON 2438
KATCINAS 2894-5
Hopi 2896
Pueblo 2520
Katzenstein, I. 4189
KA-WAIKA-A, kiva murals
2755
KECHIPAUAN PUEBLO (ZUNI),
age 691
KECHUA LANGUAGE 1496-7

Keiser, C.E. 1182
Keith, C. Minor, Collection 3713b
Keith, L. 1283
KEITH, WILLIAM 2307
Keithahn, E.L. 2739
Kelby, W. 2222
KELLER, HENRY GEORGE 2439
Kelly, A.R. 1355
Kelly, C.F. 3473
Kelly, J.C. 695
Kelly, L. 2434
KEMOHA 175, 495, 3956
KEMPTON, GRETA 2440
Kennan, G.F. 39
Kennedy, R.W. 4256, 4299-4300
KENT, FRANK 2441
KENTUCKY
archaeology 281, 289, 291, 293-4, 298, 302, 309, 332, 335, 342, 357-8, 360, 363, 370-4, 389, 399a, 410, 436-7
effigy pipe 2774
literature 1750-1840 1526, Frankfort 1538
sandals and fabrics, Indian 2833
wooden image 2775
KEPES, GYORGY 2965
Keppler, J. 2779
KERESAN INDIANS, weaving 2836
KERMA, AFRICA, excavations 1115
KERN, EDWARD M. 2308
Kern County Museum, Pioneer Village 4041
KEWEENAW WATERWAY, Old Culture 369
KHAFAJE 1136
KICHAI INDIANS 418
KICKAPOO INDIANS 388
Kidd, K.E. 452
Kidder, A. II 874-5, 3704

Kidder, A.V. 624-6, 739, 2711-2
Kidder, J.E. 3474
Kidder, M.H. 2290
Kiddle, L.B. 1505
Kimball, F. 1788, 2434, 2673, 3009, 4393
KINTETIC CONSTRUCTIONS 1979
King, A.R. 876, 2763
King, D.S. 627
King, E.S. 2186
King, M.E. 3739
Kingdon, F. 24
KINGMAN, DONG 2442
KINGS See also names of kings, as
Tizoc
African, day in life 1111
Babylonian, atonement rite 1188, reigning 3500-3000 B.C. 1192
Sumer, deified 1187
Kinietz, V. 461-2
KINSHIP See also Heraldry; Totems and Totemism
Admiralty Islands 1329
Chilkat Indian house posts 790
Guinea, twins in 1103
Hopi 717-8
Laguna 722
Northwest Indians, family hunting territories 795
Philippine Islands 1328
Tlingit Indians, clan hats 792
Zuni 715
KIOWA INDIANS
dance, Sun 569
societies 557
KIOWAN LANGUAGE 1483, 1489
KIPU See Quipu
KIRCHNER, ERNST LUDWIG 3147
KIRKUK, archaeology 1124, 1137

360

Kirstein, L. 171, 2331
KIRTLAND SOCIETY 246
KISH CEMETERY, MESOPO-
TAMIA, excavations
1086-7
Kissell, M. L. 2863
KITCHEN-MIDDENS See also
Shell-Heap Culture
Jamaica 944
KIT-SELAS, legends of 1416
KIVAS
circular, New Mexico 692
Great Kiva, Aztec Ruin 698
--Chaco Canyon 4118
mural decoration 2755
Kivett, M. F. 485, 496
KIYONAGA 3494
KLAMATH BASIN,
anthropology, bibliography
4113
KLAMATH INDIANS 740, 746
ethnography 4088a
petroglyphs 758
Klapper, W. 3936
Kleinschmidt, J. 4339
KLETZIEN MOUND, WIS 339
KNATHS, KARL 2374
Kneeland, H. T. 1915
KNIGHTS AND KNIGHTHOOD
See Arms and Armor;
Middle Ages
Knox, S.H. 1691
KOBUK RIVER
Arctic Woodland Culture 806
Forest Eskimos in 1880's
807
Kocher, A. L. 2698
Koenigswald, G.H.R. von
1396, 1400
KOLLWITZ, KATHE 3158
Korth, 3958
KORYAKS
culture and social organiza-
tion 1048
religion and myths 1049
KOURION, GREECE, prehis-
toric site 1015, 1017,
1021, 1023

figures 3197
Kraeling, E.G. 3590
Kraemer, C.J. 3226
KRAMER, HELEN KROLL
2597
Kramer, S.N. 1138-9, 1183,
1448-9, 1599
Krappe, A.H. 3888
KREDEL, FRITZ 2636, 3854
Kress, Samuel H., Collection
2926, 2931, 2934, 2936,
2941, 2944, 2947, 2957,
2963, 2966, 2970, 2975,
3258, 4046
KRIEGHOFF, CORNELIUS
2146
Kris, E. 2010
Kroeber, A.L. 249, 542, 545,
696, 715, 877-9, 1327-8,
2864-5
KUAN YIN 3373
KUAUA PUEBLO 664
Kubler, G. 1788, 3710
KUHN, JUSTUS E. 2212
KUHN, WALT 2349, 4198
Kuhnel, E. 3359, 3540, 3574
KUNIYOSHI, YASUO 2349
Kunz, F.G. 1184
KURDISTAN, IRAQ, anthro-
pology 1079
KURSI 3575
KUSH, cemeteries 3648
KWAKIUTL INDIANS, Van-
couver Island 765
KWAKIUTL LANGUAGE AND
LITERATURE 1559
KWEICHOW, MIAO PEOPLE
1064
KWOK, D. 3413
KYLIX 3208

L
Labaree, B.W. 4393
LABNA, MEXICO, cultures
921
LABRADOR

Eskimos and Indians,
anthropometry 1365
Hopedale Area archae-
ology 824
LACANDON INDIANS, derma-
toglyphics 1371
LACES AND LACE MAKING
2046
design 2031
European 2978
French 3147
modern bobbin 2040
Spanish 3358
catalogs--Hispanic Society
of America 2039-40
LA COLOMBIERE, rock shel-
ter 1008
LA CASTEUSE, N.M., site
669
LA CORUNA, costume 3357
LACQUER AND LACQUERING
3375
Chinese statue 3431
"Ladies of the Court" 3404,
3414
LADINOS, Indians and 972
La Farge, O. 942, 978
LAFAYETTE, MARIE JOSEPH
3870
LA FLORE CO, OKLA, Spiro
Mound 470
LAGUNA INDIANS
kinship 722
rites and ceremonies 723
LAHEY, RICHARD 2443
Laidlaw, S.J. 4094
La Jolla Art Center 4051
Lakokis, Michael 1986
LAKE NEMI, marbles 3240,
3247
LALANNE, MAXIME 3136
LAMA DOUSAND UP 3514
La Magdalena, archaeology
4126
LAMAISM
Newark Museum 3516
Tibet and Mongolia 3512

Tibetan art 3511
LaMar, Virginia A. 3045,
4408
LAMATA, VENEZUELA, ex-
cavations 837
LAMBAYEQUE VALLEY,
PERU, archaeology 836
Lambert, M.F. 628
LAMPS, Eskimo stone 2766,
2773
LAMUT, folk lore 1444
LANCASTER CO, NEBR,
Schrader site 487
LAND TENURE AND USE
Mexico village 979
Navaho Indians 716
New York State 1521
Northwest North America,
family hunting territories
795
LANDA, DIEGO DE 928
Landgraf, J.L. 716
LANDING MOUND, KY 374
Landivar, R. 1585
Landsberger, F. 4278
LANDSCAPE ARCHITECTURE
See also Gardens 2718
LANDSCAPE PAINTING
Egyptian 3228
English and Italian, 18th
century 2937
English watercolor 3034
Hudson River School 2220,
2260
LANE, FITZHUGH 2309
Langdon, S. 1085-7, 1185-8,
1450-3, 1600-4, 3602
LANGUAGE ARTS 1404-1633
Lapham, S. 2689
LA PLATA ISLAND, ECUA-
DOR, archaeology 867
LARSA, DYNASTY OF 1169
Larsen, H. 822
LASSEN VOLCANIC NATION-
AL PARK, CALIF
Indians 747
names, geographical 1477

road guide 3985
LATERAL DOMINANCE, Mexican Indians 1374-5
LATEX CASTS 59
LATIN AMERICA, art 4199
Sociology 4116
"Latin American Collection Paintings" 2912
Lau, R. 1164
LAU ISLANDS, FIJI
social life and customs 1326
southern ethnology 1304
LAUDERDALE CO, ALA, Perry site 415c
Laufer, B. 196,1005, 1058-60, 1063, 1109, 1649, 1879, 2076, 3387a, 3447, 3524, 3778
LAW
African, native 1110
Babylonia, documents 1166, 1183
code, oldest written 1617
Roman 3226
Zuni Indians 724
LAWRENCE, THOMAS 3030, 4252
LAWSON, THOMAS BAILEY 2310
LEADERSHIP, Palau 4140
LEATHER 2059-60
Buffalo robes 2830, Indians of North America and 267
California jackets 2599
hide dressing, Plains Indians 2835
parfleche and rawhide 2834
Leavitt, T.W. 2267, 3093
LEBDUSCA, LAWRENCE 2390
Leche, S.M. 1374-5
LECHFORD, THOMAS 2234
Lee, J.G. 3383, 3410, 3462-3
Lee, R.W. 1712
Lee, T.R. 2152
LEE MILL CAVE 407

Leechman, J.D. 797
Lefebure, E. 3147
Leff, J.C., Collection 4161
LE FLORE COUNTY, archaeology 4074
LEGENDS See Folk Literature and Folk Lore
LEGER, FERNAND 3107
Legrain, L. 1140-3, 1189-93, 1605-6, 3242, 3525, 3603-7, 3610-3, 3617-21, 3636
Leguizamon, M. 1629
Lehman, Robert and Philip, Collection 1707
Lehmann, P.W. 3231
Lehmann-Hartleben, K. 1084
Lehmann-Haupt, L. 1680
LEHN, JOSEPH 2311
Leigh, W.W. 1388
Leighton, A.H. 629
Leighton, D.C. 629
LEKANAI, Boetian 1090
Lemoine, G. 1488
LE NAIN, LOUIS 3113
LE NAIN, MATHIEW 3113
LENAPE INDIANS See Delaware Indians; Pre-Lenape Culture
Leonard, H. 1975
Leonard, S.R. 2686
LEONARDO DA VINCI 3267, 3273
influence in Spain 3321
LEONID B (LEONID BERMAN) 2971
LERIDA CERAMICS 3348
Leroy, E.D. 3912-3
Le Sueur, Jacques 272
Letcher Collection 3394
LEVANNA, N.Y., Algonquian village site 375
LEVINE, JACK 2377, 2444
Levy, J. 171
Lewin, J. 1110
Lewis, A.B. 1288-9, 1316, 3586, 3682-3, 3689, 3698

363

Lewis, O. 979
Lewisohn Collection 1748
LEYIT KIN, N.M., ruin 686
Libbey Glass Company, history 2019
LIBERIA 1097
Liberman, A. 4312
LIBERTY POLE 2674
LIBRARIES See also names
    of libraries, as Boston
    Public Library; Harvard
    University; Hispanic Society of America; Pierpont Morgan Library
    Central and South America
    1580
    Nippur temple library 1447,
    1456
    University Museum library
    164
Lichten, F. 4332
Lieberman, W.S. 4200
LILITH LEGEND 1454
Liljeblad, S. 4095
LILLOOET INDIANS 783
LIMOGES, enamels 3145
LINCOLN, ABRAHAM
    Gardner photograph 3862
    Gettysburg address in
    handwriting 3862
    in Chicago 3959
    photograph of 1936
LINCOLN-DOUGLAS DEBATES
    1518
Lindbergh, C.A. 3845
Linstrom, M. 4166
LINEN
    American, historic scenes
    2591
    flax, history 2593
Linginston Codes 990
LINGUISTICS AND GRAMMAR
    1467-1516, 4150-1
    Oregon Territory, Indian
    languages, map 769
LINTEL, Mayan 3715
Linton, R. 326, 546-8, 1290

Lionni, L. 2434
LIPIT-ISHTAR, CODE OF
    1618
LIPPITT HOMESTEAD 134
LIPSCHITZ, JACQUES 3142,
    4284e, 4317
Lipschitz, Jacques, Collection
    4284e
LIPTON, SEYMOUR 2528
LISMER, ARTHUR 2147
Lister, R.H. 518
LITCHFIELD TOWN, Colonial
    industries 3879
LITERARY LANDMARKS AND
    LOCALE
    Irving, Washington--Sunnyside 1522
    Shakespeare, William--
    1545, Anne Hathaway cottage 1543, birthplace
    1544, Stratford-upon-
    Avon 1545-6
LITERATURE 1517-1633
LITERATURE, AMERICAN
    See also names of authors, as Clemens; Hawthorne; Irving; Whittier
    Atheneum influence on 1557
LITERARY MANUSCRIPTS,
    Pierpont Morgan Library
    2097, 2986
LITHOGRAPHS See also names
    of artists, as Daumier;
    Manet; Toulouse-Lautrec
    1949-50, 1962, 4285
Little, N.F. 1797, 2187
Little, R.B. 2718
LITTLE BEAR CREEK, ALA,
    site 415b, 4096
LITTLE COLORADO, archaeology 4099
    ceramics 4352
    ruins 704
LITTLE LAKE, CALIF, site
    738
"LITTLE MASTERS," Dutch
    painting 2999

364

Livengood, W.W. 2104
Liveright, Frank I., Collection 4372
LIVINGSTON CO, N.Y., site 3894
LIZARD HUNTS, Peru 976
LLANOS, FERRANDO DO 3321
LOAN WORDS, ancient Mexico 1501
  in interpretation of history 1469
LOCK HAVEN, PA, site 303, 336
Locke, A. 3645
Locke, L.L. 190, 949-50
Lockett, H.C. 630
LOCOMOTIVES See also Railroads
  America's first, the Stourbridge Lion 2560
LOCRIAN TERRA-COTTAS 3243
LODAISKA site 493
LOGAN CO, KY, Page site 370
LOGGING, terminology 1471
LOHANS 3406
  ceramic statue 3449
LOLOS, objects 1065
LOLTUN CAVE, YUCATAN, exploration 922
Long, B. 3740
Long, C.J. 25
Long Collection 3740
LONG ISLAND, NEW YORK
  archaeology and Indians 337, 417--Easthampton cemetery 448, Shinnecock 323, Stony Brook site 381, tribes 338
  gun collections 4373
LONGHOUSE, Iroquois 2901, 4102
Longstreet, G.W. 1735
Longyear, J.M. III 880, 3741
Loo, C.T. 3407

LOOMS See also Weaving 2028
LOPEZ MEZQUITA, JOSE MARIA 3318
LORALAI, archaeology 4135
LORD OF ARATTA 1448
LOS ANGELES
  artists of, annual 2355
  history 3977
LOS ANGELES COUNTY, CALIF
  Indians, prehistoric 749
Los Angeles County Museum
  American artists, biennial 2360
  de Sylva Collection 1745
  habitat groups of North America 108
  Kress Collection 2947
  Los Angeles artists, annual 2355
  paintings, European, catalogs 2946
  sculpture, Gothic and Renaissance, catalogs 2974
LOS MANITOS 855
LOS MUERTOS, ARIZ, ruins 608
Lothrop, S.K. 881-4, 951-2, 980-1, 3742, 3762
LOUISIANA
  archaeology 310-11, 267-8, 394
LOVE CHARM 1609
Lowe, S.K. 1506, 4005
Lowenthal Collection 1820
LOWER PECOS, TEXAS, painted pebbles 684
LOWER SAN JUAN RIVER, ARIZ, sites 579
Lowie, R.H. 497, 528, 549-60, 717-8, 898, 1418-9, 2741
LOYALISTS (New Brunswick, Canada)
  3791, 3800-1, 3812, 3840
Lucas, E.L. 1852-3
Lucas, F.A. 26, 55
LUCAS Y PADILLA, EUGENIO 3319

Luce, S.B. 1022, 3194-5, 3213-8, 3224, 3232, 3249, 3571
LUCHU ISLANDS, JAPAN, anthropology 1066
LUISENO INDIANS, cremation rites and ceremonies 760
LUKS, GEORGE BENJAMIN 2312
Lumholtz, C. 982
LUMMIS, CHARLES 3860
Casa de Adobe 2704
Luomala, K. 1291-2, 1404, 1461-3
LURISTAN BRONZES 3634-6
Lustig, A. 2003
LUSTREWARE
Persian 3628
Spanish 3345
Luther, C.F. 2650
Lutz, F.E. 3713a
Lutz, H.F. 1607
LUZON, folklore 1464
Lyons, E. 4270
LYTTON, B.C. archaeology 778

M
McAllester, D.P. 1667, 4149
McAllister, J.G. 1293
McAndrew, J. 1825
McArthur, L.A. 1470
MacBeath, G. 2153, 3802-4
McBride, H. 2282
MC CARTER SITE 4105
McCarthy, R.L. 4097
McCausland, E. 2451
MC CLAUGHRY, WIS, mound 340
McClintock, W. 561
MACOMB CO, MICH, site 316
McCormack, H.G. 2305
MC CORMICK, CHAUNCEY 3071
McCormick, Elizabeth Day, Collection 2066

McCown, D. 1144
McCoy, E. 2685
McCracken, H. 2327
McCulloch, W.F. 1471
MacCurdy, G.G. 1389
McDermott, J.F. 2340, 4201
Macdonald, D.K. 2047
MACDONALD, PIRIE 2512
MacDonald, T. 2132
MC DONALD CO, MO, site 466
McFadden, G.H. 1023
MacFarlane, J. 2592
McGimsey, C.R. 940
Macgregor, G. 1294-5
McGregor, J.S. 631-2
MC GUFFEY, WILLIAM HOLMES 4063-4
MACHADO, ANTONIO 1630
MC INTIRE, SAMUEL 2651-3, 4393
McIntosh, W. 832
MACIVER, LOREN 4174, 4202
MACK, GENE 3863
Mackay, E. 1085-7
Mackay, E.J.H. 1255
Mackay, W.A. 2379
McKearin, George S., Collection 2024
McKearin, H. 2024
McKenzie, P. 1489
McKern, W.C. 339-41, 1296
McKibbin, D. 2332
McKinney, R.J. 2350
MC KNIGHT, DODGE 2446
McKown, R. 2328
McLanathan, R.B.K. 1590, 1936, 2189, 2300, 2309
MC LAUGHLIN, JOHN 2372
McLauglin, M. 1420
MC LEAN CO, KY, sites 281, 302
MacLeish, A. 40
MC LEOD, KY, site 342
McMahon, M.M. 4098, 4409
MC MANUS, JAMES GOODWIN 2445
MC MILLAN, MARY 2447

McNay, Marion Koogler,
Collection 1746
MACOA, VENEZUELA, Indians 843
MC PHERSON CO, KANS, site 514
MC QUORQUODALE MOUND, ALA, 420
MacReynolds, G. 1472
MacSherry, C. 4281
McVan, A. L. 1536, 1630
McVaugh, R. 183
MADISON CO, ALA, Flint River site 415a
Madsen, W. 4028
MADURA, INDIA, Temple of 3587
MAHICAN INDIANS 397
wood cup 2769
Mahler, J. 980-1
MAIDU INDIANS
music 1663
mythology 1413
MAILLOL, ARISTIDE 3108-9
sculpture 3143
MAINE
Indian prehistoric burial 464
MAITREYAS 3435
Majewski, L.J. 2339
MAJOLICA WARE
Italian 3287, 3289
Mexican 2716
Spanish American 3346
MAKAH INDIANS 771
MALAGAN 1297
Malbone, E.G. 4224
Maler, T. 885-8
Malo, D. 1298
MAMMALS
capture and preservation 49
skeletal preparation 55
MAMMOTH CAVE, KY, archaeology 360
MAMMATH PIT, N.M. 700
MAGDELENIAN NEEDLES 1001

Magazine Show 2637
MAGAZINES
literary, Swedish-American 1549
little 1535
MAGIC See also Charms;
Medicine Man; Religion;
Rites and Ceremonies
African fetish figures 3669
Algonkian Indian myth 1432
Aramaic 1608-9, 1611
Aymara Indians 997
Babylonian skull 3608
MAGNASCO, ALESSANDRO 2937
MAGOUN, THATCHER 2313
Magriel, Paul, Collection 1911
MAN See also Anthropology
and Archaeology 181-2, 186
MAN, CLIMATE INFLUENCE
prehistoric North America 227
MAN, ORIGIN 1378
MAN, PREHISTORIC See also
Skeletons; and names of
geographical areas and
cultures, as Ohio Valley;
Mound Builders
176, 178-80
America 1348
Boscop skull 1398
California 1358-60
Dryopithecus 1378
giant early man 1403
Gigantopithecus 1400
Hesperopithecus 1351, 1361
Homo capensis 1398
Minnesota Man 1349
New Jersey, Trenton 1352
New Mexico 658
New York 4104
North America 235, 247,
623--copper implements
264, Eastern U.S. 445,
Hudson Valley 379,
Northeast 383, Post-

367

Glacial climatic influence 227, Southwest 582
Peru 919
Pithecanthropus 1340
Sahara 1113
Solo Man 1396
Southwest 582, 662, 671, 680, 694, 1354, 1356
Tangier 1116
Texas 1362, 1368
Wisconsin 387, 1350
MAN, PRIMITIVE See also specific areas, as Africa; Australia
money 193
MANABI, ECUADOR, antiquities 956
Manakee, H.R. 343
MANCHESTER, MASS, harbor chart 3903
MANCHUS 3411
MANDAN INDIANS
painting, white influence on 2727
social life and customs 552
societies 556
MANDARIN SQUARES 3394
Mandelbaum, D.G. 498
MANET, EDOUARD 3064, 3068
lithographs 3150
MANGAIANS, social life and customs 1319
MANGAREVA
archaeology 1280
ethnology 1268
MANGUE INDIANS, pottery 2919
MANHATTAN ISLAND, Indians 395
MANICHAEANS, script 1610
MANIHIKI, ethnology 1269
MANILA CAMPAIGN 2244
MANISES, ceramics 3348
Manney, L. 1538
MANSHIP, PAUL 2540-1
MANTA 3734

MANUSCRIPTS See also Books and Book Arts; Illumination of Books and Manuscripts; and forms of Manuscripts, as Codexes, Papyri
literary 2097, 2986
science 2109
Spanish 3368
catalogs--Glazier Collection 2105
MAORIS See also Art, Maori
tattooing 1334
MAPS, ATLASES AND CHARTS
African tribes 1093
Babylonian ancient map 1185
Baltimore, defense of in 1814 3924
Berks Co, Pa, historic 3902
Berly Harbor 3903
Champlain, Lake 3910
Chittenden Co, Vt 3900
Colorado, historic 3993
Delaware, pictorial 3920
Europe, population movements 1492-1942 1006
Georgia, counties 3946
history of maps 2110
Honolulu 4001
Indians of North America 248-50-- Illinois, historic villages 489, Oregon Territory tribes and languages 769
Iran, tribes of 1069
Iraq, tribes of 1069
Lassen Volcanic National Park 3985
Manchester, Mass 3903
Marblehead Harbor 3903
Marshall Islands 1286
Mays Landing, N.J. 3915
Michigan, historic 3908
New Jersey, historic 3916
Nippur, topographical map

from 1176
North Carolina, Civil War
in 3947, counties 3927,
3949
North Dakota, historic
3997
"Northern Gateway," his-
toric 3921
Oregon Territory, military
forts and sites 3996,
pictorial 3998-4000
Pacific Northwest in 1875
4003
Palm Springs 3991
Pennsylvania--Delaware-
Hudson canals 3912,
railroad connecting 3913,
first map under Penn
3906
Penn's manors 3907
Philadelphia, time of Wm
Penn 3919
Pony Express Route 3994
Salem 3917
Salem Harbor 3903
Seattle 4002
Smith, Capt John, discov-
eries 3904
United States--Indian walk-
ing purchase 3905, Mid-
dle Atlantic Region in
1750 3911, Pennsylvania
-Maryland disputed area
in 1753 3914
Ur of the Chaldees, royal
tombs 1196
Vermont covered bridges
3918
Virginia in 1602 3950
West, trails of Old 3995
Windsor Co, Vt 3901
World 3780-5
Yellowstone Park 3992
York Road, historic 3909
York Town campaigns of
1781 3923
MAPUCHE INDIANS See Arau-

canian Indians
MARACAY, VENEZUELA, ex-
cavations 837
MARAE CHANTS 4024
MARAES 1313
MARAGATO SERIES OF GO-
YA 3337
MARASHU SONS (company),
Nippur 1171-2, 1180
MARAU CEREMONY, Oraibi
Indians 725
MARBLE
Italian statuette 3235
Lake Nemi 3240
Uloa vase 3713
MARBLEHEAD, MASS, harbor
chart 3903

Marceau, H. 2543, 2961,
3098, 3383
March, B. 207
MARCKS, GERHARD 3159
MARCOUSSIS, LOUIS 3300
Marcy, Sigbert H., Collection
2502
MARIANA ISLANDS See also
names of Islands, as
Rota, Saipan, Tinian
archaeology 1302
MARIN, JOHN 2349, 2448
MARINE PAINTING 1929, 2153
American 2172, 2189
Mariners Museum, history and
guide 109
MARINI, MARINO 3274
MARKS See also Heraldry;
Seals; Signs and Symbols
American silversmiths 2605
armorers 2077
China, Tucker 2583
Chinese painting 3421
Japanese pottery 3500
Marmon Memorial Collection
1739
MAROBAVI 4129
MAROGER, JACQUES 2388

MARQUESAS ISLANDS
  art 3681
  legends 1460
  somatology 1394
MARQUESAN LANGUAGE 1460
Marriott, A. 633
MARSH, REGINALD 2388
MARSHALL CO, KY, site 335
MARSHALL ISLANDS
  chart 1286
  fish traps 1318
Martin, Saint, altar frontal
    4315
Martin, C.J. 4357
Martin, D. 4018
Martin, G.C. 634-5, 688
Martin, P.S. 184, 499-500,
    636-43, 2802, 4099
Martin, R.A. 197
Martin, W.J. 1178
MARYLAND
  architecture, domestic, Co-
    lonial 2671
  boundary controversy with
    Pennsylvania, map 3914
  Indians, early 343
  painting in 2212
  paintings, catalog 1850
  sculpture 2527
MASKING COMPLEX, Eastern
    Woodlands 2756
MASKS 1989-91, 4318
  African 3676
  Indians of North America--
    2779-83
  Mexican 3733
  New Guinea 3698
  New Ireland 3697
Mason, D.E. 1673
Mason, G. 3763-5
Mason, J.A. 165, 185, 237,
    255, 529, 644, 889-91,
    984, 1467, 1490, 2742,
    2773, 3713b, 3714-21,
    3751-3, 3760
Mason, Leslie Lindsey, Col-
    lection 1653, 1672

Mason, R.J. 344
MASSACHUSETTS
  harbor charts 3903
  poets 1539
Massachusetts Bay Company
    records 3873
MASSACHUSETTS INDIANS 404
  burial places 463
MASSELINK, EUGENE 2449
MASSET DIALECT 1567
Mastbaum, J.E. 3144
MATHEMATICS See also
    Chronology; Quipu
  Babylonian 1596
  geometry 3777
MATISSE, HENRI 3110-12,
    4243
Matos, M. de 1496
MATTA ESCHURREN, RO-
    BERTO 1909, 2920
MATTA GROSSO EXPEDITION
    892
  primitive inhabitants 901
Matthews, D.W. 719, 1356
MATTOCKS RUIN, N.M. 655
Mau, Elizabeth C., Collection
    2395
MAUI LEGEND 1461, 1465-6
MAUI-OF-A-THOUSAND-
    TRICKS 1461
MAURER, ALBERT H. 2450
MAURER, ALFRED 2451
MAURER, LEONARD 2452
MAUSUMANE BLADE 3504
Mauzy, W.L. 3973
May, F.L. 2039, 3360
MAYA LANGUAGE AND LIT-
    ERATURE
  1500, 1502, 1569
  animal figures in 1588
  astronomy codex 999
  Book of Chilam Balam 1571,
    1578
  Dresden Codex 1575
  Perez Codex 1576
MAYAS See also Art, Maya;
    Art, Pre-Columbian;

names of tribes, as
Cholti Indians; and names
of sites, as Chichen It-
za; Copan; Palenque;
Peten
Cenote of Sacrifice 927,
952, 3756
civilization 845, 924
craniology 1370
dermatoglyphics 1371, 1374
ethnology 925
Itza Indians, Spanish con-
quest of 893, 928
jade 3756
Landa's account 928
lateral dominance 1374
Maya-Spanish crosses (ra-
cial) 998
religion 4032
temple 3774
MAYER, FRANK BLACKWELL
2508
Mayer, G.M. 4312
Mayer, J.F. 430
Mayer-Oakes, W.J. 346-7,
4128
Mayhew, E. de N. 4040
Mayor, A.H. 1884
MAYS LANDING, N.J. 3915
MAXIMS, George Washington
1556
Maxwell, M.S. 345
Mazia, V. de 3061, 3095,
3110, 3115, 4243-4
Mead, C.W. 1670, 3754
Mead, M. 1329-30, 3684
Means, P.A. 893, 3743
"Mechanical Models" 3864
MEDALS
French 2186
Renaissance 2975
MEDICINE, superstitions 4019
MEDICINE BUNDLES See
Charms
MEDICINE IN ART 1884
prints 1972
MEDICINE MAN See also

Charms; Shamanism;
Rites and Ceremonies
Blackfoot medicine-pipe
ceremony 561
Delaware Indians 460
Indians of North America
274
Pawnee Indians, annual
ceremony of 546
Medina, J.T. 1497
MEDORA, LA, site 368
MEEARMEEAR INDIANS,
folklore 461
Meeker, L.I. 562
MEETING HOUSE, QUAKER
2683, 2693-4
Meirs, Richard Waln, Collec-
tion 2859
MEISSEN PORCELAIN 3166
MELANESIA See also names
of areas and cultures,
as Java; Lau
art 4284b
canoes 1307
ethnology 1288
money, shell 1316
Mellink, M.J. 1194
Mellman, M. 1351
Mellon Collection 1767
Melton, A.W. 41, 56
MELTSNER, PAUL 2453
MEMORIALS 4160, 4394
MEMPHIS, EGYPT
excavations 1201, 1207,
1209, 1212
Merenptah throne room 3578
Mit Rahineh 1203-4
sphinx 3559
MENEHUNE OF POLYNESIA
1462
MENIFEE CO, KY, rock shel-
ter 436
MENLO PARK 4406
MENNONITES 3843
MENO, Greek potter 3207
MENIMINEE INDIANS 348
charms 456

371

dance, Dream 444
folklore 1431
material culture 440
pow wow 457
religion--medicine cere-
mony 274
rites and ceremonies 455-6
societies 455
Mera, H.P. 645, 2743, 2788,
2823-9
Mercer, H.C. 2577, 2618,
3766, 3866
Merchant Seamen of the United
Nations, art exhibition
1832
MERCHANTS
American, portraits 2226
Nippur, records 1171-2,
1180
MERENPTAH, throne room
3578
MERIDA, YUCATAN, in 1769
850
MEROITIC INSCRIPTIONS
1229
MEROITIC PYRAMIDS 3648
MEROVINGIAN PERIOD, Jew-
elry 2977
Merrill, R.S. 431
Merrill, W.M. 2654, 4410
Merritt, A.H. 3055
MERRIMACK, archaeological
survey 353
Merwin, B.W. 432, 739, 741,
809, 1671, 2830, 2868,
2884, 3767
Merwin, R.E. 894
MESA HOUSE, skeleton 1360
MESA VERDE WARE 4353
Meserve, F.G. 530
MESOPOTAMIA See also As-
syria—Babylonia; Sumeria
archaeology 1073
Kish 1086-7
ostrich egg-shell cups 3524
Messer, T.M. 4168, 4199, 4229
Metcalf, G. 484

METAL AND METALWORK
See also names of metals,
as Copper; Gold; Iron;
Silver
America, prehistoric use
946
American 2605-23, 4371,
4374
arms and armor 2077-83
Cenote of Sacrifice, Yuca-
tan 952
Chinese 3471-6
clocks and watches 2084-7
coins and medals 2088-91,
2186, 2975
Islamic 3529-31
Japanese 3501-7
Mohammedan 3529-31, 3575
Saracenic 3575
Tairona Culture, Columbia
889
Metropolitan Museum of Art,
arms and armor 4376
gems, engraved 3174
history 1747
Lewisohn Collection 1748
painting--Bache Collection
2950, European 2949,
Flemish, Dutch and Ger-
man 2951, French 3075
picture galleries 1749
MEXICO See also Indians of
Mexico, Central and
South America; and Art
--Pre-Columbian
anthropology 4126-30, cultural change 987, culture
studies 897, land use and
tenure 979
architecture, parallels with
Southwest U.S. 600
art--modern 2913, Spanish
Colonial 2910
folk art 2914
history 1585--Indian uprising in Chiapas 985, offi-
cial reports in 1580 899,

372

Spanish conquest of Yucatan 893, 928
language, ancient 1501
painting, 20th century 2915
pottery--contemporary 2917-9, Oaxaca 2916
religion 4028-9
truck drivers 4124
MEXICO, VALLEY OF, monuments 948
MEYDUM ROOM 3548
sculpture 3564
Meyer, A. 3680
Meyer, T. 3978
MEZUZAH 4278
MEZZOTINTS, English 4177
Miami University 4064
MIAO PEOPLE 1063
MICE, in plague pictures 1940
MICHIGAN
flag 3886-7
Historical Societies 3889
Indians 301, 304, 316-7, 328-9, 334, 344, 425, 450, perforated skulls 1353
map, historic 3908
Museums 66
"MICHIGAN," derivation and meaning 1475
Michigan, University, Ethnobotanical Laboratory 110
MICMAC INDIANS 829
Mickey, M.P. 1064
MICRONESIA, ethnology 1290
MIDDLE AGES See also Art, Medieval
arms and armor 2080, 4373
books 2980, 4382
ceramics, Near East 4351
MIDDLE AMERICA See Indians of Mexico, Central and South America; Spanish America
archaeology 895
chronology--Pre-Classic 914, Viru Valley, Peru 919

Pre-Columbian culture connections 4122
research records 896
Middle American Research Institute
administrative papers of New Spain 112
manuscripts 1581
philological and documentary studies 1468
Yucatan letters 111
MIDDLE VERDE VALLEY, site 591
Middlebrook, L.F. 3890
MIDDENS See KITCHEN-MIDDENS
MIDLAND, TEXAS, prehistoric man 1368
Miers, E.S. 3867
MIESTCHANINOFF, OSCAR 3301
Mileham, G.S. 3579
Miles, G.C. 3364-6
MILITARY HISTORY, museum and 35
U.S. militia 4209
West Point 4220
MILLCAYAC LANGUAGE 1499
MILLES, CARL 3304-5
MILLER, ALFRED JACOB 2314
Miller, G.S. 1340
MILLER CO, NEBR, Bone Cave site 488
Milliken, W.M. 2075
MILLING, Williamsburg 3941
MILLING-STONE, Pueblo 682
Mills, G. 646
Mills, W.C. 349
Milne, A. 4313
MILNE, DAVID 2149
Milner, W.C. 3805-7
Milwaukee Art Center
inaugural exhibition 2952
Zadok Collection 1750
MIMBRENOS INDIANS 655
pottery 2796

MIMBRES CULTURE 590
  Swarts Ruin site 595
MIMBRES VALLEY, N.M.,
  sites 590, 595, 655
MINDANAO
  Bukidon 1275
  Davao District tribes 1276
Miner, D. 1558, 1684, 2985
Miner, H.M. 198, 350, 4137
MINES AND MINING See also
  Quarries
  Africa 1114
  Indians of North America--
    Arizona salt mine 697,
    prehistoric Arizona coal
    mine 689
MING DYNASTY
  arts 3409
  ceramics 3457-8, 3463
MINIATURE ROOMS 2113,
  American 2657a
  European 2988-9
MINIATURES AND MINIA-
    TURE PAINTING See al-
    so Illumination of Books
    and Manuscripts; Por-
    traits; and names of
    artists, as Copley; Dick-
    inson, A; Ramage, J.
  Mughal 3632-3
  New England 2192
  Persian 3631-3
  Virginia, prior to 1850 2271
  catalogs--Fink Collection
    1931, Greene Collection
    1943, Heckett Collection
    1932, Pennsylvania His-
    torical Society 1784
MINNEAPOLIS I, KANS, pre-
  historic village 514
MINNESOTA
  archaeology 290,
  artists 4218-9
  authors 1537
  history in sculpture 3895
  names, geographical 1473
Minnesota Centennial Literature Group 1537

MINNESOTA MAN 1349
MINOAN ART 3183
Minorsky, V. 4279
MINTURNAE, ITALY
  Egyptian landscape 3228
  excavations 1030, 1035-6
  inscriptions 1033
  monuments 1034
  pottery 3250
  sculptures 3245
MIRO, JOAN 1909, 3312, 3320
MIRRORS
  Chinese 3475
  Japanese 3507
  Tsimshian Indian 788
MISCOU, history 3796
MISSILES 191
MISSING LINK See Man, Pre-
  historic
MISSION INDIANS, baskets
  2864-5
MISSIONARIES
  Moravian among Southern
    Indians 391
MISSIONS
  California 2714
  New Mexico 2709, 2716
  Santa Clara, Calif 2713
  Spanish in Arizona 648
MISSISSIPPI
  archaeology 312, 364
  "Mississippi Panorama" 1885
MISSISSIPPI RIVER IN ART
  1885
MISSISSIPPI VALLEY, archae-
  ological survey 366
MISSISSIPPIAN INDIANS 4096
MISSOURI
  archaeology 466, 477, 488,
    504
MISSOURI RIVER IN ART 1885
MISSOURI VALLEY, archeol-
  ogy 471, 515
MISTASSIN INDIANS, hunting
  charms 260
MIT RAHINEH 1203-4
MIWOK INDIANS 731, 734,
  material culture 752

MOANING CAVE, CALIF, ex-
cavations 742
MOBILE COUNTY, archaeol-
ogy 4121
MOBILES 1979
MOCCASINS, Plains Indians
decorations 2851
MOCHICA INDIANS, pottery
3770
MODELS See also Architec-
tural Models; Rooms
aged in paintings 1937
mechanical 3864
Morse, S. F. B., by 2315
MODIGLIANI, AMEDEO 3275,
4257
MODOC INDIANS 746, 4088a
dwellings 753
myths 4143, 4301
rock-shelter 754
petroglyphs 758
MOGOLLON INDIANS 637, 639,
641-2
pottery types 2810
stratigraphic analysis of
community 643
MOGOLLON VILLAGE, N.M.,
637, 639, 641-2
MOHAVE INDIANS
culture 703
etiquette 761
tattooing and face painting
763
MOHAWK INDIANS 377
condolence rite 446
MOHOLY-NAGY, LASZLO
3302
MOKO 3691
MOLARS See Teeth
Molina, Cristobal 985
MONASTARY, Beth-Shan 1242
MONDRIAN, PIET 3011
MONET, CLAUDE 3064, 3068
MONEY See also Coins and
Medals
Greek tetradrachms 1012
Melanesian, shell 1316

Palau 1317
primitive 193
U.S. penitentiaries 4072
wampum 432--criteria of
2841, belt 2842-3, Penn
Indian 2894
MONGOLIA
Lamaism 3512
stone artifacts 1061
Mongan, E. 1965, 3039
MONTAGNAIS INDIANS
birchbark art 2757
hunting charm 260
MONTAGNAIS LANGUAGE
1488
MONTANA, PERU, Indians
929
MONTARDIT (ARIEGE),
FRANCE, skeleton 1380
MONTAUK INDIANS, ceme-
tery 448
Montclair Art Museum 1751
Montgomery, C.F. 4204
Montgomery, J.A. 1145, 1454,
1608-11, 3608
Montgomery, R.G. 648
MONTGOMERY CO, KY,
Ricketts site 372-3
MONTEZUMA MOUNDS 477
Montpetit, E. 3808
MONUMENTS See also Mound
Builders; and types of
monuments, as Stelae;
Sepulchral Monuments
Caracol 3724
Hispanic 2708
Mexico 948
Minturnae 1034
Mission 2709
Moodie, R.L. 208
MOON, Mayas 1587
MOON HALL MONASTARY,
fresco 3403
Moore, Ada Small, Collection
3421
Moore, Colleen 2092
Moore, C.B. 351

375

Moore, E.S., Memorial Collection 2052
Moore, H. 3037
Moore, R.R. 107
Moorehead, W.F. 352
Moorehead, W.K. 353
MORALES, LUIS DE 3321
MORAVIAN CHURCH, missionaries to Southern Indians 391
More, H. 2373
Morgadanes, D. 985
Morgan, E. 3938
Morgan, J.H. 2236, 2239
Morgan, John Pierpont See also Pierpont Morgan Library
149
Morgan, Neil 157
Morgan, R.G. 354-6
Morgan Memorial, Wadsworth Atheneum 172
Morgan Collection 1184
MORGAN STONE MOUND, KY 357
MORIORIS, anthropology 1301
MORISOT, BERTHE 3084
Morley, G.M. 1874, 2352, 2380
Morley, S.G. 649, 986, 1586, 2115
Morley Collection 2115
MORMONS, Kirtland Society 246
MORRELL CO, NEBR, site 468
Morrice, J.W. 2150
Morris, E.H. 650-1, 697-8, 2804
Morris, John Thompson, Collection 3253
Morse, C.R. 3918
Morse, Charles J. and Jared K., Collection 3490
Morse, E.S. 2081, 3500
Morse, Edward S., Collection 3500

Morse, J. 285
MORSE, SAMUEL F.B. 2315
Morse, N. 652-3, 2805
MORTUARY CUSTOMS See also Burial and Burial Mounds; Cemeteries; Cremation; Mummies; Sepulchral Monuments
Chinese 3469, 4133
Early Woodlands burial cult 453
Hopewell 451
Huron ossuary 452
Indians of North America-- New York 448, Ohio 331, Pennsylvania 447
Zapotec urns 3721
MORTUARY PILLOWS 4133
MOSAICS
Babylonian 3605
Indians, Southern California 2765
Mexico 3757
Roman 3232
Mosher, S. 2090
Moss, J.H. 501
MOTRESOR, JOHN 3828
MOUND BUILDERS See also Cairns; Earthworks; and name of mounds, as Grand River Mound; Serpent Mound; Spiro Mound 239
Florida 351
Illinois 287
Mississippi 364
Ohio 349, 392-3
Wisconsin 390
MOUNDVILLE, ALA, site 400
dwarf skeletons 1364
MT. HOREB, KY, site 358, 374
MOUNT VERNON
chinaware 2578
gardens 4411
handbook 4052
history 4407
silverware 2609

376

MOUNTAIN ARAPESH 1330
MOUNTAIN CHANT 1420
MOUNTS, catalog 2567
MOVING PICTURES, film index 1975
Movius, H.L. 1007-8, 1108
MOZART, WOLFGANG AMADEUS 2942
MUDEJAR MANUSCRIPT ORNAMENT 3368
MUEL CERAMICS 3348
MUGHAL MINIATURES 3632-3
MULLICAN, LEE 2371
MULUK AL-TAWA'IF COINS 3366
Mumford, L. 2667
MUMMIES 197
  Egyptian 208, 1226, 1230, 4134, case 1231, cloth 1277, University Museum 1232
  labels, Carnegie Museum 195
  Jivaro Indian 969
  Peruvian 208
  X-ray study 208
MUNDURUCU, expedition 861
Munro, E. 987
Munro, T. 42, 1712
Munro Collection 3049
Munson-Williams-Proctor Institute 4053
MURALS
  Boscoreale 3231
  Boston Public Library 2274
  Chinese frescoes 3403, 3405
  Detroit frescoes (Rivera) 2923
  Palace of Tirynus fresco 3184
  Pueblo kiva murals 2755
  Rio Grande Valley prehistoric frescoes 2732
  Roman 3231
  Roosevelt Memorial, American Museum of Natural History 2379

Murie, J.R. 543, 563
Murphy, M. 3148
Murphy, R.L. 3034
Murphy, R.C. 4205
Murray, C.S. 3939
Murray, G.W. 1516
Murray, H.A. 1680
Musee de Nationale de Paris 3076
Musee National d'Art Moderne 4056
MUSEUM INSTRUCTION See also Education
  12
  art 40, 43
  art projects 36, 48
  science museum, children 56
  woodcraft 38
"Museum News," index 27
Museum of Fine Arts, Boston
  Egyptian Department 3549, 3535a
  Greek and Etruscan vases 3177
  Greek and Roman--antiquities 3169, sculpture 3171
  guide leaflet 1755
  handbook 1754
  history 1753
  Hoyt Collection 3375
  Islamic textiles 3539
  Karolik Collection 2246, 2252
  painting--Attic vase 3185, European 2954, French 3077
Museum of Modern Art
  International Council 39
  painting and sculpture collection 1757
Museum of Primitive Art 3640-2
Museum of Science and Industry, Chicago, guide 113
Museum of the American Indian, guide 114

Heye Collection 115
history 116
West Indies Collection
114
Museum of the City of New
York, guide 117
"The Museum Window" 28
MUSEUM WORK 7
bibliography 34
ethics 4
handbook 25
pensions 32
salaries 21
MUSEUMOBILE EXHIBITS 29
MUSEUMS AND MUSEUM
WORK 1-175
administration and tech-
nique 1-61
attendance 3
bibliography 34
buildings 15
catalogs, guides and his-
tory 71-187
college and university 14
directories 63-70--U.S.
and Canada 4033
financing 13
loans, inter-museum pro-
cedure 10, interna-
tional 39
membership 19
publicity 19
registration methods 18
security 23
trustee-employee rela-
tions 11
visitor behavior 30, 33
United States, oldest 146
MUSIC 1650-76, 4149, 4152-
3
MUSICAL INSTRUMENTS
AND NOISEMAKERS
1653-5
Chinese, ancient 1675
Europe, ancient 1672
Inca 1670
Mexican bone rattles 941,

Pueblo, Apache, and Nava-
ho 4152
Tibetan 3516
MUSKOGEE, archaeology 4105
Mutch, J.S. 801
MYCENAEAN ART 3183
Muers, G.H. 2048
MYERS, JEROME 2316, 2454
Myhrman, F.W. 1612
MYSTERY PACKS See Charms;
Medicine Man
MYSTIC SEAPORT
figureheads 4338
scrimshaw 2529a
ships 4339
MYTHS AND MYTHOLOGY
See Folk Literature and
Folk Lore

N

NAAMAN'S CREEK, DEL,
pile structures 423
Naeseth, H.C.K. 1642
NAGA-ED-DER Stelae 3528
NAHUATL LANGUAGE AND
LITERATURE 1574,
1584
NAKANAI, death rite 1094
NAKUM, GUATEMALA, ruins
957
NALA-DAMAYANT 4291
NALAKIHU, ARIZ, site 627
NAMES, Hopi proper 1493
NAMES, GEOGRAPHICAL
Beverly, Mass 1476
Connecticut 1492
Idaho 1474
Lassen National Park 1477
Michigan 1475
Minnesota 1473
New England 1486, 4151
Oregon 1470
Vermont 1485
Yosemite 4150
NAMES, PERSONAL
Akkadian 1507

artists, pronunciation 4165
Babylonian 1511
Nippur 1509
Sumer 1508
NANTACK VILLAGE 4079
NANTICOME INDIANS 4119
Naples, painting 4245
NAPOLEON, Egypt in his time
1224
NARCOTICS, Peyote 273
NARRAGANSETT INDIANS,
Sachems of 292
Nash, P. 502
Nash, R.C. 988
NASKAPEE (NASKAPI) INDI-
ANS 433
NATAL CUSTOMS AND CERE-
MONIES
Hawaii 1333
Hopi (Oraibi) 726
NATCHITOCHES, LA 394
National Academy Galleries
1830
National Academy of Design
1758
National Association of Por-
trait Painters 2196, 4210
National Baseball Hall of
Fame and Museum 118
National Collection of Fine
Arts
Adams-Clement Collection
1762
catalog 1761a
Gellatly Collection 1759
Johnston, Harriet Lane,
and 1760
Widener Collection 1761
National Committee on Art Ed-
ucation 4169
National Gallery of Art 1769
Booth Collection 1768
Dale Collection 3081
guide 1686
Kress Collection 2957
Medieval art 2955
Mellon Collection 1767

painting--1763-5, American
2191, British 3022, 4247,
Dutch 3001, 4242, Flem-
ish 3000, French 16th-
18th century 3078, 18th
century 3078, 18th centu-
ry 3079, 19th century
3080, German 3152, 4246,
Impressionism and post
impressionism 2956, Ital-
ian 3263, early 3264,
later 3265, Spanish 4249
Renaissance bronzes 2975
Rosenwald Collection 1965
sculpture 1987
Widener Collection 1766
National Gallery of Canada
engagement calendar 1770
paintings and sculpture catalog 1771
NATIONAL PARKS See also
names of parks, as Las-
sen National Park; Yel-
lowstone
Cliff Cities, proposed 618
National Print Annual 2487
National Serigraph Society International, annual 1961
National Society of the Colonial Dames in the State of
Delaware 1938
NATIVISM 4125
NAUSET INDIANS 404
NAUTICAL INSTRUMENTS
4038
NAVAHO INDIANS 633, 654,
676
art 646
blankets 2823, 2832, 4235
culture 646
ethnobotany 687, Ramah
Navaho 707
Gregorio, a psychobiological
study 629
land use 716
music 1667, 4149, 4152
mythology 1435, 4146, 4149

picture writing 2760
pottery 2814
religion 1435-8, 4020
rites and ceremonies, night
chant 719
ritual objects 2760
sand painting 2760, 4241
sex beliefs and practices
710
silver work 2789-90
spinning, dyeing, weaving
2831
social life and customs 720
star lore 1410
symbolism 2760
textiles 2823-5, 2831-2,
2840
veterans, a study of changing values 674
weaving 2837--blanket 2832,
twilled 2825
NAVAHO LANGUAGE AND
LITERATURE 1482, 1563
NAVAHO RESERVOIR DIS-
TRICT, archaeology 4085
NAVIGATION AIDS See also
Map, Atlases and Charts
4007-10, 4038
NAYARIT INDIANS See Cora
Indians
NAZCA PERIOD, PERU
burial 981
textiles 877
Neal, A. 57, 2816
NEALE MOUND, WIS 340
Nealle, J.E. 4412
NEAR EAST, anthropology and
archaeology 1068-1264
NEB-NETERU, mummy case
1231
NEBRASKA
Archaeology and Indians
486-8, 471, 496, 513--
early man 468, human
and animal remains 530,
532, Dismal River Aspect
484, Woodland-like mani-

festations 485, 496
Hesperopithecus 1340, 1351,
1361
Press Association, history
3952
schools, pioneer 1407
Nebraska State Historical So-
ciety Museum 119
Nebraska State Museum 120-1
NEBUCHADREZZAR (NEBU-
CHADNEZZAR)
boundary stone of 1161
proclamation 1181
NECKLACES, Illinois Indian
2890
Osage 4238
NECROPOLIS See Cemeteries
NEEDLES, ANCIENT 1001
NEEDLEWORK 2043
American, 18th century 2259
English 3047
quilts, applique and patch-
work 2587
technique 2050
NEGRITOS, skulls 1401
NEGRO ART See also Art,
African
American contemporary
2382
NEGROES See also Africa
dialect verse of Southern
1554
Negro-White families, U.S.
3852
NEITH, TEMPLE OF 3561
Nelson, B.E. 2112, 2579, 2619
Nelson, N.C. 359-60, 3652
Nelson, N.M. 699
Nelson, William Rockhill, Gal-
lery of Art 1772
NEMAHA CO, NEBR, site 486
NEOSHO RIVER, OKLA, site
494
Nequatewa, E. 1422
"NEPTUNE," ship 3827
Nesbitt, P.H. 655
NETHERLANDS See also Art,
Dutch and Flemish

17th century life 2998
NETSUKES 3496-7
Neuberger Collection 1821
Neuman, G. 656
Neustatter, O. 1940
NEUTRA, RICHARD 2701
NEVADA, archaeology 4107-9
  Indians 748--Gypsum Cave
    737, pottery types 2794,
    4344
Nevada State Museum 122
NEW BRITAIN, death rite
  1094
NEW BRUNSWICK, CANADA
  3817
  history 3794, 3798, 3806-7,
    3810, 3826
  implements 832
  Loyalists 3791, 3800-1,
    3812, 3840
  Portland Point 3799
  settlers 3791, 3805
New Brunswick Museum 123
NEW CALEDONIA, anthropol-
  ogy 1300
NEW ENGLAND See also Pil-
  grim Fathers; United
  States--History--Colonial
  Period
  art 2167, 4229
  Colonial treasures 2654
  flag of 3883
  in art 2211
  Indians--houses, forts, vil-
    lages 2903, tribe names
    and locations 361
  miniatures 2192,
  place names, Indian 4151
  portraits 2210
  Puritans 3892-3
  rarities 2660
  silver 2617
NEW GUINEA
  art 4284b
  canoes 1307
  commerce and trade 1335
  craniometry 1384

decorative art 3683
designs 3682
Dutch New Guinea art 3677
ethnology 1283
masks 3698
oracle 1331
sago, use of 1289
NEW HAVEN
  painting, 20thcentury 2396
NEW HEBRIDES
  art 4284b
NEW IRELAND
  Malagan 1297
  masks 3697
NEW JERSEY
  artists 2181, 2401
  arts and crafts, early 2557-
    8
  ceramics 2578-9
  furniture, early 2557-2648
  history 307, 4398
  Indians 299-300, 307, pot-
    tery 2799, Pre-Lenape
    Culture 326
  iron work 2619
  man, prehistoric 1352
  map, historic 3916
  paintings 2558
  sculpture 2522
New Jersey Collections 1859
New Jersey State Museum 124
NEW MEXICO 3969, 3980
  archaeology 580, 590, 594-
    5, 597, 599, 602, 611-2,
    614-5, 622, 624-6, 628,
    636-9, 641-2, 655, 658,
    660, 669-70, 679, 686,
    692, 699-700--Anasazi
    Culture 628, Reserve
    Phase 589, 638, 640
  bridges, early 3964
  folk art, Colonial 2250
  Franciscans 3978
  history--Hawikuh 619, Rio
    Grande Pueblos, bibliog-
    raphy 585
  Indians, Ramah area land
    use 716

landmarks 3973
missions 2709, 2716
music teaching, 17th century 1657
religion 4021
Spanish language 1504
santos 2267, 2517, 2523
tinware 2606
New Mexico Museum
Borrowdale Collection 2082
dedication 126
history 125, 127
New Mexico State Highway Department 212
NEW WORLD CIVILIZATION
216-7
NEW YEARS, Japanese festival 1067
NEW YORK
archaeology 375, 378, 380,
382, 384-5, 398, 424,
4104, 4120--Algonkian
Village 375, Argillite
Culture 406, Trent
Waterway, Ontario, Canada, relation to prehistory 827
museums 69
octagonal buildings 2686
painters 2261, 4180
painting--central 2353, upstate 2199
NEW YORK CITY
archaeology 308, 321, 381
architecture, modern 4392
arts and crafts, 1726-76
2551, 4331
in art 2209, 4220
Indians--Long Island 337,
381, 417, 448, Manhattan
Island 395, Shinnecock
323
museums 68
obelisk 2699
paintings, 20th century 2396
somatology, native and foreign born 1345

views 3884
New York Historical Society
California Gold Rush Centennial exhibition 1891
catalog 1773
library catalogs 128-32
portraits in 2205, 2216
Stuart Collection 1774
NEW YORK SCHOOL, paintings
and sculpture 2362
New York State Historical Association
Cooperstown 133, 2646-7
Lippitt Homestead and
Farmer's Museum 134
Primitive paintings, American 4197
New York State Museum
Iroquois Indian groups 135
New York World's Fair of
1938
3851
art 1857--British 3031
painting, European 2948
NEW ZEALAND, anthropology
1309
NEWARK
jewelry industry 2575
medals made in 2610
Newark Arts Festival 4054
Newark Museum
acquisitions 1775, 1777-8,
4055
American Indian 251
Bamberger Memorial 1776,
1780
bridal gowns 2598
coverlets 2589
crosses 4328
education 43
garden 136
Glass collection 2020
history 138
Jaehne Collections 1779
planetarium 137
quilts and counterpanes
2595

school house 136
Tibetan art 3516
Ward Bequest 1781
Newberry, John S., Collection 4308
Newcomb, F.J. 2760
Newcomb, W.W. 362
NEWCOMEN SOC. OF NORTH AMERICA 2654, 4410
Newman, H. 4097
Newman, M.T. 1376
NEWMAN, ROBERT LOFTIN 2317
Newman, S.A. 724
NEWPORT NEWS, views 3948
Newton, D. 4284f
Niarchos Collection 1756
Nichols, F.D. 2675
Nichols, H.W. 2076
Niehoff, A. 1236, 2067
NIGHT CHANT 1423
NIMIB, Sumerian God 1615-6
Nimuendaju, C. 898
NINE HEROES TAPESTRIES 3021
NINETEENTH CENTURY
  drawings 4302
  paintings 1697, 2265, 2961
NIPPUR
  arch, archaic 3622
  archaeology 1143-4, 1149-50, 1154
  documents 1166, 1169, 1171, 1175, 1180, 1183--map 1176, royal inscriptions 1193, tags and labels 1182, temple archives 1773-4, 1195
  drugstore 1162
  gold treasure 3620
  names, personal 1507-9
Nebuchadrezzar boundary stone 1161
  physical anthropology 1402
  religion 1610-11--Aramaic incantations 1608
  tablets 1596, 1600, 1619

terra cottas 3613
NITSCHKE, WIS, mound 339
NIZA, MARCOS DE 3963
NO DRAMA, costumes 3502
NOISE-MAKER, Indians of North America 1666
Norbeck, E. 1464
NORTH AFRICA See also Africa
  prehistoric sites 1113
NORTH AMERICA See also Canada; United States; Indians of North America
  anthropology and archaeology 218-833
  climatic influence, Post-Glacial 227
  ethnography, Pacific Coast 215
  man, prehistoric 247, 623-- copper implements 264, Eastern U.S. 445, Northeast 383, Southwest 582
  physical anthropology 1348-69
  prehistory, Hudson Valley 379
NORTH ARABIAN DESERT, archaeology 4138
NORTH CAROLINA
  archaeology 280--Haywood Co 327, Town Creek 411
  authors 1555
  Civil War--battles, map 3947, pictures 2253
  counties--origin chart 3927, outline map 3949
  flag 3940
  gemstones 2574
  Indians 400a
  seal 3935
North Carolina Artists' Exhibition, annual 2383
North Carolina Museum of Art
  catalog of painting 1782
  opening 139
North Carolina State Museum,

guide leaflet 140
NORTH DAKOTA
   flag 3961
   Indians 492
   map, historic 3997
"North Shore Legends" 1406
NORTHEAST, UNITED
   STATES See also East-
   ern Woodlands Culture
   Area
   early man 383
NORTHWEST, UNITED
   STATES See also North-
   west Coast Culture Area
   770
   Indians 766, 768, 772-3
   poetry 1540
NORTHWEST COAST CUL-
   TURE AREA 765-99,
   4081
   arts 2744
   baskets 2876
NORTHWEST GUN 2624
Northwestern Indian Expedi-
   tion 3979
NOVA SCOTIA, history of
   administration 3825
Noyes, E. 985
NTLAKYAPAMUK INDIANS
   Thompson Indians, B.C.
   785, mythology 1434
NUBIA
   archaeology 1219, 1235
   churches 3579
NUBIAN LANGUAGE 1516
NUMISMATICS See Coins
   and Medals
NURI, excavations 3648
Nute, G. L. 2745
Nuttall, Z. 216, 899, 953,
   1052, 3755, 4029
NUTTALL CODEX 1572
Nykl, A. R. 1628, 1631

O
"OAK HILL" 2651

Oak Knoll Collection 1551
OAQOL CEREMONY, Oraibi
   Indian 727
OAXACA
   black pottery 2916
   monuments 948
Oakland Art Museum
   California painters' exhibi-
   tion 1907
   California Sculptors', annual
   2524
   Honeyman Collection 1783
OBELISKS, New York 2699
OBSERVATORIES, ASTRONOM-
   ICAL See Astronomical
   Observatories and Plane-
   tariums
OCCUPATIONS See also Indus-
   tries; Williamsburg
   canoe-making 1310
   in art 1882, 4156
   scribe--Egypt 1221, Sumer
   1599
   United States--artists 2222,
   arts and crafts 2551,
   Litchfield Town 3879,
   pioneer 3847, spinning
   3880
OCEANIA See also Pacific
   Area
   anthropology 214
   art 3687
   canoes 3107
OCONTO CO, WIS, site 284
OCTAGONAL BUILDINGS, New
   York 2686
ODESS, DEL, Corbit House
   2692
"Ode to the World" 1604
OENSLAGER, DONALD 1643-4
Oetteking, B. 1341, 1357-60
OFFERINGS LODGE CERE-
   MONY 538
OGEMAU CO, MICH, earth-
   works 425
OGLALA INDIANS
   games 562

rites and ceremonies 573
Teton Dakota, Sun dance
573
Teton Sioux 521
O'Hara, F. 4258
OHIO
archaeology 393, 4112--
bibliography 356, early
man 392, Fort Ancient
319, 354, Fort Hill 355,
Glacial Kame Culture
301, Hamilton Co 419,
Hopewell Culture 352,
Madisonville 331, Mound
Builders 393, mound and
village sites 349, She-
nango River Reservoir
area 346, Serpent Mound
315, Turner earthworks
419
capitol, architecture 2669
costume, early 2603
Indians engraved bone 2768
OHIO CO, KY, Chiggerville
site 293
Indian Knoll site 332
OHIO VALLEY
archaic hunters 306
Indians, prehistoric 416
prehistory Upper Ohio
Valley 347
OJIBWA INDIANS 295
crafts 2746
medicine ceremony 274
OJIBWAY INDIANS See also
Chippewa Indians
buffalo robes 2830
O'KEEFE, GEORGIA 4207
Okladnikov, A. P. 4132
OKLAHOMA
archaeology and Indians
467, 470, 491, 494-5,
502
history 3956
Oklahoma Artists Competi-
tion, annual 2384
OKVIK, Eskimo site 811

OLD BIRCH ISLAND, ONT,
cemetery 826
OLD BLUE CHINA 3055
OLD COPPER CULTURE 369
OLD WORLD CIVILIZATION
216-7
Oliver, D. L. 1332
Oliver, F. E. 2284
OLIVEROS DE CASTILLA 3336
Olsen, E. C. 1084
Olson, E. 4280
Olson, R. 3129
O'Neal, W. B. 2675
ONEIDA INDIANS 285, 386
ONSLOW-FORD, GORDON
1909, 2371
ONTARIO, CANADA
antler spoons 2778
archaeology 4401
copper celt, native 833
handweaving 2119
textiles 4364
trade route 826
Trent Waterway 827
ONTARIO CO, N. Y., Canan-
daigua site 380
ONTONG JAVANESE, physical
anthropology 1391
ONYX JAR, Mexico 3726
OPALS 2011
OPERA, St. Louis 1639
OPIS, archaeology 1146
Opler, M. E. 721
ORACLES, New Guinea 1331
ORAIBI INDIANS See Hopi Indi-
ans
Orchard, W. C. 2817, 2833,
2849, 2885
OREGON
history 3968
Indian basketry 2857, --eth-
nography 4088a
military forts and sites,
map 3996
names, geographical 1470
theater in 1640
OREGON TERRITORY

Indian tribes and languages
map 769
map, pictorial 3998-4000
ORFUSS, ELSIE 4208
ORIENT See also Asia
and the West 1874, 1877,
1894
anthropology and archae-
ology 1054-1264, 4133-
9
art 3372-3638
ORIENTAL RUGS 3378-9
OROZCO, JOSE CLEMENTE
2921-2
Orr, P.C. 742-3, 762, 4100
ORRERIES See Astronomical
Observatories and Plan-
etariums
Ortega, J. 3980
ORTHOGRAPHY
Navaho 1482
Zuni 724
ORVIETO
amphora 3211
bowls 3206
vases 3205, 3214
OSAGE INDIANS
dance, War 565
folk literature and folk
lore 541
necklace 4238
Osborn, H.F. 1361
OSBORN, ROBERT 2389
OSCEOLA, Indian leader 4083
Osgood, S. 2193
Osma, G.J. de 3352
OSSUARY See also Burial
and Burials; Ceme-
teries
Huron 452, 4093
Ostego County Historical So-
ciety 133
OSTRICHES IN ART 3524
OTTAWA CO, KANS, site
514
OTO (OTOE) INDIANS 483
war club 527

OTSU-E, Japanese peasant
painting 3483
OTTER-MAN, Tlingit myth
1429
OUTDOOR SCULPTURE 1981
Outerbridge, A.E. 2091
OAQUOL CEREMONY, Hopi
(Oraibi) 727
OWASCO SEQUENCE, N.Y.
385
"Over the Rockies," the dis-
covery and mapping of
the Canadian West 3809
Overly, C. 2677
OVIMBUNDU, ANGOLA 1106
anthropometry 1399
Owen, R.C. 4129
OX CARTS 2568
OZARK BLUFF DWELLERS
350, 482

P

PAA-KO VILLAGE, site 628
PAALEN, WOLFGANG 2371
PACH, WALTER 3087
PACHACAMAC, PERU, archae-
ology 859
PACIFIC AREA See also
names of islands and
areas, as Fiji; Mela-
nesia; and Ethnology
anthropology and archaeology
1265-1335, 4040-1
art 3677-98
explorers 1270
folk literature and folk lore
1404, 1458-66
linguistics and grammar
1512-5
physical anthropology 1382-
97
social life and customs 1299
PACIFIC COAST
art 2380, 2386
craniology 1357
PACIFIC NORTHWEST See al-

386

so Northwest Coast
Culture Area
in 1875 4003
painting and sculpture
2386
PACKAGING 4326
"Fifty packages of the
Year" 2634
graphics in 2635
PADDLE, Eyak Indian 786
PAGE, KY, site 370
Paine, R.T. 3376
PAINTED PEBBLES, Texas
Indians 684
Painter, M.T. 4101, 4147-8
"PAINTER OF THE DEAD"
3330
"Painters' Painters" 1910
PAINTING See also media,
as Pastels; Tempera
Painting; Watercolor;
designations of subject
matter, as Animals in
Art; Genre Painting;
Marine Painting; Minia-
tures; Portraits; Still
Life Painting. See also
Folk Art; Illumination
of Books and Manu-
scripts; and schools of
painting; as Impression-
ism; New York School;
School of Paris. See
also names of Galleries
and collections, as
Frick Collection; Metro-
politan Museum of Art;
Pennsylvania Historical
Society; Widener Col-
lection
aged models 1937
appreciation 1688
architecture 1928
birds, American 2194
15th century 1696
flower 1926, 1930
history 1919

mice in plague pictures
1940
Mississippi and Missouri
Rivers 1885
19th century 1697, 2265,
2961
"painters' painters" 1910
pictures within pictures
1942
16th century 1696
theory 1688
trompe l'oeil 1935
yarn 2597
PAINTING, AMERICAN 2158-
2484
colonial 4177
contemporary (1925-   )
2346-2484
European background 2217
folk art 2161, 2164-5; 2208,
2248
expressionism 2182, 2374
history 2202, 2252
Japanese origin, painters
of 2367
New England 4229
19th century to 1925 2244-
2345
17th and 18th centuries 1908,
2217-43
turn-of-the-century 4226
20th century 4232
catalogs--See also names of
Galleries, as Brooklyn
Museum of Art, Corcor-
an Gallery of Art, Na-
tional Gallery of Art,
Whitney Museum of Amer-
ican Art--Gellatly Col-
lection 1759, Mellon Col-
lection 1767, Newark Mu-
seum 1775, Wellesley
College 1825
PAINTING, BALINESE 4273
PAINTING, BAROQUE 4245
PAINTING, BRITISH See Painting, English

PAINTING, CANADIAN 2116-
    1157
    abstract 2121
    contemporary 2117
    history 2133
    Quebec 2118
PAINTING, CHINESE 3397-8,
    4271
    bird and flower 3412
    fresco 3403, 3405
    modern 3413
    scroll 3404, 3414
    catalogs--Moore Collection
        3421, Vassar College
        Art Gallery 3419
PAINTING, CONTEMPORARY
    catalogs--Arensberg Col-
        lection 1788, Carnegie
        Institute International
        1896, Detroit Institute of
        Arts 1723, Dotrement
        Collection 1921, Phila-
        delphia Museum of Art
        1786
PAINTING, DUTCH AND
    FLEMISH 2990-3114,
    4242
    early 2994
    Golden Age of 17th century
        2991-3, 3002
    Little Masters 2999
PAINTING, EGYPTIAN 3554-
    5
PAINTING, ENGLISH 3024-42,
    4247
    contemporary 3026, 3028,
        3031
    18th century 3027--conver-
        sation pieces 3029,
        landscapes 2937
    George III, time of 1908
    Pre-Raphaellites 3033, 3035
PAINTING, ETRUSCAN 3234
PAINTING, EUROPEAN 2925-
    73
PAINTING, FLEMISH See
    Painting, Dutch and
    Flemish
PAINTING, FRENCH 3060-
    3127, from 1860 to 1960
    4259
    18th century 3072-4, 3079
    15th century to 18th century
        3075
    impressionism 1745
    romantic 3083
    19th century 3063, 3065,
        3068, 3080, 3082
    School of Paris 3085, 4250
    17th century 4265
    16th to 18th century 3078
    20th century 3069
PAINTING, GERMAND AND
    AUSTRIAN 3151-60, 4246
PAINTING, GREEK
    archaic to Graeco-Roman
        3186
    ceramic 3185, 3199, 3204,
        3207, 3215, 3221
    Tiryns frescoes 3184
PAINTING, ISRAELI 3599
PAINTING, ITALIAN 3257-82,
    4245
    landscape, 18th century 2937
PAINTING, JAPANESE, 4282
    Kamakura period 3484
    peasant 3483
PAINTING, LATIN AMERICA
    2912
PAINTING, MEXICAN, 20th
    century 2915
PAINTING, MODERN 1905
    European 2953
    catalogs--de Sylva Collec-
        tion 1745
    Gallatin Collection 1786a,
        Museum of Modern Art
        1757, Pulitzer Collection
        1728
PAINTING, NEW ENGLAND
    2168
PAINTING, PERSIAN 3630,
    4279
    miniatures 3631

PAINTING, RENAISSANCE
2943
PAINTING, ROMAN, Bosco-
reale 3231
PAINTING, SAND 2736
PAINTING, SCOTTISH 3036
PAINTING, SIENESE 3259
PAINTING, SPANISH 3306-35,
4249, 4267
contemporary 3312, 4258
School of Madrid 3311
PAINTING, THAI 4270
PAINTING, TIBETAN 3515
PAINTING, VENETIAN 3271-
2
Painting in the United States,
annual 2364
PAIUTE INDIANS
ethnology 4092
myths 1427
PAJARITAN CULTURE 614-5
PAKISTAN
anthropology 1077
archaeology 4135
Quetta Valley excavations
1074
"Palace Ladies" 3404, 3414
PALACES
Kourion 1017
Rameses II 3570
Sumerian 1087
Tirynus 3184
Palacios, E.J. 989
PALATE, HARD, normal and
feebleminded 1337
PALAU, money 1317
PALENQUE, bibliography 908
PALEOGRAPHY
Spanish manuscripts, 14th-
17th century 1506
PALEOLITHS See also Indi-
ans of North America;
Stones and Stone Work
Kansas, weathering of 536
PALEONTOLOGY
Royal Ontario Museum 153
PALESTINE

archaeology 1237-50
pottery 3592-3
temples 3593, 3596
PALM SPRINGS
history 3981
map 3991
views 3967
PALM SPRINGS INDIANS,
stories and legends 1433
PALMYRA, tomb sculpture
3242, 3612
Pan American art 4227
PANAMA
archaeology 881-3, 940
Panama-California Interna-
tional Exposition 2710
PANTOMIMES, Holland, 17th
century 2998
Pantorba, B. de 3868
PANUCO, MEX, excavations
857
Paolozzi, Eduardo 1986
PAPAGO INDIANS
baskets 2863
Vikita ceremony 711
PAPAGO LANGUAGE 1490
PAPER DOLLS See Dolls
PAPUA
Arapesh 1330
skull preservation 1322
PAPUAN LANGUAGE 1332
PAPYRI
Aramaic 3590
Egyptian 1621
PARACAS
costumes and textiles 3745
manta 3734
PARADISE LEGEND, Sumer
1453
PARAGUAY, Guarani Indians
911
PARAMONA INDIANS
Patomana Indian string
figures 3713a
PARFLECHES 2834
PARIS, SCHOOL OF 3085,
4250

PARK HOUSES 2678
Parker, A.C. 1424
Parker, B.N. 2229
Parker, H. 1538
Parker, H. 1887
Parker, T.H. 171
Parks, R.O. 4303-4, 4281
PARRISH VILLAGE, KY,
  site 363
PARS VASILARIS 1341
Parslow, V. 2592-4, 2596
PARSONS, CHARLES 4209a
Parsons, E.C. 722-3
PASQUA VILLAGE 4101
PASTELS See also names of
  artists, as Abbey, E.A.,
  Barney, A.P., Degas,
  E.
  catalogs--Freer Gallery of
  Art 1730, Museum of
  Fine Arts, Boston 2954
PATAGONIA, cloaks 3742
PATAWATOMI INDIANS See
  Potawatomi Indians
PATCHWORK QUILTS 2587
PATHOLOGY See Deforma-
  tions and Pathology
PATINA, MALIGNANT, care
  of 2076
PATOMANA INDIANS See
  Paramona Indians
Patrick, R. 700
PATTERNS, Near East silk
  4368
Paul, J.G.D. 1850
PAULSEN, ESTHER ERIKA
  2455
PAVIOTSO INDIANS
  material culture and per-
  sonalities 744
PAWNEE INDIANS
  medicine man 546
  purification of sacred
  bundles 547
  Skiki Pawnee Society 543
  societies 563
  Thunder ceremony 548,
  572

PAXTON, WILLIAM MC-
  GREGOR 2318
Payne, L. 3941
Peabody, C. 364
Peabody, R.E. 4337
PEABODY, MASS
  "Oak Hill," Samual McIn-
  tire Rooms 2651
Peabody Museum of Natural
  History, Yale Univer-
  sity
  exhibits 41
  visitor behavior 30
Peabody Museum of Salem
  East India Marine Collec-
  tion 142-3
  instruments - nautical 4038
  ship portraits 2221
  shipmasters and merchants
  2226
PEACOCK ROOM 2658
Peale, Franklin, Collection
  263
PEALE, RAPHAELLE 2319
PEALE, REMBRANDT, por-
  traits by 2262
PEALE FAMILY 2320
Peale's Museum 144-6
Peare, C.O. 2680
Pearson, Billy, Art Collec-
  tion 1831
Pease, Z.W. 2525, 2679
PEBBLES, PAINTED 684
Peck, E.J., 801
PECOS, PUEBLO 624-6
Peeso, P.E. 365
Pell, Alfred Duane, Collec-
  tion 3166
PELLETREAU, ELIAS 2620
Pellicer, C. 2924
PELVIS, human evolution
  1342
Penalba, Alicia 1986
PEND D'OREILLE INDIANS
  See Kalispel Indians
PENITENTES 4027, 4030,
  Mexico 4029
PENITENTIARIES, U.S., ex-

change media 4072
Penney, C. L. 1002, 1031,
1531, 2106, 3367
PENN HOUSE 2680
PENN INDIANS, wampum
belts 2849
PENN'S MANORS, map 3907
PENNSYLVANIA
archaeology 288, 303, 336,
346, 4119
architecture 2666
capitol, tiled pavement
2577
Indians 330, 415, 435, 447
map, first under Penn
3912
1784-5 boundary contro-
versy with Maryland,
map 3855a
PENNSYLVANIA DUTCH
art 2311, 4322
stoves, biblical scenes
2618
Pennsylvania Historical Society
paintings and miniatures
1784
PENNSYLVANIA RIFLE 2625
PENOBSCOT INDIANS 405
art symbolism 2758
canoe 427, birchbark 426
treasure of Chief Gabriel
Paul 443
THE PEOPLE See also Nava-
ho Indians 633
PEOPLE OF THE LONG-
HOUSE See also Iro-
quois Indians
New York State Musuem
135, 4102
PEOPLE OF THE MYST
(Macoa, Venezuela) 843
Pepper, G.H. 564, 2774-5
PEREIRA, I. RICE 2456,
4174
PEREZ CODEX 1576
"Periplus of Hanno" 4008

"Periplus of the Erythrian
sea" 4009
Periplus of the Outer Sea"
4010
Perkins, D., Jr. 163
Perley, S. 1539, 2681, 3891
PERLMUTTER, JACK 2457
PERRY SITE, ALA, 415c
PERSEPOLIS 1257
PERSIA See also Iran
archaeology 1253--Chanhu-
daro 1255, Damghan
1262, Indus Valley 1255,
Persepolis 1257, Tepe
Hissar 1254, 1259,
1261-3, Tol-E-Bakun
1264
art 3375, 3626-38
PERSIAN LANGUAGE AND
LITERATURE 1590
PERSONALITY
Algeria 4137
Arapesh, Rorschach test
1330
Navaho, psychobiological
study 629
Paviotso 744
Pertzoff, C.A. 1828
PERU See also Art, Pre-
Columbian; Incas
anthropology 852
archaeology 877-burials
963, Callejon de Huayles
840, Canete Valley 877,
Chavin de Huantar 840,
Chavina 981, Cuzco 905,
ethnobotany 975, Huaca
Prieta 960, Lambayeque
Valley 836, Nazca Peri-
od 877, 981, North
Coast 836, North High-
lands 840, Pachacamac
859, Puno 930, Proto-
Lima 878, Trujillo 877,
Viru Valley 836, 919,
943, Zapallan 980
art, ancient 3699-3700,
4236

costume 3772
gold--and copper ornaments
3752, breastplate 3757
Indians--Aymara 997,
Chucuito 997, Eastern
tribes 865, lizard hunts
976, Montana 929, skele-
tons 1376, spear-
thrower 255
painting 3706
pottery whistles 3764
quipu 190, 949-50
textiles 3735, 3739, 3743-4
PETEN, GUATEMALA, ex-
plorations 885-6
PETERDI, GABOR 2509
Peterson, 2626
Peterson, C.A. 239
Peterson, F.A. 388
Peterson, H. 256, 4103
PETO, JOHN F. 2321
PETRIFIED FOREST NA-
TIONAL MONUMENT,
ARIZ
archaeology 677
PETROGLYPHS See also In-
scriptions; Painted
Pebbles
British West Indies 977
Sanilac, Michigan 450
Tule Lake, California 758
PETROLOGY See also Stones
and Stone Work
stone artifacts, Mongolia
1061
Petrullo, V.M. 900-2
Pew, W.A. 3892-3
PEWTER
American 2615
New Jersey 2557
PEYOTE, Indians of North
America use 273
PHILADELPHIA
silver 2621
time of William Penn, map
3919
Philadelphia Academy of

Natural Sciences
history of publications 147
Philadelphia Museum of Art
Arensberg Collection 1788
Gallatin Collection 1786a
handbook 1787, Far Eastern
3383
Middle Ages, art 2960,
2962
painting 1785, European
2961, 20th century 1786
Philadelphia Commercial Museum, African collec-
tions 3653
Philadelphia Zoo, guide book
148
Philbrook Art Center
guide 1789
Kress Collection 2963
PHILIP II, KING OF SPAIN
official reports to, Mexi-
can towns 899
PHILIPPINE ISLANDS
anthropology 1327--Bagobo
1284, Bukidon 1275,
Davao District tribes
1276
folklore 1464
forging 1308
Indic languages 1514
kinship 1328
PHILIPPINE LANGUAGES, re-
ligious nomenclature
1327
PHILIPSBURG MANOR 4396
Phillips, D. 3550
Phillips, Henry L., Collec-
tion 3491
Phillips, J.M. 2237
PHILLIPS, MARJORIE 2458
Phillips, M.E. 147
Phillips, P. 366
Phillips, S.W. 2221
Phillips, W.J. 2151
Phillips Gallery, catalog 1790
PHILIPSBURG MANOR 2677
Phoenix Art Museum

guidebook 4057
Rubel Collection 1791
PHOTOGRAPHY 1973-5
American 2512-4, 4311
Mississippi and Missouri
Rivers 1885
PHYSICAL ANTHROPOLOGY
1337-1403, 4142
methodology 1346-7
PIANO 1655
PIAZZETTA, GIOVANNI
BATTISTA 3268
PICASSO, PABLO 2952,
3332-3
ceramics 3349
drawings 3340
graphic art 3341
lithographs 3342
PICKMAN SILVER 2622
PICTOGRAPHS See PICTURE
WRITING
PICTURE WRITING See also
Hieroglyphics; Petro-
glyphs; Writing; Aztec
Language and Litera-
ture; Signs and Symbols
Crooked Lake rock 2745
Navaho, symbols 2760
Quetico pictographs 2725
"Pictures within Pictures"
1942
PIECED WORK, Quilts 2587
PIEDRAS NEGRAS 4123
excavations 858
Expedition 860, 903, 906
incense burning 992
jades 3751
stelae 3717-8, 3723
thrones 3725
Pierce, Edith Choun, Collec-
tion 2128
Pierce, L. 3810
Pierpont Morgan Library 149,
2097, 2984
PIETA, Doccio porcelain
3290
PIG, BLACK 1094

PIGS
Solomon Islands 1332
PILE-DWELLINGS, Delaware
423
PILGRIM FATHERS See also
Plymouth Colony
2874
arms and armor 2626
Plymouth rock 3878
PILGRIM HALL 150
PILLARS OF BEN 3773
PILLOWS, MORTUARY 4133
PIMA INDIANS, baskets 2863,
2869
PINDI PUEBLO, N.M., ex-
cavations 670
PINE LAWN VALLEY, N.M.,
site 589, 638-9, 641
PINOLE FIESTA, Azqueltan
984
PINSKY, MRS. ALFRED See
Caiserman, Ghitta
PINTO SITE, CALIF 738
PIONEERS See The West
PIPELINE ARCHAEOLOGY
Chama Valley, N.M. 678
El Paso Natural Gas Com-
pany Projects 679
Southwest 679
PIPES, TOBACCO See also
Tobacco 4237
Blackfoot ceremony 561
calumet 272
effigy pipes 2774
PIRANESI, GIOVANNI BAT-
TISTA 3281
PIRATES, BARBARY 3855
PISSARO, CAMILLE 3064,
3068
PITHECANTHROPUS 1340
Pittsburgh Sesqui-Centennial
3896
PLACE NAMES See Names,
Geographical
PLAINS AND PLATEAU CUL-
TURE AREA 466-577
PLAINS-CREE INDIANS See
Cree Indians

393

PLAINS INDIANS 481, 503
   arms and armor--shields 525
   art, decorative 2734
   beadwork 2835, 2886
   clothing 2846, women 523
   dance, Sun 480, 570
   earthlodge 2904
   hide dressing 2835
   moccasins 2851
   painting, white influence on 2727
   population changes 516
   societies, age 553
   tepee 2902, 2905
PLAINS-OJIBWAY INDIANS See Chippewa Indians
PLAINS SHOSHONE INDIANS See Shoshoni Indians
PLANETARIUMS See Astronomical Observatories and Planetariums
PLANT NAMES, Yuki Indian 1479
PLANTATIONS, South Carolina 2689
PLANTS IN ART 1875
Plass, M. 1111, 3654, 3671
PLATTE CO, NEBR, site 496
PLAYING CARDS 3776
Pleasants, J.H. 1850, 2212
PLOWS
   Abraham, invention of improved 1145
   ancient 1160
PLUMBATE WARE 2797
Plummer, J. 2105
PLYMOUTH COLONY 3877, inventories 3876
PLYMOUTH ROCK 3878
PO SHAN LU 3415
POE, EDGAR ALLEN 3150
POETRY
   Essex Co, Mass 1539
   Hispanic 1633
   Hispano-Arabic 1631

Northwest 1540
Poebel, A. 1166, 1455, 1510, 1613-4
POINT BARROW ESKIMOS, prehistoric 805
POINT OF PINES
   archaeology 4079
POKEMOUCHE, history 3795
POLAR ESKIMOS,
   archaeology 813
Polish Committee for Cultural Relations ... 4305
Pollard, A.L. 58
Pollock, W.W. 3919
POLYNESIA
   anthropology 1292, 1300
   ethnology 1290
   folk literature and folk lore 1461-3
POLYNESIAN LANGUAGES 1513, 1515
POMO INDIANS
   material culture 751
   myths 1409
POMPEO LEONI 3283
PONCA INDIANS
   dance, Sun 540
   medicine ceremony 274
   societies 568
Pond, A.W. 1112-3
PONTEVEDRA, costume 3357
PONTI, GIOVANNI 2965
PONTORMO (JACOPO CURRICCI) 3266
PONY EXPRESS, map route 3994
Poole, E.L. 2311
Pope, A.H. 3128
Pope, J.A. 3465-6
POPLAR NECK, PA, rock shelter 435
POPULATION See also Demography 187
   Europe, major movements 1006
   Fiji 1278
   Northwest Coast Indians 773

Plains Indians 516
Puerto Rico 4131
Rio Grande, Glaze Point
  Area changes 645
Southwestern Indian tribes
  666
Porada, E. 3609
PORCELAINS See Ceramics
PORCUPINE QUILLWORK
  2887
PORT MOLLER, ALA, Hot
  Springs site 818
Porter, M.C.B. 30
Portland Art Museum
  Kress Collection 2966
PORTLAND POINT, N.B.
  3799
PORTRAITS See also Minia-
  tures; Silhouettes; Indi-
  ans of North America in
  art; and names of art-
  ists, as Goya; Law-
  rence
  American--colonial 1933,
    2225, 2552, 4177, 4180,
    4228, colonists before
    1701 1924, Delaware
    1716, 1718, 1938, early
    1927, 2218, 2227, in
    New York Historical So-
    ciety 2205, New Eng-
    land 2210, 1933 con-
    temporary in New York
    Historical Society 2216,
    of Americans 2195 by
    Americans 2196, 4210,
    Presidents and wives
    2197, Revolution to Civil
    War 1936, Richmond
    1944, shipmasters and
    merchants 2226, 20th
    century 4190, Vermont
    artists 2223
  catalogs--Delaware Public
    archives Commission
    1718, Essex Institute
    1725-6, Art Museum
    Harvard portraits 1727

Canadian, 18th century 2125
Greek 4253
Holland, 17th century 2998
Jay, John, of 1934
Newark Museum 2262
photographic, NY City 2512
Renaissance 4256
Roman 3233, 3236-7, 3241,
  4253, 4263
Syrian 3246
Wolfe, James, of 2157
PORTUGUESE CHAPEL 4394
Postel, A.W. 1114
POSTERS
  Toulouse-Lautrec 3124, 3140
POST-IMPRESSIONISM
  National Gallery of Art 2956
POSTURE
  human pelvis and erect pos-
    ture 1342
  lumbar breakdown and erect
    posture 1344
POTAWATOMI INDIANS
  material culture 439
  medicine ceremony 274
  mythology & folk lore 1430
POT-8-O CLUB 1558
POTSHERDS 201
  Zuni 696
Potter, W.B. 504
POTTERY See also Ceramics
  ancient, Missouri 504
  Boetian 1090
  Cocle 883
  Conebo 3761
  Hopi 4235
  Jemez Pueblo 660
  Mimbres Culture 590
  Peru 877
  Pueblo 2803, 2808, 2816
  Rio Grande 4235
  San Juan Area 2804, 2811,
    4353-4
  Santo Domingo 2792
  Tairona Culture 889
  Viru Valley 943
  Zapallan 980

POUSSIN, NICOLAS 2967, 3114
POVERTY POINT, LA, site 311
Powell, J. 3685, 3708
Powell, L.H. 4074, 4237
POWELL CO, KY, rock shelter 437
POWERS, ASAHEL 2223
Powers, M. 1425
POWHATAN INDIANS 401
POWWOW, Menominee 457
POZZATTI, RUDY 2510, 4260
POZZUOLI RELIEF 3238
Pratt, Charles M., Collection 3388
Pratt, Lillian Thomas, Collection 4355
PRATT, MATTHEW 2235
Praus, A.A. 2747
PRAYERS See also Chants, Rites and Ceremonies
Babylonian 1612
Lamaist 3516
Sumerian 1615-6
Tuamotuan 4024
PRECIOUS STONES See Gems and Precious Stones
PRE-COLUMBIAN ART AND CULTURE 220, 3644, 3699-3775, 4122-3, 4126, 4128
Meso-American and Ecuador 844, Peru 4236
catalog--Arensberg Collection 788
PRE-LENAPE CULTURE 326
PREHISTORIC MAN See Man, Prehistoric
PRENDERGAST, MAURICE 2321a-b, 4214
Prentisse, Elizabeth S., Bequest 1709
PRE-RAPHAELITES 3033, 3035
PRESERVATION (NATURAL HISTORY)
birds 52
casts, latex 59

hide tanning 51
mammals 49, 55
PRESERVATION OF ART OBJECTS, LANDMARKS, ETC.
historic house keeping 31
PRESIDENTS OF THE UNITED STATES, portraits 2197
PRESSED GLASS, American 2585
PRICE, CLAYTON S. 2459
Price, I.M. 1184
Price, L. 2257
Price, Mary and Vincent, Collection 1854, 1970
Priest, A. 3400, 3438, 3445, 3491
PRIMATES See Man, Prehistoric
Prime, P.O. 2621
PRINCE REGENT'S STYLE 3044
"Primer for Preservation" 31
Pritchett, H.S. 32
PRIMITIVE ART 3639-3775, 4284a-g
Africa 3645-76, 4284c-g
Indians of North America 2719-2897, 4233-41
Pacific Area 3677-98, 4284b
Pre-Columbian 3699-3775, 4236
PRIMITIVES See also Painting, American--Folk Art
French 3061
Prince, J.D. 1164
Princeton Art Museum, ancient art 4161
Kienbusch Memorial Collection 1792
Print Council of America 4286
PRINTING See also Books and Book Arts; Incunabula
America, history in 2638

art, modern, influences
of 2108
Bible, influence of 2096
English in Spain 3369
music 1652
Williamsberg, 18th cen-
tury 3936
PRINTS See Graphic Arts
Prior, W. L. 2223
Pritchard, J.B. 1245-6,
1591
PRIVATE COLLECTIONS See
name of Collection, as
Buckingham; Chrysler;
Clark, W.A.; Mellon;
Rosenwald; Yale Alum-
ni
PROFESSIONS See Occupa-
tions
PROFILES See Silhouettes
PRO HELVETIA FOUNDA-
TION 3371
PRONOUNS, suffixed in Poly-
nesian languages 1513
PROPAGANDA, anti-English
in Spain 3369
Proske, B.G. 1982-3, 2518,
2532, 2538, 3343, 3527
PROSTRATE FIGURES, Afri-
can art 3667-8
PROTO-LIMA CULTURE 878
PROVENCAL TROUBADORS,
Hispano-Arabic poetry
related to 1631
PROVERBS, French 1558
Sumerian 4136
PSYCHICAL RESEARCH 3779
PSYCHOLOGY
Navaho Indian 629
Rorschach Test 1330
PTOLEMY II, relief 3558
PUBLIC WORKS ART PRO-
JECT 2381
PUEBLA, Aztec Indians 3737
PUEBLO INDIANS See also
Anasazi Culture 582,
613, 616, 656-7, 4107,
4117

beadwork 2888
Cliff Cities National Park,
proposed 618
clothing 2847
cotton 2821
embroidery 2827
food 701
katcinas 2520
kiva murals 2755
milling stone 682
modern villages 647
music 4152
pottery 2803, 2808, 2816
Pueblo, Arizona, I site
596; II site 592, 681
rainbird design 2743
ruins, N.M. 699
textiles weaving 2836
wool 2822
PUEBLO OF PECOS, N.M.,
archaeology 524-6
PUEBLO PLATEAU, archaeo-
logical survey 602
PUEBLO I, site 596; II 592,
681
PUERTO RICO, population
4131
PUGET SOUND, archaeology
779
PUGET SOUND INDIANS 774
houses 2906, 2908
PUKAPUKA
anthropometry 1390
ethnology 1267, 1295
Pukui, M.K. 1310, 1333
Pulas, A.J. 2620
Pulitzer, Louise and Joseph,
Jr., Collection 1728
PUNIN CALVARIUM 1377
PUNO, PERU, archaeology
930
PUNUK INDIANS, Okvik site
811
PUPPETS AND PUPPET
PLAYS
Chinese 3428
Holland, 17th century 2998
Java 3696

PURIFICATION, Pawnee sa-
cred bundles 547
PURITANS, New England
3892-3
PURCELL, WILLIAM GRAY
2682
PURCELL & ELMSLIE,
ARCHTS 2682
Putnam, F.W. 2749
PYLE, HOWARD 2322-3
PYRAMIDS, Meroitic 3648
PYXIS 3218

Q
Qadi, Ahmad 4279
QUAKERS 2683
meeting house 2683, 2693-
4
Quandt, R.J. 44
QUARRIES See also Mines
and Mining
flint, North American
Indians 252
quartzite, Wyoming abo-
riginal 522
QUARTZITE, aboriginal Wyo-
ming quarry 522
QUEBEC 3813
painting 2118
Tetes de Boule Indians
decorative art 2722
QUECHUA LANGUAGE See
Kechua Language
QUEEN CHARLOTTE IS-
LANDS, B.C., Haida
Indians 782
QUEENSLAND, canoes 1307
QUELPA, spindle whorls
3741
QUETICO, pictographs 2725
QUETTA VALLEY, PAKI-
STAN, excavations 1074
QUIDOR, JOHN 2324
QUILL AND BEADWORK See
also Embroidery;
Featherwork

beadmaking 2882, Pueblo
2888
beadwork 2878, 2883,
2885, 2891--Crow 2892,
Plains 2835, 2886, Sauk
and Fox garters 2881
Indians of North America
2878-92
quillwork 2884--bird quill
2880, porcupine quill
2887, Illinois quilled
necklace 2890, Sauk and
Fox belt 2880
Sioux 2889
QUILTS AND COVERLETS
applique 2587
handwoven 2588-9
Newark Museum 2595
patchwork 2589
Quimby, G.I. 192, 367-9,
917, 2285, 2750, 2809
QUINAIELT (QUINAULT)
DIANS, folk literature
and folk lore 796
Quinn, R.M. 4211
QUIPU See also String Re-
cords 190, 949-50
modern Bolivia 958
QUIROS, CESAREO BER-
NALDO DO 3324-5
QUIXOTE, DON 1624

R
RABINOVITS, HAROLD 2460
RACE AND RACES See also
Ethnology
race mixture, Texas 1355,
U.S. 3852
race problem, Australia
1388
racial affinities 1394
Rackliffe, H. 4189
Radau, H. 1195, 1456, 1615
RADIOCARBON DATING
Middle and South America
938

Santa Rosa Island, Calif
  743, 4100
RAFFAELI, JEAN FRAN-
  COIS 3064
RAILROADS, connecting Dela-
  ware and Hudson Canal,
  Pa., map 3913
RAIN CHANT 1438
RAIN CLOUD, Indian myth
  1408
Rainey, A. 3526
Rainey, F.G. 810-1, 821-2,
  904
RAINBIRD, Pueblo design
  2743
RAINBOW PLATEAU, ARIZ,
  archaeology 653
RAINFOREST, PERU, Indi-
  ans of 929
RAKAHANGA, ethnology 1269
RAMESES II, palace tiles
  3570
RAMAGE, JOHN 2236
RAMAH NAVAHO INDIANS
  See Navaho Indians
Rambo, E.F. 3196, 3219-21,
  3253
Rancho Santa Ana Botanical
  Garden, history 151
RANGER, HENRY WARD
  2325, 4212
Randall-MacIver, D. 1219-
  20, 1235, 3551
Ranke, H. 1166, 1511, 3556,
  3563
RANKE, R., biography of
  1202
Rantoul, R.S. 1476, 1541,
  2622, 2655
RAPPAHANNOCK INDIANS,
  taking devices 442

RATA, legend 1466
Rathbone, P.T. 2266, 2321b,
  2332, 3112, 4213
Rathbun, M.C. 1685
RATTLES, Mexican, bone
  941

Pueblos, Apache and Nava-
  ho 4152
RATTNER, ABRAHAM 2374,
  2461
Ravenel, B.S.J. 2684
RAWHIDE ARTICLES 2834
RAWINSKY, HANS 4413
Raymond, W.C. 3811
RAYY, archaeology 1252-3,
  1256, 1258, 1260
Read, C. 4413
Read, H. 3312
READ SHELL MIDDEN, KY
  371
Reading Public Museum and
  Art Gallery 1793
Reagan, A.B. 659, 775
RECORD ALBUMS
  "Fifty Record Album Cov-
  ers of the Year" 2634
RECORDS AND RECORD
  KEEPING See Petro-
  glyphs; Writing; and
  specific forms of re-
  cords, as Libraries;
  Stele (Archaeological);
  Quipu
RECREATION See also Games
  and Sports
  Egyptian, ancient 1221
  English 4414
  in art 1941
  Japanese 1067
  Kourion amusement area
  1023
RED ANT CHANT 1426
RED CEDAR RIVER CUL-
  TURE 297
RED-FIGURE POTTERY See
  Ceramics, Greek
REDON, ODILON 3068, etch-
  ings and lithographs
  3137
Reeds, C.A. 3789
Regenos, G.W. 1585
Regeran, J.Q. von 3016
Reid, A. 59
Reina, R.E. 4130

Reisner, G.A. 1115
Reiss, John J., Collection 4858
Reiter, P. 580, 660, 4118
"Relacion de las Cosas de Yucatan" 928
RELIGION See also Charms; Folk Literature and Folk Lore; Holy Cities and Holy Lands; Magic; Medicine Man; Oracles; Rites and Ceremonies; Superstition; and names of religions, as Christian Art and Symbolism; Buddha and Buddhism; and holidays, as Easter 4021-32
Babylonia, king's atonement 1188
Chukchi Indians 1037
Crow Indians 554
Iroquois 4097
Koryaks 1049
Mexican 4028 and Navaho 4021
Navaho 1435, Mexican and 4021
Nippur, temple archives 1173-4, texts 1600, 1602-4
Penitentes 4027
Philippines, nomenclature 1327
Rome 3226
Sumer, deified kings 1187
Tinguianes 1320
Tuamotuan 4024
Yukaghir 1051
RELIGION AND SOCIETY 1680
RELIGIOUS ART See also Christian Art and Symbolism; Buddha and Buddhism; Judaism; Lamaism; etc.

Far East, wood blocks 3386
REMBRANDT VAN RIJN 2952, 2997, 3012
and his pupils 3013
drawings 3017-8, 4306
REMINGTON, FREDERIC 2255, 2326-30
Remington, P. 2976, 2047
REMINICK, SEYMOUR 2377
RENAISSANCE See also Illumination of Books and Manuscripts
arms and armor 2080, 4376
art 2968, 3062, 3284, 4256
Rendon, S. 1498, 2918
RENE-JEAN 3087
RENOIR, AUGUSTE 3064, 3068, 3115-7, 4244
RESERVE PHASE VILLAGE, N.M. 589, 638, 640
RESPIRATION, New York City, native and foreign born 1345
RESTIGOUCHE RIVER 3804
RESTORATION OF ART OBJECTS See Art Cleaning and Restoration
RETABLOS See Santos
REVERE, PAUL, silver 2213, 4377
REVERSING FALLS PORTAGE 3814
REVOLUTION, AMERICAN See United States--History--Revolution
Rewald, J. 3007, 3091, 3108, 3126, 4261
Rewald, John, Collection 1898
Reynolds, E. 1342
Reynolds, H. 1542
REYNOLDS, JOSHUA 3030
Reynolds, Mary, Collection 3086
RHODE ISLAND, seals, arms and flag 3882

Rhode Island School of Design Museum 1794
Rhys, H.H. 2321b, 4214
RIBERA, JOSE DE 3326-7
Ribicoff, B.K. 2396
Rice, D.S. 3531
RICE LAKE, WIS, site 297a, 4084
Rich, D.C. 3005
Richards, A.F. 3983
Richards, C.R. 2002
Richardson, E.P. 1722, 1888, 2175, 2201-2, 2270, 2276, 3267
RICHIER, GERMAINE 3118
RICHMOND, VA, in Civil War times 4405
  portraits 1944
  Thackeray in 1552
  views 3931
Richter, E.H. 2498
Richter, G.M.A. 2174, 2186, 3233, 4262
RICHTER, MISCHA 2389
Ricketson, E.B. 2977
RICKETTS SITE, KY 372-3
RICO Y ORTEGA, MARTIN 3328
RIDGE RUIN SITE, ARIZ 631
  pottery 2795
Ridgley, F.S. 2086
Riefstahl, E. 1221, 3552, 3572
Riegel, J. 3920
Ries, M. 4005
RIF, tribes 1098
RIFLES See Guns
RIGHT-AND LEFT-HANDED-NESS See Lateral Dominance
RILEY MOUND, KY 374
Rimmer, W. 2331
Rinaldo, J.B. 505, 638-9, 661, 2810, 4099
RINEHART, WILLIAM HENRY 2542

Ringling, John and Mabel, Museum of Art 1795-6
RIO GRANDE GLAZE PAINT AREA, population changes 645
RIO GRANDE PUEBLOS, N.M., history, bibliography 585, pottery 4235
RIO GRANDE VALLEY, Pre-Hispanic frescoes 2732
RIOTENCO SAN LORENZO, pottery 2918
"Rise of Civilizations" 186
Ritchie, A.C. 1969
Ritchie, W.A. 375-85, 453, 827, 3894, 4114
RITES AND CEREMONIES
  See also Charms; Dances and Dancing; Medicine Man; and names of religion, as Buddha and Buddhism; and names of customs, as Mortuary Customs
  Africa, death rite 1093
  Arapaho, organization 545
  Babylonia, atonement 1188
  Blackfoot, medicine-pipe 561
  Cheyenne, organization 539
  Crow 551
  Delaware, Bear 459, medicine 460
  Diegueno, death image 759
  Eastern Woodlands, Green Corn 465
  Eyak, paddle 786
  Hopi 714--(Oraibi) Marau 725, natal 726, Oaqol 727, Soyal 712, summer Snake 728
  Indians of North America --Offerings Lodge 538, upward-reaching 1435
  Laguna 723
  Menominee 455-6, powwow 457

Mohawk, condolence 446
Navaho, night chant 719
Oglala 573
Papago, Vikata 711
Pawnee, purification 547,
Thunder 572
Plains-Cree 567
Plains-Ojibway 567
Tlingit, bridal 799
Tutelo adoption 4110
Yaqui Easter 4147
Ritzenthaler, R.E. 199, 240,
258, 386-8, 434, 454,
1317, 2776, 2780, 3647
RITTENHOUSE ORRERY 167
RIVERA, DIEGO 2923
ROADS, England 4408
Roberts, H.H. 2870
Roberts, J.M. 724
Roberts, James E., Collec-
tion 2208
Robinson, E. 757
Robinson, E.S. 33
Robinson, F.W. 1643, 1929,
2078, 2616
Robinson, G. 2962
Robinson, H.S. 4320, 4378
Robinson, J. 3380
Robson, A.H. 2139, 2146,
2148, 2152
ROBUS, HUGO 2462
Roby, Sara, Collection 4059
Roby, Sara Foundation, Col-
lection 4060
ROCK See also Stones and
Stone Work
African pictures 3652
ROCK SHELTERS See Shel-
ters
Rockefeller, Abby Aldrich,
Folk Art Collection
1797, 2203-4
Rockwood, P.C. 4001
ROCOCO ART 2925
Rodabaugh, J.H. 356
RODIN, AUGUSTE 3144
Rodin Museum 3144

Rodriguez, M. 990
ROENTGEN RAYS See X-
Rays
ROGERS, BRUCE 2630
Rogers, Lauren, Library and
Museum of Art 1798
Rogers, M.B. 3510
Rojas, F. de 3367
ROMANESQUE ART 2960
ROMANTICISM IN ART
French painting 3083
United States, 1800-1875
2273
ROME AND ROMANS 1032
in 1764 1893
necropolis, Carmona 1031
Romano-Nubian cemetery
1235
town house 3256
Romer, A.S. 1112
ROMNEY, GEORGE 3030
Rood, J. 3895
Rood, John and Dorothy, Col-
lection 1819
ROOMS See also Architec-
tural Models
ball 2655
boudoir of Queen Shubad
3603
Gothic 2987
McIntire 2651
Merenptah throne room
3578
Meydum 3548
Temple of Madura, India
3587
Thorne, miniature 2113,
American 2657a, Euro-
pean 2988-9
Whistler Peacock Room
2658
Roosevelt, Franklin D., Col-
lection 1842
ROOSEVELT, THEODORE
3869
Roosevelt, Theodore, Me-
morial Murals, Ameri-

402

can Museum of Natural
History 2379
Root, W.C. 854
Roplogle, W.F. 745
Rorimer, J.J. 2969, 3021,
3149
RORSCHACH TEXT 1330
Rose, J.H. 2585
Rosenbach, A.S.W. 167
ROSENBERG, JAMES N.
1872
Rosenthal, A. 2218
Rosenthal, G. 1700-1, 1866,
1937, 3070
Rosenwald Collection 1965
Rosenwald, L.J. 1965
Ross, M. 2134
Ross, M.C. 2186, 2314,
2542, 3289, 3297
ROSS MOUND, OKLA 502
Rossiter, H.P. 2259, 3064
Roswell Museum and Art
Center 1799-1800
ROSZAK, THEODORE 2463
ROTA ISLAND, archaeology
1302
Roth, H.L. 3655
ROTHKO, MARK 4217
Rothschild, L. 4216
ROUALT, GEORGES 3119
Rouart, D. 3084
Rouart, Denis, Collection
3084
ROUND VALLEY, CALIF,
Yuki Indians 1479
Round, R.M. 2686
Rouse, P. 3942
Rousseau, T. 1748-9, 2991,
3005, 4265
Rowe, A. 1222-3, 1247-50,
3596-7
Rowe, C.W. 390
Rowe, J.H. 905
Rowland, B. 3377
Royal Ontario Museum 4061
handbook 155
Paleontology 153

Palestine Collection 3598
silver catalog 4379
Zoology 152, 154
RUBBER-CAMP, Amazon
4004, Mexico 4005
RUBBINS, Chinese 3399
Rubel Collection 1791
RUBENS, PETER PAUL
2967, 3014,
drawings 3014, 3019
RUGS AND CARPETS See al-
so Blankets
analysis, method 2044
Ecuador 3740
history, bibliography 2049
oriental 3378-9, 4365
Persian 3628, 3637
preservation, display and
storage 2048
exhibits--Egyptian 3373-4,
International Exhibition
of Contemporary 2002
RUINS See also names of
specific ruins, as Az-
tec Ruin; Cannon Ball
Ruins; Hidden House
Ruin; Leyit Kin Ruin;
Little Colorado Ruins;
Mattocks Ruin; San
Jose Ruin; White Moun-
tains Ruins
Copan 954
Holmul 894
Nakum 957
Pecos 2711-2
Society Islands 1312
Tikal 886, 912
Skichmook 923
RUSH, WILLIAM 2543
RUSSELL, CHARLES M. 2255
RUSSELL, EDWARD JOHN
2153
RUSSIA See also, Art, Rus-
sian; Siberia; Union of
Soviet Socialist Repub-
lics
archaeology 1043, 1052-3

bronze bird figures 3293,
3295
Caucasus, anthropology
1045
Imperial jewels 4355
prehistoric 1046
Rutledge, A. W. 2542
Ryder, H. 2153
Ryerson Collection 3382

S
Sabean Collection 3525
SAC INDIANS See Sauk Indi-
ans
SACHEMS, Narragansett
Indians 292
SACKVILLE, N. B. 3807
SACRED BUNDLES See
Charms
SACRIFICE, Cenote of, Yu-
catan 927, 951, 3756
SAGO, New Guinea use 1289
SAHAGUN, BERNARDINO DO
1568, 1574, 1583
SAHARA DESERT
Bedouins 1068
prehistoric sites 1113
SAILING SHIPS
American, rigs 2569
yachts 2573
ST. AUGUSTINE, FLA, ar-
chaeology 322
ST. JOHN RIVER, CANADA
3802, wood boats 3803
ST. JOHN'S, NEWFOUND-
LAND 3832
ST. LOUIS
history 3953
opera 1639
St. Louis City Art Museum
arms and armor 2083
Chinese bronzes 3474
handbook 1801-2
medieval art 2935
modern art 1803, 1862-3
SAINT-MEMIN, CHARLES
3139

engraved portraits 3138
ST. VINCENT, petroglyphs
977
STE. CROIX ISLAND 3797
SAIPAN
archaeology 1302
ethnology 1303
SAIS, statue of 3561
SAKAGAWEA (SAKAKAWEA)
506
Salas, E. P. 2911
SALEM
church silver 2607
Derby Mansion 2673
harbor chart 3903
houses 3605
map 3917
meeting house, first 2694
music societies 1660
Sanderson, Elijah and
Jacob, cabinetmakers
2653, 2656
witches 3891, 3897, 3899
SALEMME, ATTILIO 2464-5
SALINA FOCUS, trait list
2716
SALINA I, protohistoric vil-
lage site, Kans 514
Salinger, M. 2951
SALISH INDIANS
baskets 2858
blanket 2817
Sohon's portraits of Flathead Indians 2338
Salmony, A. 3416, 3436,
3441-2, 3467-9, 3475-6
SALT, aboriginal mine 697
SALTEAUX INDIANS See
Chippewa Indians
SALVADOR
archaeology 848, 880
pottery 3762
spindle whorls 3741
SALVAGE ARCHAEOLOGY
See Pipeline Archaeol-
ogy
Samford, C. 3943

SAMOA, somatology 1394
SAMPLERS, New Jersey early 2557
SAN AGUSTIN, COLUMBIA, INDIANS 936
San Antonio Collections of American Art 2160
SAN CARLOS APACHE INDIANS See Apache Indians
SAN CARLOS, GUATEMALA, culture 972
San Diego Fine Arts Gallery, catalogue 4062
San Diego Zoo 156-7
SAN FRANCISCO
architecture, domestic 2667, landscape 2718
SAN FRANCISCO MOUNTAINS, ARIZ, Pueblo II site 592, material culture 681
San Francisco Potters, Association of 4342
SAN GREGORIO DE ABO MISSION 2716
SAN JUAN AREA POTTERY 2804, 2811, 4353-4
SAN JUAN TEOTIHUACAN, MEXICO, report in 1580 899
SAN JOSE RUIN SKELETON 1373
SAN MIGUEL CHAPEL, N.M., site 669
SAN MIGUEL ISLAND, CALIF. artifacts 755, craniology 1358
SANA EULALIA INDIANS, dermatoglyphics 1371
Sanborn, H.W. 2108
SAND PAINTING 2736
SANDALS See Boots and Shoes
Sandburg, C. 4312
SANDERSON, ELIJAH AND JACOB 2653, 2656

SANILAC INDIANS, petroglyphs 450
SANTA BARBARA, CALIF, physical anthropology 1359
SANTA CLARA MISSION 2713
SANTA CLARA POTTERY 2811
SANTA FE 3976
architecture 2715
chapels 2717
La Castreuse site 669
SANTA MARIA DE MUR, CATALONGIA, painting 3310
SANTA MARTA, COLUMBIA, Tairona Culture 889
SANTA ROSA ISLAND, CALIF, radiocarbon dates 743, 4100
SANTO DOMINGO PUEBLO
pottery 2792
songs 1664
SANTOS See also Folk Art and Pueblo Indian katcinas 2520
New Mexican folk art 2267, 2517, 2523
Southwest, Bultos and Retablos 2264, 4211
Sao Paulo Biennial, Pacific Coast Art 2380
SAO PAULO MUSEUM, paintings 2958
Sapir, E. 1427, 1491, 1566, 2871
SARACENIC ART See Art, Mohammaden
SARCOPHAGI See also Tombs and Coffins
Egyptians 3554
Etruscan 3234
SARGENT, JOHN SINGER 2269, 2332
Boston Public Library decoration 2333-4

SARPY CO, NEBR, sites
486-7
SARSI INDIANS
dance societies 544
Sun dance 480
Satterlee, J.V. 1431
Satterthwaite, L. 531, 906-8,
991-3, 3723-5, 3768,
3774-5
SAUK INDIANS
beaded garters 2881
ethnology 509
quill belt 2880
sacred bundles 428
Saville, M.H. 908-10, 955-6,
3726-8, 3757
Sawitsky, W. 1784, 2230,
2235, 2243
SAW MILL, N.M., site 589
Sawtell, R.O. 1380
Sayce, A.H. 1197, 3385
SCALPING, evidence at
Moundville 400
Scarff, J.H. 4385
SCEPTRES See Staffs and
Sceptres
Schaefer, Eugene, Collection
2018, 3181
Scheil, V. 1617
Scherer, M.R. 2995
Schmidt, E. 1153, 1262-3,
2812
SCHMIDT, JULIUS 2528
Scholz, Janos, Collection
4310
SCHOOL OF MADRID, and
Van Dyck 3311
SCHOOL OF PARIS (CON-
TEMPORARY) 3085,
4250
Schoolcraft, H.R. 2813
SCHOOL-HOUSES, Newark
Museum 136
SCHOOLS See also Education
England, Tudor 4011, Uni-
versities 4012
Nebraska pioneer 1407

U.S. pioneer 3898
SCHOR, RHEA IRESS 2528
SCHRADER, NEBR, site 487
Schubert, H. 1449
Schuetz, M.K. 241, 438, 702,
2815, 2837
Schuller, R.R. 1499
Schultz, C.B. 468, 519, 532
Schulz, 747, 1477, 3985
Schwarze, W.N. 391
Schwartz, M.D. 2620
SCIENCE, history of 2109
SCIENCE AND SOCIETY 1680
SCIENCE MUSEUMS 49-62
SCOTT, site 4078
Scott, Alexander, Collection
3514
Scott, D.C. 2151
Scott, M.W. 2687
Scott, N.A. 3553
SCOTT, SAMUEL 2937
SCREENS, Chilkat Indian 790
SCRIBES
Babylonian 1599
Egyptian 1221
Scribner, H.S. 3175
SCRIMSHAW 2525
Mystic Seaport 2529a
SCROLL PAINTING See Il-
lumination of Books and
Manuscripts; Painting,
Chinese
Sculptors of Maryland, Wash-
ington and Virginia 2527
SCULPTURE See also Masks;
Santos; Scrimshaw;
and materials as Bronze
1866, 1976-91, 1986, 4313-
23
American birds 2194
domestic animals 2535
Minnesota history in 3895
occupations, history of
1882
catalogs--Brookgreen Gar-
dens 1976, Cleveland
Museum of Art 1709-10,

Detroit Institute of Arts 1722, National Gallery of Art 1987, National Gallery of Canada 1771, Niarchos Collection 1756, Walker Art Center 2530, Whitney Annual 4323

SCULPTURE, AFRICAN 3644, 3662-76, 4284c, 4321

SCULPTURE, AMERICAN 2515-45, 4187, 4313, 4319
  California 2524
  New England 4229
  New Jersey 2522
  modern 2521
  catalogs 2162--Mellon Collection 1767, Newark Museum 1775, Wellesley College 1825

SCULPTURE, ASSYRIAN 3614

SCULPTURE, BABYLONIAN 3609-14

SCULPTURE, CHINESE 3375, 3423-37

SCULPTURE, CLASSICAL 3172, 4322

SCULPTURE, CONTEMPORARY 1689-92, 1788

SCULPTURE, EGYPTIAN 3554-5, 3557-68

SCULPTURE, EUROPEAN 1775, 1767, 1825

SCULPTURE, FRENCH 3141-4, 4265, 4317
  contemporary 4314

SCULPTURE, GOTHIC 2962, 2974, 3343

SCULPTURE, GREEK 3191-5, 3171, 4320

SCULPTURE INDIAN 3582-4

SCULPTURE, INDIANS OF NORTH AMERICA 790, 2764-83

SCULPTURE, ITALIAN 3260

SCULPTURE, JAPANESE 3498, netsukes 3496-7

SCULPTURE, MODERN 1728, 1745, 1757, American 2521

SCULPTURE, ORIENTAL 3387

SCULPTURE, PERSIAN 3629

SCULPTURE, PRE-COLUMBIAN 3643, 3711-33

SCULPTURE, PRIMITIVE 3639-44

SCULPTURE, RENAISSANCE 2974-5, 3343

SCULPTURE, ROMAN 3171, 3235-47

SCULPTURE, SPANISH 3343
  contemporary 4258

SCULPTURE, SUMERIAN 3611

SCYTHOPOLIS See Beth-Shan

Seager, R.B. 1024-5

SEALS See also Tablets and Cylinders
  animals in 1873
  Babylonian 3604, 3617-8, 3621
  Chinese 3421
  cylinder seals 1083
  Hebrew 1591
  North Carolina 3935
  Rhode Island 3882

SEASONS, Hokusai prints 3493

SEATTLE, map 4002

Seattle Art Museum
  Backus Collection 1805
  handbook 1804, 1806-7
  Japanese art 4272, painting 3484
  Kress Collection 2970

Seattle Ceramics Society 4347

Seaver, E.I. 1881, 2287, 2968

Sebbelov, G. 565, 1300, 1334

Seckel, H.W. 2688

Seder, T. 217

Sellar, R. 3813

Seltzer, C.C. 662, 1088-9

Selz, P. 4217

SENECA INDIANS

Dutch Hollow site 3894
myths and folk tales 1424
SENGAI 3495
SENUFO (African tribe),
   sculpture 3664
Senyurek, M.S. 1116
SEPULCHRAL MONUMENTS
   See also Cemeteries
   Babylonian 3610
   Chinese 3432-3, 3478
   Egypt 3547, 3557, 3563
   Greek 3188, 3190, 3196
   Mohammedan 3527
   Palmyra tomb sculpture
      3242, 3612
   Pompeo Leoni 3283
   Sudan 3649
SERENTE INDIANS 898
SERI INDIANS 879
SERICULTURE, history 2041
SERIGRAPHS 1961
SERPENT MOUND, OHIO 315
SERPENTS
   art motif 3703
   worship 4026
Service, E.R. 911
SETI I, Beisan excavations
   1216
SEVENTEENTH CENTURY,
   art, French 4265
   Holland, life in 2998
   painting, Dutch 2291-3,
      3002
Severance, John L., Bequest
   1710
SEVILLE
   ceramics 3348, prehistoric
      3350
SEURAT, GEORGES 3068,
   3120
SEX, Navaho beliefs and
   practices 710
Seymour C. 1987
Seymour, George Dudley,
   Collection 4395
SHABHONA (INDIAN) 512
SHABLUL, archaeology 1229

Shaeffer, J.B. 4105
SHAHN, BEN 2466-7
SHAKERS, drawings 4304
SHAKESPEARE, WILLIAM
   See also England; Fol-
   ger Shakespeare Li-
   brary; Globe Playhouse
   1543
   age of, English dress 3045
   Anne Hathaway cottage 1543
   biography 1525
   birthplace 1544
   music in time of 1673
   play scenes 4316
   recreation in time of 4221
   roads and travel in time
      of 4408
   theatre in time of 1648
SHAKESPEAREAN GARDENS
   3059
SHAKER HANDCRAFTS 2554
SHAMANISM 276
SHAMSHIR GHAR, AFGHAN-
   ISTAN, cave site 1070
Shapiro, H.L. 187, 242, 812,
   1343, 1381, 1390-3,
   2068
Shapley, F.R. 3264-5
Shapley, J. 1686
SHARK HELMET 791
SHASTA INDIANS 733
SHAWANO CO, WIS, archae-
   ology 284
SHAWNEE INDIANS, folk lore
   462
Shead, R.B. 4106, 4238-9
Shelburne Museum
   blacksmith and wheelwright
      tools 4371
   carriages 2561
   decoys 2549
   hatboxes and bandboxes
      2548
   history 158
   quilts 2587
   woodworking tools 2623
SHEDIAC, N.B. 3826

SHEELER, CHARLES 3609
Shell, C. 1825
SHELL-HEAP CULTURE See
    also Little Bear Site
    Fraser River, B.C. 781
    Kentucky 293, 371
    trait list 332
Shelley, D.A. 2205
SHELLS AND SHELL ARTI-
    FACTS
    California coast fish hooks
    757
    Huasteca ornaments 3747
    Melanesian money 1316
    Mexican gorget 3727
    Miao People cowrie shell
    1064
    Monagrillo Culture 940
    ostrich egg-cups 3524
    Pueblo Indian 2888
    Spiro engraved 4239
    Tairona Culture 889
SHELTERS See also Archi-
    tecture, Domestic;
    Dwellings
    rock shelters--Kentucky
    436-7, La Colombiere
    1008, Nevada 4108,
    Pennsylvania 435, Tex-
    as 520
SHENANGO RIVER RESER-
    VOIR AREA 346
Shepard, A.O. 660
Shepard, C. 2265
SHEPPEGAN, history 3796
SHERATON FURNITURE 2641
SHERBRO, Sierra Leone 1102
Shetrone, H.C. 392-3
SHIELDS
    Dakota Indians 533
    Plains Indians 525
    Southwest Indians 525
SHIKLER, AARON 2377
SHINNECOCK INDIANS 323
SHIP MODELS 2570
    river boats 1885
    sailing, American 4337

SHIPMASTERS, American,
    portraits 2226
SHIPS See also types of
    ships, as Canoes; Sail-
    ing Vessels; Steam-
    ships; Submarines
    in art 2221
    Mystic Seaport 4339
    "Tyre" 2571
    yachting 2573
SHIRAZ PAINTING 3630
Shook, E.M. 912
SHOSHONEAN INDIANS, eth-
    nography 497
SHOSHONI (SHOSHONE) INDI-
    ANS
    dance, Sun 559
    dances, Plains Shoshone
    550
    societies, Plains Shoshone
    550
SHOOTING CHANT 1426
Shotridge, F. 790, 798
Shotridge, L. 776-7, 790-2,
    799, 1428-9, 2752-3,
    2872
SHRINES, See also Altars and
    Altarpieces; Chapels
    Ardebil 3465
    Hidatsa Indian 564
SHRUNKEN HEADS 199
SHUBAD, QUEEN 3603
SHUMLA CAVES, TEXAS 634,
    688
SHUNGOPOVI 1422
SHUSWAP INDIANS 784
Shutler, R. 4107-9
SIBERIA
    archaeology 1047, 4132
    blond race 1042
    Chukchi--religion 1037,
    social organization 1038
    Eskimo 1039
    folklore 1444
    Koryaks 1048-9
    Tungus 1051
    Yakuts 1050
    Yukaghir 1051

Sibley, J. 394
SICARD, PIERRE 3121
SICHOMOVI WARE 4354
SIENA, paintings 3259
SIERRA LEONE
  archaeology 1101
  Sherbro 1102
SIGILLATE POTTERY 3251
SIGNAC, PAUL 3122
SIGNS AND SYMBOLS See
    also Flags; Heraldry;
    Marks; Totems and
    Totemism
  art 2760
  Babylonian 3602, 3605
  Chilkat Indian 790
  Eastern Woodlands 2756
  Huichol Indians 982
  Indians of North America--
    art 2731, 2761, double
    axe 2731
  Indians of the Americas
    270
  Muslim art 3509
  Navaho Indian 2760, 2814
  Penobscot Indian 2758
  Pre-Columbian serpent
    3703
  Religions in illuminations
    2107
  Tibetan Buddhist art 3516
  Tlingit 792, 2752
  United States, tavern 4334,
    unity and freedom 3853
SILHOUETTES
  American sailing ship rigs
    2569
  time of James Madison
    2249
SILK
  American, historic scenes
    2591
  Chinese 3446
  history 2041
  Near East 4368
  Spanish 3360
  weaving 2055, 2057

Silsbee, E.A. 1864
SILVER AND SILVERSMITH-
    ING See also silver-
    smiths, as Pelletrean,
    E.; Revere, P. 2074
  American 2073, 2184,
    4370, 4375, 4377--
    church 2605, 2607, co-
    lonial 2608, early 2552,
    2611-3, 18th century
    2259
  Byzantine 3529
  Danish 3303
  English 3048-51
  European 2073
  French 2616
  Indians of North America
    2788
  marks 2605
  Maryland 1850
  Mount Vernon 2609
  Navaho 2789-90
  New England 2617
  New Jersey 2558
  Pennsylvania 2621
  Pickman 2622
  Royal Ontario Museum
    4379
  Spanish 3362
  Winterthur Museum 2614
  Woburn Abbey 4069
Silvert, K.H. 994
Simmons, P. 3446
Simons, A. 2689
SIMONSON, LEE 1644
Simms, S.C. 566
Simpson, G.G. 748
Simpson, R.D. 663
SINAGUA CULTURE 593
SINALOA, MEXICO, excava-
    tions 856
Sinclair, J.L. 664
SINGER, WILLIAM HENRY
    2335
Sinibaldi, G. 4298
SIOUX INDIANS See also Da-
    kota Indians; Oglala In-

dians
anthropometry 1366
myths and legends 1420
quill and bead work 2889
SIPPAR
documents 1166
inscriptions 1179
SISLEY, ALFRED 3068
SISOPDUYENHAB, STELA
OF 1233
SITIO CONTE, PERU, excavations 882-3
Sitwell, O. 171
SIUAI, BOUGAINVILLE, anthropology 1332
SITTING BULL 2747, 2759
Sizer, T. 2341, 4220
SKELETONS See also Craniology; and parts of skeleton, as Pelvis; Skulls; Spine; Teeth
America's oldest 1349
British Honduras 1373
dwarf, Moundville 1364
France 1380
Guatemala 854
Indian Knoll, Ky 332
Mexico 4115
Moundville, Ala 400, 1364
Nippur 1402
Peru 1376
Santa Barbara 1359
Southwest U.S. 4115
Swartz Ruin, N.M. 595
Turner Earthworks, Ohio 419
Yellow House Canyon, Texas 1362
SKETCHBOOKS
Cezanne 3097
Prendergast 2321a
SKIKI PAWNEE INDIANS See Pawnee Indians
Skinner, A. 274, 284, 395-7, 440, 455-6, 508-9, 567-8, 828, 833, 913, 1430-1, 2754, 2777-8, 2781, 2890, 3729

Skinner, H.D. 1301
SKULL, See also Craniology
magic Babylonian 3608
SKYPHOS 3219
SLATE MIRRORS, Tsimshian Indians 788
Slawson 2011

Sleepy Hollow Restorations 4396
Sleight, F.W. 313
SLOAN, JOHN 2336-7
Sloniker, Mr. and Mrs. Ross W., Collection 1968
Slotkin, J.S. 457
SLUIS, GEORGE VANDER 2468
Smart, C. 1547
SMIBERT, JOHN 2237
SMIT, PHILIPPE 4264
Smith, A.R. H. 2296
Smith, C.S. 398
Smith, D.E.H. 3944
SMITH, GODWIN 3818
Smith, H.G. 399
Smith, H.I. 399a, 778-81, 793
Smith, H.V., Museum. Fire Engines 2564
Smith, J.B. 2575
Smith, Captain John, map of discoveries 3904
Smith, R. 1624
Smith, R.C. 34
Smith, R.E. 3769
Smith, Ray W., Collection 2022
SMITH, SAMUEL DAVID 2469
Smith, W. 665, 724, 2755, 4076
Smith, W.E. 4063-4
Smith, W.S. 3553a - 54
Smith Alumnae Collections 1912
Smith College Museum, drawings, European 4294, drawings and watercolors, American 4285,

411

British 4293
Smith, Kline & French Laboratories 1972
SNAKE CEREMONY 728
SNAKES See also Serpents
worship 4026
SNELLINGS, OLD FORT,
archaeology 290
Sniffen, H.S. 2278, 2529
Snow, C.E. 400,1363-4
SNOWSHOES 259
SNUFFING TUBE, Tihuanaco
959
Soby, J.T. 171, 3320, 4065
Soby, James Thrall, Collection 4065
SOCIAL CLASS, Latin America 4116
SOCIAL LIFE AND CUSTOMS
See Indians of North
America, and other culture groups
SOCIAL SCIENCES See History, Social Sciences
and Technology
Societe Anonyme Collection
1827
SOCIETIES
Arikara 555
Blackfoot 576
Crow 556, tobacco society
560
Hidatsa 556
Indians of North America
--dancing society 276,
544, 549-50, shamanistic 276
Iowa 568
Kansa 568
Kiowa 557
Mandan 556
Menominee 455
Pawnee 563
Plains Indians, age societies 553
Salem music society 1660
SOCIETY

and art 1680
SOCIETY ISLANDS
physical anthropology 1396
ruins 1312
SOHON, GUSTAVE 2338
SOLANO, JOSE 3363
Solar, C.H. 2911
SOLO MAN 1396
SOLOMON ISLANDS
anthropometry and blood
types 1386
Bougainville, anthropology
1332
SOMATOLOGY
Anasazi Culture 628
Arabs 1080
Asia 1056
SOMMER, WILLIAM 1865
Sommerville Collection 2012
"The Song of Songs" 1592
SONGS See also Chants; Folk
Literature and Folk
Lore
Creek and Yuchi Indian
1668
Dahomey 1674
Mapuche 1669
Pacific Area 1457
Santo Domingo Pueblo 1664
Sonnenschein, Edward and
Louise B., Collection
3441
SONORA, anthropology 4127,
4129
Soper, A.C. 4322
Sorenson, J.L. 914
SOROLLA Y BASTIDA, JOAQUIN 3329
costumes in Provinces of
Spain 3356
SORG site 407
SOSAKU, HANGA 4307
SOTIRA, GREECE, site
1015-6
South, S.A. 400a
SOUTH AMERICA
Museum Directory 64

Social class 4116
SOUTH CAROLINA
Agricultural Society, history 3939
plantations 2689
SOUTH DAKOTA
archaeology 510
SOUTH PACIFIC See Pacific Area
"SOUTHERN CULT" INDIANS 470
Southern States Art League, annual 2392
SOUTHWEST CULTURE AREA 578-729, 4079, 4099
basketry 2867, 2873
clay figurines 2805
dwellings 2907
man, prehistoric 582, 662, 671, 680, 694, 1354, 1356
pottery 2793-5, 2806-7, 2815
regional culture 3982
shield 525
silverwork 2788
weaving 2838
Southwest Museum, handbook 159
SOYAL CEREMONY, Hopi (Oraibi) 712
Spalding, F. 3368
Spang Collection 3175
SPAIN See also Art, Spanish
archaeology 1002, 1004
Provinces of Spain 3329
SPANISH AMERICA See also Mexico; Peru; etc.
art 2910-24, 3868
history to 1830--Florentine Codex 1568, official reports in 1580 899, Spanish conquest of Yucatan 899, Landa's "Relacion..." 928, Spanish-Guarani relations in Colonial Peru 911, Sahagun 1574, majolica 3346

Maya-Spanish crosses, Yucatan 998
SPANISH AMERICAN WAR
See United States--History--War of 1898
SPANISH COLONIAL ART See also Santos and Pueblo Indian art 2520
architecture 2703-17
ecclesiastical 2115
liturgical 2268
Mexico 2910
New Mexico 2250
SPANISH LANGUAGE AND LITERATURE
"Jicara," derivation and meaning 1505
New Mexico and Colorado 1504
paleography 1506
poetry 1633
Spaulding, A.C. 369, 510
Spaulding, William S., and John T., Collection 3480
SPEARTHROWERS See also Atlatl
Indians of the Americas 255
SPECIMEN IDENTIFICATION (ARCHAEOLOGY) 204
Speck, F.G. 4110
SPEICHER, EUGENE 2470
Speiser, E.A. 3616
Speck, F.G. 260, 401-5, 441-2, 458-9, 829, 1432, 1668, 2756-8, 2848-9
Spell, L.M. 1657
Spencer, E.P. 2672
Spendlove, F. St. G. 2135-6, 2138
SPHINX 3559
SPHOUNGORAS, GREECE, excavations 1019
SPICKETT, RON 2154
Spier, L. 406, 569-70, 667, 703-6
Spinden, H.J. 995, 1587

413

SPINE, HUMAN
lumbar breakdown and
erect posture 1344
SPINNING See Fibres and
Spinning
SPINNING WHEELS 3880,
history 2047
SPIRIT BOAT, Dwamish Indi-
an 787
SPIRO MOUND 470, 4111,
4239
"Splendid Century, French
art: 1600-1715 4265
Spock, E.L. 1061
Spoehr, A. 192, 543, 1302-3
SPOONS, Antler, Ontario
2778
Sports in Art 1890, 1941,
2206, 4221
Sports Illustrated 2206
SPORTSCARS 4341
"Spring Festival on the River"
3400-1
SPRING LAKE, archaeology
407
Springer, F. 668, 3869
Springfield Museum of Fine
Arts, handbook 1808,
4067
SQUARE DANCING 4153
SQUARES
Mandarin 3394
Mary Ascher 2407
Squires, W.A. 123, 3814
Stackpole, E.A. 2529a, 4338-
9
Stacy, H.G. 4340
STAFFS AND SCEPTRES
Chinese sceptre 3439
Maori 3693
Tlingit 2753
STAGE COACHES, California
3986
STAGE DESIGN, U.S. 1637,
1643-4
STAINED GLASS 4360, Bar-
nard Collection 2962

STAIRWAYS, Mayan at Copan
962, 1579
Stallings, W.S. 209, 660
STALLING'S ISLAND MOUND,
GA 296
STAMNOS 3209
STAMOS, THEODORE 4222
STANDARDS, pottery descrip-
tion 207
Stanford Museum, catalog
1809
Stanton, Edwin M; letter from
Grant 3860a
"Star Spangled Banner" 1658,
origin 1656
Starr, F. 1065
Starr, S.F. 4112
STARS
fixed 1593
legend, American Indian
1440
lore, Navaho 1410
myth and chant of Great
Star 1411, 1436
Statler, O. 4307
STATUETTES See Figurines;
Sculpture
STEAMBOATS
American, paddle box dec-
orations 2519
Bard, James and John
2278
models 1885
Stedelije Museum 1914
Steefel, Ernest, Collection
1969
Steele, F.R. 1154, 1618-9
STEENWYCK, CORNELIUS
3823
Stefansson Collection 265
STEICHEN, EDWARD 2513,
4312
STEIN, GERTRUDE 1917
Stein, Gertrude, Collection
1917
Steindorff, G. 3566, 3568
Steinhart Aquarium, guide 160

STELE (ARCHAEOLOGY)
  Abydos 1233
  Beth-Shan 3597
  Chinese 3434
  Egypt 1225
  Greek funerary 3188, 3190,
    3196
  Middle East 3528
  Piedras Negras 3717-8,
    3723
  Tikal 993
STELLA, JOSEPH 2471
Stenzel Collection 3968
Stephens, Charles H., Col-
  lection 262
Sterling, A. 4314
STEUBEN FACTORY (GLASS)
  94
Stevens, Gerald, Collection
  2128
Stewart, D. 2084, 3896
Stewart, T.D. 854, 1365,
  4240
Stieff, F.P. 1655
STIEGLITZ, ALFRED 2514
Stieglitz Collection 2582
STILL, CLIFFORD E. 2472
STILL LIFE PAINTING See
  also Flowers in Art
  1939, 1947-8, 4163
Stimson, J.F. 1465-6
Stirling, C. 3075
Stirling, M.W. 2759
STOCKBRIDGE INDIANS 285
STOCKINGS, Indian 3534
Stoddard Collection 3178
Stoller, M.L. 571, 4141
Stolper, J. 60
Stone, A.J. 1348
Stone, D.Z. 915-8, 2919
Stone, George Cameron, Be-
  quest 3506
Stone, L.C. 4414
Stone, Lillian Newton, Col-
  lection 2095
STONE AGE
  Africa, Northwest, races
  1096

Russia 1046
Spain 1004
Tangier cave site 1108
STONES AND STONE WORK
  See also Rocks
  Alaskan lamp 2766, 2773
  California, Southern, in-
    laid work 2765
  Costa Rica 3713b
  Kentucky effigy pipe 2774
  Lenape masks 2781
  Mexico, sculpture 3731,
    3734
  Mongolia 1061
  primitive sculpture 3641
  Tairona culture 889
Stoney, S.G. 2689-90
STONY BROOK, site 381, 408
"STOURBRIDGE LION,"
  America's first locomo-
  tive 2560
STOVES, Pennsylvania Dutch
  2618
Stow, H.H. 3187
Stowell, W.H.H. 1548
STOWELL FAMILY 1548
STRATFORD-UPON-AVON
  1545-6
STRATIGRAPHIC ANALYSIS
  (ARCHAEOLOGY)
  Mogollon community 643
Straus, Edith A. and Percy
  S., Collection 2943
Strauss, J. 2025
Strauss, Jerome and Ruth
  Bryan, Memorial Foun-
  dation 2025
Streitmann, Albert P., Col-
  lection 1949
STRING FIGURES, Patomana
  Indians 3713a
STRING RECORDS See also
  Quipu
  Northwest Indians 797
Strohmer, E.V. 2928
STROZZI, BERNARDO 3268
STUART, rock shelter 4108

STUART, GILBERT 2238-9
true name 2239
Stuart Collection 1774
Stubbs, B.A. 1730, 2342
Stubbs, S.A. 669-70
STUYVESANT FAMILY, portraits 4228
SU, N.M., site 637
SUBMARINES
Holland 2565, 4340
SUCANEB 870
SUDAN
Bambara sculpture 3664, 4284c
Kush cemeteries 3648
SUFFIELD, CT, antique furniture 2642
Suffolk Museum at Stony Brook
carriage catalog 2562
Sugden, R.P. 45-6
SUGIMOTO, TETSURO 4223
SUIKO PERIOD, sculpture 3498
SUN DANCE
Arapaho 538
Blackfoot 577
Cheyenne 539
Crow 558
Hidatsa 559
Kiowa 569
Oglala 573
Osage 541
Ponca 540
Shoshoni 559
Ute 559
SUN SNARING MYTHS 1404
SUNG DYNASTY, ceramics 3452
"SUNNYSIDE," 2657, 2691
Sullivan, L.R. 1366-7, 1377, 1394-5, 1397, 1402
SULLIVAN, LOUIS 2702
SUMATRA, sacred Batak edifices 1054
SUMER
arts 3606-7

axe-head, inscribed 1184
deified kings 1187
names, personal 1508-9
palace 1087
sculpture 3611
SUMERIAN LANGUAGE AND LITERATURE 1599, 1601-4, 1607
Bible parallels 1446, 1453
epic of Gilgamesh 1450-1
epic tale 1448
hymns and prayers 1615-6
Paradise, Flood and Fall of Man epic 1453
proverbs 4136
tales, man's oldest 1449
SUNNYSIDE 4396
SUPERNATURALISM
Arapesh 1330
Tlingit ghost legend 1428
SUPERSTITIONS, medicine 4019
SURREALISM 3086
SUSQUEHANNA INDIANS 4082
SUTHERLAND, GRAHAM 3037
Suydam, F.D. 2586
SUZUKI, JAMES 2393
Svendsen, L.A. 1738
Swan, G.N. 1549
Swan, M.M. 1699, 2656
Swanson, E.H. 210, 511
Swanton, J.R. 782, 1567
SWARTS RUIN, site 595
Swartz, B.K. 4113
Swauger, J.L. 409
SWEATHOUSES, Piedras Negras 3775
SWEDISH THEATER, Chicago 1642
SWEDISH-AMERICAN LITERARY PERIODICALS 1549
Sweeney, J.A.H. 2692, 3870
Sweeney, J.J. 1737-8, 1786a, 2403, 2973, 3087, 4047
Sweet, F.A. 2269

416

Sweet, L.E. 4139
"Sweet Water," Great Lakes
    discovery and mapping
    3815
Swindler, D.R. 1402
Swinton, G. 4300
SWORDS
    Japanese sword mounts
        3480, 3505-6
    Washington, George 3856
SYCAMORE CANYON, ARIZ,
    ruin 685
SYMBOLISM, French Art
    3089
SYMBOLS See Signs and
    Symbols
SYNCRETISM 4125
SYRIA 3521
    archaeology 4138-9
    Baalbeck 3521
    ethnology 1089
    sculpture portraits 3246
SZINCA LANGUAGE 1496

T
TABLES, Egyptian 3575
TABLES, MATHEMATICAL,
    Babylonian 1596-7
TABLETS AND CYLINDERS
    See also Inscriptions;
        Seals
    1445-56
    Babylonian--historical 1598,
        interpretation of dreams
        1186
    Cappadocia 1197
    Enkhegal 1168
    Nebuchadrezzar proclama-
        tion 1181
    Sumer on deified kings
        1187
Taft Museum, catalog 1810
TAHAKI LEGEND 1465-6
TAHITI, featherwork breast-
    plate 2879
TAHITIAN LANGUAGE 1512

TAINO FIGURES 3732
TAIRONA CULTURE 889
TAJUMULCO, GUATEMALA,
    excavations 854
TAKAL, PETER 2473
TAKELMA LANGUAGE AND
    LITERATURE 1566
TALAMANCA INDIANS 918
TALAVERA CERAMICS 3348,
    3351
TANOAN LANGUAGE 1483
TAMPICO, MEXICO, excava-
    tions 857
TANAGRA FIGURINE 3195
T'ANG DYNASTY
    ceramics 3448, 3461, 3469
    mortuary figures 3432
    sculpture 3430
TANGIER
    fossil man 1116
    stone age site 1108
TANGUY, IVES 1909
TANKAS 3515
Tannenbaum, L. 3004
Tantaquidgeon, G. 460
TAPA, BOOK OF 1285
TAPESTRY
    2061-3
    Albers, J.A. 1818
    French--contemporary
        3146, 17th century 4265,
        Unicorn 3149
    Gothic-Flemish 3020--Nine
        Heroes 3022
    Roman 3254
    catalogs--North Carolina
        Museum of Art 1782
    Woburn Abbey 4069
Tapley, H.S. 1550-1
TARAHUMARE (TARAHU-
    MARA) INDIANS
    dermatoglyphics and later-
        al dominance 1374
TARASCO INDIANS, religion
    4022
TARBELL, EDMUND
    CHARLES 2257

417

Tarbell, F.B. 2072, 3234
TASSELS 2033
TASTE IN ART
2179
American in 1900's 2265
TATTOOING AND BODY
MARKINGS See also
Face Painting
Asia, Southwestern, body
markings 1057
Hawaii 1323
head ornamentation 2067
Maoris 1334
Mohave Indian tattooing 763
TAWAKONI INDIANS 418
Taylor, A.H. 3939
Taylor, Charles H., Collec-
tion 2221
Taylor, E. 2069
Taylor, E.S. 763
Taylor, F.H. 1748, 1834
Taylor, H. 4169
Taylor, J.C. 4266
Taylor, P. 3787
Taylor, W.W. 672
TAYLOR CHEST 2650
Taylor Museum, Balinese
painting 4273
TCHELITCHEW, PAUL 2971
TE RANGI HIROA See Buck,
P.H.
TEA CEREMONY 4284
"Teaching Anthropology" 211
"Teaching conservation" 61
TEETH See also Craniology
Dryopithecus 1378
Guam, prehistoric 1388
Hawaii 1382
Hesperopithecus 1340
Indians of No. America 1369
Maya 1370
Pithecanthropus 1340
TEFFT, THOMAS, archt 2213
Teit, J. 783-5, 1434
TELL BILLA
archaeology 1123, 1125-6,
1129

first Assyrian level 1122
pottery 3616
TELL EL-OBEID, archeology
1157
TELL TOQAAN 4139
TEMPERA PAINTING
European 2954
Temple, W. 512
Temple, W.C. 489
TEMPLE OF BABYLONIA
3624-5
TEMPLE OF HIBIS 3576
TEMPLE OF MADURA, IN-
DIA 3587
TEMPLE OF NEITH 3561
TEMPLES See also Monu-
ments; Ruins; Shrines
Mayan 3774-5
Mexico 942
Palestine 1247, 3593, 3596
Tenenbaum, F. 3674
TENNESSEE
Cherokee Indians 325
Tennessee River 325, 4086,
4096
TEOTIHUACAN, MEXICO, re-
port in 1580 899
TEPE GAWRA
acropolis 1165
archaeology 1123, 1125-6,
1129-30, 1155-6
Great Mound 1132
TEPE HISSAR, archaeology
1254, 1259, 1261-3
TEPECHPAN, MEXICO, re-
port in 1580 899
TEPEE, Plains Indians 2902,
2905
TEQUIZISTLAN, MEXICO, re-
port in 1580 899
Terenzio, A. 4189
TERRACOTTAS
Greek 3181
Kourion 3197
Locrian 3243
Nippur 3613
TERRARIUMS 50

Tessai, T. 4282
TETES DE BOULE INDIANS, decorative art 2722
TETON DAKOTA INDIANS See Oglala Indians
TETON SIOUX INDIANS See Oglala Indians
TEWA INDIANS, weaving 2836
TEWA LANGUAGE 1480-1
TEXAS
  history 3987-8, 4415
  Mexican population 1355
  Midland, human remains 1368
  Yellowhouse Canyon skeleton 1362
TEXAS CANYON, ARIZ, archaeology 604
Texas Collections 1901
TEXAS INDIANS 229, 241, 336, 594, 644--Bexar County 421 Big Bend 635, 684, 695, Brewster Co 520, Coast People 314, guide 229, Hasinai 320, Karan Kawa 314, Lower Pecos 684, Shumla Caves 634, 688, Val Verde Co. 634, 688, 702
Texas Memorial Museum, guide 161
Texas Technological College, Mural 2435
TEXTBOOKS 2104
  annual show 2628
Textile Museum 2051, 3540
TEXTILES See also Costume and Adornment; and types of textiles, as Cotton; Embroidery, Leather; Needlework; Rugs and Carpets; Silk; Tapestry; Wool
2027-70, 4361-8
  American 2587-97, 4367--Historic scenes and events 2591, quilts

2587, samplers 2557, Williamsburg historic 2590
Bible sources 3536
Canadian 2119, 4364
cleaning 2051, cotton 2053, color use 4362
design 2032, 2035, 4368-9, Egyptian 3532-3, 3535, 3573-4
Europe 4367
Hispano-Islamic 3538
history 2034
India prints 3586
Indians of North America 2817-39
Italian Renaissance 3292
Japanese 3503
Javanese 3689
Navaho 2824
Near East 3534-40, 4368
Persian 3637-8
Peru--Nazca period 877, Proto-Lima Culture 878, Zapallan 980
Pre-Columbian 3734-40
prehistoric, Kentucky 436
printed 4367
Spanish colonialization 4366
terminology, ancient and primitive fabrics 2036
Tiraz 3537, 3540, 3573
trimmings 2033
catalogs--Moore Memorial Collection 2052
"Texts of the Navajo Creation Chants" 4149
THACKERAY, WILLIAM MAKEPEACE 1552
THANKFULL TAYLOR CHEST 2650
THEATER ARTS 1634-49
THEATERS, Indian proposed at Santa Fe 617
Thieme, F.P. 1344, 4131
Thomas, E.B. 2474
Thomas, E.S. 355
Thomas, H. 1626

Thomas, Sir Henry 1632,
3369
Thomas, I. 2638-9
Thomas, L. O. 3817
Thompson, A. 2104
Thompson, C.R. 1553, 4011-
2, 4031
Thompson, D.E. 4032
Thompson, E.H. 920-3
Thompson, E.K. 2667
Thompson, J.E. 924-5, 996,
1469
Thompson, L. 1304
THOMPSON INDIANS See
Ntlakyapamuk Indians
THOMPSON RIVER, B.C.,
archaeology 780
THOMSON, TOM 2130
Thomson, V. 171
THON, WILLIAM 2393
Thorne, N. 2113, 2657a,
2988-9
THORNE ROOMS 2113, Amer-
ican 2657a, European
988-9
THRONES
Guatemala 3716
Piedras Negras 3725
THUMB AREA, MICHIGAN,
Sanilac petroglyphs 450
THUNDER CEREMONY,
Pawnee 548, 572
TIAHANACA
excavations 838
snuffing-tube 959
TIBET
art 3511-6
human skulls and bone use
1060
Lamaism 3512
TICOMAN, excavations 931
TICS, Navaho hand-trembler
629
TIEPOLO, GIOVANNI BAT-
TISTA 2937, 3282
TIEPOLO, GIOVANNI DO-
MENICO 2937, 3282

TIERRA DEL FUEGO INDI-
ANS 884
TIERRADENTRO INDIAN
RESERVATION, Colum-
bia 936
Tietza, H. 3268
TIGARA WHALE HUNTERS
822
TIGRIS See Euphrates-Tigris
Region
TIKAL, GUATEMALA
archaeology 886, 904, 912
stelae 993
TIKI LEGEND 1466
TILES
Egyptian 3570
Han Dynasty 3470
Pennsylvania, capitol of
2577
Westminster Abbey 3053
Tillich, P.T. 1680
TIN AND TINWARE, New
Mexico 2606
TINGUIANES
anthropology 1320
folk lore 1321
TINIAN, archaeology 1302
Tinker, S. 1318
TIPI See Tepee
TIRAZ FABRICS 3537, 3573
TIRYNIS, PALACE OF 3184
TITICACA LAKE, sites 875
Titiev, M. 926, 1669
TIZOC, Lord of the Aztecs
910
TLINGIT INDIANS
basket 2872, 2874
bridal ceremony 799
clan hats 792
dance baton 2753
legends 1428-9
signs and symbols, culture
emblems 2752
University Museum exhibit
168
war helmets 792
TLINGIT LANGUAGE 1478

TOBACCO See also Pipes,
　　Tobacco
　　Africa 1109
　　Asia 1059
　　Europe, introduction 1005
　　Indians of North America--
　　　Crow society 560, culti-
　　　vation and use 266
TOBACCO-POUCH, Iroquois
　　2754
TOBEY, MARK 2474
Tobler, A.J. 1156
Toda, K. 3382
TOILET ARTICLES, Egyptian
　　3552
TOKELAU ISLANDS, ethnol-
　　ogy 1294
TOLE WARE
　　French and English 2979
TOL-E-BAKUN, prehistoric
　　mound 1264
Toledo Museum of Art
　　1811-2, 1897
　　American contemporary
　　　painting 2394, Mau Col-
　　　lection 2395
　　Dutch art 3003
Tolman, R.P. 4224
TOLTECS, Mayas and 927
TOLU SITE 410
TOMAHAWKS 256, 4103,
　　Iowa Indian 526
TOMBS AND COFFINS See al-
　　so Cemeteries; Sepul-
　　chral Monuments
　　Dionysiac sarcophagi 1084
　　Royal Tombs, Ur 1141,
　　　1196, 1199-2000
TOMIOKA TESSAI 3485
TOMITA, K. 3407
TOMLIN, BRADLEY WALKER
　　2475
TOMYRIS, QUEEN 1590
TONALA, MEXICO, archae-
　　ology 866
TONEY, ANTHONY 2476
TONGA

　　archaeology 1296
　　ethnology 1305
　　folk literature and folk
　　　lore 1458
　　somatology 1394
TONITA OF THE HOLY
　　FAITH 588
TONHY, KRISTIANS 2971
TOOLS
　　carpenters, 18th century
　　　3866
　　Indians of North America
　　　--Ontario native copper
　　　celt 833, flint tools 252,
　　　New Brunswick chipped
　　　and flaked 832, stone
　　　tools 511, 531, 536, 709
　　woodworking 2623, 3872
TOPKAPU SARAYI MUSESI,
　　Istanbul 3466
Torday, E. 3658
Toronto Art Gallery 1897,
　　2972
　　handbook 4068
TOTALITARIANISM, art and
　　1680
TOTEMS AND TOTEMISM
　　See also Heraldry;
　　Signs and Symbols
　　261
　　Chilkat Indian house posts
　　　790
　　totem poles 2776
Touceda, E. 2053
Toulouse, J.H. 2716
TOULOUSE-LAUTREC, Henri
　　3064, 3068, 3123-6
　　posters and lithographs
　　　3140
Tourtelot, H.A. 420
TOWN CREEK MOUND, N.C.
　　411
TOWNLEY, HUGH 2544
TOWAKONI INDIANS See
　　Tawakoni Indians
TOYS, DOLLS, SHIPS, ETC
　　See also Dolls

2092-5
Hopi Indian dolls 2897
Tozzer, A.M. 886, 927-8,
957, 1500, 1588
TRADE See Commerce and
Trade
TRADE ROUTES, Ontario,
Canada 826
TRADITIONS See Folk Litera-
ture and Folk Lore
TRAILS, of Old West 3995
TRAJAN, ARCH OF, Benven-
tum 1028
Trapier, E. du G. 3308-9,
3868
TRAPS AND TRAPPING
Catawba Indian 458
Marshall Islands fish 1318
Rappahannock Indian 442
TRAVEL IN ART 1941
U.S., Colonial 2601
TREATY BELTS, Huron 2848
TREE RING DATING See
Dendrochronology
TRENT WATERWAY, Ontario,
Canada 827
TRENTON ARGILLITE CUL-
TURE 406
TRIBES See also Indians of
Mexico, Central and
South America; Indians
of North America
Africa, map 1093
Africa, East 1117
Indians of North America
228, 250--in first con-
tact with whites 249,
Great Lakes 412, New
England 361, Northwest
Coast 773, Old Oregon
Territory, map 769,
Plains Indian 503, Puget
Sound 774, Southeastern
666, tribal names 243,
Virginia tribes of 17th
century 413
Iran, map 1069
Iraq, map 1069

Mindanao 1276
Rif 1098
Tripp, R.A. 2693
TROMPE L'OEIL PAINTING
1935
Trowbridge, C.C. 361-2
Trowbridge, L.J. 673
TROYVILLE-COLES CREEK
PERIOD, site 310
TRUCK DRIVERS, Mexican
4124
TRUJILLO, PERU, pottery
877
Trumbull, J.H. 1492
TRUMBULL, JOHN 2240-1
TSATCHELA INDIANS See
Colorado (Ecuador) Indi-
ans
TSATTINE INDIANS
Beaver Indians 825
Tschopik, H. 244, 929, 997,
2814
Tschopik, M.H. 930
TSEGI WARE 4354
TSEGL CANYON, ARIZ, site
630
TSENG YO-HO 4283
TSHI-ZUN-HAU-KAU, calen-
dar stick 431
TSIMSHIAN INDIANS 777, slate
mirrors 788
Tsuji, Shindo 1986
TUAMOTU ARCHEPELAGO
dwellings 1313
legends 1465-6, 4024
music 1676
religion 4024
TUBAI, ethnology 1265
Tucker, S.J. 489
TUCKER CHINA 2583
Tuckerman, L.D. 47
Tueting, L.T. 1335
TULE BOAT 756
TULE LAKE, CALIF 758
TUN-GHAT MASK 2783
TUNGUS See Yukaghir
"Tunnel in the Desert" 62
Tupper, E.H. 3417
422

TURKEY, archaeology 1138
TURKEY FOOT RIDGE, N.M.
   site 639
Turnbull, G.H. 2477
Turner, C.G. 4115
Turner, E.H. 2240, 2389,
   3407
TURNER, WILLIAM 3042
TURNER EARTHWORKS,
   OHIO 419
TURNER-LOOK SITE 517
TURQUOISE WORK
   Hawikuh, of 2786
   Mexican mosaic 3753
TUSAYAN WARE 4352
Tushingham, A.D. 830
TUTELO INDIANS 4110
TUTHILL, ABRAHAM 2223
TWILLED WEAVING, Navaho
   Indian 2825
TWINS, Guinea 1103
TYPE AND TYPE FOUNDING
   See also names of Type
   designers as Rogers,
   B.; Thomas, Isiah;
   Zapf, H.
   American designers 2427
"TYRE," ship 2571
TYUONYI, N.M., excava-
   tions 612
TZELTAL INDIANS, derma-
   toglyphics 1371
TZENTAL LANGUAGE AND
   LITERATURE
   Maya-Tzental Codex Perez
   1576

                  U

U.S.S.R. See Union of Sovi-
   et Socialist Republics
"U505," ship 2572
UAXACTUN, ceramic se-
   quences 3769
Uffizi Gallery 4298
Uhle, M. 859, 958-9
UINTA CO, UTAH, natural
   history 170

ULOA VALLEY, HONDURAS
   archaeology 869
   skull 1370
UMAYYAD COINS 3364
UNCOMPAHGRE PLATEAU,
   archaeology 518
Underhill, R. 4117
Ungnad, A.1198
UNICORN TAPESTRIES 1349
UNICORNS
   Muslim art 3519
UNION OF SOVIET SOCIAL-
   IST REPUBLICS
   physical anthropology 4142
UNITED NATIONS CHARTER
   SIGNING, Commemora-
   tive Exhibit 2352
United Seamen's Service 1832
UNITED STATES See also
   Art, American; Indians
   of North America;
   North America; Maps
   civic heraldry 3849
   civilization, Amish influence on 3843
   coinage, curiosities of
   2091
   flag 3848
   folk literature and folk lore
   1045-7
   linguistics and grammar
   1470-7
   literature 1517-57
   Negro-White families 3852
   symbols of unity and freedom 3853
   theater arts 1637-44
UNITED STATES --HISTORY
   See also Portraits
   3841-3990
   artist in 2174-5
   French in America 2616
   textiles 2591
   Colonial Period See also
   Pilgrim Fathers; Ply-
   mouth Colony; Williamsburg; and names of mu-
   seums, as du Pont;

Ford; Shelburne; British Colonists 3867 conflict with Algonkian Indians 3875; dress and travel 2601; Maryland houses 2671; Massachusetts Bay Company records 3873; occupations 3847; Royal proclamations, 1604-1783 3842; woodworking tools 2623

French and Indian War, 1755-1763 3841

Revolution
    Liberty pole 2674
    naval actions 2224
    Yorktown campaign 3923

Civil War 4289, 4399
    Baltimore 4287
    Berks Co 4404
    North Carolina 2253, 3947
    Richmond 4405

War of 1898, Manila campaign 2244

UNITED STATES ARMY DEPARTMENT 2930

UNITED STATES NAVY
    Revolution--naval actions 2224, defense 2357
    War of 1898--Manila campaign 2244

UNIVERSITY INDIAN RUINS 4089

University Museum
    African Collections and Gallery 3656-7, art 3659
    Babylonian Section 1134, 1140
    buildings 167
    Chinese collections 3418
    Congo Galleries 3658
    Education Department 166
    Egyptian Collections 3556, mummy room 1232
    Etruscan art 3230, inscriptions 1029
    Greco-Roman Section 3170
    guide 169
    Italic art 3230
    library 164
    Luristan bronzes 3636
    Middle American Collections 165
    North American Collections 168
    Oriental art 3385

UNIVERSITIES, Tudor England 4012

UNSHAGI, N.M., Jemez Pueblo 660

Untermann 170

Upham, C.W. 2694-5, 3897

UPPER GILA, cave sites 594

UPPER REPUBLICAN COMPLEX, Nebraska and Kansas 514

Upton, J.M. 1593

UR OF THE CHALDEES
    archaeology 1127, 1131, 1135, 1142, 1148, 1151, 1158-9, 1163
    architecture 3623
    gem cutters 3619
    Royal Tombs, description 1196, discovery 1141, 1199-2000

URBANIZATION, Valley of Mexico, Pre-Spanish 4128

Ure, A.D. 1090

URNS
    Etruscan 3175
    Zapotec 3721

Usilton, B.M. 3408

USUMATSINTLA VALLEY, GUATEMALA, explorations 887-8

UTAH
    archaeology 479, 652, 739
    Indians--pottery types 2794, 4344, spearthrower 255

Utah State Museum of Natural History, guide 170
UTE INDIANS 513
Sun dance 559
UTE LANGUAGE 1484
UTRILLO, MAURICE 3077
Utterback, M. 2815
UVEA (WALLIS ISLAND)
ethnology 1272
Songs 1457
UXMAL, games and sports 965

V

Vail, R. 1891, 2330, 4228
VALDES LEAL, Juan de 3330, 4267
VALDVIA, LUIS DE 1499
VALENCIA
ceramics 3348
glass 3355
Hispano-Moresque pottery 3352
Valentine, B.B. 1554
Valentine, C. 1867, 3097
Valentine, E.G. 3945
Valentine, E.P. 3930
Valentine, E.V. 3945
Valentine Museum 4405
Valentiner, W.R. 1783, 1837, 1929, 3013, 3057, 3270
bibliography of writings 1837
Memorial Exhibition 1837
VALENTINES 2095
Valliant, G.C. 894, 931-3, 3709
Valliant, S.B. 933
VALUES
changing, a study of Navaho veterans 674
Zuni law 724
VALVERDE CO, TEXAS
caves 702
Shumla Caves 634, 688
VAN COURTLANDT MANOR 4396-7

VANCOUVER ISLAND, Kwakiutl Indians 765
Van de Put, A. 3352
VANDERLYN, JOHN 2339
VANDERLYN, PIETER 2242
Vanderpool 3898
VAN DYCK, ANTON, School of Madrid and 3311
VARDA, JEAN 1909
"Varia Africana" 1118
VARLEY, F.H. 2155-6
VASES
Babylonian 3615
classical 4356
Etruscan 3177
Greek 3175-8, 3181, 3198, 3200-3, 3205, 3210, 3214-7, 3220-1, design 3203, 3220
painting 3185, 3199, 3204, 3207, 3215, 3221
Mayan 3759
Roman 3175-6, 3178, 3210, 3249
Uloa 3713
VASILIKI, GREECE, excavations 1025
Vassar College Art Gallery
catalog 1813, Centennial catalog 1814
Chinese painting 3419
Vates, W.N. 3247
VAUQUELIN MONUMENTS 3831
VEGETABLE DYES, Indian 2820
VELASCO, JOSE MARIA 2924
VELAZAUEZ, DIEGO RODRIGUEZ 3331-2
Velde, H.R. Van de 2916
Velde, P. Van de 2916
VENARD, CLAUDE 3127
VENETIAN GLASS 3291
VENEZUELA
archaeology 837, 874, 902
Indians--People of the Myst 843

VENICE, ITALY 1888, 1892
  drawings 4309-10
Venice Biennale, catalog,
  American artists 1956
  2346
VENTANA CAVE 4090
Venturi, L. 3098
VENUS (PLANET), Mayas
  1587
VENUS CALENDAR, Maya 983
VERAGUAS, PANAMA, archae-
  ology 881
Verde Valley site 591
Verhelst, W. 48
Vermeule, C.C. 2012
VERMONT
  artists, portraits by 2223
  covered bridges--map
    3918, stamps 3922
  maps 3900-1
  names, geographical 1485
VEROCCHIO, ANDREA 3267
VERSAILLE, Vanderlyn's
  painting 2339
VERY, JONES 1517
Vestal, P.A. 707
VICES, tapestry 3020
Victoria and Albert Museum
  4297
Vienna Collections 2928
VIERGE, DANIEL URRABI-
  ETA 3333-4
"VIGILANT," fire engine 2566
"Vignettes in the 18th cen-
  tury..." 4230
VIKING FUND 206
VIKITA CEREMONY, Papago
  Indians 711
VILADRICH, MIGUEL 3335
VILLAGES, Pueblo 647
Villebon, J.R. de 3819
VILLON, JACQUES (pseudo-
  nym of Gaston Duchamp)
  1899, 3087
VIRGINIA See also Williams-
  burg
  architecture, Old Dominion
    2675

boundary controversey with
  Pennsylvania, 3885a
court minutes 3928-9
family life, 18th century
  3938
families 3930
genre painting, 19th cen-
  tury 2263
in 1602-22, map 3950
Indians--Powhatan ethnol-
  ogy 401, Rappahannock
  403, tribes of 17th century 413
miniatures, prior to 1850
  2271
sculpture 2527
square of Capitol 2687
Virginia Museum of Fine Art
  Aldrich Collection 1815
  Biennial exhibition of con-
    temporary American
    painting 2359
  Jones Collection 1817
  painting 1816
VIRTUES AND VICES, tapes-
  try 3020
VIRU VALLEY, PERU, sites
  836, 919, ceramics 943
VISHNU, statuette 3582
VISIGOTH COINS 3365
VISUAL ARTS 1677-3775,
  4151-4397
Vivian, G. 4118
Voegelin, E. 462
Vogt, E.Z. 674
Volk, E. 414
von Hagen, V.W. 934-5
von Kienbusch, Carl Otto,
  Memorial Collection
  1792
VOODOO DRUM 1671
Voth, H.R. 675, 712, 725-9,
  1493
VOYAGES AND TRAVELS See
  also Explorations and
  Discoveries
  Hawaii in 1819 1287

426

VROKASTRO, GREECE, ex-
cavations 1020

W

Wace, A.J.B. 3254
WACO INDIANS 418
WADE CUP 3531
Wadsworth Atheneum
    Austin, A.E., exhibit 171
    costume collection 2065
    guide: Colt, Morgan and
        Avery Memorials 172
    handbook 173
    history 174
WAGONS See Carriages,
    Wagons and Carts
WAHPETON INDIANS, medi-
    cine ceremony 274
Walde-Waldegg, H. von 936
WALLHALLA GLADES, ar-
    chaeological survey 607
Wallace, W.J. 763
Walker, E.F. 245, 275, 749-
    50
Walker, J. 1761, 1763-4,
    1766-7, 1769, 2164,
    2282, 2514, 2957, 3081,
    4289
Walker, J.R. 573
Walker Art Center
    Biennial of paintings and
        prints 1922
    Lowenthall Collection 1820
    Neuberger Collection 1821
    Rood Collection 1819
    sculpture exhibition 2530
    Zacks Collection 1822
Wall, C.C. 4407
Wallace, D.T. 878
Wallace, E. 3818
Wallace, P.A.W. 415
Wallace, W.J. 764
Wallerstein, L. 2979
Wallis, W.D. 831
WALLIS ISLAND
    ethnology 1272

songs 1457
WALLS, Constantinople 3522
WALRUS IVORY CARVINGS
    2784
Walser, R. 1555
Walters, Henry, Library of
    2983
Walters Art Gallery,
    altar 4315
    American art 2186
    bronze sculpture 3172
    Egyptian sculpture 3568
    Italian Majolica 3289
    paintings 1823
WAMPANOAG INDIANS 404
WAMPUM 432
    belt 2842
    criteria of 2841
    Penn Indian 2849
WANAMAKER EXPEDITION
    472
WAR AND WARFARE See al-
    so Arms and Armor
    Hupa Indian 764
WAR BONNETS, Indian 2850
WAR CLUBS
    British Guiana 955
    Oto Indian 527
WAR DANCE, Osage Indian
    565
War Shipping Administration
    1832
Warburg, J.P. 1680
Ward, Marcus L., Bequest
    1781
Wardle, H.N. 262-3, 443,
    533, 2762, 2783, 2875-
    7, 2896, 3731-2, 3746,
    3770
Wark, W.H. 1184
WARNEKE, HEINZ 2478
Warner, L. 3498
Warner, W.L. 1387
Warren Collection 3222
Washburn, G.B. 2245
WASHINGTON, MARTHA,
    will 4416

WASHINGTON, GEORGE
maxims 1556
military memorabilia 3856,
Mount Vernon 4407
portraits 2225, "Athenae-
um" portrait 1936,
etched portrait 2493
silverware 2609
will 4416
WASHINGTON
archaeology 775--cairns
793
Indian basketry 2857
Washington County Museum of
Fine Arts 4376
catalog 1824
WASHINGTON, D.C.
Artists of Washington, an-
nual 2356
collections 1861
sculpture 2527
Washington University Collec-
tion 1803
WASHO INDIANS 730
WATCHES 2084-7
WATER STREET, U.S.A. 74
WATERCOLOR PAINTING
American 2350, 4285
British 4293
Canadian 2126, 2138
English 3031, Landscape
3034
catalogs--Allyn Museum
4040, Brooklyn Museum
International biennial
1904, 1920, Museum of
Fine Arts, Boston 1752
Waterman, T.T. 2908-9
Waters, H.F. 2696
WATERWAYS, Keweenaw 369
Watkins, C.L. 2007
Watkins, F.E. 676, 2987
Watson, N. 4231
Wauchope, R. 937-9, 2763,
3771
Waugh, A.S. 2340
"Way of Tea" 4284

WEAPONS See Arms and
Armor
WEATHER
Babylonian meteorological
table 1596
Indians of North America
folklore 1408
New York folklore 1405
WEAVING See also Basket
Making and Baskets;
Blankets; Tapestry;
Textiles
2042
Acoma Indians 2836
American, coverlets 2588-
9
Canadian handweaving 2119
Hopi Indian 2818
jacquard 2045
Jemez Indians 2836
Keresan Indians 2836
Navaho Indians 2831,
twilled 2825
New York, early 2594
Pueblo Indians 2836
Southwestern 2838
Tewa Indians 2836
Zoque Indians 3738
Zuni Indians 2836
Webb, C.A. 311
Webb, W.S. 415a-416
WEBER, MAX 2349
Webster, J.C. 2157, 3819-38
Webster, John Clarence, Col-
lection 3790, 3821, lec-
tures 3808, 3810, 3839
Wedel, W.R. 514
WEDGWOOD WARE 3056,
4350
Wegeforth, H.M. 157
Wehle, H.B. 1931, 2507, 2951
WEI DYNASTY, ceramics
3469
Weibel, A.C. 2057
Weidenreich, F. 1396, 1403
Weil, Milton, Collection 2010
Weinberger, M. 2962

WEIR, JULIUS ALDEN 2511, 4220
WEIR, JOHN FERGUSON 2341
Weiss, M.H. 4020
WEISZ, EUGEN 2479
Weitzner, B. 535
Wellesley College. Department of Art 1825
WEN MING, Empress of China 3420
Wendell, B. 1557, 3899
Wendorf, F. 212, 677-9, 1368
Wenley, A.G. 3420
Werner, B. 417
Weslager, C.A. 4119
THE WEST See also Oregon Territory; Southwest Culture Area; and names of artists, as Mayer, F.B.; Miller, A.J.; Remington, F.; Russell, C.M.
  3965
  antiques of 2640
  architecture, Early Empire 2663
  artists depicting 2251, 2272, 4158
  Indians 234, 236, artists depicting 2285
  trails, map 3995
THE WEST (CANADIAN), discovery and mapping 3809
WEST, ELIZABETH DERBY 2651
West, G.A. 264
WEST BATON ROUGE PARISH, LA, Medora site 368
WEST INDIES
  figures 3732
  exhibits--Museum of American Indian 114
WEST POINT 4220

Westermann, W.L. 3226
Western Artists, Society of 4066
WESTMINSTER ABBEY, Chapter House tiles 3053
Wexberg, E. 4369
Weyer, E.M. 818, 823
WHALE HOUSE, Chilkat Indians 789
WHALE HUNTERS
  Arctic 821
  Tigara 822
Wheeler, A.B. 2229
Wheelwright, M.C. 1435-8, 2760, 4149
WHEELWRIGHT TOOLS 4371
Whiffen, M. 2697
Whipple, G.M. 1660
WHISTLER, JAMES MCNEILL 1730, 2269, 2342-3
  Peacock Room 2658
WHISTLES, Peru 3764
Whitaker, T.W. 960
Whitcomb, Edgar B. and Anna S. 1722
Whitcombe, J.D. 1305
White, M.E. 4120
WHITE MOUNTAIN APACHE INDIANS See Apache Indians
WHITE MOUNTAINS, ARIZ, ruins 706
Whitehill, W.M. 143, 2226, 4170
Whitford, A.C. 2839
Whiting, A.F. 708
WHITNEY, GERTRUDE VANDERBILT 2545
Whitney Annual Exhibition of Contemporary American Paintings and Sculpture, Watercolors and Drawings 1870
Whitney Museum of American Art 4183
  catalog 2315

429

Friends of the Whitney 2397-8
Roby Foundation Collection 2214
Sculpture and drawing annual 4323
Whitridge Collection 3464
WHITTIER, JOHN GREEN-LEAF
biography 1541
Oak Knoll Collection 1551
Whorf, B. L. 1501-2
WICHITA INDIANS 418
grass houses 2899
Wichita Mountains, arrastra 4091
Wick, P.A. 1971, 2321a
Wickenden, R.J. 3132, 3135
Widener Collection 1761, 1766, 2955, 3456
Wielgus, R. 4284g
Wielgus, Mr. and Mrs. Raymond, Collection 3646, 4284g
Wieschoff, H.A. 193, 1119, 3660
Wight, F.S. 2399, 2413, 2419, 2444, 2701, 4257
WILDE, JOHN 2491
Wildschut, W. 574, 2892
Wildung, F.H. 2623, 3872
Wilkins, E.P. 1224
Will, G.F. 515
WILL CO, ILL, Indians 333
Willard, A. 3837
Willcox, H. 3724
Willey, G.R. 919, 940
Williams, A.B. 246
Williams, C.M. 2557-8
Williams, F.B. 3038
Williams, G.D. 998
Williams, R. 1494
WILLIAMS, WILLIAM 2243
WILLIAMS CAVE, archaeology 584
WILLIAMSBURG 3925, 3933, 3942
antiques 2659
architecture 2698, Public Buildings 2697
cookery 3846
fabrics, historic 2590
flower and fruit arrangements 3932
gardens 2698
guide and map 92
in 18th century 3926
occupations--book binding 3943, milling 3941, printing 3936, silversmithing 3937
views 3945a
windmills 3941
WILLIAMSON CO MOUND 438
Willis, E.S. 2802
Willoughby, C.C. 331, 419, 463-4
Willson, R.E. 999
WILSON, EDWARD A. 2630
Wilson, G.L. 534-5, 575
Wilson, J. 2584
WILSON, RICHARD 2937
WIMAR, CHARLES 2344
Wimberly, S.B. 420, 598, 4121
Winchell, N.H. 536
WIND MYTH 1439
WIND MILLS, Williamsburg 3941
WINDSOR CO, VT, map 3901
Wingert, P.S. 3661, 3673, 3675, 3687
Wingfield, V. 2660
WINGREN, DAN 2480
Winlock, H.E. 3576
WINNEBAGO INDIANS, calendar stick 431
WINONA VILLAGE, ARIZ
pottery 2795
ruin 631-2
Winslow, J. 3838
WINSLOW WARE 4354
Winston, Mr. and Mrs. Harry Lewis, Collection 3279

WINTER, GEORGE 2345
Winterbotham Collection 1698
Winterthur See du Pont, Henry Francis, Winterthur Museum
WINTHROP, MASS, Indian burials 463
Indian Mounds Park 4084
WISCONSIN
archaeology--Aztalan 283, Effigy Mound Culture 390, Hopewell Culture 297, 341, Kletzien Mound 339, McClaughry Mound 340, Neale Mound 340, Nitschke Mound 339, Oconto Co 284, Red Cedar River Culture 297, Shawano Co 284
drawings 2491, 4070
Indians 305--Indian Mounds 297a, Oneida 386, prehistoric 387, 1350
Wisconsin Designer-Craftsmen, annual 2559
Wisconsin Painters and Sculptors, annual 2400
Wisconsin Printmakers Exhibition, annual 2499
Wisconsin Prints and Drawings 4070
Wisconsin Salon of Art, annual 1871
Wissler, C. 213, 265, 276, 516, 576-7, 813, 1337, 1345, 3469, 1395, 1397, 1440, 1991, 2851
WITCHES AND WITCHCRAFT, Salem 3891, 3897, 3899
Witt, Sir Robert, Collection 3043
Wittman, O. 2270
Witthoft, J. 277-8, 465
Woburn Abbey 4069
Wolf, E.R. 1000
WOLF, JAMES 2157
WOLF, MICH, site 316

WOLFE CO, KY, rock shelter 437
Wolff, E.G. 194
Wood, C.E. 1100
Wood, W. 3839
WOOD AND WOOD WORK 38
African carving 3663
Austral Islands carving 3692
Easter Island 3694
Inca cups 3720
Kentucky image 2775
Mahican cups 2769
Maori carving 3691
Mexico, ancient, carving 3728
Pacific Area fishhooks 1315
primitive sculpture 3642
tools 2623, 3872, carpenters, 18th century 3866
WOOD CHUCK CAVE, ARIZ, site 630
WOODBOATS 3803
Woodbury, R.B. 709
Woodbury, N. 4076
WOODCUTS AND WOODENGRAVINGS See also Engravings; Graphic Arts 4297
American, 1670-1750 2495, 4290
15th century books 3336
oriental 3386
WOODLAND CULTURE See also Eastern Woodland Culture Area 4086, 4096
Arctic, Kobuk River 806
Nebraska 485, 496
Woods, W. 3850
"Woods Words" 1471
Woodward, A. 2790
WOODWORKING TOOLS
American Colonial 2623
carpenters, 18th century 3866

Shelburne Museum 3872
WOOL
  textiles 2039--American
    handprocessed 2592,
    Pueblo Indian 2822
Woolaroc Museum, Indian
    exhibits 175
Woolford, S. 35, 421
Woolley, L. 1220, 3551
Woolley, C.L. 1157-9, 1199-
    1200, 1234-5, 3624-5
Woolworth, Norman, Collec-
    tion 4196
WORCESTER, DR. WALL,
  PORCELAIN 2582
WORLD, maps 3780-5
WORLD WAR
  artist at war 2127
  battlefront artists 2391
  naval defense 2357
Wormington, H.M. 247, 517-
    8, 680, 2816
WOTRUBA, FRITZ 3160
WRANGEL ISLAND, discovery
    3974
Wright, E.C. 3840
Wright, L.B. 1648
WRIGHT, S(TANTON) MAC-
  DONALD 2481
Writers' Program. Nebraska
    1407
WRITING See also Language
    and Language Arts; and
    types of writing, as
    Calligraphy; Cuneiform;
    Hieroglyphics; Inscrip-
    tions; Petroglyphs; Pic-
    ture Writing
  Egyptian hieroglyphics 1221
  Iran 1073
  Maya 1502--Copan hiero-
    glyphs 962
  Mesopotamia 1073
Wulsin, F.R. 1120
WUPATKI NATIONAL MONU-
  MENT, ARIZ, archae-
  ology 627, 665

Wurster, W.W. 2667
Wurtzburger Collection of
    African Sculpture 3675
Wurtzburger Collection of
    Oceanic Art 3687
Wurtzburger Collection of
    Pre-Columbian Art 3710
Wurtzburger Collection of
    Primitive Art 3644
Wuthenau, A. von 2717
WYETH, HENRIETTE 2482
Wyman, D. 70
Wyman, L. 4241
WYOMING
  archaeology--Eden Valley
    501, 531, Finley site
    531, Quartzite quarry
    522

X
XERXES, vase of 3615
XICAQUE INDIANS 934
XKICHMOOK, YUCATAN,
    ruins 923
XOCHICALCO, MEXICO, 846
  Bibliography 909
X-RAYS
  archaeological application
    202
  study of mummies 208

Y
YACHTING 2573
YAKAGNIR, 1051, folk lore
    1444
YAKUTS 1050
Yale University, excavations
    at Dura-Europos 1091,
    Gerasa 1092
  School of Fine Arts 4220
Yale University Alumni Col-
    lections 1916
Yale University Art Gallery
    Chinese paintings 3421
  guide 1826

432

Societe Anonyme Collection 1827
Yanagi, S. 4284
YANEZ, FERNANDO 3321
YAQUI INDIANS 4145, 4147-8
YARN PAINTINGS 2597
YARNS, warp 2028
YAU CHANG FOO 3421
"Ydioma Zapotec del Valle" 1503
YEAR BEARER'S PEOPLE 978
YELLOWHOUSE CANYON, skeleton 1362
YELLOWSTONE AREA
   Indians 732--Bannock Indians 745
YELLOWSTONE PARK, guide 3992
YENESEI OSTYAK, bird figures 3295
YORK ROAD, historical map 3909
YORKTOWN CAMPAIGN, map 3923
YORUBAS, Gods of 4025
YOSEMITE REGION, Indians 731, 734
   Place names 4150
Young, J.H. 3197
YOUNG, MAHONRI 2483
Young, R.S. 1026-7
Young, S.H. 3197
YOUNG, MICH, site 317
YUCATAN, MEXICO See also Chichen Itza
   Cave of Loltun 922
   Caves 872a
   Cenote of Sacrifice 927, 952, jade 3756
   crosses, Maya-Spanish 998
   Landa's Relacion de las Cosas de Yucatan 927
   letters in Middle American Research Institute Library 111
   monuments 948

potter's wheel 3766
Spanish conquest of 893, 928
travel in 1769 850
Uxmal 965
Xkichmook ruins 923
YUCHI INDIANS, songs 1668
YUGOSLAVIA
   archaeology 1044
   First International Exhibition of Prints, Modern Gallery, Ljubljana 1966
YUKAGHIR 1051, folk lore 1444
YUKIAN LANGUAGE 1479

Z

Zabriskie, G.A. 2699
ZACATENCO, excavations 932
Zacks Collection 1822
ZACUALPA, GUATEMALA, excavations 937
Zadok Collection 1750
ZAO WOU-KI 3422
ZAPF, HERMANN 2636
ZAPALLAN, PERU, grave 980
ZAPOTEC INDIANS, urns 3721
ZAPOTEC LANGUAGE 1503
ZEN See also Art, Buddhist
   Sengai drawings 3495
ZEREGA, ANDREA 2484
ZHOB, archaeology 4135
ZIGGURAT, Babylonia 3624-5
Zigrosser, C. 1972, 3322
Zimmermann, A. 2511
Zimmern, N.H. 3772
ZINNEMAN, FRED 1641
ZOOLOGICAL PARKS
   Philadelphia 148
   San Diego 156-7
ZOOLOGY, Royal Ontario Museum 152, 154
ZOOMORPHIC DESIGN See also Animals in Art

Mimbrenos Indians 2796
ZOQUE INDIANS, costumes
    and weaving 3738
ZORACH, WILLIAM 4176
ZUNI INDIANS 673
    agriculture 690--food 683,
    fetish 4106
    Hawikuh Zuni--bone work
        2770, ethnology 662,
        turquoise work 2786
    history 586
    kinship 715
    law 724
    medical observations of 603
    orthography 724
    potsherds 696
    ruins chronology 705
    weaving 2836
ZUPANICH, DOROTHY 2491